In this edition the original volume in the Oxford English Texts edited by J. B. Wharey (1928) has been completely revised and augmented. The text, revised and reset, represents a return to the first edition of 1678, and, for Bunyan's afterthoughts and additional episodes, to the earliest edition in which they appear. It has thus been possible to restore Bunyan's colloquial and ungrammatical forms.

The revised introduction places the composition of the First Part during Bunyan's first imprisonment and soon after the completion of *Grace Abounding*; while incorporating most of the very full bibliographical information which was a feature of the earlier edition, it includes a new section on the text. The full commentary takes account of Bunyan's background of Puritan homiletic literature, Biblical allusion, and proverbial lore.

THE PILGRIM'S
PROGRESS

JOHN BUNYAN
From the Pencil Drawing by Robert White

British Museum, Cracherode Collection

THE
PILGRIM'S
PROGRESS

from this World
to That which is to Come

BY

JOHN BUNYAN

Edited by
JAMES BLANTON WHAREY
Second Edition
Revised by
ROGER SHARROCK

OXFORD
AT THE CLARENDON PRESS
1960

Oxford University Press, Amen House, London E.C.4

GLASGOW NEW YORK TORONTO MELBOURNE WELLINGTON
BOMBAY CALCUTTA MADRAS KARACHI KUALA LUMPUR
CAPE TOWN IBADAN NAIROBI ACCRA

FIRST EDITION   1928
SECOND EDITION   1960

Bunyan, Joh. Pilgrim's Progress —
Bibliography

PRINTED IN GREAT BRITAIN

PREFACE TO THE SECOND EDITION

THE editor of the first edition, the late Professor J. B. Wharey, stated that his object was 'to write the history of the editions of *The Pilgrim's Progress* that were issued in England from 1678 to 1688 and to discover as far as may be possible their relative textual value'. His efforts in this direction have made it easier for those who come after to build upon his work. The chief purpose of the present revision is to complete the task by establishing a sound text. Professor Wharey relied almost exclusively on the third edition of 1679, as the latest to include substantial additions by Bunyan. He thus offered what is practically a diplomatic text of the third edition. The present text is based on the first edition, or, for passages introduced later, the earliest edition in which the new matter occurs. It is the first edition of *The Pilgrim's Progress* to do so (if one discounts a few facsimile reprints) and to retain as undoubtedly superior readings the spellings, loose grammar, and provincial forms which were normalized in the later editions.

The Introduction has been revised and two new sections have been added: a discussion of the date when *The Pilgrim's Progress* was written, and an explanation of the choice of copy-text. Wharey's very full apparatus has been drastically reduced by purging it of insignificant variants in the editions subsequent to the seventh and of most indications of changes in italicization.

A Commentary has been added. Notes to Bunyan, so simple and unadorned in his English, may seem to some of little use; but his wish was that the reader should

> ... Look within my Vail,
> Turn up my Metaphors ...

In the late eighteenth and the first half of the nineteenth century the evangelical editors of many reprints took the business of exegesis seriously, combining piety and information. Today Bunyan's theology, his use of the Bible, his allusions to contemporary events and to his own spiritual experience, all require some degree of exposition.

Among many who have put their time and knowledge at my disposal I should like specially to thank the following: the staffs of the Bodleian Library, the British Museum, and the John Rylands Library, Manchester; the Huntington Library, San Marino, California, the Pierpont Morgan Library, and the New York Public Library for microfilms and photostats; Messrs. Maggs Bros.; Messrs. Bernard Quaritch; the Rare Books Division of the Library of Con-Congress; M. Martin Bodmer; Dr. E. Lehmann of the Bibliothèque Bodmer (Geneva); Sir Arthur Howard for his kindness in allowing me to examine the Warner copy of the first edition; Dr. Richard Offor; Mr. Herbert Cahoon of the Pierpont Morgan Library; Miss Joyce Godber, Bedford-shire County Archivist; Mr. H. G. Tibbutt, F.R.Hist.S.; the Rev. A. W. Argyle; Mr. David Jenkins, Keeper of Printed Books, National Library of Wales; Mr. William H. McCarthy, Jun., of the Rosenbach Foundation of New York and Philadelphia.

I owe special gratitude to the Clarendon Press, its readers and advisers, for the care and skill they have shown during the whole work of revision.

ROGER SHARROCK

Southampton
September 1959

PREFACE TO THE FIRST EDITION

IN comparatively few of the multitude of editions of *The Pilgrim's Progress* have the editors made any serious attempt to secure an authentic text. One of the earliest to do so was the editor of the 'two and twentieth edition adorned with twenty-two copper plates engraved by J. Sturt', published in 1728 by J. Clarke. Until the close of the century this was regarded as the standard edition, and the text was frequently reprinted. Despite its claims to accuracy many errors, destined to be repeated in subsequent editions, were allowed to creep into the text. Throughout the latter half of the eighteenth and the first quarter of the nineteenth century several handsome editions appeared, but the publishers of these editions were less concerned with the text than with the illustrations. Robert Southey's edition, published by Murray and Major in 1830, in the importance attached to securing a trustworthy text, was epoch-making in the history of the editing of *The Pilgrim's Progress*. Writing to Major, 21 May 1829, in regard to his work on the proposed edition, Southey says: 'It has put me upon a careful collation of the text, and I do not repent of the unexpected labour which has thus been occasioned, as it will be the means of presenting the work in Bunyan's own vigorous vernacular English, which has been greatly corrupted in the easiest and worst of all ways—that of compositors and correctors following inadvertently their own mode of speech. . . . A *correct* text has appeared to me (who, both as a verseman and a proseman, am a weigher of words and sentences) of so much consequence since I undertook the collation, that I should like to correct the proofs myself.'[1] Southey's efforts received merited praise from Sir Walter Scott in his review of the edition. Scott makes particular mention of the 'skill with which Mr. Southey has restored much of Bunyan's masculine and idiomatic English, which has gradually dropped out of successive impressions by careless, or unfaithful, or what is as bad, conceited correctors of the press'.[2] But admirable as his efforts were, Southey was

[1] *Gentleman's Magazine* (July 1844), New Ser., xxii. 15–16. Also quoted by George Offor, *The Pilgrim's Progress*, Hanserd Knollys Edition (1847), p. v.
[2] *Quarterly Review* (October 1830), xliii. 489.

hopelessly handicapped in not having access to the early editions, the eighth being the earliest he was able to find.

In the edition of George Godwin and Lewis Pocock, 'illustrated by Engravings in Outline and Woodcuts from Drawings by Henry C. Selous, Esq.', London, 1844, some interest was manifested in matters textual, or at least bibliographical. The Introduction, written by Pocock, contained an account of the Holford copy of the first edition, and a list of all known copies of the first fourteen editions. Besides the Holford copy, the list included two copies of the second edition, none of the third, one of the fourth, one of the fifth, none of the sixth or of the seventh, two of the eighth, one of the ninth 1683 (no mention is made of the ninth 1684), one copy of the tenth, none of the eleventh or twelfth, one each of the thirteenth and fourteenth.

Ignoring for the present the valiant work of George Offor, we come next to the edition published in 1848 by George Virtue, with a life of the author by the Rev. Robert Philip. On the title-page this edition claimed to have been 'most carefully collated with the Edition containing the Author's last Additions and Corrections'. But nowhere did the editor give any information as to what edition contained the author's last revisions. Messrs. Macmillan, in 1862, under the editorship of the Rev. H. Bothamley, published an edition with a carefully corrected text in the Golden Treasury Series. In 1879 Canon Venables prepared for the Clarendon Press an edition based chiefly upon the second edition for Part One and upon the first edition for Part Two. The text of this edition has been several times reprinted, notably in the edition issued by Methuen & Co. in 1898 with an admirable introduction by Sir Charles Firth, and in the very handsome edition published by the Oxford Press in 1903. The Elstow edition, unique because of its binding in oak boards cut from the timber of the old Elstow Church, issued from the press of John Walker & Co. in 1881. In the 'bibliographical notice' prefixed to this edition the editor asserted that in preparing his text he had had before him nine of the first eleven editions.

Other editions in which a conscientious effort was made to obtain an authentic text might be mentioned, but among the editors and students of Bunyan two men tower far above their fellows. The first of these was George Offor.[1] His earliest work on Bunyan was the edition of *The Pilgrim's Progress* published by the Hanserd Knollys Society in 1847. This was followed by an edition in three volumes of Bunyan's *Works*, large 8vo (1853, reprinted 1862), and by two other editions of *The Pilgrim's Progress* published in 1856 and 1861. In the Hanserd Knollys volume Offor undertook a critical edition of the *Progress*. 'The edition now presented to the Society', so reads the 'advertisement' (p. vi), 'is carefully corrected from Bunyan's first copy, which is followed literally, in the orthography, capitals, italics, and punctuation. Every omission or alteration that the author made during his life is noted, as well as the edition in which such alterations first appeared.' The 'first copy' referred to is the Holford copy of the first edition, which Offor made the basic text. The additions of all subsequent editions down to and including the eleventh are included in the text, but placed within inverted commas, the particular edition in which the addition was first inserted being indicated in the foot-notes. The result is a text that has no parallel in any of the editions and that at times makes Bunyan guilty of grammatical anomalies of which he was innocent. The third edition, for example, was the first to introduce the three companions of Mr. By-ends. In the paragraph beginning, 'By this time By-ends was come again within sight', the words 'and his companions' were inserted after 'By-ends'. This addition, of course, changed the subject from singular to plural and necessitated a corresponding change in the following verbs and pronouns. As printed in the Hanserd Knollys volume the paragraph is as follows:

By this time By-ends 'and his companions' was come again within sight, and he at the first beck went over to *Demas*. Now whether he fell into the Pit by looking over the brink thereof; or whether he went down to dig, or whether he was smothered in the bottom, by the damps that commonly arise, of these things I am not certain: But this I observed, that he never was seen again in the way.

1 George Offor (1787–1864), after amassing a competence as a bookseller, retired from active business. He acquired an extensive knowledge of black-letter literature, particularly in theology. His fine library, including a remarkable collection of Bunyaniana, was offered for sale at Sotheby's the year after his death, from 27 June to 8 July. It was destroyed by fire in the auction-rooms 29 June 1865, and the remnants sold as salvage for £300. (*D.N.B.*)

In the footnotes the reader is informed that the phrase 'and his companions' was added in the third; that 'was come' appears as 'were come' in the eighth and subsequent editions (it so appears in the fifth and sixth); that 'was smothered' and 'was seen' became 'were smothered' and 'were seen' in editions subsequent to the third (the change was, in fact, not made until after the fourth); and finally that the pronoun 'he' throughout the passage was replaced by 'they' in the third and subsequent editions. Surely, such a method of printing the text does Bunyan an injustice.

Many of the variants reported as having been introduced in the eighth edition were introduced in the fifth, and not infrequently as early as the fourth. It looks as though Offor, not finding them in the seventh, inferred that they were added in the eighth. The only copies of the fourth and fifth editions known to him were in the library of Lea Wilson, and from a statement made in the Introduction[1] one is led to believe that these copies had not been accessible. Of the sixth edition Offor simply says no copy has 'been found in a perfect state', and of the eleventh 'date unknown'. In the three-volume edition of Bunyan's *Works* published six years later Offor was prepared to give a much fuller account of the early copies. In 1847 he did the best he could with the material at hand, but his work was necessarily far from final.

The second person who, through a lifetime devoted to Bunyan research, linked his name for ever with that of the great allegorist was the late Dr. John Brown. His great contribution to Bunyan scholarship, however, had to do not so much with textual problems as with the facts of Bunyan's life and times and with placing him in his true light before the world.[2]

In addition to his biography of Bunyan, Dr. Brown edited *Grace Abounding, The Pilgrim's Progress, The Holy War*, and *The Life and Death of Mr. Badman*. His edition of the *Pilgrim's Progress*, published in the Cambridge English Classics Series in 1907, chose as the basic text of the First Part the eleventh

---

[1] 'It is much to be regretted that the lamented death of Mr. Wilson has for the present shut up his library' (p. cxxii).

[2] The Tercentenary Edition of Dr. Brown's great study *John Bunyan, his Life, Times, and Work* revised by Frank Mott Harrison (1928) is one of the notable Bunyan books of that year.

edition, which being the last to appear before the author's death was supposed to represent his last revision, and as the basic text of the Second Part the second edition, 1687. In notes appended at the end of the volume were included about five pages of variants chiefly from the first three editions of Part One, and two pages of variants between the first and second editions of Part Two. No attempt was made to discover the relationship of the early editions to one another or their relative value.

Obviously much still remained to be done towards a critical edition. The excessive rarity of the early editions has been the chief hindrance to any thoroughgoing study of them. With the advent of the photographic reprint this difficulty is in a large measure obviated. While I have examined as many of the original copies as were accessible, for the bulk of the present work I have had to rely upon photographic reprints. The aim of the present edition is quite definite: it is to write the history of the editions of *The Pilgrim's Progress* that were issued in England from 1678 to 1688 and to discover as far as may be possible their relative textual value. The editions published outside England during this decade have been disregarded, as have the hundreds of editions that have appeared since the author's death. This deliberate limiting of the scope of the work is done in the hope that its aim may be the more successfully attained.

It is pleasant to recall the many persons who have aided me in this work. To Sir Leicester Harmsworth, Bart., I am deeply indebted for permission to examine the Warner copy of the first edition; to Mr. Joseph Whiting, Honorary Secretary of the Bunyan Trustees, for the opportunity of examining the rare copies of *The Pilgrim's Progress* in the library of Bunyan Meeting; to the officials of the Henry E. Huntington Library for valuable information concerning the Huntington copies and for permission to reproduce the 'sleeping portrait' of the Palmer-Nash copy of the first edition; to Miss Lucy Eugenia Osborne, Custodian of the Chapin Library, Williamsburg, Mass., for collations and other helpful information concerning the Chapin copies; to the Librarian of the John Rylands Library for the opportunity of seeing

the Rylands copies of the first editions of both the First and
Second Parts and to the Pierpont Morgan Library for
many courtesies extended me while examining the rare
Bunyaniana in the Morgan Collection. The most abundant
sources of Bunyan material, however, are the British Museum
and the New York Public Library. In both libraries
I have met with a spirit of the greatest kindness and helpfulness. To the Syndics of the Cambridge University Press
I am under obligation for the privilege of using the text of
Part Two of the edition of *The Pilgrim's Progress* prepared
by Dr. Brown for the English Classics Series. I feel that
special acknowledgement should be made of the generous
treatment received at the hands of Mr. E. W. Winkler,
Librarian of the University of Texas, who has supplied
me with photographic reprints of many of the rare editions
in the Lenox Collection of the New York Public Library.

J. B. W.

1928

CONTENTS

CONTENTS

REFERENCES AND ABBREVIATIONS

In the Introduction and Commentary Bunyan's works are referred to by title and with volume and page references to the *Complete Works of John Bunyan*, edited by George Offor (3 vols. Edinburgh and London, 1860–2), except for the following:

Grace Abounding, edited by John Brown (Cambridge, 1907)	G.A.
The Life and Death of Mr. Badman, edited by John Brown (Cambridge, 1905)	Badman
The Holy War, edited by John Brown (Cambridge, 1905)	H.W.
The Baptist Quarterly	B.Q.
John Brown, *Bunyan, his Life, Times and Work*. Revised by F. M. Harrison (1928)	Brown
The Church Book of Bunyan Meeting 1650–1821, edited in facsimile by G. B. Harrison (1928)	Church Book
A Catalogue of Books . . . forming a part of the library of E. D. Church (2 vols., New York, 1909)	Church Catalogue
The Works of that Eminent Servant of Christ, Mr. John Bunyan (1692)	Folio
A Bibliography of the Works of John Bunyan, by F. M. Harrison (Bibliographical Society, Oxford, 1932)	Harrison
Journal of English and Germanic Philology	J.E.G.P.
Modern Language Review	M.L.R.
Modern Philology	M.P.
Notes and Queries	N. & Q.
The Oxford English Dictionary	O.E.D.
H. R. Plomer, *Dictionary of Printers and Booksellers, 1668–1720*	Plomer
Review of English Studies	R.E.S.
Sotheby, Wilkinson and Hodge, *Catalogues* (various dates)	Sotheby Cat.
Henri A. Talon, *John Bunyan, the Man and his Work* (1951)	Talon

LIST OF ILLUSTRATIONS

INTRODUCTION

INTRODUCTION

A. THE FIRST PART 1678–88

I. THE COMPOSITION OF
THE PILGRIM'S PROGRESS

(i) Bunyan's Imprisonments

THE copy for the first edition of the First Part of *The Pilgrim's Progress* was entered in the Stationers' Register on 22 December 1677:

> Nathaniel Ponder entered then for his Coppy by vertue of a licence under the hand of Mr. Turner, and which is subscribed by Mr. Warden Vere, One Book or Coppy Intituled The Pilgrim's Progress from this world to that which is to come, delivered in ye Similitude of a Dream, by John Bunyan, vjd.[1]

The book was licensed and entered in the Term Catalogue for the following Hilary Term, 18 February 1678;[2] this date would customarily indicate the time of publication, or only slightly precede it.[3]

The composition of *The Pilgrim's Progress* is connected by tradition, by the testimony of Bunyan's earliest biographers, and by his own statement in the work itself, with the period of his imprisonments. The Den in which the Dreamer lays him down at the beginning is glossed in the margin of the third edition 'The Gaol'. The authenticity of other additions and marginalia in that edition support the trustworthiness of this note. Bunyan does not, however, mention imprisonment in the prefatory verses where he talks freely and intimately about the genesis of the work, his zest in writing it, and the shocked criticisms of some who read his manuscript.

---

[1] *A Transcript of the Stationers' Register 1640–1708* (1913–14), iii. 49.

[2] *T.C.* i. 299. By licensing the book, an unusual step with a work of this nature, Ponder acquired the exclusive right to publish it, which suggests that he may have foreseen its popularity.

[3] Entries in *T.C.* were sometimes made a short time before publication; see R. B. McKerrow, *An Introduction to Bibliography* (Oxford, 1928), pp. 138–9.

To ascertain when Bunyan wrote the book and to attempt to trace its history up to the time of its publication, it is necessary to establish as far as is possible the dates of his arrest and release and the nature of his confinement.

Bunyan underwent two imprisonments. The first was the longer and more celebrated, and can be precisely dated. For his refusal to give an undertaking against preaching to conventicles he remained in jail from November 1660 to March 1672. The second imprisonment of about six months is much more obscure and the documentary evidence remains scanty and ambiguous. Recent research has assigned it to between 1675 and 1677. The older view, as for example that of Southey in 1830, was to ignore the second imprisonment and assume dogmatically that *The Pilgrim's Progress* was a product of the first.[1] Since John Brown's discussion of the problem in 1885 was followed by the discovery of a warrant of arrest,[2] the tendency has been to assume that Bunyan must have composed it in the second, shorter imprisonment, because it was the later one, and because its somewhat shadowy nature was now given a more definite outline.[3] A later article by an eminent Baptist historian, Dr. W. T. Whitley, corrected some of the assumptions of Brown's theory and put forward the view that the imprisonment was the result, not of a civil, but of an ecclesiastical prosecution;[4] but Whitley still took for granted that the work was written in this period of six months.

But the seventeenth-century biographers of Bunyan were aware of the six months' imprisonment, and yet state that the book was written during the one that ended in 1672.

---

[1] Robert Southey in *The Pilgrim's Progress* (1830), Introduction, pp. lxxii–lxxiii.

[2] The warrant is described by W. G. Thorpe, *Proceedings of the Society of Antiquaries*, Second Series (1887), xii. 11–17. There is a facsimile reproduction in Brown, p. 267.

[3] F. M. Harrison in revising the biography by John Brown did not modify Brown's view (Brown, pp. 266–8); the case for earlier composition has, however, been stated by Gwylim O. Griffith, *John Bunyan* (1927), pp. 221–6; Daniel Gibson, 'On the Genesis of the *Pilgrim's Progress*', *M.P.* xxxii (1935), 368 ff., and Henri A. Talon, *John Bunyan: the Man and his Works* (1951), pp. 315–18, retain the theory that Bunyan wrote during the second imprisonment, though the latter acknowledges recent objections and bases his position on a psychological appreciation of the immediacy of Bunyan's inspiration.

[4] W. T. Whitley, 'Bunyan's Imprisonments', *Trans. Bapt. Hist. Soc.* vi (1918–19), 1–24.

The value of these earliest lives of Bunyan and other contemporary sources must be briefly summarized. First there
is *A Continuation of Mr. Bunyan's Life* in the seventh edition
of *Grace Abounding* (1692); this has been attributed with
some plausibility by Brown and others to George Cokayne,
minister of the Independent congregation at Red Cross
Street in Southwark and Bunyan's intimate friend;[1] it is
by someone who knew him well enough to be able to give
a close description of his features and physique. In the same
year Charles Doe, a comb-maker of Southwark whose ardent
discipleship of Bunyan had led him to turn publisher,
brought out in folio *The Works of that Eminent Servant of
Christ, Mr. John Bunyan* as the first volume of a collected
edition which was never completed; the concluding section
of this volume is entitled *The Struggler* (referring to Doe
himself, 'the struggler for the preservation of these labours'):
it consists of a catalogue of Bunyan's books, 'Reasons why
Christian people should promote by subscription the printing in folio the labours of Mr. J. B.', and a short biography,
valuable for its first-hand account of Bunyan's preaching in
London. *An Account of the Life and Death of Mr. John
Bunyan* was added to Doe's posthumous edition of *The
Heavenly Footman* (1698). Though it appears after items
reprinted from *The Struggler* (the catalogue and 'Some
Account of Mr. Bunyan and his Ministry') it is not by Doe,
since the author speaks of first meeting Bunyan in prison,
and Doe had described his first sight of his hero when he was
in the pulpit.[2] Apart from some unique information about
the prison period this account dwells on conversion experience and is largely a rewording of *Grace Abounding*.

An Account of the Life and Actions of John Bunyan (1692)
is bound up with the spurious third part of *The Pilgrim's
Progress*. As might be expected from this ill company it is
without authority; it is pompous and full of padding, and
there is no sign that the writer had much more information
than could be gained from reading Bunyan's autobiography;

---

[1] There are references to Cokayne in the *Church Book*, ff. 46, 74. For Bunyan's
connexion with other London meeting-houses, particularly Pinner's Hall, see
Walter Wilson, *History and Antiquities of Dissenting Churches and Meeting Houses in
London, Westminster and Southwark* (1808–14), ii. 249–55, 572.

[2] Charles Doe, *A Collection of Experience of the Work of Grace* (1700), p. 52.

the only exceptions are references to Bishop Barlow's intervention for Bunyan's release and to Bunyan's visits to
London: the intervention is also mentioned in *A Continuation*, and the visits are dealt with by both the anonymous
biographers and by Doe. The full story of the approach to
Barlow on Bunyan's behalf is to be found in Robert Asty's
Life of Owen (1721). Bunyan's *A Relation of My Imprisonment*, which remained in manuscript until 1765,[1] is
misleading in its title: it consists of five letters to the
brethren of the Bedford church written early in the first
imprisonment; they describe the circumstances of his
arrest and examination before the justices, and his wife's
attempt to have his case brought up again at the assize;
they do not continue the story beyond 1662. They may
however be supplemented by allusions to the duration of
his confinement in the prefaces to some of his later
works.

The manuscript minutes of the Bedford church meeting
are less informative than might have been expected: they
provide a sparse record of meetings to break bread, of the
admission of new members, and of the visitation of those in
trouble or error. Since Bunyan's first imprisonment was at
times so lenient that he was able to attend meetings and
even to be sent on missions to absent members, the record is
less useful for the corroboration of dates of imprisonment or
release; also in 1675–7, under Bunyan's own pastorate and
in the period when the second incarceration is conjectured
to have taken place, the minutes were most irregularly
maintained and there are but few entries.

Finally, a body of oral tradition in the Bedford locality
found its way into later works, notably John Jukes's *A
History of Bunyan's Church* (1849), and continued to exist
into the time of John Brown, who was the minister of Bunyan
Meeting between 1864 and 1903. Traditions concerning
Bunyan's relations with the London Nonconformist churches
have likewise found their way into Walter Wilson's *History
and Antiquities of Dissenting Churches and Meeting Houses in
London, Westminster and Southwark* (1808–14).

---

[1] Thomas Gurney the shorthand-writer bought the manuscript for five guineas
from Bunyan's great-granddaughter (*Evangelical Magazine* (1813), p. 148).

Thus there are three almost contemporary accounts apparently based on personal knowledge, two anonymous and one by Charles Doe. We have Doe's statement that he only came into contact with Bunyan during the time of persecution at the end of Charles II's reign (1683–5), so his testimony is not reliable for the imprisonment period. Cokayne, however, the probable author of *A Continuation*, was in constant communication with the Bedford church from 1660 onwards and received several of its members who had moved to London into communion with the Red Cross Street congregation.[1] The two other anonymous accounts are of considerably less authority. The aim of all five writers is hagiography and in their treatment of fact they are disappointingly vague; but where their testimony is united and unequivocal it is hard to reject it.

The date of the first imprisonment is established beyond any shadow of doubt. On 12 November 1660, at Lower Samsell in south Bedfordshire, Bunyan was arrested while preaching and committed by a local magistrate, Francis Wingate. This was before general measures had been undertaken against the Nonconformists, and at quarter sessions in January 1661 he was sentenced to imprisonment under the Elizabethan act against conventicles.[2] He was freed under the Declaration of Indulgence in March 1672. Doe and the author of *A Continuation* divide this twelve-year imprisonment into two. The former says:

... they put him in Bedford Gaol, and there he continued about six years, and then was let out again ... They took him again at a Meeting, and put him in the same Gaol, where he lay six years more. . . . And after he was released again, they took him again, and put him in Prison the third time, but that proved but for about half a year.[3]

And in a note appended to *A Catalogue of all Mr. Bunyan's Books* he makes confusion worse confused by saying that Bunyan was called to the pastoral office at Bedford in 1671,

[1] *Church Book*, p. 46.
[2] 35 Eliz. c. i. Since he refused to plead either guilty or not guilty, abjuration proceedings were started against him but seem to have been interrupted by the coronation. On the legal penalties against Nonconformists see also G. R. Cragg, *Puritanism in the Period of the Great Persecution* (1957), pp. 50–56.
[3] Doe, *The Struggler* (*Works*, iii. 765).

'being the 11th of his 12 Years and a half Imprisonment at 3 times'. Bunyan was indeed elected pastor in 1671 (Old Style), being chosen by a meeting of the congregation on 21 January 1671–2. But all the other evidence points to a date later than 1672 for the six months' imprisonment. It may be that the notion of a short interval of freedom in 1666 was connected with a period when Bunyan was allowed to move on parole among his family and friends, and seemed to be more out of the county jail than in it. Yet the *Church Book* records his presence at meetings and other business many times in the whole period 1660–72; there is no special concentration on the central years, and in fact he is not mentioned at all under 1666; he was temporarily at liberty in August and September 1661, and then towards the end of his sentence in October 1668 and frequently between then and the end of 1671.[1] Bunyan speaks of this period as a single imprisonment both in the Epistle to the Reader of *A Confession of My Faith and a Reason of My Practice* (1672) where he speaks of 'so weighty an argument as above eleven years' imprisonment' and later of 'almost twelve years' imprisonment';[2] and in the third and subsequent editions of *Grace Abounding* he alters the statement 'was had home to Prison, and there has lain now above five year and a quarter' to 'compleat twelve years'.[3] The author of *A Continuation* contradicts himself in a passage where he speaks of 'his being freed from his twelve years' imprisonment and upwards';[4] and finally we have the clear testimony of one of his official captors, Paul Cobb, Clerk of the Peace for Bedfordshire, writing in 1670: 'he hath lain in prison upon that conviction ever since Christmas Sessions, 12 Chas. II.'[5]

According to legend Bunyan was imprisoned in the little town jail on Bedford Bridge. However, since his crime came under the county jurisdiction, he would serve his sentence in the county jail; the gate-house on the bridge was only a

---

[1] *Church Book*, ff. 25, 27–29.
[2] *A Confession of My Faith*, ii. 593.
[3] *G.A.*, § 320. The third edition is undated but is listed in *T.C.* for Trinity Term 1679 under the heading 'reprinted'.
[4] *A Continuation of Mr. Bunyan's Life* (1692), p. 179.
[5] *Historical MSS. Commission 14th Report*, Appendix, Part IV, *Kenyon MSS.*, p. 86·

town lock-up whereas Bunyan's prison could accommodate at one time 'above 60 Dissenters besides himself'.[1]

The second imprisonment, though vouched for by Doe and the author of *A Continuation*, who call it the third, is not explicitly referred to by Bunyan. There are, however, two legal documents of great importance: a warrant for Bunyan's arrest dated 4 March 1674–5, and a bond entered into by sureties for his good behaviour on release and dated 21 June 1677.[2] The latter came to light in 1949 and before that it had been believed by Brown and F. M. Harrison that Bunyan was arrested on the warrant of 1675 and imprisoned for six months some time later in that year. But the warrant refers to teaching at a conventicle, and under the Conventicle Act of 1670 only fines were imposed, though these could lead to the distraining of goods and other hardships.[3] In the preface to *Instruction for the Ignorant* (1675) Bunyan addresses the Bedford brethren as one being 'in the Kingdom and Patience of Jesus Christ', and as one 'driven from you in presence, not affection', and signs himself: 'Yours, to serve you by my ministry, when I can.'[4] This does not necessarily imply, as advocates of an imprisonment in 1675–6 have maintained, that he was again in jail; it could equally well mean that he was in hiding in order to avoid arrest.

A Continuation and *The Life and Actions* both refer to Barlow's intervention, and this episode is related with circumstantial detail in Asty's *Life of Owen*;[5] all three wrongly associate it with the twelve years' imprisonment. From Asty's narrative and the bond of 1677 the pattern of

---

[1] The prison on the bridge was only large enough to hold about eight; in 1672 it was damaged by floods and remained dilapidated till 1675 when the council agreed that it should be rebuilt (*Act Book of Bedford Corporation*, 13 May 1675); Brown's suggestion that it might have been rebuilt specially to accommodate Bunyan seems far-fetched.

[2] Now in the Aylesbury Museum MS. 31/24, a formulary into which Richard Heywood, the Buckingham Registrar, has copied the bond. William Foster who proceeded against Bunyan later became Commissary in the Archdeaconry of Buckingham. See Joyce Godber, *Trans. Cong. Hist. Soc.* xvi (1949), pp. 23 ff.

[3] The Bedford separatists suffered extreme hardships immediately after the law was put into effect and attempted to resist its application: *A True and Impartiall Narrative of Some Illegal and Arbitrary proceedings . . . in and near the Town of Bedford* (1670), passim. See also G. R. Cragg, op. cit., pp. 55–56.

[4] *Instruction for the Ignorant*, ii. 676.

[5] In *The Complete Sermons of Dr. John Owen* (1721), i. xxx.

events emerges: Bunyan was arrested and condemned on an ecclesiastical charge for refusal to hear divine service and receive the Sacrament; his obstinacy was certified to the Bishop (of Lincoln) and a *significavit* for a writ *de excommunicato capiendo* was transmitted into Chancery; he was then taken into custody by the sheriff of the county. It was possible for release to be obtained if two persons offered a cautionary bond to the bishop of the diocese, and with this intention friends of Bunyan prevailed on Owen to intervene with Barlow. Barlow seems to have prevaricated, pleading the suspicion he might incur, and to have advised the more circuitous and expensive method of making application to the Lord Chancellor, who would then transmit his order to the bishop for the prisoner's release. This, according to Asty, was the course adopted.

There is therefore the strongest possible presumption that Bunyan was released as a result of the cautionary bond on or soon after 21 June 1677, though, if the bond was that presented to Barlow by Owen, one would have to allow for the delay in applying to the Lord Chancellor. Were it not for the supplementary evidence of the part played by Barlow, the fact that request was thus made for his release would not of course mean that it was obtained, any more than the existence of a warrant for his arrest signifies that he was arrested. Barlow had been consecrated to the see of Lincoln on 27 June 1675. His continuing interest in Bunyan is shown by the number of Bunyan's works among the books which Barlow bequeathed to the Bodleian and which now form the Lincoln collection.[1] His caution in preferring not to act directly is attributed by Asty to the critical situation 'soon after the discovery of the Popish Plot'. This must be a lapse of memory on the part of one writing over forty years after the event; it would place the incident later than June 1678 and none of the documents refers to a period later than June 1677. Asty's memory is a year out and he explains personal caution (Barlow speaks of his 'many enemies') by the reasons for fear all men in office were to have during the Whig

---

[1] Barlow's sympathy is illuminated by the fact that earlier in his career he had expressed doubts on paedobaptism and had had connexions with the Baptist theologian John Tombes. (*D.N.B.* s.v. Barlow.)

terror a year later. The sureties to the bond are both Londoners, Thomas Kelsay and Robert Blaney; thus they would be outside the jurisdiction of the archdeacon of Bedford and less liable to the consequences of Bunyan's further refusal to conform after his release. Both were in the parish of St. Giles, Cripplegate, where George Cokayne's meeting-house was situated. William Foster, Commissary of Bedford, would have been the official empowered to execute a *significavit* against Bunyan; he took a prominent part in the first prosecution of 1660–1,[1] and apparently in the unsuccessful proceedings of 1675 too, as Justice of the Peace, for his is the last of the signatures on the warrant of that year.

Since the ecclesiastical prosecution would deliver him into the hands of the sheriff, Bunyan would once more be detained in the county jail: the tradition that *The Pilgrim's Progress* was written in the gate-house on the bridge over the Ouse remains a pleasing legend.

(ii) *The Date when the First Part was written*

Thus it appears probable that the second imprisonment ran from late December 1676 or January 1677 to June or July 1677. Now that the discovery of the bond of 1677 has proved that Bunyan was never incarcerated in the town lock-up, and so could not have written *The Pilgrim's Progress* there, there is no longer any special reason for holding that it was written during the second imprisonment. The more knowledgeable of the early biographers assign its composition to the longer imprisonment; and they were fully conversant with the shorter one. Doe writes:

> Whilst he was thus twelve years and a half in prison, he writ several of his published Books (as by many of their Epistles appears) as Pray by the Spirit, Holy City, Resurrection, Grace abounding, and others; also the Pilgrim's Progress, as himself and many others have said.'

And Cokayne, or whoever wrote *A Continuation*, says:

> During these confinements he wrote these following books, viz.: Of Prayer by the Spirit, The Holy City, Resurrection, Grace Abounding, Pilgrim's Progress, the first part.[2]

[1] *Relation of My Imprisonment,* edited by John Brown (Cambridge, 1907). pp. 109–12.   [2] *A Continuation,* p. 185.

Presented with the author himself as witness at one remove it should be unnecessary to argue the matter further. The chief objection to an outright acceptance of these contemporary statements that the First Part was written before 1670 is the long delay of eight years or more in sending the book to the printer. But this is not really extraordinary when the novel and controversially 'amusing' character of the book is considered. Bunyan feared that to contemporary readers the humour and the whole-hearted fictional projection of his message would seem a shockingly frivolous treatment of sacred things. As he says in the prefatory verses:

> Well, when I had thus put my ends together,
> I shew'd them others, that I might see whether
> They would condemn them, or them justifie:
> And some said, let them live; some, let them die:
> Some said, John, print it; others said, Not so:
> Some said, It might do good; others said, No.
> Now was I in a straight, and did not see
> Which was the best thing to be done by me:
> At last I thought, Since you are thus divided,
> I print it will, and so the case decided.

We cannot guess how long a deliberation is indicated by that 'at last'; certainly it implies enough time for the manuscript to have passed through several hands. Earlier in the verses Bunyan speaks of warming to his theme so that the book was written without difficulty:

> Thus I set Pen to Paper with delight,
> And quickly had my thoughts in black and white.

This rapidity, though, is restricted to the act of composition, and is qualified by the statement that he only devoted 'vacant seasons' to the work; his time in prison would also be portioned out for the necessary business of maintaining his family by 'making many hundred Gross of long Tagg'd laces'.[1]

In any case, Bunyan, though a prolific writer, often left his manuscripts unpublished. Doe found sixteen unpublished works among his papers at his death, and one, *The Heavenly*

---

[1] *An Account of the Life and Death of Mr. John Bunyan*, pp. 126–8.

Footman, appears from its tentative use of the metaphor of the journey of the Christian life to be prior to *The Pilgrim's Progress*.

There is also the question of the pause in the narrative two-thirds through when the Dreamer awakes and dreams again:

And I slept, and Dreamed again, and saw the same two Pilgrims going down the Mountain along the High-way towards the City.

The break does not correspond with any pause in the journey unfolding before the Dreamer; it seems, in fact, somewhat clumsy and abrupt. We can conclude with Brown that when the Dreamer awoke Bunyan was released from his 'Den', but that this release took place, not as Brown believed in 1675, but in 1672. If it had been in 1677 when the second imprisonment ended there would have been less than six months for the final third of the book to be written, hardly a year for the whole work to be begun and finished, read and criticized by several people, and for it to reach the hands of the bookseller. In fact, however much Bunyan's thoughts multiplied

Like sparks that from the coals of Fire do flie

it would seem an instance of extreme speed for the whole process from the genesis of his inspiration to the printing-house to fall within the compass of a year. Finally there is the evidence of the new episodes introduced into the second edition: it would be difficult to explain why Bunyan should have added considerable sections to an edition which came out in the same year as the first if he had only finished the original version a short while before sending it to the press. This is a more solid criticism of the theory of composition during and after the second imprisonment than any objection to an earlier dating on the grounds of the long interval of time allowed to elapse before publication.

However, firmer grounds than the time factor appear when we compare the internal character of *The Pilgrim's Progress* with that of the other works produced by Bunyan in the whole period 1660–77. The prefatory verses tell how in beginning one book about the journey of the saints he was led insensibly to develop the imagery into an allegory:

> And thus it was: I writing of the Way
> And Race of Saints in this our Gospel-Day,
> Fell suddenly into an Allegory
> About their Journey, and the way to Glory . . .

Now the treatise which Brown and others selected as this predecessor of *The Pilgrim's Progress* was *The Strait Gate* (1676). But this title might be either an echo or an anticipation of the Wicket Gate by which Christian gets into the way (in *The Strait Gate*, the entrance into grace is compared to 'some little pinching wicket'); and though *The Strait Gate* contains portraits of false professors which resemble in brief the character-sketches of Worldly Wiseman, By-ends, Talkative, and others,[1] many of the latter appear only in the second and third editions of the allegory. But above all *The Strait Gate* is not at all about 'the Way and Race of Saints'.

The only book by Bunyan which develops the theme of salvation under St. Paul's figure of a race for a prize is *The Heavenly Footman*. Gradually, as if Bunyan cannot help himself, the metaphor turns from a cross-country race to a long journey. The Christian is exhorted to 'beware of by-paths',[2] and the lanes that run out of the way. This recalls By-path Meadow and other incidents. The runner in the race for a heavenly prize must go by the cross, the standing way-mark.[3] Through all the directions given him runs the notion of striving towards a goal across difficult and dangerous country: the grand central metaphor of *The Pilgrim's Progress* had been conceived.

The Heavenly Footman was published posthumously by Doe in 1698 and the date when it was written is a matter of conjecture. It seems to be early rather than late. Bunyan speaks of 'that little time which I have been a professor'. He recommends to his readers his own early books *A Few Sighs from Hell* and *The Doctrine of the Law and Grace Unfolded* (1658–9). Also he employs at times a levelling tone about the relations of masters and servants which is characteristic of his earlier phase and the revolutionary

---

[1] *The Strait Gate*, i. 388–9.
[2] *The Heavenly Footman*, iii. 384–5.   [3] Ibid. 386.

epoch in which he grew up. It points to a period not later than the first imprisonment, and since *The Pilgrim's Progress* grew out of the *Footman*, the earlier dating of the former receives further confirmation. During the latter part of that time, the six years between the publication of *Grace Abounding* and his release from prison, Bunyan published only the controversial pamphlets *A Confession of My Faith* and *A Defence of Justification by Faith* (1672); he may also have contributed to *A New and Useful Concordance to the Holy Bible* (1673) by Vavasor Powell.[1] In 1675–8 he published *Light for them that Sit in Darkness* (1675), *Instruction for the Ignorant* (1675), *Saved by Grace* (1676), *The Strait Gate* (1676), and *Come and Welcome to Jesus Christ* (1678), as well as *The Pilgrim's Progress*.[2] It is of course possible that all or some of these last five treatises were written earlier, even during the imprisonment years, and were printed when liberty gave him easier communication with the London booksellers. But confinement had not hindered him from publishing nine books and two broadsheets in those twelve years; so it is proper to note this comparative breathing-space of six years in Bunyan's highly productive career, occurring just after the composition of his autobiography and in a period which a concurrence of evidence from other sources marks as the creative time of his masterpiece.[3]

[1] This was the second edition of a work first published in 1671 after Powell's death; it contains additional scriptures and the title-page carries a recommendation by Bunyan's friend Owen (Harrison, p. xvii). The Bunyan signature in the copy of the *Concordance* in the library of the Baptist College, Bristol, is considered by Sir Hilary Jenkinson more likely to be that of his son: Joyce Godber, 'John Bunyan's Signature', *Bedfordshire Magazine*, vi (1957), 47–49.

[2] Harrison, pp. 24–40.

[3] Bunyan's Victorian editor, George Offor, thought that the work concerning 'the way and race of saints' was 'most probably his own spiritual experience', *Works*, iii. 7.

One further piece of internal evidence may be mentioned. In Part One Giant Pope is old and decrepit and sits at his cave's mouth 'biting his nails'. In Part Two Giant Maul, representing Catholic power, is a much more dangerous opponent. The latter of course belongs to the age after the Popish Plot, but the increasing fear of Catholic subversion in the whole period after the Treaty of Dover suggests that a weak Giant Pope would be more likely to be invented before that date. On 10 March 1671 both houses of Parliament presented a petition against the growth of Popery which was attributed to the great numbers of priests and Jesuits frequenting London and Westminster; the Test Act was passed in 1673; and Marvell was declaring in 1677 that fear of 'downright Popery and French slavery with it had existed since the King's meeting at Dover with his sister in 1670' (*An account of the*

Driven in on himself, condemned by the respectable world, and partly separated from his co-religionists, he had just composed an apologia in the form of his spiritual autobiography. Now, in his cell, the powerful physical imagery in which he had conceived his conversion took on a new dimension. The relation of the allegory to *Grace Abounding* is more profound than is its relation to the *Footman*. The latter brought into the forefront of Bunyan's mind a metaphor which countless Christian writers, Puritans and others, had employed before him. The former contains the whole drama of the quest for personal salvation which is the subject of *The Pilgrim's Progress*. As F. M. Harrison has said: '*The Pilgrim's Progress* is but another version of Bunyan's spiritual autobiography, written not like that, in sombre hue, nor yet—as he claims it to be—'in black and white'—but in colours so vivid as to bring division among his contemporaries.'[1] The good and evil presences haunting the depths of his consciousness in *Grace Abounding* put on flesh in the allegory. Among reminiscences in the later work there may be mentioned his dream of the door in the hill which shuts him off from the good people of the Bedford church, and which reappears early in *The Pilgrim's Progress* as the Wicket Gate, and the voices murmuring blasphemies in his ear, which are met again by Christian in the Valley of the Shadow of Death. There is also a structural relationship: mere legal Christianity subject to the terrors of the law is succeeded by more intense Bible reading, as the encounter with Mr. Worldly Wiseman is followed by the stay at the Interpreter's House; and, though the various types of hypocrite and unawakened Christian who take the by-paths are adequately dealt with, the real peril for Christian as it had been for his creator is the temptation to spiritual despair.[2]

This intimate, step-by-step relation to the spiritual autobiography of *Grace Abounding* does not extend to the additional matter incorporated into the second and third editions.

growth of popery and arbitrary government in England, 1677, and see David Ogg, *England under Charles II*, i. 350, ii. 541).

[1] 'John Bunyan in the Light of Recent Research', unpublished typescript in Bedford Public Library, p. 64.

[2] The relation between *The Pilgrim's Progress* and *Grace Abounding* is treated in full by the present editor in *R.E.S.* (1948), xxiv. 102–20.

These new sections are different in tone; they lack the
confessional urgency of the main narrative and display
humorous moral observation; they show us Bunyan's mind
broadened by the pastoral experience that came to him after
1672. Worldly Wiseman is to some extent a portrait of a
Latitudinarian divine: it is probable that Bunyan had in
mind Edward Fowler, the ethical religion of whose *Design
of Christianity* (1670) he had fiercely attacked,[1] and that the
passage was written shortly after his controversy with
Fowler in 1670–1; but that for some reason, perhaps the
disapproval of sectarian critics for its satiric gaiety, it was
not included in the first edition: success gave Bunyan the
courage to print it. The principal insertion in the third
edition, the episode of By-ends's companions, treats of the
same themes as *Mr. Badman*: how the hypocrite may justify
himself in getting a rich wife or more custom to his shop.
By-ends's speech in that episode, when he declares that he is
for religion 'when he walks in his golden slipers in the
Sunshine, and with applause', recalls the vignette of the
time-serving professor in the gallery of portraits in *The
Strait Gate*:

> He can be for anything for any company; he can throw stones with
> both hands; his religion alters as fast as his company; he is a frog of
> Egypt, and can live in the water and out of the water. . . .[2]

The episode seems to have been written certainly after 1676
and probably in 1678–9 when Bunyan was giving the major
part of his attention to the writing of *Badman*.

On the evidence so far available, the facts of the imprisonments and the character of the allegory, we can conclude
that Bunyan wrote the greater part of the First Part before
he was set at liberty in 1672. The effort to review his own
spiritual history set in motion the creative force which pro-
jected his experiences into fiction.

---

[1] Fowler was rector of Northill from 1656 and a moderate Presbyterian who
favoured compromise with the Establishment. In 1662 his father was ejected, but
Fowler, after apparently giving up his own living for a time, finally conformed
(*D.N.B.* s.v. Edward Fowler). Fowler's theology is a pale version of Cambridge
latitudinarianism; to Bunyan he was suspect as a local turncoat and he attacked him
in a tract written in the last days of his first imprisonment, *A Defence of the Doctrine
of Justification by Faith* (1671), ii. 281–334. He replied violently to Bunyan in a
pamphlet *Dirt Wip't Off* (1671).   [2] *The Strait Gate*, i. 389.

II. EDITIONS OF *THE PILGRIM'S PROGRESS*
1678–88

AFTER *The Pilgrim's Progress* was licensed on 18 February 1678 editions appeared in rapid succession, the eleventh being reached before Bunyan's death on 31 August 1688. In reality there were more than eleven editions issued during these years, for there were two of the fifth and two of the ninth. The name of Nathaniel Ponder is found on the title-page of them all. The twelfth edition is described as printed for Robert Ponder, supposedly his son, and the thirteenth as printed for Robert Ponder, 'and are to be sold by Nich. Boddington at the Golden Ball in Duck Lane, 1693'. Nathaniel Ponder's name appears once more, and for the last time, on the fourteenth edition, 1695.[1]

THE FIRST EDITION, 1678

BRITISH MUSEUM COPY: Small octavo. First Edition.

Collation by signatures: A–P⁸, Q⁴.

Collation by pagination: blank, recto [A]; blank, verso [A]; title-page [as reproduced opposite], recto [A2]; blank, verso [A2]; Author's Apology, recto A3—verso [A6]; text, pp. 1–232; FINIS, p. 232; The Conclusion. THE END, p. [233]: blank p. [234]. Last leaf, cut away.

No errors either in signature-marking or in pagination. The following misprints are found in this copy: pra^y (p. 30, l. 1), '*paht*' for '*path*' (p. 86, l. 6); 'befit' for 'benefit' (p. 102, l. 23); 'Prophanes' for 'Prophane' (p. 104, l. 4); 'troden' for 'untroden' (p. 172, l. 9); 'they often' for 'they have often' (p. 173, l. 29); 'Hogoblins' for 'Hobgoblins'

---

[1] Nathaniel Ponder was the son of a Nonconformist mercer, of Rothwell, in Northamptonshire. On the expiration of his apprenticeship to Robert Gibbs, bookseller, of Chancery Lane, he set up a shop of his own in Chancery Lane at the sign of the Peacock, and a second shop in 1676 in the Poultry. Early in his career he became associated with the great Nonconformist leader, Dr. John Owen, most of whose writings he published. The year before the manuscript of *The Pilgrim's Progress* was placed in his hands, Ponder was committed to prison for printing Andrew Marvell's *Rehearsal Transpros'd*, described as 'an unlicensed Pamphlet tending to Sedition and Defamation of the Christian Religion'. He was frequently involved in litigation, notably against one of his printers, Thomas Braddyl. In consequence of the phenomenal success of *The Pilgrim's Progress*, he became known, John Dunton tells us, as 'Bunyan Ponder'. See Plomer, pp. 240–1; F. M. Harrison, 'Nathaniel Ponder: the Publisher of *The Pilgrim's Progress*', *The Library*, xv (1934), 257–94.

Joseph Middleton
1784.

THE
Pilgrim's Progress
FROM
THIS WORLD,
TO
That which is to come:

Delivered under the Similitude of a

DREAM

Wherein is Discovered,
The manner of his setting out,
His Dangerous Journey; And safe
Arrival at the Desired Countrey.

I have used Similitudes, Hos. 12. 10.

By *John Bunyan.*

Licensed and Entred according to Order.

LONDON,
Printed for *Nath. Ponder* at the *Peacock*
in the *Poultrey* near *Cornhil*, 1678.

First Edition, 1678

British Museum

(p. 223, l. 20); 'away' for 'a way' (p. 232, l. 18); catchword, p. 226, 'phets', first word, p. 227, 'Prophets'. On the title-page is the inscription 'Joseph Middleton 1784'. This copy was purchased by the Museum authorities in 1884 from the Rev. Ernest S. Thies, a Wesleyan minister, for about £60. Mr. Thies, according to Dr. Brown,[1] had it from his brother-in-law, Mr. Thorne, of Dalston, who had acquired it through a kinsman, a book-collector.

OTHER COPIES. The first edition is the least rare of all the editions that were issued before Bunyan's death. Offor in 1847 knew of but one copy; in his three-volume edition of Bunyan's *Works* (second edition 1862), he states that he had discovered a second. In 1901 Victor H. Paltsits located five copies.[2] An anonymous contributor to *The Times Literary Supplement*, 13 October 1921, accounted for nine copies. A tenth copy, the Davenport-Wheeler-Thomas, came to light in 1922;[3] still another, the Warner copy, in 1926.[4] In the Ter-centenary edition of Brown's *John Bunyan* (pp. 440, 492) two additional copies are recorded. Of these additional copies I have examined personally those marked with asterisks.

1. *The Holford copy.* This is said to be a perfect copy in the original sheepskin binding. It was originally the property of Lord Vernon, from whom it was purchased about 1840 by Robert Holford, father of Sir George Holford. On Sir George Holford's death it passed into the hands of an American purchaser. It is now in the possession of the estate of John H. Scheide of Titusville, Pennsylvania. It was from this copy that Elliot Stock made his so-called fac-simile in 1875.

2. *The Lenox copy.** This was bought by James Lenox, of New York, from William Pickering, the bookseller, some time before July 1855. The title-page, first two leaves of the Author's Apology, and leaf of the Conclusion have been supplied in facsimile from the Holford copy. In 1855 Lenox compared the two copies and found that 'they are exactly alike'.[5] The collation of the Lenox copy differs from that

---

[1] Brown, p. 440.   [2] *The Literary Collector* (1901), ii. 61–66.
[3] *T.L.S.*, 19 June 1922, p. 432.
[4] *N. & Q.*, 17 July 1926, p. 38; 31 July 1926, p. 74.
[5] *Contributions to a Catalogue of The Lenox Library* (1877–80), No. IV. *Bunyan's Pilgrim's Progress, &c.*, p. 6

of the British Museum copy as to page-numbering. In the Lenox copy page 223 is misnumbered 222, 226 is 227, 227 is 226; page 83 is printed 8ε, and 231 is 23¹. It also has the corrected state of the inner forme of sheets A and B.

3. *The John Rylands Library copy.** This is in perfect condition. It is the copy formerly in the possession of Elliot Stock, who bought it from Coombs a bookseller for £25. Coombs had acquired it with a lot of miscellaneous articles for about sixpence. The facsimile published by Elliot Stock in 1895 with an Introduction by John Brown is a reproduction of this copy. This copy, like the Lenox, has signatures A and B, inner forme, in the corrected state.

4. *The Palmer-Nash copy.* This copy, now in the Henry E. Huntington Library, is described in detail in the *Church Catalogue* (i. 227–9, No. 198a). The collation differs from that of the British Museum copy in the pagination, and in having, like the two previous copies, the corrected state of signature B. The errors in page-numbering in the Lenox copy are also found in this copy. The only misprint reported is that of the catchword on p. 226, identical with the one already mentioned as occurring in the British Museum copy. Facing the title-page is a portrait of Bunyan the Dreamer. It is further described as 'Bound in old calf; in green crushed levant morocco solander case, elaborately tooled. The inside covers, the recto of the frontispiece, and p. [234] are scribbled over; the frontispiece is torn and mended and mounted on a stub; laid in is an account of Ann Palmer, the former owner of the book, by her grandson, John Nash.'

This copy, formerly the property of the Nash family, of Upton Court, Slough, was sold at Sotheby's 6 May 1901 to Cockerell for £1,475. It passed next to the library of E. D. Church, and finally to its present location, the Henry E. Huntington Library.

That which makes this copy unique is the presence of the portrait of the Dreamer, better known as 'the sleeping portrait', engraved by Robert White, opposite the title-page. According to Lowndes, 'the first edition with a portrait was the third (1679)',¹ and so far the portrait has been found in no other copy earlier than the copies of the third. In all copies

¹ *Bibliographer's Manual* (1869), i. 312.

Frontispiece to the Palmer-Nash copy
of the First Edition

Huntington Library

Frontispiece to the British Museum copy
of the Third Edition, 1679

of the third and subsequent editions in which the portrait occurs, the city from which the pilgrim is fleeing has the word 'Destruction' printed beneath it; in the Palmer-Nash copy the name of the city is 'Vanity'. The British Museum copy of the third edition shows, however, in 'Destruction' slight remains of the upper parts of the *V* and the tail of the *y*. This suggests that the word 'Vanity' was taken out of the plate for the engraving for the third edition, and that the plate had originally been engraved for the first edition and the alteration subsequently made on discovery of the mistake. The absence of the portrait in any of the other known copies of the first edition may be accounted for by supposing either that only a portion of the first edition was so illustrated, the plate having been withdrawn on discovery of the mistake in it, or that the other copies had, in the course of a couple of centuries, lost their plate, probably at the hands of a collector, and been rebound.[1]

The traces of *V* and *y* in the portrait of the third edition are unmistakable (see Plates). There are still good reasons for doubting whether the plate in the Palmer-Nash copy was originally made for the first edition. No portrait has ever been found in any other copies of the first edition, nor any in the copies of the second edition. Significant, too, is the fact that Ponder in the 'Advertisement from the Bookseller' prefixed to the fourth edition makes no mention of a portrait in either the first or second edition, but says 'this Fourth Edition hath as the third had, The Authors Picture before the Title'. It may well be that the portrait in this copy of the first edition was, as Brown suggested,[2] 'added when the book was rebound'.

5. *The Pierpont Morgan Library copy.** This copy, which has three leaves [B, Q2, Q3] in facsimile, is the copy that was sold at Sotheby's to Quaritch, 26 July 1907, for £520.

6. *The Thomas Kingsford copy.* This copy is imperfect, lacking the title, first leaf, and the whole of signature L, nine leaves in all. Across the fly-leaf is written the name of the original owner: 'Thomas Kingsford, his Book, 1678, April 8.' It was bought in a miscellaneous sale at Sotheby's

---

[1] *N. & Q.*, Seventh Series, i. 227, 272, 336, 376; *Church Catalogue*, i. 227–9; Paltsits, *The Literary Collector*, ii. 62.   [2] Brown, p. 440.

on 17 March 1902 by Tregaskis for £22. It reappeared at
Sotheby's on 30 June 1921, lot 498, as the property of the
late Rev. N. C. S. Poyntz, of Dorchester-on-Thames, Oxon.,
who by a piece of extraordinary good luck, probably un-
precedented in the annals of book-collecting, had another
imperfect copy which contained the leaves lacking in the
other.[1] This is

7. *The William Readding or Thomas Marsom copy.* Across
the fly-leaf is written the name of the original owner:
'William Readding His Booke, 1678', and on another blank
page: 'William Readding at Greens fordge in the parish of
Wamborne, 1679.' Leaves from it were used to perfect the
Kingsford copy which then passed to the F. J. Hogan Library.
At the Hogan sale (Parke-Bernet Galleries, New York,
23 April 1946) it was bought by the Library of Congress.

This copy was first described by Dr. Joseph Angus, former
president of Regent's Park College.[2] The volume, which
had but recently come into Dr. Angus's hands, had once
belonged to the Marsom family. A member of that family
had been a fellow prisoner of Bunyan's and had encouraged
him—according to tradition, even to the point of sharing
in the expense—to print his allegory.[3] The copy, according
to Dr. Angus, was in the original sheepskin binding and
had been a good deal used. He also called attention to the
one point in which it seemed unique: a list of 'Erata' of five
lines on the last page below the word 'FINIS'. Both copies,
Nos. 6 and 7, were sold in one lot to Messrs. Quaritch for
£2,500.

8. *The Davenport-Wheeler-Thomas copy.* This was an
imperfect copy, wanting M2–7 which have been made up
from the Marsom-Angus copy. Written across the title-page
are two inscriptions, the first in a contemporary hand, the
second much later: 'Tho. Davenport' and 'William Wheeler's
Book. November 23, 1845'. A third inscription is to the
effect that 'William Wheeler resided at Cleobury Mortimer'.
The book was sent to Sotheby's in 1922 by Mr. J. Thomas,
of 3 Queen Street, Derby, a hairdresser, who had received

---

[1] *T.L.S.*, 13 October 1921.
[2] *Book-Lore* (November 1886), p. 182.
[3] See also Offor, Hanserd Knollys edition (1847), p. xxv.

it together with other books upon the death of a relative. It was sold 20 June for £2,010 to Messrs. Quaritch,[1] and passed into the Harmsworth Bunyan collection. On 27 January 1947 it was sold at Sotheby's to Maggs for £1,800. It is now in the Bibliothèque Bodmer (Cologny, Geneva).

9. *The Warner copy*.* Among the books offered for sale at Sotheby's 26 July 1926 was an unrecorded and perfect copy of the first edition in contemporary sheepskin binding, the property of R. C. Warner, of Lombard Street. The book was sold to Messrs. Quaritch for the extraordinary sum of £6,800, exactly £5,000 more than was paid at the same sale for a Shakespeare First Folio.[2] Within two weeks it was returned by the purchasers on the ground that it was not as described in the catalogue of sale—a perfect copy of the first edition. The feature of the book which according to the terms of the sale justified its return was that at the bottom of the last page immediately below the word 'FINIS' is an insertion of five lines of Errata.

This and the Thomas Marsom volume, No. 7 of our list, are the only known copies of this so-called 'second issue' of the first edition with the errata.[3]

The Warner copy then passed to Sir Leicester Harmsworth. It was sold to Maggs at the Harmsworth sale on 27 January 1947 for £4,400. It is now in the Library of Sir Arthur Howard. The only differences discovered between it and the British Museum copy were (1) an inverted '3' in the page-number '83', as in the Lenox, Palmer-Nash,

---

[1] *T.L.S.*, London, 19 June 1922, p. 432.

[2] *N. & Q.*, 17 July 1926, p. 38; 31 July 1926, p. 74.

[3] In a letter to *T.L.S.*, 19 August 1926, p. 549, W. W. Greg questioned the justification of dubbing these copies with Errata added, 'a second issue': 'What the presence of the errata shows is that there are two states of the last sheet, not that there are two issues of the whole volume. Some pulls of the last sheet would have the errata, some would not, but the whole of the impression would be completed before any copies were "gathered". The sheets would then be sewn up indiscriminately, and the order in which the copies issued would be random. . . .

'It seems to me that the term "issue" always implies, or should imply, some temporal sequence applicable to a book as a whole. In that sense it can hardly be correct to speak of two "issues" of the first edition of *The Pilgrim's Progress*. For anything we can tell to the contrary, the copy recently returned as belonging to the "second issue" may have been the very first copy to issue from the printing-house.'

Pierpont Morgan, and Rylands copies, and (2) the following lines immediately below 'FINIS' (p. 232):

Erata

Page 86, line 6 for *paht* r. *path,* p. 102. | l. 23. 24 for *befit* r. *benefite*. p. 104. l. | 4. for *prophanes* r. *prophane*. p. 172 l. 9. for | *troden* r. *untroden.* p. 173. l. 29 after *often* r. | *have.*

10. *The John Wilson copy.* Also once in the Harmsworth collection. It was formerly owned by Robert Philip (1791–1858), and a manuscript note of his is written on the fly-leaf: 'This portion of "The Pilgrim's Progress" was presented by Bunyan himself to his friend Mr. [John] Wilson of Hitchin in Bedfordshire [*sic*]; and it was presented to me by a descendant of the Wilson family as the best way of preserving it. Robert Philip, Maberly Cottage, Dalston. Feby. 19th, 1848.'[1]

Many of the most familiar passages in *The Pilgrim's Progress* are lacking in the first edition. It makes no mention of Christian's return home and fruitless endeavour to explain his woeful state to wife and children; of his meeting with Mr. Worldly-Wiseman and being turned aside by him to the town of Morality; of his second meeting with Evangelist and being reproved for hearkening to Worldly-Wiseman; of his confession to Good-Will of his folly in allowing himself to be so misled; of Charity's talk with Christian about his wife and children; of Evangelist's meeting with Christian and Faithful and warning them of the troubles in store for them in Vanity Fair; of their recollection of this warning while imprisoned in the cage at Vanity Fair; of By-ends' long discourse with his three friends, Mr. Hold-the-World, Mr. Money-love, and Mr. Save-all, in which the pilgrims later participate; of the monument to Lot's wife and the talk between Christian and Hopeful concerning it; of Giant Despair's wife and the cruel treatment of Christian and Hopeful which grew out of her counsel to her husband; and finally of the King's trumpeters who came out from the Celestial City to greet Christian and Hopeful. All these appear in the second edition, except the By-ends passage which is added in the third.

[1] Brown, op. cit., Appendix IV, p. 492.

THE
Pilgrim's Progress
FROM
THIS WORLD,
TO
That which is to come:

Delivered under the Similitude of a

DREAM

Wherein is Discovered,
The manner of his setting out,
His Dangerous Journey, and safe
Arrival at the Desired Country.

By *JOHN BUNYAN*.

The second Edition, with Additions.

I have used similitudes, Hosea 12. 10.

Licensed and Entred according to Order.

LONDON:
Printed for *Nath.Ponder*, at the Peacock
in the *Poultrey*, near *Cornhil*, 1678.

Second Edition, 1678

Apart from the errata list in the Warner copy, some of the copies examined have minor variants in the corrected state of signature A and the inner formes of B and L. Lenox and Rylands have the revised state of A and B, the British Museum, Pierpont Morgan, and Warner copies that of L. In several cases throughout A 'mine' is altered to 'my'; in this instance I have given editorial preference to the earlier state as being Bunyan's retention of a slightly old-fashioned form. The differences in B and L are as follows:

Lenox, Davenport-Wheeler-Thomas, and Rylands Copies	British Museum, Pierpont Morgan, and Warner Copies
Page 6, l. 4: *Go back, go back*	*go back, Go back.*
Page 6, ll. 25–27: Pli. *Come then, good Neighbor, let us be going.* Then they went both together.	Pli. *Come then good Neighbor let us be going, then they went both together.*
Page 10, ll. 21, 27: Slough l. 25: Slough of *Dispondency*	Slow Slow of *Dispond*
Page 11, ll. 22–24: (Since . . . *Gate*) l. 27: *Miry slough*	Brackets omitted Miry *slow*
Page 14, l. 6: Saying (*roman*)	Saying (*ital.* and placed one line below).
Page 15, l. 3: *Beelzebub*	*Belzebub*
Page 18, ll. 28–29: the Man that stands . . . at the head of this way, That *etc.*	the Man that stands . . . at the head of this way; that *etc.*
Page 151: marginal note—*The Grievousness of their Imprisonment*—placed opposite l. 21; scripture reference to Ps. 88. 18 opposite l. 25.	Marginal note placed opposite l. 26; scripture reference opposite l. 29.

THE SECOND EDITION, 1678

Lɴᴏx copy. Small duodecimo. Second Edition with Additions.

Collation by signatures: One leaf unsigned, A–M¹². One additional leaf, blank. E5 is unsigned.

Collation by pagination: title-page [as reproduced opposite], recto [A]; blank, verso [A]; Author's Apology, recto A2–recto [A6]; blank, verso [A6]; text, pp. 1–276; The Conclusion, p. [277]. P. 60 is misnumbered 62, 212 is 112, 236 is 136, 246 is 247, 247 is 246, 260 is 160.

OTHER COPIES. Bodleian, British Museum (two copies), Pierpont Morgan Libraries, Bibliothèque Bodmer. A copy was formerly in the library of the late Dr. Joseph Angus. Another was purchased at Sotheby's by Messrs. Quaritch 25 July 1921.

The British Museum possesses two copies of the second edition. One of these, which is bound up with the spurious Third Part and with *An Account of the Life and Actions of John Bunyan*, printed for J. Deacon, J. Back, and J. Blare on London-Bridge (1692), lacks the leaf containing on its recto 'The Conclusion'. The errors in pagination in both the British Museum copies are identical with those in the Lenox copy.

The Bodleian copy is also bound up with another volume: John Flavell's *The Touchstone of Sincerity or The Signs of Grace and Symptomes of Hypocrisie* (1679). The signature and page-collation are identical with that of the Lenox and British Museum copies.

The Pierpont Morgan copy, in addition to the errors in page-numbering cited above, misprints 63 for 61; 66 and 67 for 64, 65; 70 and 71 for 68, 69; 74 and 75 for 72, 73; 78 and 79 for 76, 77; 82 and 83 for 80, 81; and 86 for 84.

The change in format, from a small octavo to a small duodecimo, and important additions to both text and marginalia are distinctive features of the second edition.

Exclusive of Author's Apology and Conclusion, it has 276 pages of text. The following are the additional passages in this edition[1] (cf. p. xlii above):

(1) P. 8, l. 12–p. 9, l. 25: 'In this plight . . . *to be saved?*'
(2) P. 16, l. 33–p. 25, l. 4: 'Now as Christian . . . Mr. *Worldly-Wiseman's* counsel.'
(3) P. 26, l. 31–p. 27, l. 23: '*Chr.* Truly, said *Christian . . . are cast out.*'
(4) P. 50, l. 33–p. 52, l. 12: 'Then said *Charity . . . from their blood.*'
(5) P. 74, l. 4: 'And when I . . . began to sing.'
(6) P. 85, l. 34–p. 88, l. 2: 'Now when they . . . a faithful Creator.'
(7) P. 92, ll. 17–27: 'Here also they . . . otherwise disposed of.'
(8) P. 99, ll. 3–9: 'Almost the whole . . . Father's side: And'
(9) P. 108, l. 21–p. 110, l. 25: 'Now I saw . . . remember *Lot's* Wife.'
(10) P. 114, l. 11–p. 117, l. 36: 'Now *Giant Despair* . . . in the morning.'
(11) P. 160, l. 25–p. 161, l. 15: 'There came out . . . joy be expressed.'

[1] References are to the text of the present edition.

THE
Pilgrim's Progress
FROM
THIS WORLD,
TO
That which is to come

Delivered under the Similitude of a

DREAM

Wherein is Discovered,
The Manner of his setting out,
His Dangerous JOURNEY,
AND
Safe Arrival at the Desired Countrey.

By JOHN BUNYAN.

The Third Edition, with Additions.

I have used Similitudes, *Hosea*, 12. 10.

Licensed and Entred according to Order.

LONDON,
Printed for *Nath. Ponder,* at the *Peacock*
in the *Poultrey* near *Cornhil,* 1679.

Third Edition, 1679

THE THIRD EDITION, 1679

BRITISH MUSEUM COPY. Small duodecimo. Third Edition with Additions.

Collation by signatures: A–M^{12}, N^6. Leaves E5 and M5 are unsigned; N2 is mis-signed N3.

Collation by pagination: blank, recto [A]; portrait, verso [A]; title-page [as reproduced opposite], recto [A2]; blank, verso [A2]; Author's Apology, recto A3–verso [A6]; text, pp. 1–285 [287]; FINIS,; *An Advertisement* [8 lines], p. 285 [287]; The Conclusion, THE END, p. [288]. Page 21 is mis-numbered 23, 24 is 22, 25 is 23, 28 is 26, 60 is 62, 92 is 62, 137 is 133, 176 is 776, 275 is 255, and the numbers 275 and 276 are repeated in the pagination, the subsequent pages being numbered 277, 278, &c.

OTHER COPIES. Bodleian, Bunyan Meeting, Huntington Libraries, Sir Arthur Howard. Two other copies purporting to be of the third edition are the George Offor copy, now in the Lenox collection, New York Public Library, and the John Pearson copy,[1] sold in America in 1923.

The British Museum copy of the third edition is a beautiful small duodecimo volume in olive morocco binding, having 287 pages of text, wrongly numbered 285 because of the repetition of the numbers 275 and 276, exclusive of The Author's Apology and the Conclusion. Pasted on a fly-leaf is a manuscript note of George Offor's, dated 'Hackney July 11th 1847', which is in part as follows:

This is a very rare volume of which I have only been able to trace this copy after forty years research. It is truely delightful to find it like the only copy of the first edition as yet discovered [the Holford copy] so beautifully perfect & clean. It is the first edition that had the portrait of which this is a peculiarly fair impression engraved by White. * * *

I am greatly indebted to Mr. Leslie for the use of this unique volume without which the Hanserd Knollys edition could not have been completed.

Offor eventually discovered another copy bearing the imprint of the third edition, the copy now in the Lenox collection. This is imperfect, lacking pages 119–22. Prefixed to the Lenox copy is another manuscript note of Offor's in which he says: 'The only copies that have been discovered are this and a very beautiful one sold by Mr. Leslie to the Revd T. Horner of Wells, Somerset, for ten guineas [the

[1] See below, pp. lxxv–lxxvi.

copy now in the British Museum]: while every page corresponds with this, these two copies are certainly from different type, although they may be from the same fount. The following selection of Bibliographical memoranda distinguished this from every other edition. It is impossible to say which of the books issued first from the press.' There follows a list of variants between the two copies several pages in length. Further discussion of the Lenox volume will be found on pp. lxxiv–lxxv.

The Bodleian and Bunyan Meeting copies are badly worn. The frayed condition of many of the leaves makes any report on the pagination untrustworthy. A comparison of the text of these copies with that of the British Museum copy revealed no differences.

The Huntington copy was formerly the Locker-Lampson copy. It thence passed to the E. D. Church Collection, and finally to the Huntington Library. The collation of this copy corresponds almost precisely with that of the British Museum copy. The errors in signature-marking and in page-numbering are the same, with the single exception that, in the British Museum Third, page 28 is wrongly numbered 26. The page-numbers and the running headlines from p. 133 to the end of the copy are in smaller type than pp. 1–132, indicating that the work was set up by two different printers.[1] This is also true of the British Museum copy.

The third edition enjoys the distinction of being virtually the first complete edition of *The Pilgrim's Progress*. It was the first to insert the long discourse between Mr. By-ends and his companions and their subsequent talk with Christian and Hopeful (p. 100, l. 35 to p. 106, l. 20), the last addition of any consequence Bunyan made to the text. After the third edition the additions consist of a few phrases inserted in the text, of marginal notes, and scripture references.

THE FOURTH EDITION, 1680

BRITISH MUSEUM COPY. Small duodecimo. Fourth Edition with Additions.

Collation by signatures: A–M^{12}, N^6; N2 is mis-signed N3.

---

[1] *Church Catalogue*, i. 233–4.

THE
Pilgrim's Progress
FROM
THIS WORLD,
TO
That which is to come

Delivered under the Similitude of a

DREAM

Wherein is Discovered,
The Manner of his setting out,
His Dangerous JOURNEY,
AND
Safe Arrival at the Desired Countrey.

By JOHN BUNYAN.

The Fourth Edition, with Additions.

I have used Similitudes. *Hosea*, 12. 10.

Licensed and Entred according to Order.

DONDON,
Printed for *Nath. Ponder*, at the *Peacock*
in the *Poultrey* near the Church, 1680.

Fourth Edition, 1680

Collation by pagination: [*Advertisement from the Bookseller*], recto [A]; portrait, verso [A]; title-page [as reproduced opposite], recto [A2]; blank, verso [A2]; Author's Apology, recto A3–verso [A6]; text, pp. 1–287; *An advertisement* [13 lines]; FINIS, p. 287; The Conclusion. THE END, p. [288]. Page 2 is misnumbered 28, 3 is 25, 6 is 32, 7 is 29, 10 is 36, 11 is 33, 48 is 47, 49 is 48, 52 is 51, 53 is 52, 56 is 55, 57 is 56, 58 is 85, 60 is 59, 176 is 177, 177 is 176, 234 is 243, 241 is 141.

The Advertisement from the Bookseller, Ponder's warning against the spurious copies of Braddyl and his confederates, printed, without heading, on the reverse side of the portrait, is signed 'N. P.' Two lines follow the signature and exemplify the difference between brevier type and long primer: 'This is Brevier, and the true copy | This is Long Primer letter.' The portrait of the dreamer has only two inscriptions: the name of the city—'*Destruction*', and the initials of the engraver—'*R. W.*' On the title-page 'LONDON' is misprinted 'DONDON'.

A peculiar error marks the title-page of this copy. The initial T of line 10 has slipped to a little below the beginning of line 11, so that the two lines are made to appear as follows:

he Manner of his setting out,

ᴛHis Dangerous Journey.

From this error, as well as from certain other features such as the worn condition of the plate containing the sleeping portrait, H. R. Plomer[1] draws the inference that this copy represents a late issue of the fourth edition. This particular error, however, might just as well have occurred in the first copies off the press. The erratic state of the pagination and the retention of the misprint 'DONDON' would indicate that it was one of the earlier uncorrected copies. Much more convincing evidence of 'lateness of issue' is the presence of the six-line advertisement on the reverse of the title-page.

OTHER COPIES.[2] Lenox (two copies), Huntington, British Museum (another copy), Yale University (Elizabethan Club).

[1] 'A Law-suit as to an Early Edition of *The Pilgrim's Progress*', *The Library*, Third Series (1914), v. 60–69.

[2] A copy of the fourth edition with the portrait by Robert White, but with the preliminary matter often missing or much torn, and lacking pages 221–52, was listed for sale in Mayhew's book-catalogue, 1922, at £20. See *T.L.S.*, 'Notes on Sales', 8 June 1922.

The first Lenox copy lacks the two lines after Ponder's initials about the difference between brevier and long primer. The page-numbering is often partially or wholly defaced. Page 176 is misnumbered 177, 241 is 141, 263 is 261.

In the second Lenox copy the Bookseller's Advertisement is signed, with the full name: 'N. Ponder'. The misprint 'DONDON' on the title-page has been corrected. The verso of [A2], blank in the first copy, now contains a six-line advertisement of Owen *On Hebrews*.

The Huntington copy, described in the *Church Catalogue* (i. 237–8, No. 200), is like the second Lenox copy in having 'N. Ponder' as the signature of the Bookseller's Advertisement, together with the lines exemplifying brevier and long primer; and in having on the verso of [A2] the six lines of advertisement. In the Huntington copy the errors in signature-marking are the same as those reported in the first Lenox copy. Page 2 is misnumbered 8, 6 is 7, 7 is 6, 234 is 243, and 241 is 141.

In the British Museum is another volume claiming to be the fourth edition, 1680. It is in modern binding, press-mark C. 58. a. 23. On the reverse side of the portrait is the inscription 'Lucy Lockhart—September 1865', and on the title-page 'Thomas Wilgess'. It omits entirely the *Advertisement from the Bookseller* as well as the six-line advertisement of Owen *On Hebrews*. On the title-page occurs the misprint 'DONDON'. The errors in signature-marking are identical with those in the Lenox and Huntington copies. Page 92 is misnumbered 62, 234 is 243, and 241 is 141. Upon examination of the text, the differences between this copy and the other representatives of the fourth edition are found to extend beyond the preliminaries. Throughout one whole signature, sheet E, this copy is unlike three other copies of the fourth edition that I have examined. Further discussion of it will be found on p. lxxvi, below.

Beyond a few words or phrases the fourth edition added nothing to the text. Its additions were chiefly limited to marginal notes and scripture references. It has the same number of pages as the third, though owing to an error in pagination the third apparently has two pages fewer. The fourth edition omits a line of the Author's Apology (A3ᵛ,

l. 20), and it ascribes to Christian a speech which should be assigned to Faithful (p. 109, l. 7). The outstanding feature of the fourth edition, however, is the publisher's warning against pirated editions,[1] printed on the back of the portrait as follows:

Advertisement from the Bookseller.

The *Pilgrim's Progress*, having sold several Impressions, and with good Acceptation among the People, (there are some malicious men of our profession, of lewd principles, hating honesty, and Coveting other mens rights, and which we call *Land Pirates*, one of this society is *Thomas Bradyl* a Printer, who I found Actually printing my Book for himself, and five more of his Confederates.) but in truth he hath so abominably and basely falcified the true Copie, and changed the Notes, that they have abused the Author in the sence, and the Propriator of his right, (and if it doth steal abroad, they put a cheat upon the people.) You may distinguish it thus, The Notes are Printed in Long Primer a base old letter, almost worn out, hardly to be read, and such is the Book it self. Whereas the true Copie is Printed in a Leigable fair Character and Brevier Notes as it alwaies has been, this Fourth Edition hath as the third had, The Authors Picture before the Title, and hath more then 22 passages of Additions,[2] pertinently placed quite thorow the Book, which the Counterfeit hath not.—*N. P.* [or, as in some copies, *N. Ponder*].

This is Brevier, *and the true Copy.*
This is Long Primer *Letter.*

THE FIFTH EDITION, 1680

LENOX COPY.[3] Small duodecimo. Fifth Edition with Additions.

Collation by signatures: A⁶, B–K¹², L⁶ [last leaf blank]. G4 is mis-signed K4, H5 is H4, and I5 is I4.

Collation by pagination: *Advertisement* [11 lines], recto A; portrait, verso A; title-page [as reproduced, p. lii], recto [A2]; *Advertisement* [6 lines], verso [A2]; Author's Apology, recto A3–verso [A6]; text, pp. 1–220; The Conclusion. THE END, p. [221]; Books Printed, pp. [222–6]; FINIS, p. [226]; one blank leaf, [L6]. The numbering of p. 39 is blurred; page 48 is misnumbered 58, 144 is 141, 147 is 127, 159 is 157, 162 is 160, 163 is 161, 166 is 164, 167 is 165, 217 is 117.

[1] This warning is not found in the Lockhart-Wilgess copy in the British Museum which is a made-up copy and not a genuine fourth.

[2] These 'Additions' are, with a very few exceptions, scripture references and marginal notes.   [3] Known as the Lea Wilson copy.

Besides the sleeping portrait, with the inscription 'R. W. Sc.', the name of the city 'Destruction', and 'Printed for Nat. Ponder in the Poultry', is a woodcut representing the martyrdom of Faithful, p. 128, with these four lines of verse beneath:

> Brave Faithful, Bravely done in word and deed,
> Judge, Witnesses and Jury have insteed
> Of overcoming thee, but shewn their rage,
> When they are dead thou'lt live from age to age.

OTHER COPIES. Lenox, British Museum,[1] Huntington, Pierpont Morgan, and Chapin (Williamsburg, Mass.) Libraries.

The second Lenox copy has no portrait. In all other respects the description of it in Contributions to a Catalogue (p. 11) coincides with that of the Lea Wilson copy.

The British Museum copy is imperfect, lacking leaves C6 and C7, [L5] and [L6]; the lower third of leaf L4 is torn away. The errors in signature-marking and in pagination show slight differences from those of the Lenox copy. G4 is correctly signed, but H5 and I5, as in the Lenox copy, are mis-signed H4 and I4. The numbering of pages 39 and 40 is entirely gone, the leaf being worn through at this point. Page 48 is misnumbered 58, 106 is 109, 147 is 127, 159 is 157, 162 is 160, 163 is 161, 166 is 164, 167 is 165, and 217 is 117. This copy and the Lea Wilson copy are identical as to text.

The Huntington copy is described in the Church Catalogue (i. 238–9, No. 201). It lacks the eleven-line advertisement concerning the copper cuts, the recto of [A] being blank. The frontispiece is not the sleeping portrait, but 'a portrait of John Bunyan; bust, directed and facing slightly to the right, looking to the front; with inscription: | I Sturt Sc.: | John Bunyan | Printed for Nath: Ponder in the Poultrey | Printed for Nath: Ponder in the Poultrey. (repeated); line engraving. The errors in signature-marking and in page-numbering coincide with those of the Lea Wilson copy.

---

[1] In addition to the copy of the genuine fifth printed by Ponder, the British Museum possesses a copy calling itself the fifth and with the date 1680 on the title-page, printed in Edinburgh by John Cairns. It bears no resemblance to any copies of the genuine fifth.

A woodcut of Faithful's martyrdom is found, as in the other copies, on page 128.

The Chapin Library copy, formerly in the library of John Pearson, was bought at Sotheby's 7 November 1916. The signature and page-collation coincides with that of the Lea Wilson copy in every particular except that H5 is not mis-signed. The eleven-line advertisement of the 'copper cutts' is found on the recto A; the frontispiece is the sleeping portrait, but the plate is unsigned. Inscribed below are the words '*Printed for Nat. Ponder* in the Poultri'. On p. 128 occurs the woodcut of Faithful's martyrdom. Loosely laid in are eight of the advertised thirteen 'Copper Cutts' (taken from a bound copy) as follows:

1. Christian meeting Evangelist (Page 4 & 5).
2. Christian meeting Worldly Wiseman (Page 22 & 23).
3. Christian at the Wicket Gate (Page 30 & 31).
4. Christian in the Valley of the Shadow of Death (Page 104 & 105).
5. Faithful before Judge Hategood (Page 122 & 123).
6. Giant Despair before his Castle (Page 150 & 151).
7. Pilgrims with Shepherds of the Delectable Mountains (Page 158 & 159).
8. The Pilgrims riding the Clouds (Page 218 & 219).

Each plate is paged as above and bears four lines of verse at its foot.

Several features of the fifth edition call for special mention. The size of the volume has been considerably reduced, 220 pages of text as against 287 pages in the third and fourth editions. In this edition and, with the exception of the seventh, in all subsequent editions, the text proper begins with sheet B. The first illustration of the text and the first mention of the 'Copper Cutts' occur in the fifth edition. The advertisement of the cuts in the Lea Wilson copy is as follows:

Advertisement.

The *Pilgrims Progress* having found | good Acceptation among the People, | to the carrying off the Fourth Impression, | which had many Additions, more | than any preceding :And the Publisher ob-|serving that many persons desired to have it | illustrated with Pictures, hath endeavoured to | gratifie them therein: And besides those that | are

THE
Pilgrim's Progress
FROM
THIS WORLD,
TO
That which is to come :
Delivered under the Similitude of a
DREAM.
Wherein is Discovered,
The Manner of his setting out,
His Dangerous JOURNEY,
AND
Safe Arrival at the Desired Countrey.

By *JOHN BUNYAN.*

The Fifth Edition with Additions.

I have used Similitudes, Hosea 12. 10.

Licensed and Entred according to Order.

LONDON,
Printed for *Nath. Ponder,* at the *Peacock*
in the *Poultrey* near the Church, 1680.

Fifth Edition, 1680

ordinarily printed to this Fifth Impression, | hath provided Thirteen
Copper Cutts curi-|ously Engraven for such as desire them.

The fifth edition repeats one of the errors made in the
fourth: the omission of a line of the Author's Apology
[A3ᵛ, l. 20]. It begins an error which is repeated in all the
subsequent editions, the seventh excepted: the omission of
four lines of the dialogue between Christian and Evangelist
upon the occasion of their second meeting.

THE FIFTH EDITION, 1682

L E N O X C O P Y. Small duodecimo. Fifth Edition with Additions.

Collation by signatures: A⁶, B–K¹², L⁶ [last leaf blank]. Sigs. C, D, E, F,
H, I, K signed up to 7; sigs. B and G to 6.

Collation by pagination: *Advertisement* [11 lines], recto A; portrait, verso
A; title-page [as reproduced, p. lv], recto [A2]; *Advertisement* [7 lines],
verso [A2]; Author's Apology, recto A3–verso [A6]; text, pp. 1–220; The
Conclusion. THE END, p. [221]; Books Printed, pp. [222–6]. FINIS, p. [226].
Some of the pages are cut so close, and others so badly frayed, that many of the
page-numbers are either partially or wholly defaced. Numbers 35, 85, 86,
131, 135, 138, 139, 154, 155, 156, 157, 158, 159, 160, 166, 167, 199, 201,
202, 203, 206, 207, 208 are no longer decipherable.

The portrait is that of the dreamer, with the inscription:
'R. W. Sc.', the name of the City—'*Destruction*', and below,
'*Printed for Nat: Ponder in the Poultry*'. There are thirteen
copper plates, each with a descriptive stanza of four lines.
These, with the directions in the upper right-hand corner
of each plate as to its placing, are as follows:

1. Christian meeting Evangelist (Page 4 & 5).
2. Christian meeting Worldly Wiseman (Page 22 & 23).
3. Christian at the Wicket Gate (Page 30 & 31).
4. Christian in the Arbour (Page 50 & 51).
5.¹ Christian losing his Burden (Page 54 & 55).
6. Christian passing the lions (Page 56 & 57).
7. Christian in complete Armour (Page 70 & 71).
8.² Christian in the Valley of the Shadow of Death [written at
    the top of the plate '104–105'].
9. Faithful before Judge Hategood (Page 122 & 3).

---

¹ No. 5 is wrongly placed. It should come between pp. 44 and 45.
² No. 8 is also wrongly placed. The text it illustrates is found on pp. 80 and 81.

10. Martyrdom of Faithful. [No directions on plate as to position.]
11. Giant Despair before his Castle (Page 150 & 151).
12. Pilgrims with Shepherds of the Delectable Mountains (Page 158 & 159).
13. The Pilgrims riding the Clouds (Page 218 & 219).

No. 10, the Martyrdom of Faithful, is on p. 128; the recto of the leaf, p. 127, is filled with letter-press. The verses accompanying this cut are printed; those accompanying the other plates, engraved.

The advertisement concerning the copper cuts, recto A, is reprinted from the fifth edition, 1680, with a few changes in spelling and the substitution of 'the' for 'this' in line 9. The title-page, except for the change in date and a period instead of a comma after 'London', is the same as that of the earlier fifth. An examination of the texts proves that the later copy, though differing on nearly every page from the earlier, is undoubtedly reprinted from it.

OTHER COPIES. British Museum, Bunyan Meeting, Pierpont Morgan Libraries.[1] In both the British Museum and the library of Bunyan Meeting, Bedford, are two little volumes claiming to be the fifth edition of 1682. Although each has the name of Ponder on the title-page, they are totally unlike all other editions bearing the imprint. The British Museum copy is printed in small type on very inferior paper. The pages have no marginals; the notes and scripture references are placed either in the body of the text or in spaces made by indentations of the text. There are no advertisements and no portrait. The recto of the first leaf contains the title-page; the verso, the first of the seven pages of the Author's Apology. There are 183 pages of text, besides the Conclusion, p. [184]. On the verso of a leaf between pages 40 and 41 is a woodcut of Christian in the Arbour, but without the usual verses. The text differs on practically every page from that of the fifth of either 1680 or 1682. On the inside cover is pasted a manuscript note to the effect that 'this edition is unknown to Offor and others', and that 'it is either a counterfeit issue of ed. 5; or one struck off

---

[1] A copy of the fifth edition of 1682, from the library of William Edward Buckley, was sold at Sotheby's to Quaritch, 27 February 1893, for £3. 5s. (*Book Prices Current*, vii, Lot 2033).

THE
Pilgrim's Progreſs
FROM
THIS WORLD,
TO
That which is to come:
Delivered under the Similitude of a

DREAM.

Wherein is Diſcovered,
The Manner of his ſetting out,
His Dangerous JOURNEY,
AND
Safe Arrival at the Deſired Countrey.

By *JOHN BUNYAN*.

The Fifth Edition with Additions.

I have uſed Similitudes, Hoſea 12. 10.

Licenſed and Entred according to Order.

LONDON.
Printed for *Nath. Ponder*, at the *Peacock* in
the *Poultrey* near the Church, 1682.

Fifth Edition, 1682

on a smaller paper and type for circulation among the poorer classes'. It was in all probability either this or the Bunyan Meeting copy that is alluded to by Dr. John Brown: 'One of these pirated editions is before me as I write, and both in type and paper is greatly inferior to those issued by Ponder himself, though it boldly bears his name on the title-page, claims to be licensed, and to be the fifth edition of 1682.'[1]

The Pierpont Morgan copy[2] of the fifth edition, 1682, resembles the Lenox copy, but the two are not identical. The advertisement of the copper cuts in the Morgan copy has been changed to read as follows:

The *Pilgrims Progress* having found good Acceptation among the People, to the carrying off the *Fifth* Impression, which had many Additions, more than any preceding: And the Publisher observing, that many persons desired to have it illustrated with Pictures, hath endeavoured to gratifie them therein: And besides those that ere ordinarily printed to this *Sixth* Impression, hath provided Thirteen Copper *Plates* curiously Engraven for such as desire them.

The portrait of the dreamer in the Morgan copy is unique. In all the other copies containing the sleeping portrait, the dreamer is leaning on his left arm, the city of Destruction is just behind his right shoulder, and the celestial gate in the upper right-hand corner. In this copy the positions are reversed: the dreamer is leaning on his right arm, the city of Destruction is behind and a little to the right of his left shoulder, the celestial gate is in the upper left-hand corner.[3] In addition to the portrait are fourteen copper plates illustrative of the text, each accompanied by four lines of explanatory verse. The verses to all the plates, except the Martyrdom of Faithful, are engraved. These correspond in arrangement with those in the Lenox copy except that No. 8 in the Morgan copy is Christian's Fight with Apollyon (pp. 76 and 77), which is not found in the Lenox copy at all. For further discussion of this so-called fifth edition, 1682, see p. lxxxi.

[1] Brown, p. 444. A manuscript note on the fly-leaf of the Bunyan Meeting copy, in what appears to be the handwriting of Dr. Brown, says: 'Probably one of Braddyl's counterfeits. Ponder's fifth edition is dated 1680.'

[2] Originally in the Huth Library. See *Catalogue of the Huth Collection*, First Portion (1911), Lot 1097 (Sotheby Cat.).

[3] Unlike the portrait of the Lenox fifth, 1682, this omits the engraver's initials.

Printed for Nat. Ponder in the Poultry

Frontispiece to the Fifth Edition, 1682

Pierpont Morgan Library

THE SIXTH EDITION, 1681

First variety

LENOX COPY.[1] Small duodecimo. Sixth Edition with Additions.

Collation by signatures: A⁶, B–K¹². B5 and H5 are unsigned, and H6 is wrongly signed H5.

Collation by pagination: blank, recto [A]; portrait; verso [A]; title-page [as reproduced, p. lix], recto [A2]; *Advertisement* [6 lines], verso [A2]; Author's Apology, recto A3–verso [A6]; text, pp. 1–210; The Conclusion. THE END, p. [211]; Books Printed, pp. [212–16]. Page 145 is misnumbered 135, 194 is 2.

The portrait is not the sleeping portrait of Robert White, but a portrait of Bunyan, with the inscription of the engraver '*I. Sturt Sc.*', and beneath, '*John Bunyan. Printed for Nath. Ponder in the Poultrey*', the same portrait already described as appearing in the Huntington copy of the fifth edition, 1680. In line 4 of the title-page occurs the misprint 'WORL,D'. The woodcut of Faithful's martyrdom with the descriptive verses appears in this edition on p. 121. Sheet D, pp. 49–72, is in smaller type than the rest of the volume. OTHER COPIES. British Museum, Huntington, Chapin Libraries.

The collation of the British Museum copy is identical with that of the Lenox except in a few particulars. It contains the advertisement of the copper plates on the reverse side of the portrait, reprinted without alteration from the fifth edition, 1680, except for slight changes in spelling and the substitution of 'the' for 'this' in line 9. The portrait is that of the dreamer with the inscription '*R. W. Sc.*', '*Destruction*', '*Printed for Nat. Ponder in the Poultrey*'. Page 145 is misnumbered 135, but the numbering of 194 is correct. A careful comparison of the texts reveals no differences.

The Huntington copy, described in the *Church Catalogue* (i. 240–1, No. 202), also has the advertisement concerning the extra plates and the portrait of the dreamer, but without the inscription of the engraver. The Chapin copy, formerly

---

[1] This copy was presented to the New York Public Library by Alexander Maitland. It is not listed among the other editions of the Lenox Collection in *Contributions to a Catalogue of the Lenox Library*.

in the Huth Library, likewise contains the advertisement (recto A) and the sleeping portrait signed 'R. W. f.' The advertisement of the copper plates, as in the British Museum copy, reads 'to the carrying off the Fourth Impression', and speaks of the present edition as 'the fifth Impression'.[1]

Second variety

There is another copy of *The Pilgrim's Progress*, presumably of the sixth edition, in the Lenox Library. It lacks the portrait, title-page, Author's Apology, and the Conclusion.

Collation by signatures: A¹ [leaves A2–A6 lacking], B–I¹², K⁹ [leaves K10–K12 lacking].

B3 is signed 3; B5 and H5 are unsigned; H6 is mis-signed H5.

Collation by pagination: *Advertisement* [12 lines], recto A; blank, verso A; text, pp. 1–210. [So many of the page-numbers are gone that any attempt to report them in detail would be futile.]

The wording of the *Advertisement* is precisely that of the *Advertisement* in the Morgan copy of the fifth edition, 1682, even to the misprint of 'ere' for 'are' (see p. lvi, above).

Besides the woodcut of Faithful's martyrdom, p. 121, there are eight copper plates, each supplied with the customary verses, and with inscriptions at the top of each plate as indicated below in brackets.

1. Christian meeting Evangelist (Page 2 & 3).
2. Christian meeting Worldly Wiseman (Page 18 & 19).
3. Christian at the Wicket Gate (Page 24 & 25).
4. Christian losing his Burden (Page 44 & 45).
5. Christian in the Arbour (Page 50 & 51).
6. Christian meeting the Lions (Page 56 & 57).
7. Christian in Full Armour (Page 70 & 71).
8. Giant Despair before his Castle. [Direction above plate faded out. Placed between pp. 150 and 151.]

Further discussion of this copy will be found on pp. lxxxii ff.

The sixth edition reduces still further the size of the volume, having 210 pages of text as against 220 in the fifth edition. It continues the error of the fourth and fifth

---

[1] From a collation kindly provided by the Custodian of the Chapin Library.

THE

Pilgrim's Progress

FROM
THIS WORLD, D
TO
That which is to come :

Delivered under the Similitude of a

DREAM,

Wherein is Discovered,
The Manner of his setting out,
His Dangerous JOURNEY,
AND
Safe Arrival at the Desired Countrey.

By *JOHN BUNYAN*,

The Sixth Edition with Additions.

I have used Similitudes, Hosea 12. 10

- Licensed and Entred according to Order.

LONDON;
Printed for *Nath. Ponder*, at the *Peacock*
in the *Poultrey* near the Church, 1681.

Sixth Edition, 1681

editions, the omission of a line of the Author's Apology [A3ᵛ, l. 20], and enlarges upon the error of the fifth by omitting an additional line in the dialogue between Christian and Evangelist: 'Yes dear Sir, said *Christian*.'

THE SEVENTH EDITION, 1681

LENOX COPY.[1] Small duodecimo. Seventh Edition with Additions.

Collation by signatures: A–M¹², N⁶. E, E5, M5 are unsigned.

Collation by pagination: blank, recto [A]; portrait, verso [A]; title-page,[2] recto [A2]; blank, verso [A2]; Author's Apology, recto A3–verso [A6]; text, pp. 1–285 [287]; FINIS. *An Advertisement* [8 lines], p. 285 [287]; The Conclusion. THE END, p. [288]. Page 12 is misnumbered 20, 133 is 1, 151 is 15¹, 155 is 155, 205 is 105, 228 is 229; 275–6 is repeated and the subsequent pages numbered 277, 278, &c.

The portrait of the dreamer closely resembles that in the third edition, having the inscription '*R. W. Sc.*' on the rock, the name of the city *Destruction*, and beneath, '*Printed for Nat. Ponder in the Poultry*'. The fourth line of the title-page repeats the error of the sixth edition: 'WORL,D'. Between pages 164 and 165, facing 164, is inserted a woodcut of Faithful's martyrdom, with the four lines of explanatory verse beneath and in the upper margin the direction 'Place this betwixt page 164 and 165'.

OTHER COPIES. British Museum.

The British Museum copy exhibits no differences whatever from the Lenox copy in the matter of text. The two show slight differences in the preliminaries and in the marking of signatures and in page-numbering. Sig. E is correctly marked. Leaf D5 is so worn at the bottom that the signature-marking is entirely gone. Otherwise, the two copies agree. In addition to the errors in pagination in the Lenox copy, all of which are present, page 113 appears as 11, 124 as 24, 125 as 12⁵. The frontispiece is not, as in the Lenox copy, the portrait of the dreamer, but a full-faced, bust portrait of Bunyan enclosed within a circular rim, the left hand at the breast. In the lower curve of the rim 'Bunyan' is written

---

[1] Acquired since the publication of *Contributions to a Catalogue* and consequently not listed among the editions in the Lenox Collection.

[2] The title-page of the Lenox copy is not identical with that of the British Museum copy (see opposite). In the Lenox Seventh 'Country' (l. 13) is spelt 'Countrey'.

THE
Pilgrim's Progress
FROM
THIS WORLD,D
TO
That which is to come:

Delivered under the Similitude of a

DREAM,

Wherein is Discovered,
The Manner of his setting out,
His Dangerous JOURNEY,
AND
Safe Arrival at the Desired Country.

By *JOHN BUNYAN*,

The seventh Edition with Additions.

I have used Similitudes, Hosea 12. 10.

Licensed and Entred according to Order.

LONDON,

Printed for *Nathanael Ponder* at the *Peacock* in the *Poultrey*, near the Church, 1681.

Seventh Edition, 1681

British Museum

with a pen. The other two inscriptions on the plate are: '*Burnford Sc.*' and '[Prin]*ted for Nath: Ponder in the Poultry*'. Inserted between the last page of the Author's Apology and the first page of the text is a leaf on the verso of which is the portrait of the dreamer. This shows slight modifications of the sleeping portrait as it appears in the third edition. The plate has no inscription whatever save the name of the city '*Destruction*'. The woodcut of Faithful's martyrdom, as in the Lenox copy, is placed between pages 164 and 165, but on the verso of the leaf, facing page 165, instead of, as in the Lenox, on the recto, facing page 164. On the recto of the leaf containing the portrait of the dreamer is the inscription of the original owner: '*Thomas Hayward* . . . Aug: j: j682.'[1] The title-page contains the misprint WORL,D in line 4, but differs from the Lenox copy in line 13 in printing 'Country' instead of 'Countrey'.

The seventh edition is the rarest of all the editions issued during Bunyan's lifetime.[2] In form, it returns to that of the third and fourth editions. It has the same number of pages as they, though, as in the third, through the repetition of numbers 275 and 276, the last page is numbered 285 instead of 287. The seventh, like each of the first four editions, begins the text proper with leaf 7 of sheet A, and not, as in the fifth, sixth, eighth, and subsequent editions, with sheet B. The passages omitted in the fifth and sixth editions are restored, and not a few independent readings introduced.

THE EIGHTH EDITION, 1682

LENOX COPY. Small duodecimo. Eighth Edition with Additions.

Collation by signatures: A⁶, B–K¹². B5 is unsigned.
Collation by pagination: *Advertisement* [11 lines], recto A; portrait, verso A; title-page [as reproduced overleaf], recto [A2]; *Advertisement* [6 lines],

[1] This inscription identifies this copy with that described by Offor in *Works*, iii. 43. The inscription in full reads:
Thomas: Hayward: | :his booke: Testis Jere | = miah: Hayward: His | Brother. Ex dono: of | his namesake, & kinsman | Thox Pengry: Aug. j: j682 | Pretium: s d
j. 6: | Hic nomen pono, quia librum | perdere nolo.
[2] In the British Museum is a little volume professing to be a reprint of the seventh edition. It was published in Glasgow by Alexander Carmichael in 1735. It bears no resemblance to the original seventh edition.

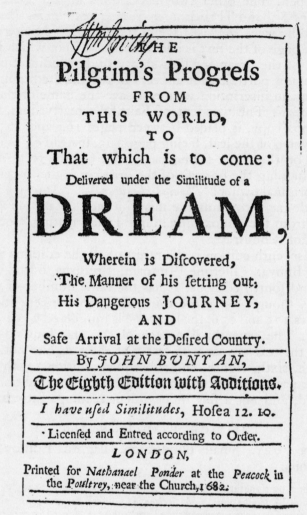

THE
Pilgrim's Progress
FROM
THIS WORLD,
TO
That which is to come:

Delivered under the Similitude of a

DREAM,

Wherein is Discovered,
The Manner of his setting out,
His Dangerous JOURNEY,
AND
Safe Arrival at the Desired Country.

By *JOHN BUNYAN*,

𝔗𝔥𝔢 𝔈𝔦𝔤𝔥𝔱𝔥 𝔈𝔡𝔦𝔱𝔦𝔬𝔫 𝔴𝔦𝔱𝔥 𝔄𝔡𝔡𝔦𝔱𝔦𝔬𝔫𝔰.

I have used Similitudes, Hosea 12. 10.

Licensed and Entred according to Order.

LONDON,

Printed for *Nathanael Ponder* at the *Peacock* in
the *Poultrey*, near the Church, 1682.

Eighth Edition, 1682

British Museum

verso [A2]; Author's Apology, recto A3–verso [A6]; text pp. 1–211; The Conclusion. THE END, p. [212]; Books printed, pp. [213–16]. Page 16 is misnumbered 6, 184 is 114, 210 is 208; numbers 135–44 are repeated, numbers 159–68 and 204 omitted.

The advertisement of the plates, recto A, is reprinted from the fifth edition (1680) without alteration save in the spelling of a word or two.

The portrait of the dreamer has no inscription other than the name of the city: '*Destruction*'. There are three woodcuts each with the usual four lines of verse: the martyrdom of Faithful, p. 121; Giant Despair before his Castle, p. 135 [145]; Pilgrims riding the Clouds, p. 204.

Sheet D, pp. 49–72, is in distinctly smaller type, sheets I and K in larger type, than the rest of the volume.

OTHER COPIES. Lenox, British Museum, Pierpont Morgan, Libraries.[1]

The second Lenox copy is a duplicate of the one just described. The British Museum copy is imperfect, lacking pages 179–82 and the last leaf, K12.

With the single exception that page 16 is correctly numbered, the errors in signature-marking and in pagination are precisely the same as those noted in the Lenox copy. The same differences in type are also seen in sheets D, I, and K. The two show no variations as to text.

The eighth edition follows the sixth in omitting five lines of the dialogue between Christian and Evangelist (p. 23).[2]

---

[1] Offor, Brown, Paltsits, and others all report a copy of the eighth edition as being in the library of Sion College. The librarian informs me that he can find no record of such a copy. According to Offor, this Sion College copy had but two woodcuts, the Martyrdom of Faithful (p. 121) and the Pilgrims riding the Clouds (p. 204), page 145 [misnumbered 135] being filled with letterpress. See Offor, *Works*, iii. 43.

[2] It is a copy of the eighth edition that is good-humouredly satirized in Gay's farce, *The What-d'ye-call-it* (Act II, sc. 1). A man condemned to be shot is offered a book to pray by. Urged to make use of it, he cries

'I will! I will!

Lend me thy handkercher. "*The pilgrim's pro-*" [*reads and weeps*]
(I cannot see for tears) "*pro—progress*": Oh!
"*The Pilgrim's Progress, eighth edi-ti-on:*
Lon-don print-ed—for—Ni-cho-las Bod-ding-ton:
With new ad-di-tions ne-ver made before":
—Oh, 'tis so moving, I can read no more.' [*drops the book.*]

As Boddington's name first appeared on the title-page of the thirteenth edition, it was suggested by Bishop Heber that Gay was alluding to the eighteenth edition,

(a) THE NINTH EDITION, 1683

LENOX COPY. Small duodecimo. Ninth Edition with Additions.

Collation by signatures: A⁶, B–K¹². B3 is mis-signed 3; B5 is unsigned.

Collation by pagination: *Advertisement* [11 lines], recto A; portrait, verso A; title-page [as reproduced opposite], recto [A2]; *Advertisement* [6 lines], verso [A2]; Author's Apology, recto A3–verso [A6]; text, pp. 1–211; The Conclusion. THE END, p. [212]; Books Printed, pp. [213–16]; FINIS, p. [216]. Page 99 is misnumbered 89, 184 is 114, 210 is 208; 126 appears as 1z6, numbers 135–44 are repeated, 159–68 and 204 are omitted.

The advertisement of the extra plates, recto A, with the word 'Seventh' substituted for 'Fourth' and for 'Fifth' in lines 3 and 9 respectively, is reprinted from the eighth.

The portrait of the dreamer is more nearly like the portrait in the sixth edition (British Museum copy) than that in the eighth. It has no inscription other than the name of the city. There are three woodcuts: the Martyrdom of Faithful, p. 121; Giant Despair before his Castle, p. 135 [145]; Pilgrims riding the Clouds, p. [204]. Sheets D (pp. 49–72) and G (pp. 121–44) are in smaller type than the rest of the volume.

OTHER COPIES. British Museum, Huntington, Pierpont Morgan, Chapin Libraries. A copy was also formerly in the Huth Library.[1]

The British Museum possesses two copies purporting to be of the ninth edition, 1683. The copy here spoken of, press-mark C. 58. a. 27, is in the original binding, and has written across the title-page two inscriptions: 'G. Pearson Croft Cottage' and 'W. Tarbutt Cranbrook Kent 1876'. Leaf A, with the advertisement of the extra plates on the recto and the portrait on the verso, and leaf K 12, containing two pages of 'Books Printed', are missing. The collation by signatures and pagination is in perfect agreement with that of the Lenox copy. Comparison of the text proves the

on which Boddington's name does appear, but for metrical reasons changed 'eighteenth' to 'eighth'. Offor (iii. 44) was of the opinion that the allusion is to the eighth edition of the Second Part.

[1] The Huth copy was sold at Sotheby's 23 November 1911, Lot 1099, to Maggs Bros. for £12. It is reported as being in the original sheepskin binding with three woodcuts and 'a portrait closely resembling that in the edition of 1681' (the sixth edition). See *Catalogue of the Huth Collection*, First Portion (1911), Lot 1099.

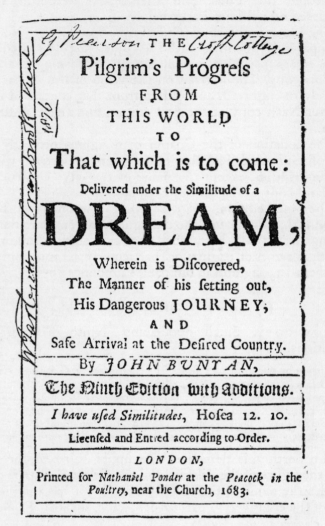

THE

Pilgrim's Progress

FROM
THIS WORLD
TO

That which is to come:

Delivered under the Similitude of a

DREAM,

Wherein is Discovered,
The Manner of his setting out,
His Dangerous JOURNEY,
AND
Safe Arrival at the Desired Country.

By *JOHN BUNYAN*,

The Ninth Edition with Additions.

I have used Similitudes, Hosea 12. 10.

Licensed and Entred according to Order.

LONDON,

Printed for *Nathaniel Ponder* at the *Peacock in* the
Poultrey, near the Church, 1683.

Ninth Edition, 1683

two copies duplicates. The other British Museum copy is discussed on pp. lxxx–lxxxi, below.

The Huntington copy (*Church Catalogue*, i. 241, No. 203) is, apparently, identical with the copies just described. The same errors in pagination and signature-marking characterize this copy. The portrait on the verso of leaf A has been entirely re-engraved, and differs from that contained in the Palmer-Nash copy of the first edition and the Huntington sixth.

The collation of the Chapin copy agrees perfectly with that of the Lenox. The plate of the sleeping portrait, without any inscription, except the name of the city 'Destruction', is a faint copy of that in the sixth edition.

The ninth edition, 1683, continues the omission, begun in the fifth, of a part of the dialogue between Christian and Evangelist. It will be noticed that this edition follows the eighth in errors of pagination, particularly in repeating page-numbers 135–44 and in omitting numbers 159–68.

(*b*) THE NINTH EDITION, 1684

LENOX COPY. Small duodecimo. Ninth Edition with Additions.

Collation by signatures: A⁶, B–K¹². F3 is unsigned. K11 is badly stained.

Collation by pagination: blank, recto [A]; portrait, verso [A];[1] title-page [as reproduced opposite], recto [A2]; *Advertisement* [6 lines], verso [A2]; Author's Apology, recto A3–verso [A6]; text, pp. 1–211; The Conclusion. THE END, p. [212]; Books Printed, pp. [213–16]. Page-numbers 135–44 are repeated, 159–68 omitted; 190 is numbered 901; 203, 204 are unnumbered.

The portrait is defective; the upper third of the plate with the figure of the Pilgrim and the Celestial Gate is gone. Besides the name of the city '*Destruction*', it has the inscription of the engraver '*W. Elder Sc.*', and beneath: '*Printed for Nat: Ponder in the Poultry*'.

There are three woodcuts: Martyrdom of Faithful, p. 121; Giant Despair before his Castle, p. 135 [145]; Pilgrims riding the Clouds, p. [204]. Sheet D, pp. 49–72, is in distinctly smaller type than the rest of the volume.

---

[1] The leaf containing the portrait is a loose leaf. The page opposite the title-page is blank, which is presumably where the portrait originally came.

THE
Pilgrim's Progress
FROM
THIS WORLD,
TO
That which is to come:
Delivered under the Similitude of a
DREAM,
Wherein is Discovered,
The Manner of his setting out,
His Dangerous JOURNEY,
AND
Safe Arrival at the Desired Country.

By *JOHN BUNYAN*,

The Ninth Edition with Additions.

I have used Similitudes, Hosea 12. 10.

Licensed and Entred according to Order.

LONDON,
Printed for *Nathanael Ponder*, at the Peacock in
the *Poultrey*, near the Church, 1684.

OTHER COPIES. Bunyan Meeting, Pierpont Morgan Libraries.

The Bunyan Meeting copy is imperfect, lacking portrait and Author's Apology. Otherwise, it seems to be identical with the copy just described.

The Pierpont Morgan copy contains a fourth woodcut, Christian and Hopeful with the Shepherds of the Delectable Mountains, inserted between pages 144 and 145, and an additional error in pagination: page 210 is numbered 208.

This edition, though called the ninth, is quite distinct from the ninth of 1683. It represents an entirely new setting up. It not only follows the example of editions five to nine in omitting five lines of the dialogue between Christian and Evangelist, but by discarding 'Evan.' at the top of page 18 combines the two speeches into one. This, of course, necessitates changing the catchword 'Evan.' at the bottom of page 17 to 'How', the first word now on page 18. It also omits a line of the quotation from 2 Cor. 4. 18 (p. 33, l. 24), and a line of Christian and Hopeful's song upon their escape from Doubting Castle: '*Lest heedlessness makes them, as we, to fare*' (p. 141, l. 16).

THE TENTH EDITION, 1685

LENOX COPY.[1] Small duodecimo. Tenth Edition with Additions.

Collation by signatures: A⁵ [A, wanting], B–I¹², K⁶. K3 is mis-signed L3.
Collation by pagination: Leaf A [presumably with portrait] lacking; title-page [as reproduced on p. lxx], recto [A2]; *Advertisement* [9 lines], verso [A2]; Author's Apology, recto A3–verso [A6]; text, pp. 1–199; The Conclusion. THE END, p. 200; Books Printed, pp. [201–4]. Page 171 is misnumbered 181.

On the title-page the author's name is spelt 'JOHN BUNIAN'. The advertisement on the reverse is an advertisement of the Second Part.[2] There are two woodcuts: Faithful's Martyrdom, p. 116, Pilgrims riding the Clouds, p. 193.

[1] Lea Wilson copy.
[2] *Advertisement*. The Pilgrims Progress, from this | World to that which is to come; The | Second Part: delivered under the | Similitude of a *Dream*, wherein is set forth | the Manner of the setting out of Christians | Wife and Children, their dangerous Journey, | and safe Arrival at the desired Countrey, by | *John Bunian*. *I have used Similitudes*, Hos. 12. | 10. Price One shilling.

OTHER COPIES.[1] Lenox (two copies), British Museum, Pierpont Morgan Libraries.

The copy just described is the second of the copies of the tenth edition in the Lenox Collection listed in *Contributions to a Catalogue* (p. 12). The first copy there described lacks the portrait, has a facsimile title-page, and at the end four pages advertising books printed, not by Ponder, but by Boddington. The third Lenox copy has the portrait.

The British Museum copy is imperfect, lacking leaves A, K5, and K6. F, F2, F3 are mis-signed G, G2, G3. Several of the leaves have been cut so close as to clip away the page-numbers. As in the Lenox copy, page 171 appears as 181 and sig. K3 as L3. As to text, the only variations between this and the Lenox copy are that the scripture reference 'Rom. 7. 24' (p. 98, l. 9) is misprinted in the Lenox 'from 7. 24', and the two marginal notes (p. 103) which in the Lenox are placed opposite lines 12 and 15 respectively, in this copy are opposite lines 15 and 23. The first of these, the misprint 'from.' for 'Rom.', is in the eleventh edition, which apparently was printed from an uncorrected copy of the tenth.

The tenth edition reduces the number of pages of text by twelve. All the omissions of the ninth edition, 1684, are repeated: the five lines of dialogue between Christian and Faithful together with the discarding of 'Evan.', and the consequent merging of Evangelist's two speeches into one; the part of the quotation from 2 Cor. 4–18 so as to read *'for the things that are seen, are Eternal'*; and the line of Christian and Hopeful's song after escaping from Doubting Castle: *'Lest heedlessness makes them, as we, to fare'.*

THE ELEVENTH EDITION, 1688

Pierpont Morgan Library copy. Small duodecimo. Eleventh Edition with Additions.

Collation by signatures: A⁶, B–I¹², K⁶.

Collation by pagination: *Advertisement*, recto A; sleeping portrait, verso A; title-page [as reproduced, p. lxxii], recto A2; Advertisement of Second Part,

[1] Two copies of the tenth edition were sold at Sotheby's 4 December 1902 and 3 June 1908. See *Church Catalogue*, i. 231.

THE
Pilgrim's Progress
FROM
THIS WORLD,
TO
That which is to Come :
Delivered under the Similitude of a
DREAM,
Wherein is Discovered
The Manner of his setting out
His Dangerous JOURNEY,
AND
Safe-Arrival at the Desired Country

By *JOHN BUNIAN.*

The Tenth Edition with Additions.

I have used Similitudes, Hosea 12. 10.

Licensed and Entred according to Order.

LONDON,
Printed for *Nathaniel Ponder,* at the *Peacock* in the
Poultry near the Church, 1685.

Tenth Edition, 1685

verso A2; Author's Apology, recto A3–verso A6; text, pp. 1–199; The Conclusion. THE END, p. [200]; Books Printed, pp. [201–4]. Page 16 is unnumbered; 139 appears as 13.

Besides the sleeping portrait are thirteen full-page cuts with four lines of verse below each.

OTHER COPIES.[1] British Museum, Huntington Libraries.

The British Museum copy is very imperfect; leaves A6, B4, B9, C2, C6, C7, D2, D6, D7, E6, E7, F2, F5, H, I2, I10, I12, K1–K6 are wanting.[2] The frontispiece, the portrait of the dreamer, has the inscriptions '*W. Elder Sc.*' and, at the bottom, '*Printed for Nat: Ponder In the Poultry*', while all that remains of the name of the city is '*truction*'.

This copy contains nine of the woodcuts:

1. Christian meeting Evangelist.
2. Christian meeting Worldly Wiseman.
3. Christian losing his Burden.
4. Christian in the Arbour.
5. Christian passing the Lions.
6. Faithful before Judge Hategood.
7. Faithful's Martyrdom.
8. Giant Despair before his Castle.
9. Pilgrims with the Shepherds of the Delectable Mountains.[3]

The omitted illustrations are: (1) Christian at the Wicket Gate; (2) Christian's fight with Apollyon; (3) Christian in the Valley of the Shadow of Death; (4) Pilgrims riding the Clouds.

The Huntington copy, formerly in the John Pearson Collection, lacks leaf A1, containing the sleeping portrait. Like the Morgan copy, it has thirteen full-page cuts.

The distinctive feature of the eleventh edition is the insertion of the thirteen illustrative woodcuts. These were reproduced from the copper plates which first appeared in

---

[1] A copy of the eleventh edition was sold at the Buckler sale (Anderson), 3 December 1907. See *Church Catalogue*, i. 231.

[2] That is, in addition to the last two pages of the Author's Apology, which are unnumbered, pp. 7–8, 17–18, 27–28, 35–36, 37–38, 51–52, 59–60, 61–62, 83–84, 85–86, 99–100, 105–6, 145–6, 171–2, 187–8, 191 ff.

[3] According to directions on the cuts these are to be placed, respectively, between (1) pp. 2 and 3, (2) 18 and 19, (3) 44 and 45, (4) 46 and 47, (5) 50 and 51, (6) 112 and 113, (7) p. 116, (8) 136 and 137, (9) 144 and 145.

Thomas THE *Harris*
Pilgrim's Progress
FROM
THIS WORLD
TO
That which is to Come:
Delivered under the Similitude of a
DREAM,
Wherein is Discovered.
The Manner of his setting out,
His Dangerous JOURNEY,
AND
Safe Arrival at the Desired Country.
By *JOHN BUNYAN.*

The Eleventh Edition with Additions, and the Cuts.

I have used Similitudes, Hosea 12. 10.

Licensed and entred according to Order.

LONDON,
Printed for *Nathanael Ponder,* at the *Peacock* in the
Poultry near the Church, 1688.

Eleventh Edition, 1688

the fifth edition, 1682.[1] It has the same number of pages of text as the tenth edition, and, with the exception of the bungled quotation from 2 Corinthians, the same omissions. Copies of this edition are extremely rare. Brown made it the basic text of his edition published in 1907 in the Cambridge Classics.

III. DOUBTFUL COPIES AND EDITIONS

THE extraordinary popularity of *The Pilgrim's Progress* is best seen in the attempts of the unscrupulous to share in its success. Their efforts took the form of imitations, of surreptitious editions of the genuine work, or of copies made up of parts of different editions. It is with the last two groups that we are at present concerned.

All the editions from 1678 to 1688 describe themselves on the title-page as printed *for* Nathaniel Ponder. From this, and from the changes of type noted in several of the editions, it is clear that these editions were set up by several different compositors and probably at different printing-

[1] Among the British Museum and Lenox copies of the *Pilgrim's Progress* is a copy of the first Dutch edition: *Eens Christens Reyse na de Eeuwigheyt*. In't Engels beschreven door Mr. Joannes Bunjan: Leeraar in Bedford. T' Amsterdam: Joannes Boekholt (1682). It has an engraved frontispiece of Christian at the Wicket-Gate and eleven small copperplate engravings printed on the same pages with the letter-press. Three years later Boekholt published what is supposed to be the first French edition, a copy of which is in the Lenox Collection: *Voyage d'un Chrestien vers l'Eternité*. Ecrit en Anglois, par Monsieur Bunjan, F. M. en Bedfort, et nouvellement traduit en François. Avec Figures. Amsterdam, Chez Jean Boekholt (1685). Avec Privilegie. This handsome edition is illustrated with eight copperplate engravings besides the frontispiece. These were the work of the Dutch engraver Jan Luiken. One of these engravings representing Christian and Hopeful struggling through the river of Death was substituted in the thirteenth edition (1693) for the English print representing them as riding the Clouds. The verses remained unchanged:

> Now, now look how the holy Pilgrims ride,
> Clouds are their chariots, angels are their guide:
> Who would not here for him all hazards run,
> That thus provides for his when this world's done!

'This absurd mistake,' writes Brown, 'was repeated in edition after edition for nearly a century.' In the fourteenth edition seven of the Dutch engravings, (1) Christian at Sinai, (2) Christian at the Wicket-Gate, (3) Hill Difficulty, (4) Parley with Apollyon, (5) Valley of the Shadow of Death, (6) Vanity Fair, (7) Crossing the River, replaced the following English engravings: (1) Christian meeting with Worldly Wiseman, (2) Christian at the Wicket-Gate, (3) Christian in the Arbour, (4) Christian in Full Armour, (5) Fight with Apollyon, (6) Christian in the Valley of the Shadow of Death, (7) Pilgrims riding the Clouds. (See Brown, pp. 442–3.)

shops. This may explain the curious fact that the fourth edition in which Ponder bitterly complains against the piracies of Braddyl and his confederates has its marginal notes in long primer (Ponder's mark of identification for fraudulent copies); so has the first, but the second has notes in brevier. In the spring of 1678 Ponder entered an action against Braddyl for violation of copyright;[1] the case was made interesting by the lapsing of the 1662 Licensing Act in 1679 (the situation was regularized by the Stationers' Ordinance in 1681–2). In 1697 Ponder instituted a suit in Chancery against Braddyl for having printed in 1688 20,000 copies of *The Pilgrim's Progress*, although authorized to print but half that number, and for having sold, without authority, 9,500 of these to Awnsham Churchill and Nicholas Boddington. He also charged Braddyl with having printed more than the authorized number of copies of the Second Part and of *Grace Abounding*, without rendering any account of the sales; lastly, he charged him with being the author and printer of the spurious Third Part of the *Progress*.[2] Plomer characterizes Braddyl's defence as 'quite open and straightforward', and as bearing out the good opinion Dunton had of him.[3]

No copies have yet been discovered which exactly satisfy the test set forth in Ponder's warning. There are copies and editions, however, that upon close examination of the text must be classed as spurious or at least doubtful.

The Lenox copy of the third edition proves to be quite different from the British Museum copy. George Offor called attention to this fact in a long bibliographical note which he prefixed to the Lenox volume. 'While every page [of the British Museum copy]', he declares, 'corresponds with this, these two copies are certainly from different type, although they may be from the same fount. . . . It is impossible to say which of the books issued first from the press.'[4]

[1] Common Pleas, Hilary Term, 30 Car. II, 1679. *The True Domestick Intelligence*, 3 Jan. 1679–80. The case was not proceeded with. Cf. W. A. Copinger, *The Law of Copyright*, 3rd ed. (1893).

[2] P.R.O. C 24/1201/41. See H. R. Plomer's 'A Law-suit as to an Early Edition of *The Pilgrim's Progress*', *The Library*, Third Series, v (1914), 60–69.

[3] *Life and Errors of John Dunton*, London (1705), pp. 332–3.

[4] From a photostat reprint of Offor's manuscript note in the Lenox copy. An extract is also printed in *Contributions to a Catalogue*, pp. 6–7.

The editions which show a page-for-page correspondence with the third are the fourth and seventh, and as far as page 171—at which point ten pages of new matter are introduced in the third—the second. It was at once noticed that two of the errors of the fourth edition, the omission of a line of the Author's Apology and the ascribing to Christian a speech of Faithful's, also appeared in the Lenox third. On the other hand, a number of misprints supposedly found only in the seventh edition, such as 're receive', 'thrt' for 'that', 'gi-en' for 'given', were also discovered in the Lenox copy. This led to a painstaking comparison of this copy with copies of the fourth and seventh editions, with the following results:

The Lenox third is identical[1] with the seventh edition in leaves A4, A5, A6; in pages 1–108 (recto A7–verso E12); in pages 157–66 (recto H–verso H5); and in pages 171–[288] (recto H8–recto N6). It is identical with the fourth in leaf A3; in pages 109–18 (recto F–verso F5) [leaves F6, F7, pp. 119–22, are lacking in Lenox 'Third']; in pages 123–56 (recto F8–verso G12), and in pages 167–70 (recto H6–verso H7). It has the portrait with the inscription 'R. W.' and, below, the words 'Printed for Nat. Ponder in the Poultry'. The title-page is that of the genuine third.

The Lenox volume is not the only third-edition copy that has borrowed freely from the fourth. On 7 November 1916 a copy of the third edition from the library of John Pearson, re-bound by Lloyd & Co., and containing the autograph of the original owner 'Dennis Melhuishe his Book, 1680', was sold at Sotheby's for £55. It reappeared at Sotheby's on 9 April 1919,[2] and was sold for £205. It was returned as having some twenty pages from the fourth edition. On 26 July 1920 it was once more offered for sale. 'This volume', ran the description in the Sale Catalogue, 'was sold in these rooms last year for £205. It has since been suggested that several leaves have been supplied from the fourth edition

---

[1] By 'identical' is meant that, judged by every possible test, they are the same and came from the same setting-up. The tests do not include an examination of watermarks, as I had before me only a photographic reprint of the Lenox copy. The paper of these early copies is in such condition that little could be learnt from the watermarks.

[2] Sotheby Cat. (1919), Second Day: Lot 421.

(1680), which reads almost identical with this third edition. The volume will now be sold not subject to return. *Seven* leaves from a third edition will be included in the lot. The difference (if any) is most difficult to detect.' The little volume was sold to Dobell for £18. 10*s*. Three years later, 16 April 1923, it was put up at public sale in America, being described as having 'very slight repairs, mainly in margins, one leaf cover restored from another copy'. It sold for $2,000.[1]

One of the copies in the British Museum bearing the imprint of the fourth edition, the Lockhart-Wilgess copy, differs throughout one entire sheet from the other British Museum copy of this edition and from the photostat of the Lenox fourth. The evidence is conclusive that sheet E in this copy is taken from the third edition. The catchwords, the line-spacing of the text and of the marginalia, and typographical defects are the same in the two sheets.[2] All the misprints in sheet E of the third edition are repeated in the Lockhart-Wilgess copy; for example, 'daw' for 'day' (p. 85, l. 25), 'too' for 'two' (p. 88, l. 8), 'Yalley' (p. 88, l. 16), 'saying' for 'saving' (p. 89, l. 3), 'though' for 'thought' (p. 101, l. 1), 'cruelty' for 'cruelly' (p. 106, l. 2), 'addressest' for 'addressed' (p. 97, l. 10), 'solitarly' for 'solitary' (p. 97, l. 23). With the exception of this one sheet, no differences were discovered between this and the genuine copies of the fourth edition. As in the case of the Lenox third, it is impossible to determine when this copy was 'made up'.

The copies claiming to be of the fifth edition, 1682, are of three varieties: (1) a very inferior edition, printed in small type, on cheap paper, without margins, and without portrait; (2) an edition, represented by the Lenox copy, with the usual portrait of the dreamer and illustrated with thirteen copper plates; (3) an edition, represented by the Pierpont Morgan copy, with a portrait based upon the sleeping portrait by Robert White but greatly modified, and illustrated with fourteen copper plates.

The first variety, copies of which are in the British

[1] *American Book-Prices Current*, xxix. 123.
[2] On p. 94, l. 6, for example, the same defect in type of 'h' in 'hand' is found in the third edition and in this copy. In the marginal note, p. 102, '*he spake*' appears as '*hespeake*' in both.

Museum and at Bunyan Meeting, Bedford, may be dismissed as spurious. It differs totally from all other known versions of *The Pilgrim's Progress* published by Nathaniel Ponder. Though it does not satisfy Ponder's test it may be one of the copies set up by his piratical rivals. Brown considered it 'one of Braddyl's counterfeits'.[1] The text is unlike that of the fifth 1680 or the fifth 1682.[2]

The Lenox copy, representative of the second variety, was formerly owned by George Offor, who has left a description of it in his edition of Bunyan's *Works*. He seems to have had no doubt of its genuineness. 'The discovery', he declares, 'of these original engravings on copper to the edition of 1682, proves that they were published under Bunyan's name and his direct sanction. Pleased with such decisive evidence that the lines were his, I cheerfully paid five guineas for a beautiful copy of this little volume, although published originally for two shillings.'[3]

A careful comparison of the text of this copy with the text of the 1680 edition shows, as Offor says, that it is 'an entire reprint' with 'variations in typography in every page', but it also shows that it is a very corrupt reprint. Omission of letters in a word is not at all uncommon; for example: 'tunder' for 'thunder' (marg. p. 93, l. 4); 'Husands' for 'Husbands' (p. 116, l. 25); '*I show itself*' for '*It shows it self*' (p. 107, l. 4); '*wose*' for '*whose*' (p. 158, l. 2). Omission, too, of words, phrases, and in one instance even of a whole line occurs. Line 25, A4, of the Author's Apology reads in the earlier text:

> *His gun, his nets, his lime-twigs, lights and bell:*

in the later:

> *His gun, his lime-twigs, light and bell.*

The eighth line of Christian's song (p. 86, l. 4) is omitted entirely.

Bunyan is made to say in the Apology that his book 'will direct thee to the Hilly-land' (A6ᵛ, l. 1). '*Tillage*' is substituted for *Village* (p. 19, l. 8); '*comply*' for '*comely*' (p. 99,

---

[1] Manuscript note on the fly-leaf of the Bunyan Meeting copy.
[2] See p. liv, above.   [3] Op. cit., iii. 43.

l. 2). Christian's promises to Apollyon were made in his 'bondage' instead of his 'nonage' (p. 73, l. 24), and the moon, when past the full, goes into the *want* instead of *into the wane* (p. 112, l. 25). The misprint of *Great-Gence* for *Great-Grace* (p. 167, l. 34) in the fifth of 1680 is blindly repeated. The text of this later edition certainly underwent no intelligent revision.

The woodcuts which were made from the thirteen copper plates, one or more of which had been inserted in all the editions subsequent to the fourth, first appeared in their entirety in the eleventh edition. These correspond to the plates in this copy. The verses accompanying the plates also correspond with the verses printed beneath the woodcuts, but in the 1682 edition contain many crudities of spelling and punctuation. In the Lenox copy these verses are as follows:

1. Christian meeting Evangelist (between pp. 4 and 5):

> Christian no sooner leaues this world but meets
> Euangelist who loueingly him greet
> with tideings of another: and doth show
> him how to mount to that from this below.

2. Christian meeting Worldly Wiseman (pp. 22 and 23):

> When Christians unto carnal men give ear
> out of their way they goe, and pay for't dear
> for master worldly wiseman, can but shew
> a saint the way to bondage and to woe.

3. Christian at the Wicket-Gate (pp. 30 and 31):

> He that will enter in must first without
> stand knocking at the gate nor need he doubt
> that is a knocker but to enter in
> for God can love him, and forgive his sin.

4. Christian in the Arbour (pp. 50 and 51):

> Shall they who wrong begin yet rightly end,
> Shall they at all have safty for their friend,
> No no in head-strong maner they set out
> And headlong will they fall at last no doubt.

5. Christian losing his Burden (pp. 54 and 55):

> Who's this. the pilgrim. how; tis veri true,
> Old things are past away; als becom new,
> Strange: hees another man upon my word,
> They be fine fethers that make afine bird.[1]

6. Christian meeting the Lions (pp. 56 and 57):

> Difficult is behinde, fear is before
> Tho hees goot on the hill the lions roer
> A christian man is neuer long at eas
> When one fright's gon another doth him seiz.

7. Christian in Complete Armour (pp. 70 and 71):

> Whilst christian is among his godly friends
> Their golden mouths make him ufficient mends
> For all his griefs and when they let him goe
> Hes clod with northen steel from top to toe.

8. Christian in the Valley of the Shadow of Death (pp. 104 and 105):

> Poor man where art thou now thy day is night
> Good man be not cast down thou yet art right
> Thy way to heavn lies by the gates of hell,
> Chear up, hold out, with thee it shall goe well.[2]

9. Faithful before Judge Hategood (pp. 122 and 123):

> Now faithful play the man speak for thy God:
> Fear not the wickeds malice nor their rod:
> Speak boldly man the truth is on thy side
> Die for it and to life in triumph ride.

10. Faithful's Martyrdom is printed on p. 128 (verso G4). The verses beneath are not engraved, but printed.

> Brave *Faithfull*; Bravely done in word and deed
> Judge. Witnesses and Jury have insteed
> Of overcoming thee, but shewn their rage,
> When they are dead thou'lt live from age to age.

---

[1] This should come between pages 44 and 45.
[2] This is placed, according to directions on the plate, between pages 104 and 105. The text it is supposed to illustrate is on pages 80 and 81.

11. Giant Despair before His Castle (pp. 150 and 151):

> The pilgrims nowto gratifie the flesh
> will seek its eas, but oh how they afresh
> doe their by plunge themselves new griefs into
> who seeken to pleas the flesh themselves vndoe.

12. The Pilgrims with the Shepherds of the Delectable Mountains (pp. 158 and 159):

> Mountains delectable they now ascend
> Where shepherds be which to them do commend
> Aluring things and things that cautious are
> Pilgrims are steddie kept by faith and feare.

13. The Pilgrims riding the Clouds (pp. 218 and 219):

> Now now look how the holy Pilgrims ride
> Clouds are their chariots Angels are their guid
> Who would not here for him all hazzards run
> That thus provides for his when this worlds don.

Of some significance is the misplacing of Nos. 5 and 8. The plate illustrating Christian's fight with Apollyon is for some reason omitted. What we have, then, in the Lenox copy claiming to be of the fifth edition, 1682, is a text representing a debased reprint of that of the 1680 fifth, illustrated with thirteen copperplate engravings, two of the plates being removed by several pages from their proper places. The verses accompanying the illustrations, while the same as those found in the later editions, are set out in a much more slovenly manner.

Despite the doubts awakened by the badness of the text, there is not sufficient evidence for denying the genuineness of this edition. The most disconcerting thing in regard to it is that it should be called the 'fifth' edition, although the sixth and seventh had each appeared the year before. It was the fifth edition, however, in which the advertisement of the copperplates first appeared, and for which the plates were made. Engraved on the upper margin of each plate is the number of the pages between which the plate is to go. The proper adaptation of the plates to the text demanded that the reprint should be made from the fifth edition. This was done, but done in very careless fashion.

The Pierpont Morgan copy, representative of the third variety of the fifth edition, 1682, is an object of far greater suspicion than the Lenox copy. First of all there is the strange anomaly of an edition calling itself 'the fifth' on the title-page but in the Advertisement of the copper plates 'this sixth Impression' (see p. lvi, above). The modification of the 'sleeping portrait' is another peculiarity of this copy. But that which chiefly discredits any claim to genuineness is the wretchedness of the text. In addition to the blunders of the Lenox copy, such as 'Hilly-Land' for 'Holy-Land', 'Tillage' for 'Village', 'tunder' for 'thunder', 'bondage' for 'nonage', the Morgan copy literally swarms with blunders of its own. 'Twenty-thousand Cartloads' appears as 'Twenty-thousald Catt-loads'; 'millions [of wholesome Instructions]' as 'minions'; *into the wane* as *into the what*. Not infrequently the misprints are so gross as to be utterly unintelligible.[1] A typical example is the distortion of the following couplet from the Apology:

> My *end*, thy *good? why may it not be done?*
> *Dark clouds bring waters, when the bright bring none.*

into

> My *end*, thy *good? why may it not be done? in me*
> *Dark clouds bring waters, whĕt he brightbring.*

The occurrence in the Morgan copy of all the errors in the Lenox copy proves that one is printed from the other. The far more debased text of the Morgan copy and the changed form of the advertisement of the copperplates indicate it to be the later of the two. The copy is undoubtedly spurious. No respectable publisher, such as Ponder undeniably was, could possibly have had any share in issuing so disreputable a version as this. It was suggested in the Sale Catalogue description of the Morgan copy that it may be one of Braddyl's pirated editions 'with the genuine plates published by Ponder introduced';[2] if not the work of Braddyl and his associates it is that of some other pirate.

[1] On virtually every page are numerous typographical blunders, such as: 'cach' for 'catch', 'trough' for 'through', 'angles' for 'angels', 'they' for 'thy', 'whith' for 'with', 'grid' for 'gird', 'Ciyty' for 'City', 'wole' for 'whole', 'tetrours' for 'terrours'.

[2] *Catalogue of the Huth Collection*, First Portion (1911), Lot 1097, pp. 308–9.

There is extant still another doubtful copy illustrated with copperplates. This is the unique little volume in the Lenox Library, lacking title-page, Author's Apology, and Conclusion, but in the advertisement of the plates calling itself 'this Sixth Impression'. In the discussion that follows, this copy of the sixth (?) edition will be called 6^b, the copy of the sixth edition without plates 6^a, and the ninth edition, 1683, 9^3. The sixth, eighth, and both ninth editions have the same number of pages and, with only slight exceptions, correspond page for page. Occasionally the catchwords vary, one edition running slightly behind or slightly ahead of the others. The interchange of whole sheets or parts of sheets could easily be effected within the group. In a manuscript note written on a fly-leaf of 6^b Offor is quoted as saying 'it [6^b] proves upon a very careful collation to be made up of 2 editions—pages 1 to 76—93 to 96—109 and 110—123 to 124—*differ with all my copies*'. A comparison of photostats of the Lenox copies of 6^a and 6^b with the British Museum copy of 6^a reveals that both copies of 6^a are from the same type, while 6^b is from a different setting up. Offor's statement is correct. Obviously, the chances are that where 6^b differs from 6^a it will be found to resemble either the eighth or one of the ninth editions. As a matter of fact, wherever 6^b differs from 6^a it is identical[1] with 9^3, and wherever it differs from 9^3 it is identical with 6^a. For example:

Pages 1–76, recto B–verso E2, 6^b and 9^3 identical.
Pages 77–92, recto E3–verso E10, 6^b and 6^a identical.
Pages 93–96, recto E11–verso E12, 6^b and 9^3 identical.
Pages 97–122, recto F–verso G, 6^b and 6^a identical.
Pages 123–144, recto G2–verso G12, 6^b and 9^3 identical.
Pages [145]–210, recto H–verso K9, 6^b and 6^a identical.

All three copies are closely related. Often the differences between any two of them have to do simply with line-spacings or arrangement of marginalia.

The following table of the variants in those pages in which 6^b and 9^3 are identical makes clear the differences in the body of the text:

---

[1] By 'identical' is meant that they give every evidence of being from the same setting up.

Sig.	Page	Line	6ᵃ	6ᵇ	9³
recto B2	3	4	solitarily	solitary	solitary
„ „	3	28	willing to die	willing to do dye	willing to do dye
verso B3	6	21	*whether*	*whith[er]*	*whither*
recto B4	7	24	*tell me now*	*tell me know*	*tell me know*
verso B4	8	4	be given	bo given	bo given
recto [B5]	9	15	go so fast	go fast	go fast
„ [B6]	11	7	*Miry slow*	*Miry Slough*	*Miry Slough*
verso [B6]	12	14	saw	say	say
„ „	12	30	solitarily	solitarary	solitarary
„ [B8]	16	15	*say*	*saw*	*saw*
„ [B9]	18	22	loden	loaden	loaden
recto [B11]	21	29	mistery	mystery	mystery
„ C2	27	23	*loose*	*lose*	*lose*
verso C3	30	27	Heart	heart	heart
„ C5	34	26	VVall	Wall	Wall
recto [C10]	43	17	*Lion*	*Lyon*	*Lyon*
„ D2	51	2	*to have trod*	*to have tread*	*to have tread*
„ D5	57	2	bosom	bosome	bosome
„ [D7]	61	33	Dunghil	Dunghill	Dunghill
„ [D10]	67	12	considerated	considerate	considerate
„ [D11]	69	29	*purpose*	*pupose*	*pupose*
verso [D12]	72	12	through	thorow	thorow
recto [E11]	93	20	Eternal	eternal	eternal
recto [E12]	95	4	That	that	that
verso [E12]	96				
	catchword		as	you	you
	Throughout pp. 97–122, recto F–verso G, 6ᵃ and 6ᵇ are identical.				
recto G2	123	19	*wealthy*	*waelthy*	*waelthy*
verso G3	126	11	minority	Minority	Minority
recto G4	127	12	Duty	duty	duty
recto G5	129	28	dissenting	disserting	disserting
verso [G6]	132	9	Devil	Divel	Divel
recto [G7]	133	20	brink	brim	brim
verso [G8]	136	3	strangeness	stangeness	stangeness ['r' faded out.]
verso [G9]	138	25	always	alwaies	alwaies
recto [G10]	139	9	marg. *lie down to sleep*	*lie to sleep*	*lie to sleep*
verso [G12]	144	36	sttipes	stripes	stripes
	Throughout pp. [145]–210, 6ᵃ and 6ᵇ are identical.				

One of the most conclusive bits of evidence that 6ᵇ is a composite of 6ᵃ and of 9³ is found in the omission of a whole line between signatures E and F. Signature E ends with page 96. At this point 9³ is running just one line behind 6ᵃ; consequently, the last line on page 96 in 6ᵃ becomes the first line of page 97 in 9³. Copy 6ᵇ, which throughout the last two leaves of signature E is identical with 9³, goes back to

6ª in signature F, and thus loses a whole line. A citation of the lines involved will make the point clearer:

The last two lines of page 96, the end of signature E, in 6ª, are:

> Had I known him no more than |
> you, I might perhaps have thought of him |
> > as [catchword]

The first line of page 97 and of signature F is:

> as at the first you did: Yea, had he re- |

In 9³ the arrangement of these lines is as follows:

> Had I known him no more than | [last line of p. 96]
> > you [catchword]
> you, I might perhaps have thought of him |
> as at the first you did. Yea, had he recei-
> > [first two lines of p. 97, sig. F].

In 6ᵇ:

> Had I known him no more than | [last line of p. 96]
> > you [catchword]
> as at the first you did: Yes, had he re-
> > [first line of p. 97, sig. F].

Another piece of evidence, almost as conclusive, for the identity of certain parts of 6ᵇ with corresponding parts of 9³, is found in the last line of page 127, in signature G. This line in 6ª reads:

> the first, yet let us be content to take fair |
> > weather [catchword]

in 6ᵇ:

> the first, yet let us be content to take fai |
> > weatherr [catchword]

in which the 'r' of 'fair' has clearly slipped and been added to the catchword 'weather'.

Turning to 9³, we find as the last line of page 127:

> the first, yet let us be content to take fai |
> > weatherr.

These results had already been reached when confirmation came from an unsuspected quarter. In 1928, Mr.

William A. Jackson, Cataloguer in the Chapin Library, attempted to determine the question of priority of editions between the Chapin copy (formerly the Henry Huth copy) and this Lenox copy which we have designated 6ᵇ. By comparison of headlines and by measurement of type he discovered that in the Lenox copy no fewer than eight different founts of type had been used. By comparing position of signatures, by measurement of type, and from typographical errors in pagination and text, he reached the conclusion that the Huth-Chapin copy and the Lenox copy were identical in only forty-six leaves. Put into tabular form the combined results are as follows:

Sig.		Pag.	Lenox type	Sheets same in both copies
recto B–verso	B12	1–12	No. 1	
„ C– „	C12	25–48	2	
„ D– „	D12	49–72	3	
„ E– „	E12	73–96	4	same (recto E3–verso E10)
„ F– „	G	97–122	5	same
„ G2– „	G12	123–144	6	
„ H– „	I12	[145]–192	7	same
„ K– „	K9	193–210	8	same
K10–K12 [lacking in Lenox copy].				

The position of the eight copperplates in 6ᵇ is significant. Inscribed at the top of each plate is the number of the pages between which it is to be placed. These place-inscriptions on the first four are different from those on the corresponding plates of the fifth, 1682, but are identical with the directions on the corresponding woodcuts first inserted in the eleventh edition. The directions on the second four are the same as those on the corresponding plates in the 1682 fifth. The position of the first four fits fairly well with the text, but not so in the case of the second four. For example, plate No. 5, Christian in the Arbour, should go, according to the inscription on the plate, between 'Page 50 and 51', and is so placed in both the 1682 fifth and 6ᵇ. To fit the text of 6ᵇ, it should come between pages 48 and 49. The sixth plate, Christian meeting the Lions, in accordance with the directions on the plate is placed in both copies between 'Page 56 and 7'. In 6ᵇ Christian passes the lions on page 52. The seventh plate,

Christian in Full Armour, is placed in both copies, according to directions, between 'Page 70 and 71'. In 6ᵇ Christian leaves the Palace Beautiful fully armed on page 65. The eighth plate, Giant Despair before his Castle, is, in accordance with the inscription at the top, placed between 'Page 150 and 151'. This is where it should come in the fifth, but in 6ᵇ it is fully six pages removed from its proper place. The verses accompanying the plates in 6ᵇ show only the slightest variations from those of the earlier copy. A single example will suffice:

Fifth 1682. [Christian meeting the Lions.]   6ᵇ
Difficult is behinde, fear is before   comma omitted
Tho hees goot on the hill the lions roer
A Christian man is neuer long at eas
When one fright's gon another doth him siez   seaz

It is clear that the plates were adapted to the text of the fifth edition. These, or others closely modelled after them, were used to make up the copy 6ᵇ. The work was so carelessly done that in four of the eight plates the inscription at the top was not changed, and regardless of the text the plates were placed according to directions. Far from being, as Offor is credited with believing, the genuine sixth edition, this 'unique copy' is a sham; it is made up of sheets from two separate editions, and illustrated with plates that were designed to go with a different edition.

The British Museum possesses in addition to the copy described above on pp. lxiv–lxvi another with the imprint of the ninth edition, 1683. This is in modern binding, with press-mark C. 58. a. 38. The sleeping portrait, without inscription save the name of the city, 'Destruction', is not identical with any of those so far described, though evidently modelled upon that by Robert White. The reverse side of the portrait, which in the other copies of this edition contained the advertisement of the extra plates, is blank. Leaf A5 is signed in this copy; but in neither the Lenox nor the other British Museum copy. Page 210, misnumbered in all the other copies 208, is correctly numbered. With these exceptions the collation of this volume shows no variation from that of the other copies.

Upon closer examination, however, far more important

variations are discovered. Leaves A4, A5, and A6, the whole of sheet C, pp. 25–48, and leaf K9, pp. 209–10, are from a different setting up.

A4 and A5 are identical with the corresponding leaves in the fifth edition, 1680; A6 with the corresponding leaf in the fifth edition, 1682. There are several bits of evidence that go to show that these leaves are not close reprints from these respective editions, but are from the same type. Sheet C is identical with the corresponding sheet in 9^4. K9, except for the corrected numbering of page 210 (208 in the eighth), is identical with K9 of the eighth edition. What we have, then, in this copy is another 'composite'. It is made up of two leaves, A4 and A5, from the fifth edition, 1680; one leaf, A6, from the fifth edition, 1682; one whole sheet, C, from the ninth edition, 1684; and a leaf, K9, from the eighth edition.

The copies that have been discovered to be 'composites' of different editions are the Lenox third, the British Museum copy of the fourth with the inscriptions 'Lucy Lockhart' and 'Thomas Wilgess', the Lenox sixth containing the copper plates, the British Museum ninth, press-mark C. 58. a. 38. The versions that appear to be spurious are the two varieties of the fifth edition, 1682, the one variety represented by the two copies in the British Museum and Bunyan Meeting, the other by the Pierpont Morgan copy. The other variety of the fifth, 1682, edition, even if genuine, has no integrity as an independent text, and consequently will be ignored in the discussion of the relationship of the genuine editions.

IV. RELATIONSHIP OF THE
GENUINE EDITIONS

In the attempt to discover the relationship of the genuine editions issued prior to Bunyan's death, two lines of investigation must be followed. First, what inferences may be drawn from the mechanical 'make-up' of these editions? Secondly, what light do the variant readings throw upon the problem?

(a) *A succession of reprints*

A very cursory examination of these twelve editions—twelve, since the ninth, 1684, should count as a separate edition—would unquestionably lead one to divide them into two groups. In size of type, quality of paper, and general appearance the first, second, third, fourth, and seventh editions show much similarity. Beginning with the fifth and, the seventh excepted, continuing to the eleventh, the number of pages grows less and less, the paper is of inferior quality, the type smaller. The degeneracy in general appearance is quite marked. The first edition, an octavo, has, exclusive of Author's Apology and Conclusion, 232 pages of text; the second, a duodecimo as are all the subsequent editions, 276 pages of text; the third, fourth, and seventh, 287 pages;[1] the fifth, 220 pages; the sixth, eighth, ninth, 1683, and ninth, 1684, 210 pages;[2] the tenth and eleventh, 199 pages. As the size of the page remains practically the same,[3] the diminishing number of pages clearly results from an endeavour to economize.[4] Again, in the first four editions and in the seventh, the compositor set up his pages continuously from the beginning, sheet B in the first edition commencing with page 5, in the other four with page 13. In all the other editions the first page of the text is the recto of leaf B.

[1] In the third and seventh wrongly numbered 285.

[2] The text in the sixth edition ends on p. 210, in the other three on p. 211. In reality the number of pages of text is exactly the same; the apparent discrepancy results from the fact that p. 204 in the sixth is filled with letterpress; in the other three with a woodcut.

[3] The size of page, for example, in the third edition is $5\frac{9}{16}$ inches $\times 3\frac{8}{16}$; in the fourth, $5\frac{3}{4} \times 3\frac{8}{16}$; in the fifth $5\frac{1}{2} \times 3\frac{8}{16}$; in the seventh, $5\frac{7}{16} \times 3\frac{1}{16}$.

[4] This desire to reduce the number of pages must be the explanation of the change to distinctly smaller type in sheet D, which is first seen in the sixth edition.

Except in the Author's Apology and the first two pages of text, the catchwords in the second rarely vary from the catchwords in the third, fourth, and seventh until page 171 is reached. At this point the addition of ten pages of new matter in the third throws the second out of harmony with the other three, but these, which have been parallel from the beginning, continue the parallelism, with slight exceptions, to the end. An examination of the catchwords indicates that for the first 170 pages the third was set up from the second, that the fourth was set up throughout from the third, and the seventh from either the third or the fourth.

It will be remembered that in the third edition, owing to the error of repeating the page-numbering of 275 and 276, the numbering of the subsequent pages is two short of what it should be. This error does not occur in the fourth, but does reappear in the seventh—evidence that the seventh was set up from the third and not from the fourth. Further evidence to the same effect is found in the last page of the text. In the third, just below 'FINIS' is printed an eight-line advertisement of Owen's Χριστολογία; in the fourth there is an additional paragraph of five lines advertising 'The Life and Death of Mr. Badman', and the whole advertisement is placed above the word 'FINIS'. The corresponding page in the seventh is precisely like that of the third in both content and arrangement.

The editions of the second group, on the basis of number of pages of text, fall into three sub-groups. The fifth with its 220 pages of text stands alone, having sixty-seven pages fewer than either the third, fourth, or seventh, ten pages more than the sixth, eighth, and both versions of the ninth, twenty-one pages more than the tenth and eleventh. The only other text with an equal number of pages is the fifth, 1682, which, as we have seen, is little more than a slavish reprint. In the absence of any testimony from catchwords, the determination of what edition the fifth, 1680, is printed from must rest solely upon the evidence furnished by the variants.

The sixth, eighth, ninth, 1683, and ninth, 1684, having each 210 pages of text, compose the second sub-group. Inasmuch as a study of the catchwords reveals a much closer correspondence between the first three than between the ninth, 1684, and the other members of the sub-group, it will be best to discuss the later ninth separately. 'Ninth' as now used refers to the ninth, 1683.

The first divergence occurs on page 96; here the eighth and ninth are exactly one line behind the sixth. The compositor of the eighth, in order to restore the parallelism with the sixth, prints line 13 of page 97 in much smaller type; the compositor of the ninth does not resort to this, but simply economizes on word-spacing. All three are again running parallel at line 14 (p. 97). On page 145 (wrongly numbered 135 in all three editions) the eighth and ninth print a wood-cut of Giant Despair and Doubting Castle. This page in the sixth edition is filled with letterpress. At the end of page 146 (wrongly numbered in the eighth and ninth 136) the eighth and ninth are one line ahead of the sixth on the page, but a whole page behind the sixth. The three are again parallel at the end of page 163 (wrongly numbered 153 in eighth and ninth) and continue so for five pages. At the end of page 169 the eighth and ninth are each two lines behind the sixth, but all three are again parallel at the close of page 171. At the bottom of page 175 the eighth and ninth are just two words behind the sixth. They are again parallel at the close of page 176 and continue so to page 187.[1] Here the eighth and ninth end the page just three words behind the sixth; they are again parallel on pages 188–9, but at the end of page 190 have fallen four words behind the sixth. Once more on page 192 the catchword is the same in all three editions. Page 204 in the eighth and ninth is filled with the woodcut of Christian and Hopeful riding the Clouds, in the sixth with letterpress; from this point to the end the sixth is one page ahead, but the catchwords are the same. In the sixth the text ends on page 210, and the Conclusion on the recto of the following leaf; in the eighth and ninth the text ends on page 211, and the Conclusion is printed on the verso of the leaf, page [212].

It will be noticed that when divergences occur the line of cleavage is between the sixth on the one hand and the

---

[1] The British Museum copy of the eighth lacks pages 179–82. Fortunately these pages are present in the Lenox copy.

eighth and ninth on the other. This remarkably close affiliation between the eighth and ninth is borne out by the errors in signature-marking and in pagination which the two have in common. Sig. B5 is unsigned in all three. In the sixth, page 145 is wrongly numbered 135, but the subsequent pages correctly numbered 146, 147, etc. In the eighth and ninth the page-numbers 135–44 are repeated. Not only so, but in these two editions page-numbers 159–68 are omitted, 184 is misnumbered 114, 210 is 208. In all three editions, sheet D, pp. 49–72, is in much smaller type than the other sheets.[1]

The ninth edition, 1684, also exhibits many bonds of close kinship with the other three editions of this sub-group. As in the rest, sheet D is in smaller type, and as in the eighth and earlier ninth page-numbers 135–44 are repeated, and 159–68 omitted. A comparison of the catchwords in the two versions of the ninth shows variations on pages 12, 17, 20, 34, 136, 144, 148, 149, 150, 154, 156, 187. On pages 148, 149, and 150 the ninth, 1683, is a line behind; on page 154, about one-and-a-half lines ahead; and on page 156, a half-line ahead. The other variations do not extend beyond a syllable or a word or two at most.

The external evidence indicates that the eighth was reprinted from the sixth; the ninth, 1683, from the eighth; the ninth, 1684, from the ninth, 1683. The sixth is certainly not a page-for-page reprint from any of the earlier editions. Whether it is, as we should naturally expect, a reprint from the fifth edition must be determined from a study of the variant readings.

The presence of the same number of pages of text in the tenth and eleventh editions would lead us to expect a similar parallelism, page for page, to that in the other sub-groups. Unfortunately, the examination cannot be so exact owing to the fragmentary condition of the British Museum copy of the eleventh, the only copy available.[2] An examination of the pages that remain of the eleventh edition reveals only the

---

[1] The change once effected in the sixth would have to be followed by all editions representing a page-for-page reprint.

[2] The edition published by the Cambridge University Press in the Cambridge Classics Series bases its text on that copy, but is not a verbatim reprint of it.

following discrepancies between the two editions: at the end of pages 74 and 75 the eleventh is precisely one line behind the tenth; at the close of page 101 the tenth is precisely one line behind the eleventh. We are fairly safe, therefore, in believing that the eleventh is reprinted from a copy of the tenth. The determination of what edition the tenth is printed from must, as in the case of the sixth edition, be sought for in a study of the variant readings.

From the evidence which this examination of the catchwords, the signature-markings, the page-numbering, the general 'make-up' of the volumes has furnished, the following tentative conclusions may be drawn:

1. The genuine editions of *The Pilgrim's Progress* published between 1678 and 1688 fall into two groups. The first group, representing the better-appearing editions, comprises the first, second, third, fourth, and seventh editions; the second group, representing the cheaper editions, comprises the fifth, sixth, eighth, ninth, 1683, ninth, 1684, tenth, and eleventh editions.

2. Both the fourth and seventh editions were reprinted from the third.

3. The fifth was reprinted from the fourth.

4. The sixth, eighth, ninth, 1683, and ninth, 1684, are very closely related. The sixth was reprinted from the fifth, the eighth from the sixth, the ninth, 1683, from the eighth, the ninth, 1684, from the earlier ninth.

5. The tenth and eleventh are also closely affiliated. The eleventh was reprinted from the tenth, the tenth from the ninth, 1684.

A study of the variants should either corroborate or overthrow these conjectures, and may possibly enable us to answer the most interesting and important question of all: What editions, if any, underwent Bunyan's personal supervision?

(*b*) *The variants*

The twofold grouping made upon the basis of external or mechanical evidence is strongly supported by that of the variants. On the basis of textual readings, the editions frequently divide into two groups. In such cases the alignments arranged in order of decreasing frequency of occurrence are:

(1) 1, 2, 3, 7 *vs.* 4, 5, 6, 8, 9^1, 9^2, 10, 11.
(2) 1, 2, 3, 4, 7 *vs.* 5, 6, 8, 9^1, 9^2, 10, 11.
(3) 1, 2, 3, 4, 5, 7 *vs.* 6, 8, 9^1, 9^2, 10, 11.
(4) 1, 2, 3, 4, 5, 6, 7 *vs.* 8, 9^1, 9^2, 10, 11.

On the other hand, such alignments as

1, 2, 3, 4, 5 *vs.* 6, 7, etc., or
1, 2, 3, 4, 5, 6 *vs.* 7, etc.,

do not occur. But for the fact that the seventh almost invariably omits additions first made in the fourth, the alignment—1, 2, 3, 4, 7 *vs.* 5, 6, 8, etc.—would be overwhelmingly preponderant.

The external evidence indicated that the seventh was printed from the third rather than from the fourth. If it contained *all* the additions of the third and omitted *all* the additions of the fourth, the matter would be beyond question. The seventh does contain nearly all the additions of the third, including marginal notes and scripture references; it omits all the additions of the fourth except three marginal notes.[1] Moreover, in those instances in which the fourth has a reading different from that of the second and third, the seventh invariably follows the earlier editions, even when the fourth is correct and the second and third wrong.

Of the additions to the text first introduced in the third, the seventh omits five. These are surprisingly petty in importance. The first omission occurs at the bottom of page 165 of the line introductory to Christian's song: 'And as he went he Sang'. The reason for the omission is obvious. On this page the seventh is a line behind the third and fourth, and the compositor catches up by dropping an unimportant line. The second and third omissions occur on page 167.

---

[1] Forty-seven marginal notes (including the insertion of an index finger) were added in the third edition. All these are included in the fourth; thirty-eight of them in the seventh. Eleven marginal notes were added in the fourth; only three of these are found in the seventh. That is, the seventh omits about 20 per cent. of the marginal notes added in the third and 70 per cent. of those added in the fourth. Scripture references are not included under 'marginal notes'.

The words '*said* Christian', lines 15 and 20, were introduced in the third but omitted in the seventh. In neither line is the insertion at all necessary for the sense. The omission might easily have resulted from the compositor's effort to economize space. On page 168, l. 8, the word 'become', introduced in the third, is omitted in the seventh. Again, the word is not essential to the meaning of the sentence. 'I am a gentleman' differs but slightly from 'I am become a gentleman'. Coming as early as it does on the page (l. 8), however, it apparently was not excluded because of the exigency of space. This may well be the reason, though, for the next and last omission. 'Said he', page 252, line 26, is found in all editions subsequent to the third except the seventh. Here again the omission in no way affects the sense but does give the printer more space.

The same explanation will not account for the omission of marginalia. It is hard to explain the absence from the seventh of the following marginal notes found in the third and all the other subsequent editions:[1]

> Envy *begins*, p. 158.
> Superstition *follows*, p. 159.
> *The Jury and their names*, p. 163.
> *Every ones private verdict*, p. 164.
> *They conclude to bring him in guilty of death*, p. 164.
> *A chariot and Horses wait to take away* Faithful, p. 165.
> *The Song that* Christian *made of* Faithful *after his death*, p. 166.
> Index finger, p. 239.[2]

Beginning with the third, all the editions except the seventh cite immediately underneath the marginal note 'Ignorance's *hope and the ground of it*', p. 253, 'Prov. 28, 29', (misprinted for 28. 26) as well as having the same scripture reference in its proper place twenty-two lines below as it is found in the first and second. The reference is omitted entirely in the seventh, suggesting editorial rather than authorial care. With these exceptions the seventh includes all the additions made in the third.

On the other hand, of the eleven additional marginal

---

[1] '*Mount* Sinai', p. 21, was added in the second, but is omitted in the seventh.
[2] It is noteworthy that all these but the last fall within the space of a single sheet.

notes found in the fourth and subsequent editions, only the
following are included in the seventh:

By-ends *and* Christian *part* [*parts* in 4th and 7th], p. 171.
He has new companions, p. 171.
By-ends *Character* [*Carracter*, 4th] *of the* Pilgrims, p. 172.[1]

The eight marginal notes added in the fourth that are
omitted in the seventh are:

He knows no way of escape, p. 2.
Obstinate *goes railing back*, p. 9.
The Valley of Humiliation, p. 88.
The Valley of the Shadow of Death, p. 97.
The ground of Ignorances *hope*, p. 214.
The flatterer finds them, p. 231.
Ignorance comes up to the River, p. 286.
Vain-hope does ferry him over, p. 286.

All of the four additional scripture references in the fourth
are omitted by the seventh.

Not only does the seventh omit, with the three exceptions
noted above, the new matter found in the fourth, but where-
ever the fourth differs from the second and third the seventh
follows the earlier reading. A good illustration is furnished
by the lines omitted in the fifth, sixth, eighth, and subsequent
editions, but restored in the seventh. The lines, a part of a
passage first introduced in the second, were continued in the
third and, slightly modified, in the fourth. In the second and
third (p. 23) they are as follows:

Chr. Yes, dear Sir, I am the man.
Evan. Did I not direct thee the way to the little Wicket-gate?
Chr. Yes, dear Sir said *Christian.*

To the first line, the fourth adds 'said *Christian*'. The seventh
restores the lines as they appear, not in the fourth, but in the
second and third.

Another example of the seventh's preference for the
reading of the second and third is found in the passage about
Lot's wife (p. 186), first introduced in the second edition.
Had we accepted the invitation of Demas, says Christian,

we had, for ought I know, been made our selves a spectacle, . . .

---

[1] It will be noted that these examples occur on successive pages and quite close to
the examples of marginal notes in the third which are omitted in the seventh.

In the fourth, fifth, sixth, eighth, and ninth (1683 and 1684) the line reads:

> We had, for ought I know, been made, ourselves, like this woman, a spectacle, . . .

In the tenth and eleventh:

> We had for ought I know been made like this Woman a spectacle, . . .

In the seventh it appears in the same form as in the second and third.

In the first and second editions the songs inserted in the text seldom, if ever, have any introductory sentence. This is true of the song which Christian and Hopeful sing about the shepherds of the Delectable Mountains (p. 212). The third inserts the line 'Then they went away and sang', which the fourth enlarges to 'Then they went away and sang this Song', and it so continues in all the subsequent editions except the seventh. In the seventh it appears in the same form as in the third.

In a few rare instances the fidelity of the seventh to the earliest editions results in a less happy reading than that of the fourth and subsequent editions. One of the best examples of Bunyan's sarcasm is seen in Judge Hategood's attitude towards Faithful at the time of his trial (p. 161). To Faithful's plea to speak in his own defence, the Judge exclaims:

> Sirrah, Sirrah, thou deservest to live no longer, but to be slain immediately upon the place; yet that all men may see our gentleness towards thee, let us see[1] what thou hast to say.

This is the reading of the first, second, and third editions. The fourth heightens the sarcasm by inserting after 'thou' of the last line the epithet 'Vile runagate', and this is kept in all subsequent editions except the seventh. The seventh returns to the more colourless reading of the first three editions.

Ordinarily, the earlier the edition the more correct is the scripture reference. There are a few instances, however, in which an error in a scripture reference in the earliest editions

[1] 'hear' in the third edition.

is corrected in the fourth and subsequent editions but is repeated in the seventh. In the fourth edition (p. 208), the scripture reference '2 Tim. 2. 17, 18' corrects 'Tim. 2. 18, 19' of the third ('2 Tim. 2. 18, 19' in the second). The fifth, sixth, eighth, and subsequent editions continued the correction of the fourth, whereas the seventh repeats the error made in the third.

Again, the first three editions insert, in the margin opposite the scripture text quoted on page 277 of the third edition, the reference 'Psal. 33. 4, 5'. This is corrected in the fourth to 'Psal. 73. 4, 5'. It is dropped altogether in the fifth, sixth, eighth, and following editions, but restored in the seventh, and restored, too, not as correctly given in the fourth, but as incorrectly given in the first, second, and third.

The differences between the third edition and the first two, particularly the second, consist for the most part of additions rather than of variations in the text. There are, however, a few instances in which the third and seventh stand alone. One such instance occurs in the text glossed by Bunyan in characteristic fashion 'Christian and Obstinate *pull for* Pliable's *Soul*' (p. 8). The first and second editions have Christian say:

Come with me Neighbour *Pliable*

The third and seventh:

Come with thy Neighbor *Pliable*

The fourth, fifth, sixth editions:

Nay, but do thou come with thy Neighbor *Pliable*

The eighth, ninth (1683 and 1684), tenth, eleventh:

Nay, but do thou come with thy Neighbor, *Pliable*

The variations are important. In the first and second editions, as in the eighth to the eleventh, Christian's remark is clearly addressed to Pliable; in the third to the seventh, to Obstinate. In the light of the gloss, the invitation is clearly meant for Pliable.

Errors, palpably misprints, held in common by the third and seventh are the use of 'prejudice' for 'prejudiced' (p. 154), and of '*Deman*' for '*Demas*' (p. 186). Another example may also be a misprint; certainly, it is not the best reading: on Thursday Giant Despair visits Christian and Hopeful in the dungeon, 'and there first falls to rating of them as if they were dogs'. The third and seventh substitute 'beating' for 'rating', although in the very next clause we are told 'then he falls upon them and beats them fearfully' (p. 196).

The evidence derived from a study of the variants in both text and marginalia appears to be overwhelmingly in support of the conclusion that the seventh was printed from a revised copy of the third edition. The only difficulty in the way of this conclusion lies in the omission by the seventh of some eight marginal notes added in the third and the inclusion of three marginal notes added in the fourth. Whether Bunyan was responsible for all the marginal glosses or for only some of them seems impossible of determination. Some of these glosses are so colourless that they might very easily have been added by another hand; others are very distinctly tinged with the Bunyan flavour. It would be difficult to persuade oneself that any other hand than Bunyan's was responsible for such glosses as:

A man may have company when he sets out for heaven, and yet go thither alone.
He is a stain to Religion.
Christian snibbeth his fellow for unadvised speaking.
Hopeful swaggers.

Certainly neither the additions of the third omitted in the seventh nor those of the fourth included in the seventh are characterized by such raciness, but it would be hazardous to say that those of the third were not contributed by Bunyan himself.

The alternative—that the seventh was printed from a copy of the fourth—is beset with difficulties far greater and far more numerous.

On the basis of similarity in general appearance, the fifth was placed in the group of later editions. The correctness of such grouping is borne out by the testimony of the variants. Wherever there is a twofold division the fifth will as a rule be found with the sixth, eighth, and subsequent editions.

Whenever it is found in the first group, it is always in conjunction with the fourth. No examples have been discovered of such an alignment as

1, 2, 3, 5, 7 *vs.* 4, 6, 8, etc.

All the marginal notes occurring in the fourth are included in the fifth, and all but three of the scripture references. The error made by the fourth in omitting a line of the Author's Apology reappears in the fifth. It is safe to say, therefore, that the fifth was printed from the fourth.

The variants furnish convincing evidence that the sixth edition was set up from a copy of the fifth. The two omissions in the fifth, a line from the Author's Apology and four lines of the dialogue between Christian and Evangelist, are repeated, but with this difference: an additional line of this dialogue is omitted in the later edition. Most convincing of all is the frequent occurrence of the combination 5, 6, 8, and subsequent editions.

The sixth, eighth, and earlier ninth editions reveal a remarkably close affinity. The variations are chiefly differences in spelling, in the use of italics, in the employment of '&' for 'and' to save space. The page-for-page correspondence proves that the eighth was printed from the sixth, and the ninth from either the sixth or the eighth. An examination of the catchwords and the signature and page-numbering shows that the ninth, 1683, was set up from a copy of the eighth rather than of the sixth. Both follow the sixth in omitting the five lines on page 18.

The ninth edition, 1684, occupies a kind of intermediary position between the sixth, eighth, and earlier ninth on the one hand and the tenth and eleventh on the other. To all outward appearances it belongs to the former group, having the same number of pages and practically the same catchwords. A comparison of texts, however, proves it a far more independent version than any of the other three. This is most conspicuous in its employment of italic and roman type, which not infrequently is just the reverse of that of the earlier editions. A notable example of this occurs in the long dialogue between Christian and Ignorance. In all the editions from the first to the ninth, 1683, the speeches of Ignorance are in roman, of Christian in italics. But from line 7, p. 186, to line 36, p. 189, in the ninth edition, 1684, the reverse is the case. Many variations of text between the two ninths occur, but few of any importance. In at least one instance the later ninth has the better reading. In all the texts from the third to the ninth, 1683, Christian tells Good-will that he was persuaded to turn aside into the way of Death 'by the carnal agreement of one Mr. *Worldly Wise-man*'. The ninth, 1684, in substituting 'argument' gives the correct reading.[1] It cannot be called a better text, however, for not only does it fail to restore the lines omitted in the fifth, sixth, eighth, and earlier ninth editions, but it carries the omission one step farther (see p. lxviii, above). It also omits a line of the quotation from 2 Corinthians (p. 33, l. 24) and from Christian and Hopeful's song (p. 141, l. 16), and makes meaningless the marginal note '*A way and a way*' (p. 158, l. 25) by misprinting it '*Away and away*'.

The recurrence of these blunders in the tenth and, with the exception of the omitted lines from 2 Corinthians, also in the eleventh edition, the inclusion of the marginal notes first added in the ninth, 1684, and a similar interchange of roman and italic type, attest the close relationship of the last sub-group to the later ninth edition. Several errors appearing for the first time in the tenth are repeated in the eleventh. Such are the bad bungling of the sentence on p. 184, ll. 22-28, of the tenth edition; the change of the marginal note 'Christian *proveth his Brother*' (p. 163, l. 34) into 'Christian *rovoketh his Brother*', despite Christian's remark on the following page, line 17; the misprint 'from. 7. 24' for 'Rom. 7. 24' (p. 98, l. 9).[2]

The tentative conclusions as to the relationship of the early editions drawn from a comparison of the catchwords, number of pages, and general appearance are fully supported by the testimony of the variants. All the evidence, both external and internal, justifies the twofold grouping: the first, second, third, fourth, and seventh editions composing the one group; the fifth, sixth, eighth, and subsequent edi-

---

[1] The second, into which edition the passage was first introduced, reads 'argu-ments'.

[2] This misprint has been corrected in the British Museum copy of the tenth.

tions the second group. The testimony of the variants confirms, too, the conjecture that both the fourth and seventh editions were printed from the third, the fifth from the fourth, the sixth from the fifth, the eighth from the sixth, the first ninth from the eighth, the second ninth from the first ninth, the tenth from the second ninth, and the eleventh from the tenth. It establishes the additional fact that within the second group the sixth, eighth, and first ninth form a sub-group, the tenth and eleventh a second sub-group, with the second ninth as intermediary between the two.

Represented graphically, the relationship appears as follows:

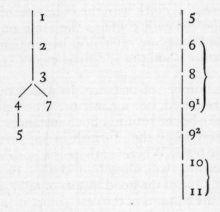

V. READINGS IN THE TWO GROUPS

THE question 'What editions, if any, did Bunyan supervise?', like most questions one would like to answer, is hedged about with many difficulties. Though a definite reply may not be given, it may at least be possible to establish a strong probability. The substantial additions to both the text and the marginalia made in the second and third editions are sufficient evidence that these editions passed through the author's own hands. After the third edition the new material is confined almost wholly to marginal notes and scripture references. A few words introduced into the body of the text, eleven marginal notes, and four scripture references constitute the additions of the fourth. The fifth makes no additions to the text or to the marginalia, but omits one marginal note of those in the fourth and four scripture references. The sixth omits two of the scripture references of the fifth. The seventh makes no additions to the marginalia, but omits one marginal note added in the second, eight of the forty-seven added in the third, and eight of the eleven added in the fourth. The marginalia of the eighth and the sixth are the same. The ninth, 1683, makes no additions to or omissions from the eighth. The ninth, 1684, adds four marginal notes to those of the first ninth and omits two scripture references. The tenth contains all the marginalia found in the second ninth with the exception of one scripture reference. The eleventh contains the same number of marginal notes and scripture references as the tenth. Evidently, after the fourth edition the additions even to the marginalia are insignificant.

In a large number of instances in which the two groups of editions are pitted, one against the other, neither may be said to give the better reading. Such instances are important only in the testimony they furnish in support of a twofold division of the texts. Wherever there is a possible preference, the better reading will almost invariably be found in the earlier group. One of the good results of talk, says Talkative, according to the editions of the first group, is that by it 'a man may learn to refute false Opinions'; in the editions of the second group, 'refute' is changed to 'refuse', a decided change for the worse (see below, p. 76, l. 25). In Hopeful's reply to Christian, 'Had he [Faithful] told me so when I was pleased and satisfied with mine own amendments, I had called him Fool for his pains' (see below, p. 140, l. 32), 'amendments' is changed in the second group to 'amendment', although on the same page Hopeful has twice spoken of his 'amendments'. According to the first group, we are told that Little-Faith, after being assaulted by Faintheart, Mistrust, and Guilt, 'made shift to scrabble on his way' (see below, p. 126, l. 15). In the second group, 'scramble' is substituted for 'scrabble'. The passage is strongly reminiscent of Bunyan's description in *Grace Abounding* of his own fear when in prison that he would not be able to face death fearlessly: 'Besides, I thought with myself, if I should make a scrabbling shift to clamber up the ladder.'[1] The words mean the same, but Bunyan shows particular fondness for 'scrabble'.

In none of the editions are all the scripture references correct. Whenever a particular reference in the two groups differs, the reference as given in the earlier group is apt to be the more nearly correct of the two. In the following list the correct reference is found in the earlier editions:[2]

P. 78, l. 16.   1 Cor. 4. 20, 1st to 4th, 7th *vs.* 1 Cor. 4. 2, other edits.
P. 80, l. 4.   Matt. 13 and ch. 25, 1st to 4th, 7th *vs.* Matt. 14, ch. 25, 5th and 6th, Matt. 14, 25, 8th to 11th.
P. 83, l. 6.   Rev. 21. 6, 1st to 4th, 7th *vs.* Rev. 1. 6, all other edits.
P. 111, l. 5.   Isa. 14. 30, 1st to 5th, 7th *vs.* Isa. 14. 13, all other edits.
P. 128, l. 28.   Jer. 2. 24, 1st to 4th, 7th *vs.* Jer. 1. 24, all other edits.
P. 134, l. 1.   Prov. 29. 5, 1st to 3rd, 7th *vs.* Prov. 29. 4, all other edits.
P. 134, l. 17.   Deut. 25. 2, 1st to 4th, 7th, 11th *vs.* Deut. 25. 1 ‖ 5, 6, 8, 9[3]: Dan. 25. 1 ‖ 9[4], 10.
P. 139, l. 30.   Gal. 2. 16, 1st to 4th, 7th *vs.* Gal. 2. 6, all other edits.

The fourth edition occasionally breaks away from its group and is found in the ranks of the later editions. One of the earliest examples of this occurs in the Author's Apology. In the first three editions and the seventh, Bunyan is made to say

Some men by feigning words, as dark as mine
Make truth to spangle, and its rayes to shine.

The fourth, followed by all the subsequent editions except the seventh, substitutes *feigned* for *feigning*. The preference, I think, lies with the reading of the earlier editions.

We have already seen that in p. 12, l. 8, the reading of the fourth, fifth, and sixth editions is no better than that of the third and seventh. In each case the insertion of a comma after 'Neighbour' would result in a correct reading.[3]

The additions to the text made in the fourth edition are for the most part unimportant. The happiest contribution it makes is probably the epithet 'Vile Runagate' inserted in

---

[1] *G.A.* § 334.   [2] References are to the text of the present edition.
[3] *Supra,* p. xcvii.

Judge Hategood's speech to Faithful. The fourth also wisely follows the second instead of the third in reading 'rating' for 'beating'. It is the fourth, too, that is the first to change 'it' to 'him' in the speech of Mr. By-ends: 'we are always most zealous when Religion goes in his Silver Slippers; we love much to walk with him in the Street, if the Sun shines and the People applaud it' (p. 99). Either pronoun makes good sense, but the remark of By-ends a little later: 'I am for him [Religion] when he walks in his golden Slippers in the Sun-shine and with applause' makes the reading of the fourth and later editions, except the seventh, plausible. The change of the marginal note, 'Christian *is still alive*', in the first three and seventh editions to 'Christian *still a Prisoner*' in all the rest results in a reading that is more apropos to the text. The fourth, however, must be held responsible for another change that is not so happy. In the first and second editions the passage in which Faithful learns from Christian who it was that had beaten him is glossed '*The temper* of *Moses*'. This is misprinted 'The thmper of Moses' in the third. In the fourth and subsequent texts, the seventh excepted, this marginal note appears as '*The thunder of Moses*', a reading wholly beside the mark. On the credit side the fourth can lay claim to the correction of two scripture references (see above, pp. xcvi–xcvii), but to offset this may be cited the omission of a whole line of the Apology and the giving of a speech of Faithful's to Christian.

The departures of the fourth from its group do not furnish convincing evidence of being the author's handiwork. Even the numerous marginal notes first introduced in this edition are rarely indicative of more than editorial helpfulness.

Let us now turn to the remaining member of this group, the seventh. Offor's assertion that it was a copy of the seventh edition Bunyan used in writing the Second Part of the *Pilgrim's Progress* since 'all the references . . . to the first part are correctly made to this edition',[1] was so often repeated as to be accepted without question. The truth of the matter is, that the references are more correctly made to the fourth edition than to the seventh, on account of the faultier pagination of the seventh.

[1] Hanserd Knollys edition (1847), p. cxxi. Cf. *Church Catalogue*, i. 231.

There are two references in Part Two to pages in Part One that are wrongly numbered in the seventh.[1] On the basis of correctness of the references in Part Two to Part One, the fourth can therefore present superior claims. Offor's further surmise that the seventh 'is very probably the last edition corrected by the pen of the Author' grew out of the discovery that the errors of the fourth, fifth, and sixth editions were all corrected in the seventh.

We have seen that the seventh edition stands closer to the third than to the fourth and was undoubtedly printed from it.

Occasionally it stands apart from all the other editions. In the seventh alone does the Man in the Iron Cage declare that nothing remains to him 'but threatnings, dreadful threatnings fearful threatnings of certain judgment'; in all the other texts 'faithful threatenings' is the reading for 'fearful threatnings'. The seventh gives an entirely independent reading of another passage. Before setting out upon his journey Christian goes home to plead with his wife and children. 'Moreover', he tells them, *'I am for certain informed that this our City will be burned with fire from Heaven, in which fearful overthrow, both my self, with thee my wife, and you my sweet babes shall miserably come to ruin.'* The second (the passage is not in the first edition) then has: 'At this his Relations were sore amazed'; the third: 'At this his Relations they were sore amazed'; the fourth and fifth: 'At this, His Relations they were sore amazed'; the sixth, eighth, and subsequent editions: 'At this, His Relations were sore amazed'. The seventh alone reads: 'At this his Revelations they were sore amazed.' Though attractive, and deriving some support from similar constructions elsewhere in Bunyan,[2] this must be treated as intelligent removal of the ambiguity introduced into the third edition: there is no reason to abandon the perfectly good reading of the second, supported as it is by Bunyan's use of 'Relations' in the same sense and similar contexts in Part Two.

A few examples of errors occurring in the third and repeated in the seventh were given above (pp. xcvii ff.).

---

[1] These are pages 12 and 275. In the seventh edition page 12 is misnumbered 20; while page-number 275 is repeated. The pagination of the third edition is much more erratic than that of either the fourth or the seventh.

[2] Cf. 'for this my conversion was as great', *Grace Abounding*, § 32; 'the truth of these his words', ibid., § 118; 'by reason of this my terror', ibid., § 164.

There are also several instances of errors occurring in the third which have been corrected in the seventh. One of these has already been alluded to in discussing the fourth, the misprint in the third of '*thmper*' for '*temper*', which the fourth, blindly followed by the fifth, sixth, eighth, and subsequent editions, changed into '*thunder*'. The seventh is the only edition which restores the correct reading, '*The temper of Moses*'. All the editions from the third to the tenth, except the seventh, have Christian say to Pliable, 'There we shall see Men that, by the Word, were cut in pieces'. The seventh restores the correct reading of the first and second, 'World' for 'Word', in which it is followed by the eleventh. Another of the extremely rare cases in which the seventh forsakes the first group is less happy. In conjunction with the second ninth, the tenth, and eleventh editions the seventh substitutes 'the desired Heaven' for 'the desired Haven' of all the other editions (p. 54, l. 38). This error is soon retrieved, however, for a little later (p. 62, l. 11) the seventh returns to the reading of the first three editions, 'the desired Haven'. The last example I shall cite in which the seventh is associated with the later editions as against the earlier occurs in the song Faithful sings of Talkative (p. 85):

> *but so soon*
> *As Faithful talks of Heartwork like the Moon,*
> *That's past the full, into the Wain he goes.*

This is the reading of editions one to four. From the fifth to the eleventh, the seventh this time not excepted, the word '*Wain*' is corrected to '*Wane*'.

The close association of the seventh edition with the first three, not infrequently the first four, editions, constituting as they do not only the better-appearing but the better-edited group; the fact that the majority of the readings peculiar to the seventh are better than those found in the other editions; the further fact that when the seventh abandons its own group for the second and later group, it does so because in those particular cases the reading of the latter is, in the majority of instances, preferable to that of the former—all this shows highly intelligent editorial supervision, but is not conclusive evidence for the intervention of the author after the third edition. The fifth, sixth, eighth, and subsequent editions are each marred by important omissions of the text, which tend to enlarge with each succeeding edition. There is not a scintilla of evidence, apart from the additional marginal notes in the ninth, 1684, that any one of the editions of the second group ever passed through the author's hands.[1]

VI. CONCLUSIONS ON THE TEXT

A SUMMING-UP can now take place. Of the thirteen editions published during Bunyan's lifetime the first three only are of substantive character. The second edition includes considerable additions; the third, too, contains further additions. The fourth edition has several fresh marginal notes, but these are removed in the fifth and its successors; the seventh is worth a certain degree of consideration because, though set up from the third, it offers a small number of intelligent corrections of readings in the earlier editions. However, the history of all the editions subsequent to the fourth (except the seventh) is that each was set up in turn from the previous edition, that printing and book production gradually deteriorated, and that errors already present were perpetuated while new ones progressively increased.

The present text is based on the first edition, and, for the additional episodes or passages, on the editions in which they first appear (whether the second or the third).[2] All the substantive editions have been collated. Apart from the general principle that a first edition is likely to give the closest approximation to the intention of the author's copy, unless there is clear indication of a subsequent total revision

---

[1] Numerous misprints are found in the seventh edition: 'Thrt' for 'That' (A5, recto); 'gi-en' for 'Gi-ven' (p. 9); 'Plain.' for 'Pli.' (p. 10); driection (p. 24); difficuties (p. 33); nrarrow (p. 36); 'were' for 'where' (p. 54); 'wither' for 'whither' (p. 57); 'fact' for 'act' (p. 65); 'the' for 'thee' (p. 71); 'gaief' for 'grief' (p. 76); 'too' for 'two' (p. 88); weakear (p. 94); Ridicle (p. 118); expouds (p. 133); 'this' for 'thus' (p. 138); 'prejudice' for 'prejudiced' (p. 154); 'Deman' (p. 186); cretificate (p. 219); 'whicy' for 'which' (p. 231). There is an important difference, as McKerrow reminds us, between 'errors of wording' and 'errors of printing'. 'A most carelessly printed book absolutely swarming with literals, may contain important corrections, and from an editor's point of view give us the best text.' *An Introduction to Bibliography* (1927), p. 185.

[2] Attention is drawn to some superior and previously neglected readings in the early pages of the first edition by John Sparrow in his review of Professor Wharey's text; but he does not question the general choice of the third as copytext (*R.E.S.* vi (1930), 219–24).

of the text by the author,[1] there are special reasons why an editor of *The Pilgrim's Progress* must decisively choose the first. First, internal ones. Some characteristic colloquial forms, particularly those for the verb 'have' and the pronoun 'he' ('would a done', 'a came', etc.) occur in the first and are altered in all the subsequent editions. The same applies to many lapses in grammar, such as errors in sequence or number, and to a few archaic or provincial forms of words. These are indubitably the idiom of Bunyan, not the lapses of a printing-house reader or compositor:

P. 7, l. 15.   drownded (1)   drowned (2), etc.
    l. 20.   loose (1)   lose (2), etc.
P. 16, l. 33.   walking solitary (2)   solitarly (3)   solitarary (9[3])
P. 25, l. 9.   *bin* (1)   *been* (2)
P. 27, l. 2.   have had you a sought (1)
P. 36, l. 14.   the Heavens was (1)   were (2 &c.)
P. 59, l. 10.   strodled (1)   stradled (2 &c.)
P. 75, l. 7.   should a been killed (1)
P. 93, l. 16.   They was then asked (1)
P. 126, l. 6.   strook (1, 2)
P. 134, l. 11. you was (1)
P. 156, l. 29. stounded (1)   stun'd (2–9)   stunned (10, 11)

The problem for an editor is to decide whether the change in the second and later editions to forms more modern or more correct was approved of by Bunyan, or at any rate accepted by him, since the revised forms occur throughout the two editions, the second and the third, which contain long additional passages from his pen. Does such connivance by the author constitute the granting of his authority for all substantive changes in the expanded text?[2] I have not considered that it does:[3] to believe in such total supervision

---

[1] See Sir Walter Greg, 'The Rationale of Copy Text', *Studies in Bibliography* (1950–1), iii. 19–36.

[2] There are parallel problems in the text of *Grace Abounding*: in a passage first appearing in the third edition there is the reading 'stounded', altered to 'stunned' by the fifth edition.

[3] Southey alone of the nineteenth-century editors appears to have taken this view and not to have believed that some correction of Bunyan's English must be accepted: 'A collation of the first part with the earliest attainable copies has enabled me in many places to restore good old vernacular English which had been injudiciously altered, or carelessly corrupted. This has also been done in the second part; but there I had the first edition before me, and this it is evident had not been inspected either in manuscript or while passing through the press, by any person capable of correct-

there would have to be evidence of intelligent and purposeful revision throughout, and this is not the case; in fact the second and third editions contain a large number of serious departures from the original text, which seem due to carelessness or to interpretative emendation by the compositor; the following instances may be given:

P. 11, l. 24.   fast (1)   safe (2), etc.
P. 12, l. 8.   me Neighbour (1, 2)   thy Neighbor (3)
P. 14, l. 1.   World (1, 2, 7, 11)   Word (3)
P. 18, l. 15.   with (2)   him (3, 4)
P. 19, l. 12.   Morality (2)   Mortality (5)
P. 26, l. 36.   arguments (2)   agreement (3)
P. 33, l. 20.   muse (1)   maze (2, 3)
P. 36, l. 22.   Fiery (1)   fierce (2 &c.) (cf. Malachi iii. 2, 3)
P. 68, l. 34.   You know what I mean (1, 2, 9)   You know that I mean (3–7, 10, 11)
P. 85, l. 19.   stumble (1)   puzzle (2)
P. 97, l. 17.   Lanced (1, 2)   Lanched (3)
P. 108, l. 19.   *so these two* (1, 2)   *do* 3
P. 114, l. 22.   rateing (1)   beating (3)
P. 118, l. 20.   creaking (1, 2)   cracking (3)
P. 132, l. 28.   *shall then a Victor be* (1)   *then shall you Victors be* (2)
P. 162, l. 6.   *your Lord* (1)   *our Lord* (2)

There is also the interesting case of Bunyan's private use of 'lumbring' for a noise which is altered to 'rumbling' (p. 122, l. 4).

Bunyan did not supervise the reprints of 1678 and 1679 carefully enough to prevent these errors being made. If he had simply gone through them in order to make the alterations in grammar and spelling noticed above, we should expect him to continue to practise the same studious avoidance of provincial forms. But the same unemphatic forms of the auxiliary verbs and looseness of sequence occur in the first edition of the Second Part.[1]

ing it.' *The Pilgrim's Progress* (1830), Introduction, p. lxxxvii. But Southey had seen no edition of the first part earlier than the eighth and could not therefore go far in restoring the original text.

1 Spelling tests are difficult to apply, but it is worth noting that several spelling forms are common to the first edition, the conjectured Bunyan entries in the *Church Book*, and the first edition of *Badman* (also published by Ponder, 1680). For instance, 'countrey', 'bin', and 'judg'. These and others are also found in those treatises in the *Folio* which Doe printed from Bunyan's uncorrected papers; in *Pauls Departure and Crown* I have counted fifty such parallel spellings (*Folio*, pp. 173–88).

It was therefore the printer of the second and third editions who was responsible for trimming and polishing Bunyan's English in this way. For this reason, naturally, the fresh passages in these editions have had some of their irregularities smoothed over: it is only in the first edition that a less officious printer allows us to see the English of Bunyan as it was in his copy.

Bunyan writes proudly in the prefatory verses to his Second Part of how his work may be known from the counterfeits which were by then in circulation:

> If such thou meetst with, then thine only way
> Before them all, is, to say out thy say,
> In thine own native Language, which no man
> Now useth, nor with ease dissemble can.

The lines imply that the native roughness of his style was his distinguishing mark; it separates him from the peculiarly insipid false elegance of Thomas Sherman's Second Part (1683); in all his doctrinal and experimental works Bunyan was content to conform more closely to standard forms, or, more likely, to allow the corrector to have his way; even in *Badman* and *The Holy War* he does not give his idiom its full play as he does in his major work, where he is deliberately easy and popular.

But though aware that the colloquial quality was his strength Bunyan had none of the conscious artist's interest in the preservation of detail and texture: his main care was that the reader should

> Put by the Curtains, Look within my Vail;
> Turn up my Metaphors . . .

For the faithful reproduction of his message he put his trust in Ponder;[1] his complete confidence in him is shown by the inscription on the verso of the title-page of the first edition of the Second Part:

[1] Ponder was a Nonconformist who had been influential in obtaining licences for meeting-houses; he was imprisoned in 1676 for publishing Marvell's attack on Samuel Parker, *The Rehearsal Transprosed*. He published Owen's books and bought land at Northill in Bedfordshire (*Index to Recoveries*, Mich. xxix Car. II, 1677), and may have come in touch with Bunyan by either means. See F. M. Harrison, 'Nathaniel Ponder, the Publisher of *The Pilgrim's Progress*', *The Library*, Fourth Series (1934), xv. 257–94.

I appoint Mr. *Nathaniel Ponder*, But no other to
Print this Book. *John Bunyan* January 1. 1684.

Furthermore, after his release from the second imprisonment Bunyan's neglected pastoral duties must have pressed
hard upon him. The last ten years of his life were also his
most productive years as an author. As well as *Badman*
(1680), *The Holy War* (1682), and the Second Part (1684)
he published seventeen other books in the last ten years of
his life. Though this was also the period of his preaching
visits to London, to the Zoar Street meeting-house and elsewhere, he must have had very little time to attend at the
printing-house to correct the sheets as they were passing
through the press. When Ponder published the *Treatise of
the Fear of God* in 1679 he made the request that the reader
might correct the errors 'occasioned by the Printer, by
reason of the absence of the author'.[1] Yet the *Treatise* has
a comparatively short errata list; *Come and Welcome to Jesus
Christ* (1678) has a list of errata about twice as long; and the
second edition of *Come and Welcome* (1684) exhibits quite a
different treatment of the original text from that in the second
of *The Pilgrim's Progress*: the meaning is clarified or ampli-
fied by new phrases, sentences, or paragraphs on almost
every page. This is quite different from the dovetailing in
of a few long episodes or passages. The only radical alteration in the First Part comparable to the type of revision
employed in the 1684 *Come and Welcome* is a sentence
(p. 110, ll. 34–37) which is not expanded but curtailed in the
second and third editions.

For reasons similar to those given above, I have retained
the spelling, punctuation, capitalization, and italicization of
the first edition and of the earliest edition in which the
passages added later appear, adopting revised readings only
where plain inaccuracy is to be corrected.

[1] There was a tradition at Braintree in Essex, Ponder's home, that Bunyan stayed
there in 1679 to write a book, probably *Badman* (Harrison *art. cit.*, pp. 283–4, and
Essex Review (1929), xxxviii).

B. THE SECOND PART

IN the final couplet of verses forming the conclusion of the
First Part of the *Progress*, Bunyan had hinted at a continuation
of his Dream. That he regarded *The Life and Death of Mr.
Badman* (1680) as a kind of sequel to *The Pilgrim's Progress*
is evident from his statement concerning the inception of this
allegory: 'As I was considering with myself what I had written concerning the Progress of the Pilgrim from this world
to glory, and how it had been acceptable to many in this
nation, it came again into my mind to write, as then, of him
that was going to heaven, so now, of the life and death of
the ungodly, and of their travel from this world to hell.'[1]
The publication of *Mr. Badman*, however, failed to satisfy the
public demand for more of the original allegory. Spurious
'Second Parts' began to appear, so that in sheer self-defence
Bunyan was compelled to resume his dream.

In the lines prefixed to the Second Part, he expresses
the belief that his manner and language cannot be successfully imitated:

> *'Tis true, some have of late, to Counterfeit*
> *My Pilgrim, to their own, my Title set;*
> *Yea others, half my name and Title too;*
> *Have stitched to their Book, to make them do;*
> *But yet they by their Features do declare*
> *Themselves not mine to be, whose ere they are.*
> *If such thou meetst with, then thine only way*
> *Before them all, is, to say out thy say,*
> *In thine own native Language, which no man*
> *Now useth, nor with ease dissemble can.*

No copy of the Second Part bearing half the author's name
has come to light, but copies flaunting his title have been
known for a long time. The most interesting of these is by
Thomas Sherman, a General Baptist, who set out to improve
both Bunyan's theology and his literary manners:

The | Second Part | of the | Pilgrims Progress, | from | This present
World of | Wickeness and Misery, to An | Eternity of Holiness and
Felicity; | Exactly Described under the Similitude | of a Dream,
Relating the Manner | and Occasion of his setting out from, | and

[1] Offor, *Works*, iii. 590.

difficult and dangerous Journey | through the World; and safe
Arrival | at last to Eternal Happiness.

They were Strangers and Pilgrims on Earth, | *but they desire a*
better Countrey, that is | *an Heavenly.* Heb. 11. 13. 16. | *Let us lay*
aside every Weight, and the Sin, | *that doth so easily beset us; and run*
with | *patience the Race that is set before us,* | Heb. 12. 7.——
LONDON, Printed by *T. H.* over | against the *Poultry,* 1682.

The four-and-a-half pages of Dedication are signed
'T. S.'; the three-and-a-half pages of verse 'To the Ingenious
Author of this Second Part of the Pilgrims Progress',
'R. B.'; and the five-and-a-quarter pages of 'The Authors
Apology for his Book' again 'T. S.' Nowhere is the claim
advanced that the work is Bunyan's. On the contrary, in the
Author's Apology the writer declares that through 'the
importunity of others' and his own desire to be more theological and 'to deliver the whole in such serious and spiritual
phrases, that may prevent that lightness and laughter, which
the reading some passages occasion [*sic*] in some vain and
frothy minds', he had been induced to issue his 'Meditations
in such a method as might serve as a Supplyment, or
a Second Part to it'. How far removed his manner is from
Bunyan's is evident in the very first sentence:

The Spring being far advanced, the Meadows being Covered with
a Curious Carpet of delightful Green, and the Earth Cloathed in Rich
and Glorious Attire, to Rejoyce and Triumph for the Return of her
Shining Bridegroom: The Healthful Air rendred more Pleasing and
Delightful by the gentle Winds then breathed from the *South,* im-
pregnated with the Exhilerating Fragrancy of the Variety of Flowers
and odoriferous Plants over which they had passed; and every Blooming
Bush, and Flourishing Grove plentifully stored with Winged Inhabitants, who with a delightful Harmony sweetly sing forth their Makers
Praise and Warble out their joyful Welcomes to the Gaudy Spring.
I one Day took a walk in the Fields. . . .

Bad as this is, it did not prevent the book from going
through several editions.

The copy described by Robert Southey in the Introduction to his edition of *The Pilgrim's Progress* is today in
the library of the Baptist Union, Southampton Row,
London. The imprint of this copy reads: 'London, Printed
for *Tho. Malthus* at the *Sun* in the *Poultry,* 1683.' It is

apparently a duplicate copy of the one described in the *Church Catalogue* (i. 245–6, No. 205), except for this difference: the six leaves of sig. *, inserted in the Church copy between leaves A and A2, in the Southey copy are placed at the end of the volume. The Lenox Library also possesses a copy dated 1683. Still another copy, printed in Edinburgh 'by the Heir of *Andrew Anderson*' and dated 1684, is described in the *Church Catalogue* as No. 206.

The genuine Second Part first appeared in 1684, and went through two editions during Bunyan's life.

THE FIRST EDITION, 1684

LENOX COPY.[1] The Second Part. Small duodecimo.

Collation by signatures: One leaf unsigned with portrait, A⁶, B–E¹², F⁵, G¹²–K¹², L⁶. D4 is signed D5, K4 is K2.

Collation by pagination: blank, recto *; frontispiece, verso *; title-page [as reproduced opposite], recto [A]; [Authorization to print] I appoint Mr. *Nathaniel* Ponder, But no other to Print this Book. | [signed] *John Bunyan.* | [dated] January 1. | 1684. |, verso [A]; [publisher's advertisement], verso [A]; The Author's Way &c., recto A2–verso [A6]; text, pp. 1–224; FINIS. ERRATA [3 lines], p. 224; [publisher's advertisement], pp. [225–7].

Page 13 is misnumbered 15, 14 is 12, 96 is 66; numbers 106–19 are omitted; number 102 is printed ¡02. Pages 100–5 and 120 are in much larger type than the rest of the text. Though the page-numbering breaks from 105 to 120, nothing is omitted.

Besides the frontispiece are two cuts. The first of these, representing Greatheart leading the pilgrims past the scene where Simple, Sloth, and Presumption were hanged, was supplied, according to a manuscript note on the fly-leaf, from another copy. It is placed, according to directions on the plate, between pages 52 and 53, although the portion of text it is designed to illustrate falls on page 60. The second cut, the dance around the head of Giant Despair, is inserted between pages 182 and 183.

The frontispiece in the lower part of the plate represents Bunyan asleep, as in the third edition of Part One, with Christiana, Mercy, and the four boys above and behind the

---

[1] This is the Lea Wilson copy described by Offor in the Hanserd Knollys edition, 1847, p. cxxvi. The present collation is made from a photographic reprint.

THE
Pilgrim's Progreſs.
FROM
THIS WORLD
TO
That which is to come
The Second Part.

Delivered under the Similitude of a

DREAM

Wherein is ſet forth
The manner of the ſetting out of *Chri*
ſtian's Wife and Children, their
Dangerous JOURNEY,
AND
Safe Arrival at the Deſired Country.

By *JOHN BUNYAN,*

I have uſed Similitudes, Hoſ. 12. 10.

LONDON,
Printed for *Nathaniel Ponder* at the *Peacock*
in the *Poultry,* near the Church, 1684.

Part Two, First Edition, 1684

dreamer setting out for the celestial gate. The plate has the name of the engraver, *Sturt Sc.*; the name of the city, *Destruction*; the inscription at the left side, *The Pilgrims Progress P^t. 2^d.*; and beneath, *Sold by N. Ponder at the Peacock in the Poultry.*

There are but five leaves of sheet F. The change to larger type begins on the verso of F2, p. 100, and continues through the remaining leaves of this sheet. Page 106, verso of F5, is numbered 120, and the following page, No. 121, is the recto of G1. It will be noticed that this occurs about the mechanical centre of the volume. Very probably the manuscript was divided between two compositors, the first to end with sig. F, the second to begin with sig. G. The matter given the first compositor proved less than had been supposed. Even after resorting to large type he succeeded in filling out only five leaves of sig. F. The remaining leaves of the signature were then, in all probability, cut away.

OTHER COPIES. British Museum, Huntington, John Rylands, Chapin, Rosenbach Foundation, and Pierpont Morgan Libraries. Another copy known as the Van Antwerp copy was sold at Sotheby's 22 March 1907.

In the Huntington copy, as described in the *Church Catalogue* (i. 243–4, No. 204), there are no significant press differences from the Lenox copy.

THE SECOND EDITION, 1686 AND 1687

Of the Second Edition of the Second Part there were two issues. The British Museum copy which claims to be the Second Edition bears the date 1686. The Lenox copy, which does not name the edition, is dated 1687.[1] So was the copy which Brown made the basis of his edition in the Cambridge English Classics Series (1907), a copy belonging to Eliot Pye-Smith Reed. A careful collation of Brown's text with the British Museum copy reveals differences few in number and insignificant in character. The edition of 1690, a copy of which is also in the British Museum, calls itself the third edition. If Brown's text is, as

[1] There is also a copy dated 1687 in the Pierpont Morgan Library. A copy dated 1687 was sold at Sotheby's, 4 December 1902.

it claims to be, a faithful reproduction of that of the 1687 copy the differences between the copies dated 1686 and 1687 represent merely minor press variants in certain formes.[1]

BRITISH MUSEUM COPY. The Second Part. The Second Edition. Small duodecimo.

Collation by signatures: One leaf unsigned with portrait facing title-page, A⁶, B–J¹², K⁶. C3 is unsigned.

Collation by pagination: blank, recto *; portrait, verso *; title-page [as reproduced opposite], recto [A]; blank, verso [A]; The Author's Way, recto A2–verso A6; text, pp. 1–201; FINIS, p. 201; Advertisement, pp. [202–4]; FINIS, p. [204]. Page 37 is misnumbered 47, 48 is 84, 90 is 99, 96 is 66, 166 is 167, and 167 is 166. Portrait the same as in first edition. Two cuts, as in first edition. Other copies: Lenox, Pierpont Morgan Libraries, Dr. Richard Offor.

The second edition has made exceedingly few alterations in the text of the first edition. It has added, however, a great many marginal notes.[2]

CONCLUSIONS ON THE TEXT

THERE is no evidence of author's revision in the second edition and therefore, as with the First Part, the present text is based on the first edition while incorporating the additional marginalia of 1686.

---

[1] Typical differences are:

1686	1687
make	made
oweth	owneth
good a	a good
above	about
bring	being
embrace	imbrace

[2] A spurious Third Part appeared in 1693. This was a brazen attempt to deceive. It described itself as 'The Third Part, to which is added The Life and Death of John Bunyan, Author of the First and Second Part; thus compleating the whole *Progress*'. Despite the strong denunciation of it printed in the form of a publisher's advertisement on the reverse of the title-page in the thirteenth edition, 1693, no fewer than fifty-nine editions of it had appeared before the end of the eighteenth century.

THE
Pilgrim's Progress.
FROM
THIS WORLD
TO
That which is to come
The Second Part.

Delivered under the Similitude of a

DREAM

Wherein is set forth
The manner of the setting out of *Chri*-
stian's Wife and Children, their
Dangerous JOURNEY,
AND
Safe Arrival at the Desired Country.

By *JOHN BUNYAN.*

The Second Edition.

I have used Similitudes, Hof. 12. 10.

LONDON,
Printed for *Nathaniel Ponder* at the *Peacock*
in the *Poultry*, near the Church. 1686.

Part Two, Second Edition, 1686

C. EXPLANATIONS

PART ONE

THE textual notes list all significant variations. The variants in the editions of the first group, because of the relatively greater importance of these editions, are recorded in much greater detail than those in the editions of the second group. No account has been taken of differences in spelling, unless the difference seemed to have some special significance, or of variations in capitalization, in the use of hyphens, in the use of the sign for 'and'. Obvious misprints, except those in the editions of the first group, have for the most part been disregarded. Obvious errors in the scripture references, which occasionally run the gamut of all the editions, have been corrected. In making these corrections, I have been greatly aided by the work of George Offor, who carefully tested every reference. The first edition indicates some but not all of the scripture references by the letters of the alphabet, and then irregularly. I have abandoned this in favour of the more convenient asterisks employed, in combination with daggers, in all the subsequent editions, and sometimes in the first also. Differences in punctuation have been recorded only in cases involving the actual sense of the passage; that of the first edition has been generally adopted.

Editions and copies collated:

First Edition, British Museum, Howard, Warner, Rylands, Lenox, and Pierpont Morgan copies.
Second Edition, British Museum (two), Lenox, and Pierpont Morgan copies.
Third Edition, British Museum and Howard copies.
Fourth Edition, British Museum and Lenox copies.
Fifth Edition (1680), British Museum and Lenox copies.
Sixth Edition, British Museum and Lenox copies.
Seventh Edition, British Museum and Lenox copies.
Eighth Edition, Lenox copy.
Ninth Edition (1683), Lenox copy.
Ninth Edition (1684), Lenox copy.
Tenth Edition, Lenox copy.
Eleventh Edition, British Museum and Pierpont Morgan copies.

These editions appear in the footnotes as 1, 2, 3, 4, 5, 6, 7, 8, 9³, 9⁴, 10, and 11. No variants have been reported from the fifth edition, 1682. As shown elsewhere, this edition, if admitted to be genuine, has no integrity as an independent text.

Whenever a certain reading is reported as occurring from one edition to another, 'inclusive' should always be understood (e.g. '4–11' means 'from the fourth to the eleventh inclusive'). The statement that a particular reading or marginal was added [*add.*] in a certain edition means, unless specifically stated to the contrary, that the reading or marginal is retained in all subsequent editions (e.g. '*marg.* Carnal Physick for a Sick soul *add.* 3' means that this marginal note was added in the third edition and retained in all subsequent editions). If a word for which a variant is recorded occurs more than once in the same line, the particular instance or instances involved will be indicated by the use of superior numbers (e.g. '11 worse¹, ² *ital.* 10, 11' means that the word 'worse' occurring twice in line 11 is in both instances printed in italics in the tenth and eleventh editions). Lemmas have been employed whenever there seemed a possibility of misunderstanding.

The following abbreviations have been used:

add.   = added.
om.   = omitted.
marg.   = marginal note.
etc.   = and subsequent editions.
rom.   = roman type.
ital.   = italics.

PART TWO

THE text has been based on the first edition into which have been incorporated the marginalia added in the second (1686).

Copies collated:

First Edition: British Museum, Lenox, Rylands, Huntington, Pierpont Morgan copies.

Second Edition: British Museum, Offor, Lenox, Pierpont Morgan copies.

The AUTHOR'S *Apology*
For His BOOK

*W*Hen *at the first I took my Pen in hand,*
    Thus for to write; I did not understand
That I at all should make a little Book
In such a mode; Nay, I had undertook
To make another, which when almost done,
Before I was aware, I this begun.

   And thus it was: I writing of the Way
And Race of Saints in this our Gospel-Day,
Fell suddenly into an Allegory
About their Journey, and the way to Glory,
In more than twenty things, which I set down;
This done, I twenty more had in my Crown,
And they again began to multiply,
Like sparks that from the coals of Fire do flie.
Nay then, thought I, if that you breed so fast,
I'll put you by your selves, lest you at last
Should prove ad infinitum, *and eat out*
The Book that I already am about.

   Well, so I did; but yet I did not think
To shew to all the World my Pen and Ink
In such a mode; I only thought to make
I knew not what: nor did I undertake
Thereby to please my Neighbour; no not I,
I did it mine own self to gratifie.

   Neither did I but vacant seasons spend
In this my Scribble; Nor did I intend
But to divert my self in doing this,
From worser thoughts, which make me do amiss.

   Thus I set Pen to Paper with delight,
And quickly had my thoughts in black and white.

The AUTHOR'S APOLOGY | For His BOOK. | 3: The Author's
Apology for | His BOOK. | 4, 5: The Author's Apology for his |
BOOK. | 6: The AUTHOR's APOLOGY | For His BOOK. | 7: The
Authors Apology for his | BOOK. | 8–10: The Authors Apology for
his BOOK. | 11   6 *this*] *thus*, 2, 6

For having now my Method by the end;
Still as I pull'd, it came; and so I penn'd
It down, until it came at last to be
For length and breadth the bigness which you see.

Well, when I had thus put mine ends together,
I shew'd them others, that I might see whether
They would condemn them, or them justifie:
And some said, let them live; some, let them die:
Some said, John, print it; others said, Not so:
Some said, It might do good; others said, No.   10

Now was I in a straight, and did not see
Which was the best thing to be done by me:
At last I thought, Since you are thus divided,
I print it will, and so the case decided.

For, thought I; Some I see would have it done,
Though others in that Channel do not run;
To prove then who advised for the best,
Thus I thought fit to put it to the test.

I further thought, if now I did deny
Those that would have it thus, to gratifie,   20
I did not know, but hinder them I might,
Of that which would to them be great delight.

For those that were not for its coming forth;
I said to them, Offend you I am loth;
Yet since your Brethren pleased with it be,
Forbear to judge, till you do further see.

If that thou wilt not read, let it alone;
Some love the meat, some love to pick the bone:
Yea, that I might them better palliate,
I did too with them thus Expostulate.   30

May I not write in such a stile as this?
In such a method too, and yet not miss
Mine end, thy good? why may it not be done?
Dark Clouds bring Waters, when the bright bring none;
Yea, dark, or bright, if they their silver drops
Cause to descend, the Earth, by yielding Crops,

5 *my* 1 (Lenox)   18–19 *fit . . . thought* om. 4, 5, 6   23 *that*]
which 2 etc.   29 *palliate*] *moderate* 9⁴ etc.   33 *My* 1 (Lenox)
may it not] *may not it* 9³

Gives praise to both, and carpeth not at either,
But treasures up the Fruit they yield together:
Yea, so commixes both, that in her Fruit
None can distinguish this from that, they suit
Her well, when hungry: but if she be full,
She spues out both, and makes their blessings null.

   You see the ways the Fisher-man doth take
To catch the Fish; what Engins doth he make?
Behold! how he ingageth all his Wits;
10 *Also his Snares, Lines, Angles, Hooks and Nets:*
Yet Fish there be, that neither Hook, nor Line,
Nor Snare, nor Net, nor Engin can make thine;
They must be grop'd for, and be tickled too,
Or they will not be catcht, what e're you do.

   How doth the Fowler seek to catch his Game,
By divers means, all which one cannot name?
His Gun, his Nets, his Lime-twigs, light and bell:
He creeps, he goes, he stands; yea, who can tell
Of all his postures? Yet there's none of these
20 *Will make him master of what Fowls he please.*
Yea, he must Pipe, and Whistle to catch this;
Yet if he does so, that Bird he will miss.

   If that a Pearl may in a Toads-head dwell,
And may be found too in an Oister-shell;
If things that promise nothing, do contain
What better is then Gold; who will disdain,
(That have an inkling of it,) there to look,
That they may find it? Now my little Book,
(Tho void of all those paintings that may make
30 *It with this or the other man to take,)*
Is not without those things that do excel,
What do in brave, but empty notions dwell.

   Well, yet I am not fully *satisfied,*
That this your Book will stand, when soundly try'd.
   Why, what's the matter? It is dark, what tho?
But it is feigned, *what of that I tro?*

---

6 *their*] her 9³   21 this *ital.* 1, 2   22 that *ital.* 1, 2, 6, 8 *etc.*
26 Gold *?* 3   29 *those*] these 8 *etc.*   *may*] they 2, 3   33–34 Well
. . . try'd *ital.* 1, 2   35 It is dark *ital.* 1, 2   36 But . . . feigned
ital. 1, 2   that I tro?] that? I tro, 8 *etc.*

Some men by feigning words as dark as mine,
Make truth to spangle, and its rayes to shine.
    But they want solidness: *Speak man thy mind:*
They drown'd the weak; Metaphors make us blind.
    Solidity, indeed becomes the Pen
Of him that writeth things Divine to men:
But must I needs want solidness, because
By Metaphors I speak; was not Gods Laws,
His Gospel-laws in olden time held forth
By Types, Shadows and Metaphors? Yet loth   10
Will any sober man be to find fault
With them, lest he be found for to assault
The highest Wisdom. No, he rather stoops,
And seeks to find out what by pins and loops,
By Calves, and Sheep; by Heifers, and by Rams;
By Birds and Herbs, and by the blood of Lambs;
God speaketh to him: And happy is he
That finds the light, and grace that in them be.
    Be not too forward therefore to conclude,
That I want solidness; that I am rude: 20
All things solid in shew, not solid be;
All things in parables despise not we,
Lest things most hurtful lightly we receive;
And things that good are, of our souls bereave.
    My dark and cloudy words they do but hold
The Truth, as Cabinets inclose the Gold.
    The Prophets used much by Metaphors
To set forth Truth; Yea, who so considers
Christ, his Apostles too, shall plainly see,
That Truths to this day in such Mantles be.   30
    Am I afraid to say that holy Writ,
Which for its Stile, and Phrase, puts down all Wit,
Is every where so full of all these things,
(Dark Figures, Allegories,) yet there springs
From that same Book that lustre, and those rayes
Of light, that turns our darkest nights to days.

---

1 *feigned* 4, 5, 6, 8 *etc.*   3–4 But . . . blind *ital.* 1, 2
4 *drown* 7: drownd 3   8 *were* 5, 6, 8 *etc.*   9 *olden times,* 3: *old*
time 2: *olden times* 11   11 *be to*] *below* 2   32 *Phrase*] *Praise*
6, 8 *etc.*

Come, let my Carper, to his Life now look,
And find There darker Lines, then in my Book
He findeth any. Yea, and let him know,
That in his best things there are worse lines too.
   May we but stand before impartial men,
To his poor One, I durst adventure Ten,
That they will take my meaning in these lines
Far better then his lies in Silver Shrines.
Come, Truth, although in Swadling-clouts, I find
Informs the Judgement, rectifies the Mind,
Pleases the Understanding, makes the Will
Submit; the Memory too it doth fill
With what doth our Imagination please;
Likewise, it tends our troubles to appease.
   Sound words I know Timothy is to use;
And old Wives Fables he is to refuse,
But yet grave Paul him no where doth forbid
The use of Parables; in which lay hid
That Gold, those Pearls, and precious stones that were
Worth digging for; and that with greatest care.
   Let me add one word more, O Man of God!
Art thou offended? dost thou wish I had
Put forth my matter in another dress,
Or that I had in things been more express?
Three things let me propound, then I submit
To those that are my betters, (as is fit.)
   1. I find not that I am denied the use
Of this my method, so I no abuse
Put on the Words, Things, Readers, or be rude
In handling Figure, or Similitude,
In application; but, all that I may,
Seek the advance of Truth, this or that way:
Denied did I say? Nay, I have leave,
(Example too, and that from them that have
God better pleased by their words or ways,
Then any Man that breatheth now adays,)

2 There] their 6   than 2, 3 etc.   6 dare 3 etc.   7 That
om. 4, 5, 6   8 than 2, 3 etc.   13 Imaginations 3   17 where]
were 9⁴   doth] did 3   25–26 transposed 8 etc.   28–29 none abuse.
Put 10, 11   29 Words] Word 7   34 Examples 6, 8, etc.
35 pleas'd 3   36 Than 3

Thus to express my mind, thus to declare
Things unto thee that excellentest are.
   2. *I find that men (as high as Trees) will write*
Dialogue-wise; yet no Man doth them slight
For writing so: Indeed if they abuse
Truth, cursed be they, and the craft they use
To that intent; but yet let Truth be free
To make her Salleys upon Thee, and Me,
Which way it pleases God. For who knows how,
Better then he that taught us first to Plow,   10
To guide our Mind and Pens for his Design?
And he makes base things usher in Divine.
   3. *I find that holy Writ in many places,*
Hath semblance with this method, where the cases
Doth call for one thing to set forth another:
Use it I may then, and yet nothing smother
Truths golden Beams; Nay, by this method may
Make it cast forth its rayes as light as day.
   And now, before I do put up my Pen,
I'le shew the profit of my Book, and then   20
Commit both thee, and it unto that hand
That pulls the strong down, and makes weak ones stand.
   This Book it chaulketh out before thine eyes,
The man that seeks the everlasting Prize:
It shews you whence he comes, whither he goes,
What he leaves undone; also what he does:
It also shews you how he runs, and runs,
Till he unto the Gate of Glory comes.
   It shews too, who sets out for life amain,
As if the lasting Crown they would attain: 30
Here also you may see the reason why
They loose their labour, and like fools do die.
   This Book will make a Travailer of thee,
If by its Counsel thou wilt ruled be;
It will direct thee to the Holy Land,
If thou wilt its Directions understand:
Yea, it will make the sloathful, active be;

15 *Do* 3   20 *I'l* 3 : *I'll* 6, 8 *etc.*   21 *into* 9³   32 lose 2, 3
33 *Traveller* 2 *etc.*   35 *Holy Land*] *Hilly Land* 5 (Lenox and
Pierpont Morgan), 9³ (B.M.)

The Blind also, delightful things to see.
  Art thou for something rare, and profitable?
Wouldest thou see a Truth within a Fable?
Art thou forgetful? wouldest thou remember
From New-years-day *to the last of* December?
Then read my fancies, they will stick like Burs,
And may be to the Helpless, Comforters.
  This Book is writ in such a Dialect,
As may the minds of listless men affect:
It seems a Novelty, and yet contains
Nothing but sound and honest Gospel-strains.
  Wouldst thou divert thy self from Melancholly?
Would'st thou be pleasant, yet be far from folly?
Would'st thou read Riddles, and their Explanation,
Or else be drownded in thy Contemplation?
Dost thou love picking-meat? or would'st thou see
A man i' th Clouds, and hear him speak to thee?
Would'st thou be in a Dream, and yet not sleep?
Or would'st thou in a moment Laugh and Weep?
Wouldest thou loose thy self, and catch no harm?
And find thy self again without a charm?
Would'st read thy self, and read thou know'st not what
And yet know whether thou art blest or not,
By reading the same lines? O then come hither,
And lay my Book, thy Head and Heart together.

                    JOHN BUNYAN

3 *Wouldst* 3   4 *Wouldst* 3   5 *the*] *th'* 3 etc.   7 *maybe* 11
15 *drownded*] *drowned* 2, 4 *etc.: drown'd* 3   17 *i th* 2: *i' th'* 7, 9⁴ *etc.*
20 *Wouldst* 3   *lose* 2, 3

THE

Pilgrims Progress:

In the similitude of a

DREAM.

The *Gaol. AS I walk'd through the wilderness of this world, I lighted on a certain place, where was a *Denn; And I laid me down in that place to sleep: And as I slept I dreamed a Dream. I dreamed, and behold *I saw* *Isa. 64. 6. *a Man *cloathed with Raggs, standing in a certain place,* Lu. 14. 33. *with his face from his own House, a Book in his hand, and* Psal. 38. 4. Hab. 2. 2. *a great burden upon his Back.* I looked, and saw him Act. 16. 31. open the Book, and Read therein; and as he read, he wept and trembled: and not being able longer to contain, *His Out-cry. he brake out with a lamentable cry; saying, *what shall 10 I do?*

In this plight therefore he went home, and refrained himself as long as he could, that his Wife and Children should not perceive his distress; but he could not be silent long, because that his trouble increased: wherefore at length he brake his mind to his Wife and Children; and thus he began to talk to them, *O my dear Wife,* said he, *and you the Children of my bowels, I your dear friend am in my self undone, by reason of a burden that lieth hard upon me: moreover, I am for certain in-* 20 *formed, that this our City will be burned with fire from Heaven, in which fearful overthrow, both my self, with thee, my Wife, and you my sweet babes, shall miserably come to ruine; except (the which, yet I see not) some way of*

2 *marg.* The Gaol *add.* 3: The Goal 4 *etc.*   3 that ital. 3   10
marg. His Out-cry *add.* 3   Acts 2. 27 *add.* 4, *om.* 7   12 In
this plight . . . *to be saved?* (p. 9, l. 25) *add.* 2   restrained 2   18
saith 3   21 marg. *This World* add. 9⁴   24 marg. *He knows no
way of escape as yet* add. 4, *om.* 7

escape can be found, whereby we may be delivered. At this
his Relations were sore amazed; not for that they
believed, that what he said to them was true, but because they thought, that some frenzy distemper had got
into his head: therefore, it drawing towards night, and
they hoping that sleep might settle his brains, with all
hast they got him to bed; but the night was as troublesome to him as the day: wherefore instead of sleeping,
he spent it in sighs and tears. So when the morning
10 was come, they would know how he did; and he told
them worse and worse. He also set to talking to them
again, but they began to be hardened; *they also *Carnal
thought to drive away his distemper by harsh and surly Physick for
a Sick Soul.
carriages to him: sometimes they would deride, sometimes they would chide, and sometimes they would
quite neglect him: wherefore he began to retire himself
to his Chamber to pray for, and pity them; and also to
condole his own misery: he would also walk solitarily
in the Fields, sometimes reading, and sometimes pray-
20 ing: and thus for some days he spent his time.

Now, I saw upon a time, when he was walking in the
Fields, that he was (as he was wont) reading in his
Book, and greatly distressed in his mind; and as he
read, he burst out, as he had done before, crying, *What
shall I do to be saved?*

I saw also that he looked this way, and that way, as if
he would run; yet he stood still, because, as I perceived, he could not tell which way to go. I looked
then, and saw a man named *Evangelist* coming to him,
30 and asked, *Wherefore dost thou cry?* He answered, Sir,
I perceive, by the Book in my hand, that I am Condemned to die, and *after that to come to Judgment; *Heb. 9. 27.
and I find that I am not *willing to do the first, nor *Job 16.
21, 22.
*able to do the second. *Ezek. 22. 14.

1–2 At this his Relations they were 3: At this, His Relations they
were 4, 5: At this, His Relations were 6, 8 *etc.*: At this his Revelations
they were 7   3 said] had said 9[4] *etc.*   10 and *om.* 5, 6, 8 *etc.*
12 *marg.* Carnal . . . Soul *add.* 3   18 solitary 8, 9[3]   24–25
Acts 16. 30, 31 *add.* 4, *om.* 7   30 doest 2   33 Job 26. 21,
22 ‖ 1–11   33 Ezek. 22. 14] Exod. 22. 14 ‖ 11

Then said *Evangelist*, Why not willing to die? since this life is attended with so many evils? The Man answered, Because I fear that this burden that is upon my back, will sink me lower then the Grave; and I shall **Isa. 30. 33.* fall into **Tophet*. And Sir, if I be not fit to go to Prison, I am not fit (I am sure) to go to Judgement, and from thence to Execution; and the thoughts of these things make me cry.

Then said *Evangelist*, If this be thy condition, why standest thou still? He answered, Because I know not 10 ** Conviction of* whither to go, Then he gave him a **Parchment-Roll*, *the necessity* and there was written within, **Fly from the wrath to* *of flying.* **Mat. 3. 7. come.*

The Man therefore Read it, and looking upon *Evangelist* very carefully; said, Whither must I fly? Then said *Evangelist*, pointing with his finger over a very **Mat. 7.* wide Field, Do you see yonder **Wicket-gate*? The Man *Psal. 119.* said, No. Then said the other, Do you see yonder *105.* *2 Pe. 1. 19.* **shining light? He said, I think I do. Then said *Evan-* **Christ and* gelist, Keep that light in your eye, and go up directly 20 *the way to him* *cannot be found* thereto, **so shalt thou see the Gate; at which when thou *without the* knockest, it shall be told thee what thou shalt do. *Word,*

So I saw in my Dream, that the Man began to run; Now he had not run far from his own door, but his Wife and Children perceiving it, began to cry after him to **Luke 14. 26.* return: **but the Man put his fingers in his Ears, and ran on crying, Life, Life, Eternal Life: so he looked **Gen. 19.* not behind him, **but fled towards the middle of the *17.* Plain.

* They that fly The Neighbors also came out to **see him run, and 30 *from the wrath* as he ran, some mocked, others threatned; and some *to come, are a* *Gazing-Stock* cried after him to return: Now among those that did so, *to the world.* there were two that were resolved to fetch him back by *Jer. 20. 10.* force. **The name of the one was *Obstinate*, and the **Obstinate* *and* Pliable name of the other *Pliable*. Now by this time the Man *follow him.*

1 saith 3, *etc.*   to die] to do dye 9³   6 (I am sure) om. 2 *etc.*
9 saith 3   11 marg. *Conviction...flying* add. 2   19 *marg.* 2 Pet.
1. 19] 2 Pet. 1. 29 || 1–10: 2 Pet. 2. 29 || 11   26 Luke 14. 26] Luke
14. 16 || 4, 5, 6, 8 *etc.*   28 Gen. 19. 17] Gen. 19. 27 || 2, 3, 7
32 Now] And 2 *etc.*   34 *marg.* Obstinate . . . *him* add. 3

was got a good distance from them; But however they were resolved to pursue him; which they did and in little time they over-took him. Then said the Man, Neighbours, *Wherefore are you come?* They said, To perswade you to go back with us; but he said, That can by no means be: You dwell, said he, in the City of *Destruction*, (the place also where I was born) I see it to be so; and dying there, sooner or later, you will sink lower then the Grave, into a place that burns with Fire 10 and Brimstone: Be content good Neighbours, and go along with me.

*What! said *Obstinate, and leave our Friends, and our* * Obstinate. *Comforts behind us!*

*Yes, said *Christian*, (for that was his name) because, * Christian. that all, which you shall forsake, is not *worthy to be * 2 Cor. 4. 18, compared with a little of that that I am seeking to enjoy, and if you will go along with me, and hold it, you shall fare as I my self; for there where I go, is *enough, and * Luk. 15. to spare; Come away, and prove my words.

20   Obst. *What are the things you seek, since you leave all the world to find them?*

Chr. I seek an **Inheritance, incorruptible, undefiled,* * 1 Pet. 1. 4. *and that fadeth not away*; and it is laid up in Heaven, **and fast there, to be bestowed at the time appointed,* * Heb. 11. 16. on them that diligently seek it. Read it so, if you will, in my Book.

Obst. *Tush*, said *Obstinate, away with your Book; will you go back with us, or no?*

Chr. No, not I, said the other; because I have laid 30 my hand to the *Plow.   * Luke 9. 62.

Obst. *Come then, Neighbour* Pliable, *let us turn again, and go home without him; there is a company of these Craz'd-headed Coxcombs, that when they take a fancy by the end, are wiser in their own eyes then seven men that can render a reason.*

---

3 a little time 2 *etc.*   saith 3   15 all *ital.* 2   which . . . forsake add. 3 16 little *ital.* 2   17 and hold it *add.* 2, rom. 3   18 Luke 15] Luke 15. 17 ‖ 4, 5, 6, 8 *etc.*   20 *all* marg. *Heb.* 11. 62 ‖ 1, 2   22 1 Pet. 1. 4] Pet. 1 ‖ 4, 6, 8–10   24 fast] safe 2, 3 *etc.*   25–26 Read . . . Book *add.* 2   29 saith 3 *etc.*   34 *than* 2, 7 *etc.*

Pli. Then said *Pliable*, Don't revile; if what the good *Christian* says is true, the things he looks after are better then ours; my heart inclines to go with my Neighbour.

Obst. *What! more Fools still? be ruled by me and go back; who knows whither such a brain-sick fellow will lead you? go back, go back, and be wise.*

Chr. *Come with me Neighbour *Pliable*, there are such things to be had which I spoke of, and many more Glories besides; If you believe not me, read here in this Book; and for the truth of what is exprest therein, behold, all is confirmed by the *blood of him that made it.

Pli. *Well Neighbour* Obstinate (*said* Pliable) *I begin to come to a point; I intend to go along with this good man, and to cast in my lot with him: But my good Companion, do you know the way to this desired place?*

Chr. I am directed by a man whose name is *Evangelist*, to speed me to a little Gate that is before us, where we shall receive instruction about the way.

Pli. *Come then, good Neighbour, let us be going:* Then they went both together.

Obst. And I will go back to my place, said *Obstinate*: I will be no Companion of such mis-led fantastical Fellows.

Now I saw in my Dream, that when *Obstinate* was gon back, *Christian* and *Pliable* went *talking over the Plain; and thus they began their discourse,

Chr. Come Neighbour *Pliable*, how do you do? I am glad you are perswaded to go along with me; and had even *Obstinate* himself, but felt what I have felt of the Powers, and Terrours of what is yet unseen, he would not thus lightly have given us the back.

---

3 than 2, 7 etc.   6 *whether* 5, 6   8 *marg.* Christian ... *Soul* add. 2   Come with thy Neighbour *Pliable* 3, 7: Nay, but do thou come with thy Neighbour, *Pliable* 4, 5, 6   12 Heb. 9. 17, 18, 19, 20, 21 || 4, 5, 6, 8 etc.; *om.* 3, 7   13 saith 3   14–15 *marg.* Pliable . . . Christian *add.* 3   marg. *consented* 7: *contented* 4, 5, 6, 8 etc.   19 instructions 3   20–21 *Come then good Neigbor, let us be going, then they went both together* 3   22 *marg.* Obstinate *goes railing back* add. 4, *om.* 7   29 you] your 1   me; had 2, 3 32 back] bag 2

Pliable. *Come Neighbour* Christian, *since there is none but us two here, tell me now further, what the things are: and how to be enjoyed, whither we are going.*

Chr. I can better conceive of them with my Mind, then speak of them with my Tongue: But yet since you are desirous to know, I will read of them in my Book.

Pli. *And do you think that the words of your Book are certainly true?*

Chr. Yes verily, for it was made by him that *can- *Tit. 1. 2.
10 not lye.

Pli. *Well said; what things are they?*

Chr. There is an *endless Kingdom to be Inhabited, *Isa. 45. 17.
and everlasting life to be given us; that we may Inhabit John 10. 27,
that Kingdom for ever. 28, 29.

Pli. *Well said, and what else?*

Chr. There are Crowns of Glory to be given us; *and *2 Tim. 4. 8.
Garments that will make us shine like the Sun in the Rev. 3. 4.
Firmament of Heaven. Matth. 13.

Pli. *This is excellent; And what else?*

20 *Chr.* There shall be no more crying, *nor sorrow; For *Isa. 25. 8.
he that is owner of the place, will wipe all tears from Rev. 7. 16, 17.
our eyes. Chap. 21. 4.

Pli. *And what company shall we have there?*

Chr. There we shall be with *Seraphims,* *and *Cheru-* *Isa. 6. 2.
bins, Creatures that will dazle your eyes to look on 1 Thess. 4.
them: There also you shall meet with thousands, and 16, 17.
ten thousands that have gone before us to that place; Rev. 5. 11.
none of them are hurtful, but loving, and holy; every
one walking in the sight of God; and standing in his
30 presence with acceptance for ever: In a word, there we
shall see the *Elders with their Golden Crowns: There *Rev. 4. 4.
we shall see the Holy *Virgins with their Golden Harps. *Chap. 14.
1, 2, 3, 4, 5.

4 marg. *Gods things unspeakable* add. 9⁴   **5** than 2, 3   spake
5, 6   **7** *Books* 6   **11** Plain. 2, 3, 4, 7: Plia. 1   **12** Isa.
45. 17 ‖ 11: Isa. 4. 5, 17 ‖ 1–10   **17** Rev. 3. 4 ‖ 1: Re. 3. 4 ‖ 2:
Rev. 23. 4 ‖ 3–11   **19** *excellent*] *very pleasant* 4, 5, 6, 8 *etc.*
20 Isa. 25. 8 ‖ 1, 2: Isa. 15. 8 ‖ 3–11   **21** places 1   **24–25**
Cherubims 5, 6, 8, 9⁴ *etc.*   **26** Rev. 5. 11 ‖ 11: Rev. 7. 17 ‖ 1: Rev.
7. 57 ‖ 2–5, 7: Rev. 5. 57 ‖ 6, 8–10   **30** there we] there, there we
2, 3   **31** Rev. 44 ‖ 4, 5: Rev. 45 ‖ 6, 8–9⁴: Rev. 4. 5 ‖ 10, 11
32 Ch. 14. 1, 2, 3, 4, 5 ‖ 11: Ch. 14. 12, 3, 4, 5 ‖ 1–10

*John 12. 25. There we shall see *Men that by the World were cut in pieces, burnt in flames, eaten of Beasts, drownded in the Seas, for the love that they bare to the Lord of the *2 Cor. 5. 2, 3, 5. place; all well, and cloathed with *Immortality, as with a Garment.

Pli. *The hearing of this is enough to ravish ones heart; but are these things to be enjoyed? how shall we get to be Sharers hereof?*

Chr. The Lord, the Governour of that Countrey, *Isa. 55. 12. John 7. 37. Chap. 6. 37. Rev. 21. 6. Chap. 22. 17. hath Recorded *that* *in this Book: The substance of which is, If we be truly willing to have it, he will bestow it upon us freely.

Pli. *Well, my good Companion, glad am I to hear of these things: Come on, let us mend our pace.*

Chr. I cannot go so fast as I would, by reason of this burden that is upon my back.

Now I saw in my Dream, that just as they had ended this talk, they drew near to a very *Miry Slough* that was in the midst of the Plain, and they being heedless, did both fall suddenly into the bogg. The name of the Slow was *Dispond.* Here therefore they wallowed for a time, being grievously bedaubed with the dirt; And *Christian,* because of the burden that was on his back, began to sink in the Mire.

Pli. *Then said* Pliable, *Ah, Neighbour* Christian, *where are you now?*

Chr. Truly, said *Christian,* I do not know.

Pli. At that *Pliable* began to be offended; and angerly, said to his Fellow, *Is this the happiness you have told me all this while of? if we have such ill speed at our first setting out, What may we expect, 'twixt this and our* *It is not enough to be pliable. *Journeys end? *May I get out again with my life, you shall possess the brave Country alone for me.* And with that he gave a desperate struggle or two, and got out of the Mire, on that side of the Slow which was next to his own House: So away he went, and *Christian* saw him no more.

1 World] Word 3   2 drowned 2 etc.   8 thereof 5, 6, 8 etc. 9 that] the 3   15 so om. 9³   16 upon] on 3   18 marg. The Slough of Despond add. 4: om. 7   20 sudenly 3, 7   21 Slough 2, 3 etc.   22 the om. 11   32 marg. It is not enough to Pliable 1

Wherefore *Christian* was left to tumble in the Slow
of *Dispond* alone; but still he endeavoured to struggle
to that side of the Slow, that was still further *from his
own House, and next to the Wicket-gate; the which he
did, but could not get out, because of the burden that
was upon his back: But I beheld in my Dream, that a
Man came to him, whose name was *Help*, and asked
him, *What he did there?*

Chr. Sir, said *Christian*, I was bid go this way, by
10 a Man called *Evangelist*, who directed me also to yonder
Gate, that I might escape the wrath to come: And as
I was going thither, I fell in here.

Help. *But why did you not look for *the steps?*

Chr. Fear followed me so hard, that I fled the next
way, and fell in.

Help. *Then*, said he, *Give me thy hand;* so he gave
him his hand, and *he drew him out, and set him upon
sound ground, and bid him go on his way.

Then I stepped to him that pluckt him out, and said;
20 Sir, Wherefore, since over this place is the way from
the City of *Destruction*, to yonder *Gate*, is it, that *this*
Plat is not mended, that poor Travellers might go
thither with more security? And he said unto me, this
Miry slow, is such a place as cannot be mended: It is
the descent whither the *scum and filth that attends
conviction for sin doth continually run, and therefore
is it called the *Slough of Dispond*: for still as the sinner is
awakened about his lost condition, there ariseth in his
soul many fears, and doubts, and discouraging appre-
30 hensions, which all of them get together, and settle in
this place: And this is the reason of the badness of this
ground.

It is not the *pleasure of the King that this place
should remain so bad; his Labourers also, have by the
direction of His Majesties Surveyors, been for above

* Christian *in trouble, seeks still to get further from his own House.*

* *The Promises.*

* Help *lifts him out.*
* Psal. 40 2.

* *What makes the Slough of Dispond.*

* Isa. 35. 3, 4.

1 wherefore 3   tumbled 3, 4, 7   3 still *om.* 9⁴ *etc.*   4 and
om. 5, 6, 8, 9³   marg. *farther* 2, 3 *etc.*   9 bid go] directed 1
13 *did not you* 2, 3, 4, 5   16 *Then*, said he, *add.* 2   16–17 so
... hand ital. 2, 3 *etc.*   marg. Help ... out add. 3: Help ... *up* 9³
25 marg. *What ... Dispond* add. 2   26 for] or 8, 9³, 9⁴   27 is
it] it is 6, 8, 9³: it was 9⁴ *etc.*   35 directions 9⁴ *etc.*

this sixteen hundred years, imploy'd about this patch of ground, if perhaps it might have been mended: yea, and to my knowledge, saith he, *Here* hath been swallowed up, at least, Twenty thousand Cart Loads; yea Millions of wholesom Instructions, that have at all seasons been brought from all places of the Kings Dominions; (and they that can tell, say, they are the best Materials to make good ground of the place,) If so be it might have been mended, but it is the *Slough of Dispond* still; and so will be, when they have done what 10 they can.

The Promises of forgiveness and acceptance to life by Faith in Christ. True, there are by the direction of the Law-giver, certain good and substantiall *steps, placed even through the very midst of this *Slough*; but at such time as this place doth much spue out its filth, as it doth against change of weather, these steps are hardly seen; or if they be, Men through the diziness of their Heads, step besides; and then they are bemired to purpose, notwithstanding the steps be there; but the ground is

1 Sam. 12. 23. *good when they are once got in at the Gate.   20

Plyable got home, and is visited of his Neighbors. *His entertainment by them at his return.* Now I saw in my Dream, that by this time *Pliable* was got home to his House again. *So his Neighbours came to visit him; and some of them called him wise Man for coming back; and some called him Fool for hazarding himself with *Christian*; others again did mock at his Cowardliness; saying, Surely since you began to venture, I would not have been so base to have given out for a few difficulties. So *Pliable* sat sneaking among them. But at last he got more confidence, and then they all turned their tales, and began 30 to deride poor *Christian* behind his back. And thus much concerning *Pliable*.

Now as Christian was walking solitary by himself, he espied one afar off, come crossing over the field

1 these 9³   hundreds 11   3 said 2 *etc.*   21 saw] say 9³ *marg.* Plyable . . . *Neighbors* add. 2: Pliable *is got home, and is visited by his Neighbours* 5, 6, 8 *etc.*: Pliable *got home & is visited by his Neighbours* 4   24 marg. *His . . . return* add. 3   30 tailes 7   33 Now as Christian. . . Mr. Worldly-Wiseman's counsel (p. 25, l. 4) *add.* 2   solitary] solitarly 3: solitarary 9³

*to meet him; and their hap was to meet just as they
were crossing the way of each other. The Gentleman's
name was, Mr. *Worldly-Wiseman*, he dwelt in the Town
of *Carnal-Policy*, a very great Town, and also hard by,
from whence Christian came. This man then meeting
with Christian, and having some inckling of him, for
Christians setting forth from the City of *Destruction*,
was much noised abroad, not only in the Town, where
he dwelt, but also it began to be the *Town*-talk in some
10 other places, Master *Worldly-Wiseman* therefore,
having some guess of him, by beholding his laborious
going, by observing his sighs and groans, and the like;
began thus to enter into some talk with *Christian*.

World. *How now, good fellow, whither away after this
burdened manner?*

Chr. A burdened manner indeed, as ever I think
poor creature had. And whereas you ask me, *Whither
away*, I tell you, Sir, I am going to yonder Wicket-gate
before me; for there, as I am informed, I shall be put
20 into a way to be rid of my heavy burden.

Worl. *Hast thou a Wife and Children?*

Chr. Yes, but I am so laden with this burden, that
I cannot take that pleasure in them as formerly: methinks, I am as *if I had none.

Worl. *Wilt thou hearken to me, if I give thee counsel?*

Chr. If it be good, I will; for I stand in need of good
counsel.

Worl. *I would advise thee then, that thou with all
speed get thy self rid of thy burden; for thou wilt never be
30 settled in thy mind till then: nor canst thou enjoy the benefits
of the blessing which God hath bestowed upon thee till
then.*

Chr. That is that which I seek for, even to be rid of
this heavy burden; but get it off my self I cannot: nor
is there a man in our Country that can take it off my

* Mr. Worldly-
Wiseman *meets
with* Christian.

Talk betwixt
Mr. Worldly-
Wiseman, *and*
Christian.

* 1 Cor. 7. 29.

* Mr. Worldly-
Wiseman's
Counsel to
Christian.

1–2 just . . . other *ital.* 3   marg. *Mr.* om. 4, 5, 6, 8 *etc.*   2
was 5, 6   2–3 The Gentleman's name that met him was 4, 5, 6,
8 *etc.*   6–10 for . . . places] (for . . . places) 4, 5, 6, 8 *etc.*   10 places.
1–11   14 marg. . . . *between* . . . 6, 8 *etc.*   24 *marg.* 1 Cor. 7. 29
om. 10, 11   28 marg. *Mr.* . . . . Christiant *add.* 3: Worldly-Wiseman's *counsel to* Christian 4, 5, 6, 8 *etc.*   35 a] any 4, 5, 6, 8 *etc.*

917.34   C

shoulders; therefore am I going this way, as I told you, that I may be rid of my burden.

Worl. *Who bid thee go this way to be rid of thy burden?*

Chr. A man that appeared to me to be a very great and honorable person; his name, as I remember is *Evangelist.*

* Mr. Worldly-Wiseman Condemned Evangelists Counsel.

Worl. **I beshrow him for his counsel; there is not a more dangerous and troublesome way in the world, than is that unto which he hath directed thee; and that thou shalt find, if thou wilt be ruled by his counsel: Thou hast met* 10 *with something (as I perceive) already; for I see the dirt of the* Slough of Dispond *is upon thee; but that Slough is the beginning of the sorrows that do attend those that go on in that way: hear me, I am older than thou! thou art like to meet with in the way which thou goest,* Wearisomness, *Painfulness, Hunger, Perils, Nakedness, Sword, Lions, Dragons, Darkness; and in a word, death, and what not? These things are certainly true, having been confirmed by many testimonies. And why should a man so carelessly cast away himself, by giving heed to a stranger.* 20

* The frame of the heart of young Christians.

Chr. Why, Sir, this burden upon my back is more terrible to me than are all these things which you have mentioned: *nay, methinks I care not what I meet with in the way, so be I can also meet with deliverance from my burden.

Worl. *How camest thou by thy burden at first?*

Chr. By reading this Book in my hand.

* Worldly-Wiseman does not like that Men should be Serious in reading the Bible.

Worl. **I thought so; and it is happened unto thee as to other weak men, who meddling with things too high for them, do suddenly fall into thy distractions; which distrac-* 3 *tions do not only unman men, (as thine I perceive has done thee) but they run them upon desperate ventures, to obtain they know not what.*

---

3 *thee*] *you* 4, 5, 6, 8¹*etc.*   *thy*] *your* 10, 11   **7** marg. *Mr.* . . . . *Counsel* add. 3: M. . . . . *Counsel* 4, 5, 6, 8, 9³, 9⁴   *beshrew* 5, 6, 8 *etc.* **10** *haste* 3   **12** *that*] *the* 3, 7   **15** *with*] *him* 3, 4   **19** *why* om. 6, 8 *etc.*   *a* om. 9³   **20** *head* 2   **21** marg. *The frame of the heart of a young* Christian 6, 8 *etc.*   **24** *so be*] *if so be* 4, 5, 6, 8 *etc.* **26** *thy*] *the* 3   **28** marg. Worldly-Wiseman . . . *Bible* add. 3: . . . *man* . . . 5, 6, 8 *etc.*   **28–29** *as to other*] *as unto other* 9³   **30** *unto* 4–6, 8, 9³: *into* 2, 7, 9⁴ *etc.*

Chr. I know what I would obtain; it is ease for my heavy burden.

Worl. *But why wilt thou seek for ease this way, seeing so many dangers attend it, especially, since (hadst thou but patience to hear me) I could direct thee to the obtaining of what thou desirest, without the dangers that thou in this way wilt run thy self into: yea, and the remedy is at hand. Besides, I will add, that instead of those dangers, thou shalt meet with much safety, friendship, and content.*

10 *Chr.* Pray Sir open this secret to me.

Worl. **Why in yonder Village, (the Village is named* Morality) *there dwells a Gentleman, whose name is* Legality, *a very judicious man (and a man of a very good name) that has skill to help men off with such burdens as thine are, from their shoulders: yea, to my knowledge he hath done a great deal of good this way: Ai, and besides, he hath skill to cure those that are somewhat crazed in their wits with their burdens. To him, as I said, thou mayest go, and be helped presently. His house is not quite a mile from* 20 *this place; and if he should not be at home himself, he hath a pretty young man to his Son, whose name is* Civility, *that can do it (to speak on) as well as the old Gentleman himself: There, I say, thou mayest be eased of thy burden, and if thou art not minded to go back to thy former habitation, as indeed I would not wish thee, thou mayest send for thy wife and Children to thee to this Village, where there are houses now stand empty, one of which thou mayest have at reasonable rates: Provision is there also cheap and good, and that which will make thy life the more happy, is, to be sure there thou* 30 *shalt live by honest neighbors, in credit and good fashion.*

*Now was *Christian* somewhat at a stand, but presently he concluded; if this be true which this Gentleman hath said, my wisest course is to take his advice, and with that he thus farther spoke.

Chr. Sir, which is my way to this honest man's house?

* Whether Mr. Worldly prefers Morality before the Straight Gate.

* Christian Snared by Mr. Worldly Wisemans Word.

10 Sir, pray open 4, 5, 6, 8, 9³, 9⁴: Sir, I pray open 10, 11   11 marg. *Whether . . . Gate* add. 3: *M.* Worldly . . . 4, 6, 8, 9⁴, 10   *Mortality* 5   12 Mortality 5   31 *marg.* Christian . . . *Word* add. 3

* *Mount* Sinai.

Worl. *Do you see yonder *high hill?*

Chr. Yes, very well.

Worl. By that *Hill* you must go, and the first house you come at is his.

So *Christian* turned out of his way to go to Mr. *Legality's* house for help: but behold, when he was got now hard by the *Hill*, it seemed so high, and also that side of it that was next the way side, did hang so
* *Christian* much over, that Christian was *afraid to venture
afraid that further, lest the *Hill* should fall on his head: wherefore 10
Mount Sinai
would fall on there he stood still, and wotted not what to do. Also
his head. his burden, *now*, seemed heavier to him, than while he
* Exod. 19. 18. was in his way. There came also *flashes of fire out of
* Ver. 16. the Hill, that made *Christian afraid that he should be burned: here therefore he swet, and did quake for
* Heb. 12. *fear. And now he began to be sorry that he had taken
   21. Mr. *Worldly-Wisemans* counsel; and with that he saw
* *Evangelist* *Evangelist coming to meet him; at the sight also of
findeth Chris- whom he began to blush for shame. So *Evangelist* drew
tian under
Mount Sinai nearer, and nearer, and coming up to him, he looked 20
and looketh upon him with a severe and dreadful countenance: and
severely upon
him. thus began to reason with *Christian*.
* *Evangelist* **Evan.** *What doest thou here? said he: at which
reasons afresh word *Christian* knew not what to answer: wherefore,
with Christian. at present he stood speechless before him. Then said *Evangelist* farther, *Art not thou the man that I found crying, without the walls of the City of* Destruction?

Chr. Yes, dear Sir, I am the man.

Evan. *Did not I direct thee the way to the little Wicket-gate?* 30

Chr. Yes, dear Sir said *Christian*.

Evan. *How is it then that thou art so quickly turned aside, for thou art now out of the way?*

Chr. I met with a Gentleman, so soon as I had got

1 marg. *Mount* Sinai *add.* 2: *om.* 7   6 *Legailty's* 2, 3: *Legalitie's* 7   11 he wot 2   16 Heb. 12. 11 ‖ 1–11   23 *marg.* Evangelist *reasons refresh with* Christian 11   dost 7 *etc.*   said he? 3 here *Christian*? said he 4, 5, 6, 8 *etc.*   24 words 3   28 *Chr.* Yes, dear Sir, I am the man, said *Christian* 4   28–30 *Chr.* Yes, ... *Wicket-gate?* om. 5   28–31 *Chr.* Yes, ... said *Christian* om. 6, 8 *etc.*

over the *Slough of Dispond*, who perswaded me, that I
might in the *Village* before me, find a man that could
take off my burden.

Evan. *What was he?*

Chr. He looked like a Gentleman, and talked much
to me, and got me at last to yield; so I came hither: but
when I beheld this Hill, and how it hangs over the way,
I suddenly made a stand, lest it should fall on my head.

Evan. *What said that Gentleman to you?*

10 *Chr.* Why, he asked me whither I was going, and
I told him.

Evan. *And what said he then?*

Chr. He asked me if I had a Family, and I told him:
but, said I, I am so loaden with the burden that is on my
back, that I cannot take pleasure in them as formerly.

Evan. *And what said he then?*

Chr. He bid me with speed get rid of my burden,
and I told him 'twas ease that I sought: And said I,
I am therefore going to yonder *Gate* to receive further
20 direction how I may get to the place of deliverance. So
he said that he would shew me a better way, and short,
not so attended with difficulties, as the way, Sir, that
you set me: which way, said he, will direct you to a
Gentleman's house that hath skill to take off these burdens: So I believed him, and turned out of that way
into this, if haply I might be soon eased of my burden:
but when I came to this place, and beheld things as
they are, I stopped for fear, (as I said) of danger: but
I now know not what to do.

30 Evan. *Then* (said Evangelist) *stand still a little, that
I may shew thee the words of God.* So he stood trembling.
Then (said Evangelist) **See that ye refuse not him that* · Heb. 12. 25.
speaketh; for if they escaped not who refused him that spake
on Earth, * *much more shall not we escape, if we turn away* * Evangelist
from him that speaketh from Heaven. He said moreover, *Convinces*
**Now the just shall live by faith; but if any man draws* *Christian of*
his Error.
back, my soul shall have no pleasure in him. He also did * Chap. 10. 38.
thus apply them, Thou art the man that art running into

this misery, thou hast began to reject the counsel of the most high, and to draw back thy foot from the way of peace, even almost to the hazarding of thy perdition.

Then *Christian* fell down at his foot as dead, crying, Woe is me, for I am undone: at the sight of which Matth. 12. *Evangelist* caught him by the right hand, saying, All Mark 3. manner of sin and blasphemies shall be forgiven unto men; be not faithless, but believing; then did *Christian* again a little revive, and stood up trembling, as at first, before *Evangelist*. 10

Then *Evangelist* proceeded, saying, *Give more earnest heed to the things that I shall tell thee of.* I will now shew thee who it was that deluded thee, and who 'twas also

* *Mr.* Worldly- to whom he sent thee. *The man that met thee, is one
Wiseman *Worldly-Wiseman*, and rightly is he so called; partly,
discribed by
Evangelist. *because he favoureth only the Doctrine of this World
* 1 John 4. 5. (therefore he always goes to the Town of *Morality* to
* Gal. 6. 12. Church) and partly *because he loveth that Doctrine best, for it saveth him from the Cross; and because he is of this carnal temper, therefore he seeketh to prevent 20
* Evangelist my ways, though right. *Now there are three things in
discovers the this mans counsel that thou must utterly abhor.
deceit of
Mr. Worldly   1. His turning thee out of the way.
Wiseman.   2. His labouring to render the Cross odious to thee.

     3. And his setting thy feet in that way that leadeth unto the administration of Death.

First, Thou must abhor his turning thee out of the way; yea, and thine own consenting thereto: because this is to reject the counsel of God, for the sake of the
* Luke 13. 24. counsel of a *Worldly-Wiseman*. The Lord says, *Strive 30
to enter in at the strait gate, the gate to which I sent thee;
* Mat. 7. 13, **for strait is the gate that leadeth unto life, and few there*
14. *be that find it.* From this little wicket-gate, and from the way thereto hath this wicked man turned thee, to

---

1 *hast begun* 6, 8, 9³, 10, 11   3 *thy*] *my* 4   5 Wo 3
6 Matth. 12, Mark 3 *om.* 5, 6, 8 *etc.*   13 'twas] it 'twas 4: it was
5, 6, 8 *etc.*   marg. *Mr.* Worldly-Wiseman . . . Evangelist *add.* 3
17 *Morality* 6, 8 *etc.*: *Mortality* 2, 3, 4, 7   18 Gol. 6. 12 ‖ 2: Col. 6.
13 ‖ 9³: Col. 6. 12 ‖ 3–8, 9⁴ *etc.*   19 him from] him best from 5,
6, 8 *etc.*   20 prevent] pervert 4, 5, 6, 8 *etc.*   21 *marg.* Evang.
. . . Wiseman *add.* 3   31 *in at*] *into* 4, 5, 6, 8, 9³   send 3

the bringing of thee almost to destruction; hate therefore his turning thee out of the way, and abhor thy self
for harkening to him.

Secondly, Thou must abhor his labouring to render
the Cross odious unto thee; for thou art to *prefer it* *Heb. 11. 25,
before the treasures in Egypt: besides the King of glory [26.]
hath told thee, *that he that will save his life shall lose* *Mark 8. 34.
it: and *he that comes after him, and hates not his father* John 13. 25.
and mother, and wife, and children, and brethren, and *Luke 14. 26.
10 *sisters; yea, and his own life also, he cannot be my Disciple.*
I say therefore, for a man to labour to perswade thee,
that that shall be thy death, without which the truth
hath said, thou canst not have eternal life, this Doctrine thou must abhor.

Thirdly, thou must hate his setting of thy feet in the
way that leadeth to the ministration of death. And for
this thou must consider to whom he sent thee, and also
how unable that person was to deliver thee from thy
burden.

20 He to whom thou wast sent for ease, being by name
Legality, is the Son of the *Bond woman which now is, *Gal. 4. 21,
and is in bondage with her children, and is in a mystery 22, 23, 24,
this *Mount *Sinai*, which thou hast feared will fall on 25, 26, 27.
thy head. Now if she with her children are in bondage, *The Bond-
how canst thou expect by them to be made free? This Woman.
Legality therefore is not able to set thee free from thy
burden. No man was as yet ever rid of his burden by
him, no, nor ever is like to be: ye cannot be justified
by the Works of the Law; for by the deeds of the Law
30 no man living can be rid of his burden: therefore Mr.
Worldly-Wiseman is an alien, and Mr. *Legality* a cheat:
and for his Son *Civility*, notwithstanding his simpering
looks, he is but an hypocrite, and cannot help thee.
Believe me, there is nothing in all this noise, that thou
hast heard of this sottish man, but a design to beguile
thee of thy Salvation, by turning thee from the way in

8 Luke 14. 26 || 2: Luke 14. 16 || 3 *etc.*   11 a *om.* 4, 5, 6, 8 *etc.*
13 life. This 2–11   23 marg. *The Bond-Woman* add. 3
27 by] to 4, 5, 6, 8 *etc.*   31 Mr. *Legality* is a cheat 4, 5, 6, 8 *etc.*
32 Son] own 2   35 this sottish men 3: these sottish men 5 *etc.*

which I had set thee. After this *Evangelist* called aloud
to the Heavens for confirmation of what he had said;
and with that there came words and fire out of the
Mountain under which poor Christian stood, that made
the hair of his flesh stand. The words were thus pro-

Gal. 3. 10. nounced, *As many as are of the works of the Law, are
under the curse; for it is written, Cursed is every one that
continueth not in all things which are written in the Book
of the Law to do them.

Now *Christian* looked for nothing but death, and 10
began to cry out lamentably, even cursing the time in
which he met with Mr. *Worldly-Wiseman*, still calling
himself a thousand fools for hearkening to his counsel:
he also was greatly ashamed to think that this Gentle-
mans arguments, flowing only from the flesh, should
have that prevalency with him as to cause him to forsake
the right way. This done, he applied himself again to
Evangelist in words and sense as follows.

* Christian
Enquired if
he may yet be
Happy. *Chr.* *Sir, what think you? is there hopes? may I
now go back and go up to the *Wicket-gate*, shall I not 20
be abandoned for this, and sent back from thence
ashamed. I am sorry I have hearkened to this man's
counsel, but may my sin be forgiven.

Evang. Then said *Evangelist* to him, Thy sin is very
great, for by it thou hast committed two evils; thou hast
forsaken the way that is good, to tread in forbidden

* Evangelist
comforts him. paths: *yet will the man at the Gate receive thee, for
he has *good will* for men; only, said he, take heed that
thou turn not aside again, lest thou perish from the way

* Psal. 2 last. when his wrath is *kindled but a little. Then did *Chris-* 30
tian address himself to go back, *and *Evangelist*, after
he had kist him, gave him one smile, and bid him God
speed; so he went on with hast, neither spake he to any
man by the way; nor if any man asked him, would he
vouchsafe them an answer. He went like one that was

5 his] the 4   stand up 4, 5, 6, 8 *etc.*   6 Gal. 3. 10 ‖ 6 *etc.*:
Solom. 3. 10 ‖ 2, 3: Solom. 3. 1 ‖ 4, 5   16 that] the 5, 6, 8 *etc.*
as to cause him *add.* 3   19 *marg.* Christian . . . *Happy* add. 3
23 sins 6, 8 *etc.*   26 the] thy 3–7   27 at] of 2   *marg.* Evangelist . . . *him* add. 3   30 Psal. 2 *last* add. 3   32 kist] kept 2

all the while treading on forbidden ground, and could by no means think himself safe, till again he was got into the way which he left to follow Mr. *Worldly-Wiseman's* counsel: so in process of time *Christian* got up to the Gate. Now over the Gate there was Written, *Knock and it shall be opened unto you.* *He knocked therefore, more *then* once or twice, *saying,*

Mat. 7. 8.

> May I now enter here? will he within
> Open to sorry me, though I have bin
> An undeserving Rebel? then shall I,
> Not fail to Sing his lasting praise on high.

10

At last there came a grave Person to the Gate: named *Good-will*, who asked, *Who was there? and whence he came? and what he would have?*

Chr. Here is a poor burdened sinner, I come from the City of *Destruction*, but am going to Mount *Zion*, that I may be delivered from the wrath to come; I would therefore, Sir, since I am informed that by this Gate is the way thither, know if you are *willing* to let 20 me in.

Good-Will. *I am *willing* with all my heart, said he; and with that he opened the Gate.

* The Gate will be opened to broken-hearted sinners.

So when *Christian* was stepping in, the other gave him a pull: Then said *Christian*, what means that? The other told him, a little distance from this Gate, there is erected a strong Castle, of which * *Belzebub* is the Captain: from thence both he, and them that are with him, Shoot Arrows at those that come up to this Gate; if happily they may die before they can enter in. Then, said 30 *Christian*, *I rejoyce and tremble. So when he was got in, the man of the Gate asked him, Who directed him thither?

* Satan envies those that enter the straight Gate.

* Christian Entred the Gate with Joy and trembling.

Chr. *Evangelist* bid me come hither and knock, (as I did;) And he said, that you, Sir, would tell me what I must do.

* Talke between Good Will and Christian.

Good Will. *An open Door is set before thee, and no man can shut it.*

Chr. Now I begin to reap the benefits of my hazzards.

Good Will. *But how is it that you came alone?*

Chr. Because none of my Neighbours saw their danger as I saw mine.

Good Will. *Did any of them know of your coming?*

Chr. Yes, my Wife and Children saw me at the first, and called after me to turn again: Also some of my Neighbours stood crying, and calling after me to 10 return; but I put my Fingers in mine Ears, and so came on my way.

Good Will. *But did none of them follow you to perswade you to go back?*

Chr. Yes, both *Obstinate*, and *Pliable*: But when they saw that they could not prevail, *Obstinate* went railing back; but *Pliable* came with me a little way.

Good Will. *But why did he not come through?*

Chr. We indeed came both together, until we came at the Slow of *Dispond*, into the which, we also suddenly 20 fell. And then was my Neighbour *Pliable* discouraged, and would not adventure further. *Wherefore getting out again, on that side next to his own House; he told me, I should possess the brave Countrey alone for him: So he went his way, and I came mine. He after *Obstinate*, and I to this Gate.

Good Will. Then said *Good Will*, Alas poor man, is the Cœlestial Glory of so small esteem with him, that he counteth it not worth running the hazards of a few difficulties to obtain it? 30

Chr. Truly, said *Christian*, I have said the truth of *Pliable*, and if I should also say all the truth of my self, it will appear there is *no betterment 'twixt him and my self. 'Tis true, he went back to his own house, but I also turned aside to go in the way of death, being perswaded thereto by the carnal arguments of one Mr. *Worldly Wiseman*.

A Man may have Company when he sets out for Heaven, & yet go thither alone.

Christian accuseth himself before the man at the Gate.

11 my Ears 2   20 Slough of *Dispond* 2: *Slough of Despond* 5 etc.
29 hazard 11   31 Truly, said *Christian . . . are cast out* (p. 27, l. 23)
add. 2   32 all *add.* 3   35 in] into 5, 6, 8 etc.   36 agreement 3: Argument 9⁴ etc.

Good Will. Oh, did he light upon you! what, he would have had you a sought for ease at the hands of Mr. *Legality*; they are both of them a very cheat: but did you take his counsel?

Chr. Yes, as far as I durst, I went to find out Mr. *Legality*, until I thought that the Mountain that stands by his house, would have fallen upon my head: wherefore there I was forced to stop.

Good Will. That Mountain has been the death of 10 many, and will be the death of many more: 'tis well you escaped being by it dasht in pieces.

Chr. Why, truly I do not know what had become of me there, had not *Evangelist* happily met me again as I was musing in the midst of my *dumps*: but 'twas Gods mercy that he came to me again, for else I had never come hither. But now I am come, such a one as I am, more fit indeed for death by that Mountain, than thus to stand talking with my Lord: But Oh, what a favour is this to me, that yet I am admitted entrance 20 here.

Good Will. *We make no objections against any, notwithstanding all that they have done before they come hither, *they in no wise are cast out*; and therefore, good *Christian*, come a little way with me, and I will teach thee about the way thou must go. *Look before thee; dost thou see this narrow way? That is the way thou must go. It was cast up by the Patriarchs, Prophets, Christ, and his Apostles, and it is as straight as a Rule can make it: This is the way 30 thou must go.

Chr. But said *Christian, Is there no turnings nor windings, by which a Stranger *may loose the way?*

Good Will. Yes, there are many ways *Butt* down upon this; and they are Crooked, and Wide: But *thus* thou

* Christian is *comforted again.*
* John 6. 37.
* Christian *directed yet on his way.*
* Christian *afraid of losing his way.*

---

5 went to] went not to 2　　Mr. *add.* 3　　21 *marg.* Christian ...*again* add. 3: Christ. *comforted again* 7　　23 *they...cast out* rom. 2: *they in no ways are cast out* 7　　and therefore] Well 1　　25 *marg.* Christian ... *way* add. 3: Christ.... *way* 7　　26 That 1　　28 and¹ *add.* 2　　31 *is*] *are* 7　　32 *lose* 2, 3, 4　　*the*] *his* 10, 11 *marg.* Christian ... *way* add. 2: Christ.... *way* 7　　33 *BUTT* 2 etc.

may'st distinguish the right from the wrong, *That* only being *straight and narrow.

*Mat. 7. 14.

*Christian weary of his Burden

Then I saw in my Dream, *That *Christian* asked him further, If he could not help him off with his burden that was upon his back; For as yet he had not got rid thereof, nor could he by any means get it off without help.

*There is no deliverance from the guilt, and burden of sin, but by the death and blood of Christ.

He told him, As to the burden, be content to bear it, until thou comest to the place of *Deliverance; for there it will fall from thy back it self.

10

Then *Christian* began to gird up his loins, and to address himself to his Journey. So the other told him, that by that he was gone some distance from the Gate, he would come at the house of the *Interpreter*; at whose Door he should knock; and he would shew him excellent things. Then *Christian* took his leave of his Friend, and he again bid him God speed.

*Christian comes to the House of the Interpreter.

Then he went on, till he came at the house of the *Interpreter, where he knocked over, and over: at last one came to the Door, and asked *Who was there?*

20

Chr. Sir, here is a Travailer, who was bid by an acquaintance of the Good-man of this House, to call here for my profit: I would therefore speak with the Master of the House: so he called for the Master of the House; who after a little time came to *Christian*, and asked him what he would have?

Chr. Sir, said *Christian*, I am a Man that am come from the City of *Destruction*, and am going to the Mount *Zion*, and I was told by the Man that stands at the Gate, at the head of this way; that if I called here, you would shew me excellent things, such as would be an help to me in my Journey.

30

*He is entertained.

Inter. Then said the *Interpreter*, *come in, I will shew thee that which will be profitable to thee. So he commanded his man to *light the Candle, and bid *Christian* follow him; so he had him into a private

*Illumination.

Room, and bid his Man open a Door; the which when
he had done, *Christian saw a Picture of a very grave   * Christian sees
Person hang up against the wall, and this was the   a brave Picture.
fashion of it, *It had eyes lift up to Heaven, the best of   * The fashion
Books in its hand, the Law of Truth was written upon   of the Picture.
its lips, the World was behind its back; it stood as if it
pleaded with Men, and a Crown of Gold did hang over its
head.

Chr. Then said Christian, What means this?

10   Inter. The Man whose Picture this is, is one of a
thousand, he can *beget Children, Travel in birth with   * 1 Cor. 4. 15.
Children, and *Nurse them himself when they are born.   * Gal. 4. 19.
And whereas thou seest *him with his eyes lift up to   * 1 Thes. 2. 7.
Heaven, the best of Books in his hand, and the Law of
Truth writ on his Lips: it is to shew thee, that his work
is to know, and unfold dark things to sinners; even as
also thou seest *him stand as if he Pleaded with Men: * The meaning
And whereas thou seest the World as cast behind him,   of the Picture.
and that a Crown hangs over his head; that is, to shew
20 thee, that slighting and despising the things that are
present, for the love that he hath to his Masters service,
he is sure in the world that comes next to have Glory
for his Reward: Now, said the Interpreter, I have shewed
thee this Picture first, *because the Man whose Picture   * Why he
this is, is the only Man, whom the Lord of the Place   shewed him the
whither thou art going, hath Authorized, to be thy   Picture first.
Guide in all difficult places thou mayest meet with in
the way: wherefore take good heed to what I have
shewed thee, and bear well in thy mind what thou hast
30 seen; lest in thy Journey, thou meet with some that
pretend to lead thee right, but their way goes down to
death.

   Then he took him by the hand, and led him into a
very large Parlour that was full of dust, because never
swept; the which, after he had reviewed a little while,
the Interpreter called for a man to sweep: Now when
he began to sweep, the dust began so abundantly to

2 a] the 2   4 lift] lifted 2   5 its] his 2 etc.   6 its¹] his 7
its²] his 1 etc.   9 meaneth 4, 5, 6, 8 etc.   13 his add. 2
1 Thess. 2. 7 || 1, 2: om. 3 etc.   31 thee] the 4

fly about, that *Christian* had almost therewith been choaked: Then said the *Interpreter* to a *Damsel* that stood by, Bring hither Water, and sprinkle the Room; which when she had done, was swept and cleansed with pleasure.

Chr. Then said Christian, *What means this?*

In. The *Interpreter* answered; This Parlor, is the heart of a Man that was never sanctified by the sweet Grace of the Gospel: The *dust*, is his Original Sin, and inward Corruptions that have defiled the whole Man. 10 He that began to sweep at first, is the Law; but She that brought water, and did sprinkle it, is the Gospel: Now, whereas thou sawest that so soon as the first began to sweep, the dust did so fly about, that the Room by him could not be cleansed, but that thou wast almost choaked therewith, this is to shew thee, that the Law, instead of cleansing the heart (by its working) from sin, *doth revive, put *strength into, and *increase it in the soul, even as it doth discover and forbid it, for it doth not give power to subdue. 20

* Rom. 7. 6.
* 1 Cor. 15. 56.
* Rom. 5. 20.

Again, as thou sawest the *Damsel* sprinkle the Room with Water, upon which it was cleansed with pleasure: This is to shew thee, that when the Gospel comes in the sweet and precious influences thereof to the heart, then I say, even as thou sawest the Damsel lay the dust by sprinkling the Floor with Water, so is sin vanquished and subdued, and the soul made clean, through the Faith of it; and consequently *fit for the King of Glory to inhabit.

* John 15. 3.
Ephes. 5. 26.
Acts 15. 9.

I saw moreover in my Dream, *that the *Interpreter* 30 took him by the hand, and had him into a little Room, where sat two little Children, each one in his Chair: The name of the eldest was *Passion*, and of the other, *Patience; Passion* seemed to be much discontent, but *Patience* was very quiet. Then *Christian* asked, What

Rom. 16. 25, 26.
John 15. 13.
* He shewed him Passion *& Patience.*
Passion will have all now.

3 the *add.* 2   4 the which *add.* 3.   it was *add.* 3   12
Gosple 3   18 Rom. 7. 9 ‖ 11   19 even *add.* 3   for it] but 1, 2
28 Ephes. 5. 26 ‖ 1: Ephes. 5. 16 ‖ 2–11   33 and the name of the
other 3   34–35 discontented 4, 5, 6, 8 *etc.*   *marg.* Passion *will
have it now* 2

is the reason of the discontent of *Passion*? The *Inter-*
preter answered, The Governour of them would have
him stay for his best things till the beginning of the
next year; but he will have all now: *But *Patience*   * Patience *is*
is willing to wait.   *for waiting.*

    Then I saw that one came to *Passion, and brought * Passion *has*
him a Bag of Treasure, and poured it down at his feet; *his desire,*
the which he took up, and rejoyced therein, and withall,
laughed *Patience* to scorn: But I beheld but a while,
10 and he had *lavished all away, and had nothing left * *And quickly*
him but Rags.   *lavishes all*
   away.
    Chr. *Then said* Christian *to the* Interpreter, *Expound * *The matter*
this matter more fully to me.   *expounded.*

    Int. So he said, These two Lads are Figures; *Pas-*
sion, of the Men of *this* World; and *Patience*, of the
Men of *that* which is to come: For as here thou seest,
Passion will have all now, this year; that is to say, in
this World; *So* are the Men of this World: they must
have all their good things now, they cannot stay till
20 next *Year*; that is, untill the *next* World, for their Portion of good. That Proverb, **A Bird in the hand is* * *The Worldly*
worth two in the Bush, is of more Authority with them, *Man for a Bird*
then are all the Divine Testimonies of the good of the *in the hand.*
world to come. But as thou sawest, that he had quickly
lavished all away, and had presently left him, nothing
but Raggs; So will it be with all such Men at the end of
this world.

    Chr. *Then said* Christian; *Now I see that* Patience *has*
the best **Wisdom, and that upon many accounts.* 1. *Because* * *Patience*
30 *he stays for the best things.* 2 *And also because he will have* *had the best*
the glory of His, *when the other hath nothing but Raggs.* *Wisdom.*

    In. Nay, you may add another; to wit, The glory of
the *next* world will never wear out; but *these* are suddenly gone. Therefore *Passion* had not so much reason
to laugh at *Patience*, because he had his good things
first, as *Patience* will have to laugh at *Passion*, *because * *Things that*
he had his best things *last;* for *first* must give place to *are first must*
give place, but
last, because *last* must have his time to come, but *last* *things that are*
last are lasting.

6 *marg*. Passion *hath his desire* 5 *etc.*   23 than 7 *etc.*   31 *hath*
1, 2, 7: *hatd* 3: *had* 4–6, 8 *etc.*   33 *these* rom. 1, 8 *etc.*

gives place to *nothing*; for there is not another to succeed: he therefore that hath his Portion *first*, must needs
have a time to spend it; but he that has his Portion *last*,
Luk. 16. must have it lastingly. Therefore it is said of *Dives*,
Dives had his *In thy life thou receivedst thy good things, and likewise*
good things first. Lazarus *evil things; but now he is comforted, and thou art*
tormented.

Chr. *Then I perceive, 'tis not best to covet things that*
are now, *but to wait for things to* come.

2 Cor. 4. 18.   Int. You say the Truth, *For the things that are seen,* 10
The first are Temporal; *but the things that are not seen, are* Eternal:
things are but
Temporal. But though this be so, yet since things present, and our
fleshly appetite, *are such near Neighbours one to another*;
and again, because things to come, and carnal sense,
are such strangers one to another: therefore it is, that
the first of these so suddenly fall into *amity*, and that
distance is so continued between the second.

Then I saw in my Dream, that the *Interpreter* took
Christian by the hand, and led him into a place, where
was a Fire burning against a Wall, and one standing 20
by it always, casting much Water upon it to quench it:
Yet did the Fire burn higher and hotter.

Then said Christian, *What means this?*

The *Interpreter* answered, This fire is the work of
Grace that is wrought in the heart; he that casts Water
upon it, to extinguish and put it out, is the *Devil*: but
in that thou seest the fire, notwithstanding, burn higher
and hotter, thou shalt also see the reason of that: So
he had him about to the back side of the Wall, where
he saw a Man with a Vessel of Oyl in his hand, of the 30
which he did also continually cast, but secretly, into
the fire. Then said *Christian, What means this?* The
Interpreter answered, This is *Christ*, who continually
with the Oyl of his Grace, maintains the work already
begun in the heart; by the means of which, notwith-
2 Cor. 12. 9. standing what the Devil can do, the souls of his people
prove gracious still. And in that thou sawest, that the

5 *hadest, or receivedest* 1: *receivedst* 3: *receivedest* 4, 9⁴   10 the
Truth] Truth 2 *etc.*   12 marg. *Temperal* 3   tho 5   17 con-
tinued] continually 11   31 (but secretly) 3

Man stood behind the Wall to maintain the fire; this is to teach thee, that it is hard for the tempted to see how this work of Grace is maintained in the soul.

I saw also that the *Interpreter* took him again by the hand, and led him into a pleasant place, where was builded a stately Palace, beautiful to behold; at the sight of which, *Christian* was greatly delighted; he saw also upon the top thereof, certain Persons walked, who were cloathed all in gold. Then said *Christian*, May we 10 go in thither? Then the *Interpreter* took him, and led him up toward the door of the Palace; and behold, at the door, stood a great company of men, as desirous to go in, but durst not. There also sat a Man, at a little distance from the door, at a Table-side, with a Book, and his Inkhorn before him, to take the Name of him that should enter therein: He saw also that in the door-way, stood many Men in Armour to keep it, being re-solved to do to the Man that would enter, what hurt and mischief they could. Now was *Christian* somwhat 20 in a muse; at last, when every Man started back for fear of the Armed Men; *Christian* saw a man of a very stout countenance come up to the Man that sat there to write; saying, *Set down my Name Sir*; the which * *The valiant* when he had done, he saw the Man draw his Sword, *man.* and put an Helmet upon his Head, and rush toward the door upon the Armed Men, who laid upon him with deadly force; but the Man, not at all discouraged, fell to cutting and hacking most fiercely; so after he had *received and given many wounds to those that at- * Acts 14. 22. 30 tempted to keep him out, he cut his way through them all, and pressed forward into the Palace; at which there was a pleasant voice heard from those that were within, even of the Three that walked upon the top of the Palace, saying,

> *Come in, Come in;*
> *Eternal Glory thou shalt win.*

8 walked] walking 2 *etc.*   9–10 Then . . . thither? *separate* ¶ 10, 11   18 Men 3 *etc.*   will 7   20 a muse]: a maze 2, 3: amaze 4, 5, 6, 8 *etc.*   22 sate 3 *etc.*   23 *Set . . . Sir* rom. 1 marg. *The valiant man* add. 2   29 Acts 14. 21 ‖ 7   33 the Three] those 2 *etc.*   34 saying, *add.* 2

917.34   D

So he went in, and was cloathed with such Garments as they. Then *Christian* smiled, and said, I think verily I know the meaning of this.

Now, said *Christian*, let me go hence: Nay stay (said the *Interpreter*,) till I have shewed thee a little more, and after that, thou shalt go on thy way. So he took him by the hand again, and led him into a very dark Room, *Despair like* where there sat a Man in an Iron *Cage.
an Iron Cage.

Now the Man, to look on, seemed very sad: he sat with his eyes looking down to the ground, his hands 10 folded together; and he sighed as if he would break his heart. Then said *Christian*, *What means this?* At which the *Interpreter* bid him talk with the Man.

Chr. Then said *Christian* to the Man, *What art thou?* The Man answered, *I am what I was not once.*

Chr. What wast thou once?

* Luke 8. 13.   *Man.* The *Man* said, I was once a fair *and flourishing Professor, both in mine own eyes, and also in the eyes of others: I once was, as I thought, fair for the Cœlestial City, and had then even joy at the thoughts 20 that I should get thither.

Chr. Well, but what art thou now?

Man. I am *now* a Man of Despair, and am shut up in it, as in this Iron Cage. I cannot get out; O *now* I cannot.

Chr. But how camest thou in this condition?

Man. I left off to watch, and be sober; I laid the reins upon the neck of my lusts; I sinned against the light of the Word, and the goodness of God: I have grieved the Spirit, and he is gone; I tempted the Devil, 30 and he is come to me; I have provoked God to anger, and he has left me; I have so hardened my heart, that I *cannot* repent.

Then said *Christian* to the *Interpreter*, But is there no hopes for such a Man as this? Ask him, said the *Interpreter*.

12 *What means this?* rom. 1   17 Luke 8.13 *add.* 2: Luke 8. 18 ||
4, 5, 6, 8 *etc.*   23 *Dispair* 3: *Despair* 2, 4 *etc.*   29
World 10   36 Nay, said *Christian*, pray Sir, do you *add.* 1:
om. 2 *etc.*

Chr. Then said *Christian, Is there no hope but you must be kept in this Iron Cage of Despair?*

Man. No, none at all.

Chr. *Why? The Son of the Blessed is very pitiful,*

Man. I have *Crucified him to my self afresh, I have *Heb. despised *his Person, I have despised his Righteous- *Luke 19. 14. ness, I have counted his Blood an unholy thing, I have done despite *to the Spirit of Grace: Therefore I have *Heb. 10. shut my self out of all the Promises; and there now 28, 29.
10 remains to me nothing but threatnings, dreadful threatnings, fearful threatnings of certain Judgement and firy Indignation, which shall devour me as an Adversary.

Chr. *For what did you bring your self into this condition?*

Man. For the Lusts, Pleasures, and Profits of this World; in the injoyment of which, I did then promise my self much delight: but now even every one of those things also bite me, and gnaw me like a burning worm.

Chr. *But canst thou not now repent and turn?*
20 *Man.* God hath denied me repentance; his Word gives me no encouragement to believe; yea, himself hath shut me up in this Iron Cage: nor can all the men in the World let me out. O Eternity! Eternity! how shall I grapple with the misery that I must meet with in Eternity?

Inter. Then said the *Interpreter* to *Christian,* Let this mans misery be remembred by thee, and be an everlasting caution to thee.

Chr. Well, said *Christian,* this is fearful; God help
30 me to watch and be sober; and to pray, that I may shun the cause of this mans misery. Sir, is it not time for me to go on my way now?

Int. Tarry till I shall shew thee one thing more, and then thou shalt go on thy way.

---

1 Chr.] *Inter.* 1　the *Christian* 2, 3, 7　*Christian*] the *Interpreter* 1
hopes 7　2 *this*] the 2 *etc.*　4 Inter. 1　5 a fresh 1　11 fearful
7] faithful 1–6, 8 *etc.*　11–12 and firy Indignation *add.* 3: fiery 4,
5, 6, 8 *etc.*　14 Chr.] Inter. 1　16 enjoyments 3　17 now
even every] now every 2　19 Chr.] Inter. 1　24 grabble 3　31
causes 1, 2　34 you 3 : you shall 7

So he took *Christian* by the hand again, and led him
into a Chamber, where there was one a rising out of
Bed; and as he put on his Rayment, he shook and
trembled. Then said *Christian*, Why doth this man thus
tremble? The *Interpreter* then bid him tell to *Christian*
the reason of his so doing: So he began, and said, This
night as I was in my sleep, I Dreamed, and behold the
Heavens grew exceeding black; also it thundred and
lightned in most fearful wise, that it put me into an
Agony. So I looked up in my Dream, and saw the 10
Clouds rack at an unusual rate, upon which I heard a
great sound of a Trumpet, and saw also a Man sit
upon a Cloud, attended with the thousands of Heaven;
they were all in flaming fire, also the Heavens was on
a burning flame. I heard then a voice, saying, *Arise ye
Dead, and come to Judgement*; and with that the Rocks
rent, the Graves opened, & the Dead that were therein
came forth; some of them were exceeding glad, and
looked upward; and some sought to hide themselves
under the Mountains: Then I saw the Man that sat 20
upon the Cloud, open the Book; and bid the World
draw near. Yet there was by reason of a Fiery flame
that issued out and came from before him, a convenient
distance betwixt him and them, as betwixt the Judge
and the Prisoners at the Bar. I heard it also proclaimed
to them that attended on the Man that sat on the Cloud,
*Gather together the Tares, the Chaff, and Stubble, and
cast them into the burning Lake*; and with that the Bottomless pit opened, just whereabout I stood; out of the
mouth of which there came in an abundant manner 30
Smoak, and Coals of fire, with hideous noises. It was
also said to the same persons *Gather my Wheat into my
Garner.* And with that I saw many catch'd up *and
carried away into the Clouds, but I was left behind.

Marginal references (left column):
1 Cor. 15.
1 Thess. 4.
Jude 15.
2 Thess. 1. 8.
John 5. 28.
Rev. 20. 11,
12, 13, 14.
Isa. 26. 21.
Mich. 7. 16,
17.
Psal. 5. 1, 2, 3.
Dan. 7. 10.
Mal. 3. 2, 3.
Dan. 7, 9, 10.
* Mat. 3. 2.
Ch. 13. 30.
Mal. 4. 1.
* Luke 3. 17.
* 1 Thess. 4.
16, 17.

2 a rising] rising 2 *etc.*   11 rackt 7   14 were 2 *etc.*   **17**
Dan. 10 ‖ 4, 5, 6, 8, 9³: *om.* 9⁴ *etc.*   22 Fiery] fierce 2 *etc.*   Mal.
3. 2, 3 ‖ 5, 6, 8 *etc.*: Maj. 50. 2, 3 *add.* 2: Mal. 50. 2, 3 ‖ 3, 4: *om.* 7
Dan. 7. 9, 10 *add.* 2   23 from *om.* 10, 11   27 Mat. 3. 12 ‖ 1:
Mark 3. 12 ‖ 2: Mark 3. 13 ‖ 3 *etc.*   31 of smoak 7   **32**
Luke 3. 17 *add.* 2   my] the 2 *etc.*   33 1 Thes. 4. 16, 17 ‖ 1:
1 Thes. 7. 16, 17 ‖ 2 *etc.*

I also sought to hide my self, but I could not; for the Man that sat upon the Cloud, still kept his eye upon me: my sins also came into mind, and my Conscience Rom. 2. 14, 15. did accuse me on every side. Upon this I awaked from my sleep.

Chr. *But what was it that made you so afraid of this sight?*

Man. Why, I thought that the day of Judgement was come, and that I was not ready for it: but this frighted 10 me most, that the Angels gathered up several, and left me behind; also the pit of Hell opened her mouth just where I stood: my Conscience too within afflicted me; and as I thought, the Judge had always his eye upon me, shewing indignation in his countenance.

Then said the *Interpreter to Christian, Hast thou considered all these things?*

Chri. Yes, and they put me in *hope* and *fear.*

Inter. Well, keep all things so in thy mind, that they may be as a *Goad* in thy sides, to prick thee forward in 20 the way thou must go. Then *Christian* began to gird up his loins, and to address himself to his Journey. Then said the *Interpreter,* The Comforter be always with thee good *Christian,* to guide thee in the way that leads to the City.

So *Christian* went on his way, saying,

> *Here I have seen things rare, and profitable;*
> *Things pleasant, dreadful, things to make me stable*
> *In what I have began to take in hand:*
> *Then let me think on them, and understand*
> 30 *Wherefore they shewed me was, and let me be*
> *Thankful, O good Interpreter, to thee.*

Now I saw in my Dream, that the high way up which *Christian* was to go, was fenced on either side with a Wall, and that Wall is called *Salvation.* Up this way *Isa. 26. 1. therefore did burdened *Christian* run, but not without great difficulty, because of the load on his back.

2 sat] set 7   3 into mind 1] into my mind 2 *etc.*: in my mind 11
6 *afraid* 2 *etc.*   12 within *om.* 2 *etc.*   30 *were* 10, 11   34 is]
was 5, 6, 8 *etc.*   Isa. 36. 1 *add.* 2

He ran thus till he came at a place somewhat ascending; and upon that place stood a *Cross*, and a little below in the bottom, a Sepulcher. So I saw in my Dream, that just as *Christian* came up with the *Cross*, his burden loosed from off his Shoulders, and fell from off his back; and began to tumble; and so continued to do, till it came to the mouth of the Sepulcher, where it fell in, and I saw it no more.

When God releases us of our guilt and burden, we are as those that leap for joy. Then was *Christian* glad *and lightsom, and said with a merry heart, *He hath given me rest, by his sorrow;* 10 *and life, by his death.* Then he stood still a while, to look and wonder; for it was very surprizing to him, that the sight of the Cross should thus ease him of his burden. He looked therefore, and looked again, even

Zech. 12. 10. till the springs that were in his head sent the *waters down his cheeks. Now as he stood looking and weeping, behold three shining ones came to him, and saluted

Mark 2. 5. him, with *Peace be to thee*: so the first said to him, *Thy sins be forgiven.* The second stript him of his Rags, and

Zech. 3. 4. *cloathed him with change of Raiment. The third also 20

Eph. 1. 13. set *a mark in his fore-head, and gave him a Roll with a Seal upon it, which he bid him look on as he ran, and that he should give it in at the Cœlestial Gate: so they went their way. Then *Christian* gave three leaps for joy, and went on singing.

A Christian can sing tho alone, when God doth give him the joy of his heart.

> *Thus far did I come loaden with my sin,*
> *Nor could ought ease the grief that I was in,*
> *Till I came hither: What a place is this!*
> *Must here be the beginning of my bliss?*
> *Must here the burden fall from off my back?* 30
> *Must here the strings that bound it to me, crack?*
> *Blest Cross! blest Sepulcher! blest rather be*
> *The Man that there was put to shame for me.*

I saw then in my Dream that he went on thus, even untill he came at a bottom, where he saw, a little out of

3 in[1] *om.* 7   15 Zech. 12. 20 || 7   18 Mark 2. 2 *add.* 2
19 *forgiven thee* 10, 11   20 Zech. 3. 4 *add.* 2   21 Eph. 1. 8 3
add. 2: Eph. 1. 8. 13 || 5, 6, 8 etc.   25 on] out 1, 2   26 *did*
I come] *I did come* 4, 5, 6, 8 etc.   29 *bliss!* 1–11

the way, three Men fast asleep, with Fetters upon their
heels. The name of the one was *Simple, another Sloth, * Simple,
and the third Presumption.

Christian then seeing them lye in this case, went to
them, if peradventure he might awake them. And
cried, You are like them that sleep on the top of *a * Prov. 23. 24.
Mast, for the dead Sea is under you, a Gulf that hath
no bottom: Awake therefore, and come away; be willing also, and I will help you off with your Irons. He
10 also told them, If he that goeth about like *a roaring * 1 Pet. 5. 8.
Lion, comes by, you will certainly become a prey to his
teeth. With that they lookt upon him, and began to
reply in this sort: *Simple said, I see no danger; Sloth * There is no
said, Yet a little more sleep: and Presumption said, perswasion
Every Fatt must stand upon his own bottom, what is the openeth not
answer else that I should give thee? And so they lay down the eyes.
to sleep again, and Christian went on his way.

Yet was he troubled to think, That men in that
danger should so little esteem the kindness of him that
20 so freely offered to help them; both by awakening of
them, counselling of them, and proffering to help them
off with their Irons. And as he was troubled thereabout, he espied two men come tumbling over the Wall,
on the left hand of the narrow way; and they made up
a pace to him. The name of the one was Formalist, and
the name of the other Hypocrisie. So, as I said, they
drew up unto him, who thus entered with them into
discourse.

Chr. *Gentlemen, Whence came you, and whither do * Christian
30 you go?   talked with
                                                            them.
Form. and Hyp. We were born in the Land of Vain-
glory, and are going for praise to Mount Sion.

Chr. Why came you not in at the Gate which standeth
at the beginning of the way? Know you not that it is written,
*That he that cometh not in by the door, but climbeth up * John 10. 1.
some other way, the same is a thief and a robber.

Form. and Hyp. They said, That to go to the Gate

---

6 Prov. 23. 24. add. 2   10 1 Pet. 5. 8 add. 2   15 what is the
answer else that I should give thee? om. 2 etc.   29 marg. Christian ...
them add. 3   29 whither] wither 7

for entrance, was by all their Countrey-men counted too
far about; and that therefore their usual way was to
make a short cut of it, and to climb over the Wall as
they had done.

Chr. *But will it not be counted a Trespass, against the
Lord of the City whither we are bound, thus to violate his
revealed will?*

They that come into the way, but not by the door, think that they can say something in vindication of their own Practice.

Form. and *Hyp.* They told him, *That as for that, he
needed not to trouble his head thereabout: for what
they did they had custom for; and could produce, if 10
need were, Testimony that would witness it, for more
then a thousand years.

Chr. But said Christian, *Will your Practice stand a
Trial at Law?*

Form. & *Hyp.* They told him, That Custom, it being
of so long a standing, as above a thousand years, would
doubtless now be admitted as a thing legal, by any
Impartial Judge. And besides, said they, so be we get
into the way, what's matter which way we get in; if we
are in, we are in: thou art but in the way, who, as we 20
perceive, came in at the Gate; and we are also in the
way that came tumbling over the wall: Wherein now
is thy condition better then ours?

Chr. I walk by the Rule of my Master, you walk by
the rude working of your fancies. You are counted
thieves already, by the Lord of the way; therefore
I doubt you will not be found true men at the end
of the way. You come in by your selves without his
direction, and shall go out by your selves without his
mercy.
　　　　　　　　　　　　　　　　　　　　　　　　　　30

To this they made him but little answer; only they
bid him look to himself. Then I saw that they went on
every man in his way, without much conference one
with another; save that these two men told *Christian*,
That, as to *Laws and Ordinances*, they doubted not,
but they should as conscienciously do them as he.
Therefore said they, We see not wherein thou differest
from us, but by the Coat that is on thy back, which was,

3 over as 1: over it as 2　　　17 any] an 2　　　18 say, 6, 8 *etc.*
so be 1: if 2

as we tro, given thee by some of thy Neighbours, to hide
the shame of thy nakedness.

Chr. By *Laws and Ordinances, you will not be *Gal. 2. 16.
saved, since you came not in by the door. And as for
this Coat that is on my back, it was given me by the
Lord of the place whither I go; and that, as you say,
to cover my nakedness with. And I take it as a token of
his kindness to me, for I had nothing but rags before;
and besides, *thus I comfort my self as I go: Surely, *Christian *has*
10 think I, when I come to the Gate of the City, the Lord *got his Lords*
thereof will know me for good, since I have his Coat on *Coat on his*
my back; a *Coat* that he gave me freely in the day that *comforted there-*
he stript me of my rags. I have moreover a mark in my *with, he is*
forehead, of which perhaps you have taken no notice, *with his Mark,*
which one of my Lords most intimate Associates fixed *and his Roll.*
there in the day that my burden fell off my shoulders.
I will tell you moreover, that I had then given me a Roll
sealed to comfort me by reading, as I go in the way;
I was also bid to give it in at the Cœlestial Gate, in
20 token of my certain going in after it: all which things
I doubt you want; and want them, because you came
not in at the Gate.

To these things they gave him no answer, only they
looked upon each other, and *laughed.* Then I saw that
they went on all, save that *Christian* kept before, who
had no more talk but with himself, and that somtimes
sighingly, and somtimes comfortably: also he would
be often reading in the Roll, that one of the shining
ones gave him, by which he was refreshed.

'0   I believe then, that they all went on till they came to
the foot of an Hill, *at the bottom of which was a *He comes to*
Spring. There was also in the same place two other *the hill*
ways besides that which came straight from the Gate; *Difficulty.*
one turned to the left hand, and the other to the right,
at the bottom of the Hill: but the narrow way lay
right up the Hill, (and the name of the going up
the side of the Hill, is called *Difficulty.*) *Christian* now

1 trow 7   3 Gal. 1. 16 ‖ 1–11   4 come 7   7–8 of
kindness 3   18 in] on 4, 5, 6, 8 *etc.*   26 *marg.* Christian *has*
talk with himself add. 9⁴   31 an Hill] the Hill Difficulty 2

*Isa. 49. 10. went to the *Spring and drank thereof to refresh himself, and then began to go up the Hill; saying,

> This Hill, though high, I covet to ascend,
> The difficulty will not me offend:
> For I perceive the way to life lies here;
> Come, pluck up, Heart; lets neither faint nor fear:
> Better, tho difficult, th' right way to go,
> Then wrong, though easie, where the end is wo.

The other two also came to the foot of the Hill. But when they saw that the Hill was steep and high, and 10 that there was two other ways to go; and supposing also that these two ways might meet again, with that up which Christian went, on the other side of the Hill: Therefore they were resolved to go in those ways; (now the name of one of those ways was Danger, and the *The danger name of the other Destruction) So *the one took the way of turning out which is called Danger, which led him into a great of the way. Wood; and the other took directly up the way to Destruction, which led him into a wide field full of dark Mountains, where he stumbled and fell, and rose no 20 more.

I looked then after Christian, to see him go up the Hill, where I perceived he fell from running to going, and from going to clambering upon his hands and his knees, because of the steepness of the place. Now about the midway to the top of the Hill, was a pleasant *Award of *Arbour, made by the Lord of the Hill, for the refresh- grace. ing of weary Travailers. Thither therefore Christian got, where also he sat down to rest him. Then he pull'd his Roll out of his bosom, and read therein to his comfort; 30 he also now began afresh to take a review of the Coat or Garment that was given him as he stood by the Cross. Thus pleasing himself a while, he at last fell into a slumber, and thence into a fast sleep, which detained him in that place untill it was almost night, *He that sleeps and in his sleep his *Roll fell out of his hand. Now as is a loser. he was sleeping, there came one to him & awaked

him, saying *Go to the Ant, thou sluggard, consider her * Prov. 6. 6.
ways, and be wise: and with that Christian suddenly
started up, and sped him on his way, and went a pace
till he came to the top of the Hill.

Now when he was got up to the top of the Hill, there
came two men running against him amain; the name
of the one was *Timorous*, and the name of the other * Christian
Mistrust. To whom Christian said, Sirs, what's the matter *meets with*
you run the wrong way? Timorous answered, That they *Mistrust and* Timorous.
10 were going to the City of Zion, and had got up that
difficult place; but, said he, the further we go, the more
danger we meet with, wherefore we turned, and are
going back again.

Yes, said *Mistrust*, for just before us lye a couple of
Lions in the way, whether sleeping or wakeing we
know not and we could not think, if we came within
reach, but they would presently pull us in pieces.

Chr. Then said *Christian*, You make me afraid, but
whither shall I fly to be safe? If I go back to mine own
20 Countrey, *That* is prepared for Fire and Brimstone; and
I shall certainly perish there. If I can get to the Cœlestial City, I am sure to be in safety there. *I must * Christian
venture: To go back is nothing but death, to go forward *shakes off fear.*
is fear of death, and life everlasting beyond it. I will
yet go forward. So *Mistrust* and *Timorous* ran down the
Hill; and *Christian* went on his way. But thinking
again of what he heard from the men, he felt in his
bosom for his Roll: that he might read therein and be
comforted; but he felt, and *found it not. Then was * Christian
30 *Christian* in great distress, and knew not what to do, *missed his Roll,*
for he wanted that which used to relieve him, and that *wherein he used to take comfort.*
which should have been his Pass into the Cœlestial
City. Here therefore he began to be much *perplexed, * He is per-
and knew not what to do; at last he bethought himself *plexed for his Roll.*
that he had slept in the *Arbour* that is on the side of the
Hill: and falling down upon his knees, he asked God

1 Prov. 6. 6 *add.* 2   7 *Timorus* 1   *marg.* Christian ... Timorous *add.* 2   7 and the other 2 *etc.*   11 farther 2 *etc.*
14 lie 2: lies 3   21 get] *go* 6, 8 *etc.*   22 *marg.* Christian ... *fear*
add. 2   33 marg. *He ... Roll* add. 2

forgiveness for that his foolish Fact, and then went back to look for his Roll. But all the way he went back, who can sufficiently set forth the sorrow of *Christians* heart? somtimes he sighed, somtimes he wept, and often times he chid himself, for being so foolish to fall asleep in that place which was erected only for a little refreshment from his weariness. Thus therefore he went back, carefully looking on this side, and on that, all the way as he went, if happily he might find his Roll, that had been his comfort so many times in his Journey. He went thus till he came again within sight of the *Arbour*, where he sat and slept; but that sight renewed *his sorrow the more, by bringing again, even a fresh, his evil of sleeping unto his mind. Thus therefore he now went on, bewailing his sinful sleep, saying, *O wretched Man that I am*, that I should sleep in the day time! that I should sleep in the midst of difficulty! that I should so indulge the flesh, as to use that rest for ease to my flesh, which the Lord of the Hill hath erected only for the relief of the spirits of Pilgrims! How many steps have I took in vain! (Thus it happened to *Israel* for their sin, they were sent back again by the way of the Red-Sea) and I am made to tread those steps with sorrow, which I might have trod with delight, had it not been for this sinful sleep. How far might I have been on my way by this time! I am made to tread those steps thrice over, which I needed not to have trod but once: Yea now also I am like to be benighted, for the day is almost spent. O that I had not slept! Now by this time he was come to the *Arbour* again, where for a while he sat down and wept, but at last (as *Christian* would have it) looking sorrowfully down under the Settle, there he *espied his Roll; the which he with trembling and haste catch'd up, and put it into his bosom; but who can tell how joyful this man was, when he had gotten his Roll again! For this Roll was the assurance of his life, and acceptance at the desired Haven. There-

*Christian
*bewails his
foolish sleeping.*
Rev. 2. 2.
1 Thess. 5.
7, 8.

*Christian
*findeth his Roll
where he lost it.*

---

7 from] for 3   9 his] *the* 10, 11   **14** into 1   **15**
1 Thess. 5. 7, 8 *add.* 2   21 Thus] This 3   33 *marg.* Christian
. . *it* add. 2   34 it *om.* 3 *etc.*   37 *Heaven* 10

fore he laid it up in his bosom, gave thanks to God for directing his eye to the place where it lay, and with joy and tears betook him self again to his Journey. But Oh how nimbly now did he go up the rest of the Hill! Yet before he got up, the Sun went down upon *Christian*; and this made him again recall the vanity of his sleeping to his remembrance, and thus he again began to condole with himself: *Ah thou sinful sleep! how for thy sake am I like to be benighted in my Journey! I must walk with-*
10 *out the Sun, darkness must cover the path of my feet, and I must hear the noise of doleful Creatures, because of my sinful sleep!* Now also he remembred the story that *Mistrust* and *Timorous* told him of, how they were frighted with the sight of the Lions. Then said *Christian* to himself again, These Beasts range in the night for their prey, and if they should meet with me in the dark, how should I shift them? how should I escape being by them torn in pieces? Thus he went on his way, but while he was thus bewayling his unhappy mis-
20 carriage, he lift up his eyes, and behold there was a very stately Palace before him, the name whereof was *Beautiful*, and it stood just by the High-way side.

So I saw in my Dream, that he made haste and went forward, that if possible he might get Lodging there; Now before he had gone far, he entered into a very narrow passage, which was about a furlong off of the Porters Lodge, and looking very narrowly before him as he went, he espied two Lions in the way. Now, thought he, I see the dangers that *Mistrust* and *Timorous*
30 were driven back by, (The Lions were chained, but he saw not the Chains) Then he was afraid, and thought also himself to go back after them, for he thought nothing but death was before him: But the *Porter* at the Lodge, whose name is **Watchful*, perceiving that   * Mark 13. 14. *Christian* made a halt, as if he would go back, cried unto him saying, Is thy strength so small? fear not the Lions, for they are Chained; and are placed there for

4 nimble now did 3: *nimbly did* 6, 8 *etc.*   8 *Oh* 2, 3, 4: Oh 5, 6,
8: O 9³ *etc.*   11 of the doleful 8 *etc.*   13 *Timorus* 1   17
them! 1   18 on in 2   21 whereof] of which 2   34 Mar. 13 ‖ 1

trial of faith where it is; and for discovery of those that have none: keep in the midst of the Path, and no hurt shall come unto thee.

Then I saw that he went on, trembling for fear of the Lions; but taking good heed to the directions of the *Porter*; he heard them roar, but they did him no harm. Then he clapt his hands, and went on till he came and stood before the Gate where the *Porter* was. Then said *Christian* to the *Porter*, Sir, What house is this? and may I lodge here to night? The *Porter* answered, This House was built by the Lord of the Hill: and he built it for the relief and security of Pilgrims. The *Porter* also asked whence he was, and whither he was going?

Chr. I am come from the City of *Destruction*, and am going to Mount *Zion*; but because the Sun is now set, I desire, if I may, to lodge here to night.

Por. What is your name?

Chr. My name is, now, *Christian*; but my name at the first was *Graceless*: I came of the Race of **Japhet*, whom God will perswade to dwell in the Tents of *Shem*.

Por. But how doth it happen that you come so late, the Sun is set?

Chr. I had been here sooner, but that, wretched man that I am! I slept in the *Arbour* that stands on the Hill side; nay, I had notwithstanding that, been here much sooner, but that in my sleep I lost my Evidence, and came without it to the brow of the Hill; and then feeling for it, and finding it not, I was forced with sorrow of heart, to go back to the place where I slept my sleep, where I found it, and now I am come.

Por. Well, I will call out one of the Virgins of this place, who will, if she likes your talk, bring you in to the rest of the Family, according to the Rules of the House. So *Watchful* the *Porter* rang a Bell; at the sound of which, came out at the door of the House, a Grave and Beautiful Damsel, named *Discretion*, and asked why she was called.

The *Porter* answered, This Man is in a Journey from the City of *Destruction* to Mount *Zion*, but being weary,

* Gen. 9. 27.

19 Gen. 9. 27 *add.* 2: Gen. 9. 2. 7 || 5, 6

and benighted, he asked me if he might lodge here to night; so I told him I would call for thee, who after discourse had with him, mayest do as seemeth thee good, even according to the Law of the House.

Then she asked him whence he was, and whither he was going, and he told her. She asked him also, how he got into the way and he told her; Then she asked him, What he had seen, and met with in the way, and he told her; and last, she asked his name, so he said, It is *Christian*; and I have so much the more a desire to lodge here to night, because, by what I perceive, this place was built by the Lord of the Hill, for the relief and security of Pilgrims. So she smiled, but the water stood in her eyes: And after a little pause, she said, I will call forth two or three more of the Family. So she ran to the door, and called out *Prudence*, *Piety* and *Charity*, who after a little more discourse with him, had him in to the Family; and many of them meeting him at the threshold of the house, said, Come in thou blessed of the Lord; this house was built by the Lord of the Hill, on purpose to entertain such Pilgrims in. Then he bowed his head, and followed them into the House. So when he was come in, and set down, they gave him somthing to drink; and consented together, that until supper was ready, some one or two of them should have some particular discourse with *Christian*, for the best improvement of time: and they appointed *Piety* and *Prudence* and *Charity* to discourse with him; and thus they began.

Piety. *Come good* Christian, *since we have been so loving to you, to receive you in to our House this night; let us, if perhaps we may better our selves thereby, talk with you of all things that have happened to you in your Pilgrimage.* Piety *discourse him.*

Chr. With a very good will, and I am glad that you are so well disposed.

Piety. *What moved you at first to betake yourself to a Pilgrim's life?*

3 thee] the 7   7 into] in 8 *etc.*   15 the] my 3 *etc.*   23 sate 3
25 one or two *om.* 2   28 and *Charity* add. 2   30 *marg.* Piety *discourses him* add. 2   36 *your self* 2

*How Chris-
tian *was driven*
out of his own
Countrey.

Chr. I was *driven out of my Native Countrey, by a dreadful sound that was in mine ears, to wit, That unavoidable destruction did attend me, if I abode in that place where I was.

Piety. *But how did it happen that you came out of your Countrey this way?*

Chr. It was as God would have it; for when I was under the fears of destruction, I did not know whither to go; but by chance there came a man, even to me, (as I was trembling and weeping) whose name is 10

*How he got
into *the way*
to Sion.

*Evangelist, and he directed me to the Wicket-gate, which else I should never have found; and so set me into the way that hath led me directly to this House.

Piety. *But did you not come by the House of the Interpreter?*

Chr. Yes, and did see such things there, the remembrance of which will stick by me as long as I live;

*A rehearsal
of what he saw
in the way.*

specially three *things; *to wit,* How Christ, in despite of Satan, maintains his work of Grace in the heart; how the Man had sinned himself quite out of hopes of Gods 20 mercy; and also the Dream of him that thought in his sleep the day of Judgement was come.

Piety. *Why? Did you hear him tell his Dream?*

Chr. Yes, and a dreadful one it was, I thought. It made my heart ake as he was telling of it, but yet I am glad I heard it.

Piety. *Was that all that you saw at the house of the Interpreter?*

Chr. No, he took me and had me where he shewed me a stately Palace, and how the People were clad in 30 Gold that were in it; and how there came a venturous Man, and cut his way through the armed men that stood in the door to keep him out; and how he was bid to come in, and win eternal Glory. Methought those things did ravish my heart; I could have staid at that good Mans house a twelve-month, but that I knew I had further to go.

4 I] he 7   11–12 marg. *got in* 2, 7   24 it was. I thought it 1: it was; I thought, it 3, 4: it was, I thought, it 5, 6: it was, I thought; it 8 *etc.*   27 *all that you*] *all you* 10, 11   31 venterous 2 *etc.* 35 could] would 2 *etc.*   36 twelve-moneth 4

Piety. *And what saw you else in the way?*

Chr. Saw! Why, I went but a little further, and I saw one, as I thought in my mind, hang bleeding upon the Tree; and the very sight of him made my burden fall off my back (for I groaned under a weary burden) but then it fell down from off me. 'Twas a strange thing to me, for I never saw such a thing before: Yea, and while I stood looking up, (for then I could not forbear looking) three shining ones came to me: one of 10 them testified that my sins were forgiven me: another stript me of my rags, and gave me this Broidred Coat which you see; and the third set the mark which you see in my forehead, and gave me this sealed Roll (and with that he plucked it out of his bosom.)

Piety. *But you saw more then this, did you not?*

Chr. The things that I have told you were the best: yet some other matters I saw, as namely I saw three Men, *Simple, Sloth,* and *Presumption,* lye a sleep a little out of the way as I came, with Irons upon their heels; 20 but do you think I could awake them? I also saw *Formalist* and *Hypocrisie* come tumbling over the wall, to go, as they pretended, to *Sion,* but they were quickly lost; even as I my self did tell them, but they would not believe: but, above all, I found it *hard* work to get up this Hill, and as *hard* to come by the Lions mouths; and truly if it had not been for the good Man, the Porter that stands at the Gate, I do not know, but that after all, I might have gone back again: but now I thank God I am here, and I thank you for receiving of me.

30   Then *Prudence* thought good to ask him a few questions, and desired his answer to them.   Prudence *discourses him.*

Pru. *Do you not think somtimes of the Countrey from whence you came?*

Chr. Yes, *but with much shame and detestation; * Christians *thoughts of his Native Countrey.* *Truly, if I had been mindful of that Countrey from whence I came out, I might have had opportunity to have returned; but now I desire a better Countrey; that is, an Heavenly.* Heb. 11. 15. 16.

---

1 *ye* 8 *etc.*   5 weary] heavy 2 *etc.*   15 *than* 2, 3, 4, 5   17 small matters 1: matter 3   20 them! 1 *etc.*   21 *Formality* 3 26 mouth 2 *etc.*   30 *marg.* Prudence ... *him* add. 2   34 Yea 7

Pru. *Do you not yet bear away with you some of the things that then you were conversant withal?*

Chr. Yes but greatly against my will; especially my inward and *carnal cogitations; with which all my Countrey-men, as well as my self, were delighted; but now all those things are my grief: and might I but chuse mine own things, I would *chuse never to think of those things more; but when I would be doing of that which is best, that which is worst is with me.

* Christian distasted with carnal cogitations.

* Christians choice.

Pru. *Do you not find sometimes, as if those things were* 10 *vanquished, which at other times are your perplexity?*

Chr. Yes, but that is but seldom; but they are to me *Golden hours, in which such things happens to me.

* Christians golden hours.

Pru. *Can you remember by what means you find your anoyances at times, as if they were vanquished?*

Chr. Yes, when *I think what I saw at the Cross, that will do it; and when I look upon my Broidered Coat, that will do it; also when I look into the Roll that I carry in my bosom, that will do it; and when my thoughts wax warm about whither I am going, that 20 will do it.

* How Christian gets power against his corruptions.

Pru. *And what is it that makes you so desirous to go to Mount Zion?*

Chr. Why, *there I hope to see him *alive,* that did hang *dead* on the Cross; and there I hope to be rid of all those things, that to this day are in me, an anoiance to me; there they say there is no *death, and there I shall dwell with such Company as I like best. For to tell you truth, I love him, because I was by him eased of my burden, and I am weary of my inward sickness; 30 I would fain be where I shall die no more, and with the Company that shall continually cry, *Holy, Holy, Holy.*

* Why Christian would be at Mount Zion.

* Isa. 25. 8.
Rev. 21. 4.

* Charity discourses him.

Then said *Charity* to *Christian, Have you a family? are you a married man?*

Chr. I have a Wife and four small Children.

Cha. *And why did you not bring them along with you?*

8 be a doing 6, 8 *etc.*   9 Rom. 7 add. 4, *om.* 7   **13**
happen 2   18 also] and 3   27 say] saw 3   Isa. 25. 8 *add.* 2
Rev. 21. 4 *add.* 2   33 Then said *Charity . . . from their blood*
(p. 52, l. 12) add. 2

Chr. Then *Christian* *wept, and said, Oh how willingly would I have done it, but they were all of them
utterly averse to my going on Pilgrimage.

*Cha. But you should have talked to them, and have en-
deavoured to have shewen them the danger of being behind.*

Chr. So I did, and told them also what God had
shewed to me of the destruction of our City; but I
seemed to them as one that mocked, and they believed
me not.

10 *Cha. And did you pray to God that he would bless your
counsel to them?*

Chr. Yes, and that with much affection; for you must
think that my Wife and poor Children were very dear
unto me.

*Cha. But did you tell them of your own sorrow, and
fear of destruction? for I suppose that destruction was
visible enough to you?*

Chr. Yes, over, and over, and over. They might
also *see my fears in my countenance, in my tears, and
20 also in my trembling under the apprehension of the
Judgment that did hang over our heads; but all was
not sufficient to prevail with them to come with me.

*Cha. But what could they say for themselves why they
came not?*

Chr. Why, *my Wife was afraid of losing this World;
and my Children were given to the foolish delights
of youth: so what by one thing, and what by another,
they left me to wander in this manner alone.

*Cha. But did you not with your vain life, damp all that
30 you by words used by way of perswasion to bring them away
with you?*

Chr. Indeed I cannot commend my life; for I am
conscious to my self of many failings: therein, I know
also that a man by his conversation, may soon overthrow
what by argument or perswasion he doth labour to
fasten upon others for their good: Yet, this I can say,
1 was very wary of giving them occasion, by any

* Christian's
love to his
Wife and
Children.

Gen. 19. 14.

* Christian's
fears of perish-
ing might be
read in his very
countenance.

* The cause
why his Wife
and Children
did not go
with him.

1 marg. *loves* 3   15 Cha.] Chr. 2   19 marg. . . . *fear* . . . 4 *etc.*
23 Cha.] Chr. 5   33 failings therein; 4–6, 8, 9³: failing therein;
9⁴: failings therein: 7, 1C, 11

Christian's good conversation before his Wife and Children. unseemly action, to make them averse to going on Pilgrimage. Yea, for this very thing, they would tell me I was too precise, and that I denied my self of things (for their sakes) in which they saw no evil. Nay, I think I may say, that, if what they saw in me did hinder them, it was my great tenderness in sinning against God, or of doing any wrong to my Neighbor.

* 1 John 3. 12.
Christian clear of their blood if they perish.
* Ezek. 3. 19.

Cha. *Indeed *Cain hated his Brother, because his own works were evil, and his Brothers righteous; and if thy Wife and Children have been offended with thee for this,* 10 *they thereby shew themselves to be implacable to *good; and thou hast delivered thy soul from their blood.*

* What Christian had to his supper.
* Their talk at supper time.

Now I saw in my Dream, that thus they sat talking together until supper was ready. So when they had made ready, they sat down to meat; Now the Table was furnished *with fat things, and with Wine that was well refined; and all their talk *at the Table was about the Lord of the Hill: As namely, about what he had done, and wherefore he did what he did, and why he had builded that House: and by what they said, 20 I perceived that he had been a *great Warriour*, and

* Heb. 2. 14, 15.

had fought with and slain *him that had the power of Death, but not without great danger to himself, which made me love him the more.

For, as they said, and as I believe, (said *Christian*) he did it with the loss of much blood; but that which put Glory of Grace into all he did, was, that he did it of pure love to his Countrey. And besides, there were some of them of the Household that said, they had seen, and spoke with him since he did dye on the Cross; and 30 they have attested, that they had it from his own lips, that he is such a lover of poor Pilgrims, that the like is not to be found from the East to the West.

They moreover gave an instance of what they affirmed, and that was, He had stript himself of his glory that he might do this for the Poor; and that they heard him say and affirm, That he would not dwell in the Mountain of *Zion* alone. They said moreover, That

3 things] sins 2   **11** Ezek. 4. 19 ‖ 1–11   **22** Heb. 2. 14, **15** add. 2   **28** out of 5, 6, 8 *etc.*   **29** seen] been 3

he had made many Pilgrims *Princes, though by nature *Christ makes
they were *Beggars born, and their original had been Princes of
the Dunghil.   Beggars.
                                                    * 1 Sam. 2. 8.
    Thus they discoursed together till late at night; and Psal. 113. 7.
after they had committed themselves to their Lord for
Protection, they betook themselves to rest. The Pilgrim they laid in a large upper *Chamber, whose *Christians
window opened towards the Sun rising; the name of Bed-Chamber.
the Chamber was *Peace*, where he slept till break of
10 day; and then he awoke and sang,

> *Where am I now? is this the love and care*
> *Of Jesus, for the men that Pilgrims are?*
> *Thus to provide! That I should be forgiven!*
> *And dwell already the next door to Heaven.*

So in the Morning they all got up, and after some more
discourse, they told him that he should not depart, till
they had shewed him the *Rarities* of that place. And
first they had him into the Study, *where they shewed *Christian had
him Records of the greatest Antiquity; in which, as I into the Study,
                                                       and what he
20 remember my Dream, they shewed him first the Pedi- saw there.
gree of the Lord of the Hill, that he was the Son of the
Ancient of Days, and came by an eternal Generation.
Here also was more fully Recorded the Acts that he
had done, and the names of many hundreds that he had
taken into his service; and how he had placed them in
such Habitations that could neither by length of Days,
nor decaies of Nature, be dissolved.
    Then they read to him some of the worthy Acts that
some of his servants had done: As how they had sub-
30 dued Kingdoms, wrought Righteousness, obtained
Promises, stopped the mouths of Lions, quenched the
*violence of Fire, escaped the edge of the Sword; out *Heb. 11.
of weakness were made strong, waxed valiant in fight, 33, 34.
and turned to flight the Armies of the *Aliens*.
    Then they read again in another part of the Records
of the House, where it was shewed how willing their

2 1 Sam. 2. 8 *add.* 2   Psal. 113. 7 *add.* 2   10 sung 11   17
shew'd 3   22 an] that 3   32 Heb. 11. 33, 34 || 1, 2, 5, 6, 8 *etc*.:
Heb. 11. 37, 34 || 3, 4, 7   33 fight] sight 3, 7   36 willingly 4, 5, 6, 8, 9³

Lord was to receive into his favour, any, even any,
though they in time past had offered great affronts to
his Person and proceedings. Here also were several
other Histories of many other famous things; of all
which *Christian* had a view. As of things both Ancient
and Modern; together with Prophecies and Predictions
of things that have their certain accomplishment, both
to the dread and amazement of enemies, and the comfort and solace of Pilgrims.

The next day they took him, and had him into the 10
* Christian ***Armory**; where they shewed him all manner of Furni-
had into the
Armory. ture, which their Lord had provided for Pilgrims, as
Sword, Shield, Helmet, Brest plate, *All-Prayer*, and
Shooes that would not wear out. And there was here
enough of this, to harness out as many men for the
service of their Lord, as there be Stars in the Heaven
for multitude.

They also shewed him some of the Engines with
which some of his Servants had done wonderful things.
* Christian *is* *They shewed him *Moses* Rod, the Hammer and Nail 20
made to see
Ancient things. with which *Jael* slew *Sisera*, the Pitchers, Trumpets,
and Lamps too, with which *Gideon* put to flight the
Armies of *Midian*. Then they shewed him the Oxes
goad wherewith *Shamger* slew six hundred men. They
shewed him also the Jaw bone with which *Sampson* did
such mighty feats; they shewed him moreover the Sling
and Stone with which *David* slew *Goliah* of *Gath*: and
the Sword also with which their Lord will kill the Man
of Sin, in the day that he shall rise up to the prey. They
shewed him besides many excellent things, with which 30
Christian was much delighted. This done, they went
to their rest again.

Then I saw in my Dream, that on the morrow he
got up to go forwards, but they desired him to stay till
the next day also; and then said they, we will, (if the
* Christian day be clear) shew you the *delectable Mountains;
shewed the
delectable which they said, would yet further add to his comfort;
Mountains. because they were nearer the desired Haven, then the
place where at present he was. So he consented and

20 *Moses's* 3   38 Heaven 7, 10, 11

staid. When the Morning was up, they had him to the top of the House, *and bid him look South; so he did; *Isa. 33. 16, 17. and behold at a great distance he saw a most pleasant Mountainous Country, beautified with Woods, Vinyards, Fruits of all sorts; Flowers also, with Springs and Fountains, very delectable to behold. Then he asked the name of the Countrey, they said it was *Immanuels Land*: and it is as common, said they, as this *Hill* is to, and for all the Pilgrims. And when thou 10 comest there, from thence, thou maist see to the Gate of the Cœlestial City, as the Shepherds that live there will make appear.

Now he bethought himself of setting forward,* and * Christian they were willing he should: but first, said they, let us *sets forward.* go again into the Armory, so they did; and when he came there, they *harnessed him from head to foot, * Christian *sent* with what was of proof, lest perhaps he should meet *away Armed.* with assaults in the way. He being therefore thus accoutred, walketh out with his friends to the Gate, 20 and there he asked the *Porter* if he saw any Pilgrims pass by; then the *Porter* answered, Yes.

Ch. Pray did you know him?

Por. I asked his name, and he told me it was *Faithful.*

Chr. O, said *Christian*, I know him, he is my Townsman, my near Neighbour, he comes from the place where I was born: how far do you think he may be before?

Por. He is got by this time below the Hill.

Chr. Well, *said *Christian*, good Porter the Lord be * *How* Chris-
30 with thee, and add to all thy blessings much increase, *tian and the* for the kindness that thou hast shewed to me. *Porter* greet *at parting.*

Then he began to go forward, but *Discretion*, *Piety*, *Charity*, and *Prudence* would accompany him down to the foot of the Hill. So they went on together, reiterating their former discourses till they came to go down the Hill. Then said *Christian*, as it was *difficult* coming up, so (so far as I can see) it is *dangerous* going down. Yes, said *Prudence*, so it is; for it is an hard matter for

5 with *add.* 2   **7** say 10, 11   **10** thence, said they, thou 1, 2
22 said he *add.* 2   **31** for] *of* 10, 11

a man to go down into the valley of *Humiliation*, as thou
art now, and to catch no slip by the way; therefore,
said they, are we come out to accompany thee down
the Hill. So he began to go down, but very warily, yet
he caught a slip or two.

Then I saw in my Dream, that these good Companions (when *Christian* was gone down to the bottom of
the Hill) gave him a loaf of Bread, a bottle of Wine, and
a cluster of Raisins; and then he went on his way.

But now in this Valley of *Humiliation* poor *Christian* 10
was hard put to it, for he had gone but a little way
before he espied a foul *Fiend* coming over the field to
meet him; his name is *Apollyon*. Then did *Christian*
begin to be afraid, and to cast in his mind whether to
go back, or to stand his ground. But he considered
again, that he had no Armour for his back, and therefore thought that to turn the back to him, might give
him greater advantage with ease to pierce him with his
* Christians Darts; therefore he resolved to venture, and *stand his
resolution at
the approach ground. For thought he, had I no more in mine eye, 20
of Apollyon. then the saving of my life, 'twould be the best way
to stand.

So he went on, and *Apollyon* met him; now the
Monster was hidious to behold, he was cloathed with
scales like a Fish (and they are his pride) he had Wings
like a Dragon, feet like a Bear, and out of his belly
came Fire and Smoak, and his mouth was as the mouth
of a Lion. When he was come up to *Christian*, he beheld
him with a disdainful countenance, and thus began to
question with him. 30

Apol. *Whence come you, and whither are you bound?*
* Discourse Chr. I come from the City of *Destruction*, *which is
betwixt the place of all evil, and am going to the City of *Zion*.
Christian
and Apollyon. Apol. *By this I perceive thou art one of my Subjects,*
for all that Countrey is mine; and I am the Prince and God
of it. How is it then that thou hast ran away from thy

1 marg. *The Valley of* Humiliation *add.* 4, *om.* 7　　5 two] too 1, 2,
3, 7　　　　14 whither 1　　　　16 *marg.* Christian *no Armor for his back*
add. 9⁴　　19 marg. . . . . *on* 2 *etc.*: . . . *in* . . . 11　　21 than 2　　saying 3
26 feet like a Bear *add.* 2　　　32 am come 2　　　36 *run* 8 *etc.*

King? Were it not that I hope thou maiest do me more ser-vice, I would strike thee now at one blow to the ground.

Chr. I was born indeed in your Dominions, but your service was hard, and your wages such as a man could not live on, *for the wages of Sin is death;* therefore when I was come to years, I did as other considerate persons do, look out, if perhaps I might mend my self.

* Rom. 6. 23.

Apol. There is no Prince that will thus lightly lose his Subjects; neither will I as yet lose thee. But since thou 10 *complainest of thy service and wages, *be content to go back; what our Countrey will afford, I do here promise to give thee.*

* Apollyons flattery.

Chr. But I have let my self to another, even to the King of Princes, and how can I with fairness go back with thee?

Apol. Thou hast done in this, according to the Proverb, *changed a bad for a worse: but it is ordinary for those that have professed themselves his Servants, after a while to give him the slip; and return again to me: do thou so too, 20 *and all shall be well.*

* Apollyon undervalues Christs service.

Chr. I have given him my faith, and sworn my Alle-giance to him; how then can I go back from this, and not be hanged as a Traitor?

Apol. Thou didest the same to me, *and yet I am willing to pass by all, if now thou wilt yet turn again, and go back.

* Apollyon pretends to be merciful.

Chr. What I promised thee was in my none-age; and besides, I count that the Prince under whose Banner now I stand, is able to absolve me; yea, and to pardon also what I did as to my compliance with thee: and 30 besides, (O thou destroying *Apollyon*) to speak truth, I like his Service, his Wages, his Servants, his Govern-ment, his Company, and Countrey better then thine: and therefore leave off to perswade me further, I am his Servant, and I will follow him.

Apol. Consider again when thou art in cool blood, what

Apollyon pleads the grievous ends of Christians, to diswade Christian from persisting in his way.

5 Rom. 6. 23 *add.* 2   6 considerated 3 *etc.*   13 let] left 3–8, 9⁴, 10   17 *change . . . worse* rom. 10, 11   *change* 3   19 *too]* to 1 24 *didst* 2   to] by 5, 6, 8 *etc.*   25 *wilt yet]* wilt 1   *marg.* Apollyon *pretends to be merciful* om. 2 *etc.*   26 promise 3, 4 32 than 2, 4 *etc.*   35 marg. . . . *end* . . . 11

thou art like to meet with in the way that thou goest. Thou knowest that for the most part, his Servants come to an ill end, because they are transgressors against me, and my ways: How many of them have been put to shameful deaths! and besides, thou countest his service better then mine, whereas he never came yet from the place where he is, to deliver any that served him out of our hands: but as for me, how many times, as all the World very well knows, have I delivered, either by power or fraud, those that have faithfully served me, from him and his, though taken by 10 *them; and so I will deliver thee.*

Chr. His forbearing at present to deliver them, is on purpose to try their love, whether they will cleave to him to the end: and as for the ill end thou sayest they come to, that is most glorious in their account: For, for present deliverance, they do not much expect it; for they stay for their Glory, and then they shall have it, when their Prince comes in his, and the Glory of the Angels.

Apol. *Thou hast already been unfaithful in thy service* 20 *to him, and how dost thou think to receive wages of him?*

Chr. Wherein, O *Apollyon*, have I been unfaithful to him;

Apollyon *pleads* Christian's *infirmities* against him.

Apol. *Thou didst faint at first setting out, when thou wast almost choked in the Gulf of Dispond. Thou didst attempt wrong ways to be rid of thy burden, whereas thou shouldest have stayed till thy Prince had taken it off. Thou didst sinfully sleep, and loose thy choice thing: thou wast also almost perswaded to go back, at the sight of the Lions; and when thou talkest of thy Journey, and of what thou* 30 *hast heard, and seen, thou art inwardly desirous of vainglory in all that thou sayest or doest.*

Chr. All this is true, and much more, which thou hast left out; but the Prince whom I serve and honour, is merciful, and ready to forgive: but besides, these infirmities possessed me in thy Countrey, for there I suckt them in, and I have groaned under them, been

---

4 *way* 5, 6, 8 *etc.*   5 *than* 2   7 *our*] *their* 2 *etc.*   15 too 1
21 *doest* 3   24 marg. . . . *again* . . . 3   25 *didst* 3: diddst 8
28 *lose* 2, 3, 4   *things* 3   37 been] being 6, 8 *etc.*

sorry for them, and have obtained Pardon of my
Prince.

Apol. Then *Apollyon* broke out into a grievous rage, Apollyon *in a*
saying, *I am an enemy to this Prince: I hate his Person,* Christian.
his Laws, and People: I am come out on purpose to with-
stand thee.

Chr. Apollyon, beware what you do, for I am in the
Kings High-way, the way of Holiness, therefore take
heed to your self.

10   *Apol.* Then *Apollyon* strodled quite over the whole
breadth of the way, and said, I am void of fear in this
matter, prepare thy self to dye, for I swear by my In-
fernal Den, that thou shalt go no further, here will I
spill thy soul: and with that he threw a flaming Dart
at his brest; but *Christian* had a Shield in his hand,
with which he caught it, and so prevented the danger
of that. Then did *Christian* draw, for he saw 'twas time
to bestir him; and *Apollyon* as fast made at him, throw-
ing Darts as thick as hail; by the which, notwith-
20 standing all that *Christian* could do to avoid it, **Apollyon * Christian
wounded him in his *head,* his *hand* and *foot;* this made *wounded in his*
Christian give a little back: *Apollyon* therefore followed *faith and*
his work amain, and *Christian* again took courage, and *conversation.*
resisted as manfully as he could. This sore Combat
lasted for above half a day, even till *Christian* was almost
quite spent. For you must know, that *Christian,* by reason
of his wounds, must needs grow weaker and weaker.

Then *Apollyon* espying his opportunity, began to
gather up close to *Christian,* and wrestling with him, Apollyon
30 gave him a dreadful fall; and with that *Christian's* *casteth down*
Sword flew out of his hand. Then said *Apollion, I am* Christian.
sure of thee now; and with that, he had almost prest him
to death; so that *Christian* began to despair of life. But
as God would have it, while *Apollyon* was fetching of
his last blow, thereby to make a full end of this good
Man, *Christian* nimbly reached out his hand for his Christians
victory over
Apollyon.

10 stradled 2 *etc.*   12–13 by . . . that *add.* 2   21 *head* rom. 1
hand rom. 1   *foot* rom. 1   29 marg. . . . *the Christian* 1: . . . *casteth*
Christian *down to the Ground* 11   30 have him 3   34 of *om.* 10, 11
36 retched 3: stretched 4, 5 (6 *illegible*), 8 *etc.*   marg. Christ.'s . . . 7

*Mich. 7. 8. Sword, and caught it, saying, *Rejoyce not against me, O mine Enemy! when I fall, I shall arise*; and with that, gave him a deadly thrust, which made him give back, as one that had received his mortal wound: *Christian*

*Rom. 8. 37. perceiving that, made at him again, saying, *Nay, in all these things we are more then Conquerours, through him that*

James 4. 7. *loved us.* And with that, *Apollyon* spread forth his Dragons wings, and sped him away, that *Christian* saw him no more.

A brief relation of the Combat by the spectator. In this Combat no man can imagine, unless he had seen and heard as I did, what yelling, and hideous roaring *Apollyon* made all the time of the fight, he spake like a Dragon: and on the other side, what sighs and groans brast from *Christians* heart. I never saw him all the while give so much as one pleasant look, till he perceived he had wounded *Apollyon* with his two-edg'd Sword, then indeed he did smile, and look upward: but twas the dreadfullest sight that ever I saw.

Christian gives God thanks for deliverance. So when the Battel was over, *Christian* said, I will here give thanks to him that hath delivered me out of the mouth of the Lion; to him that did help me against *Apollyon*: and so he did, saying,

> Great Beelzebub, *the Captain of this Fiend*,
> *Design'd my ruin; therefore to this end*
> *He sent him harnest out, and he with rage*
> *That hellish was, did fiercely me Ingage:*
> *But blessed* Michael *helped me, and I*
> *By dint of Sword did quickly make him flye;*
> *Therefore to him let me give lasting praise,*
> *And thank and bless his holy name always.*

Then there came to him an hand with some of the leaves of the Tree of Life, the which *Christian* took, and applyed to the wounds that he had received in the Battel, and was healed immediately. He also sat down in that place to eat Bread, and to drink of the Bottle

---

1 Mich. 7. 8 *add.* 2   5 Rom. 8. 37 *add.* 2: Rom. 8. 34 ‖ 4: Rom. 8. 3 ‖ 5–9³: Rom. 8. 8, 9 ‖ 9⁴ *etc.*   6–7 *through . . . us* add. 2   8 *Christian* for a season saw 1   14 burst 2   19 marg. . . . . *for* his deliverance 10, 11   30 *thanks* 3, 7

that was given him a little before; so being refreshed, he addressed himself to his Journey, with his *Sword drawn in his hand; for he said, I know not but some other enemy may be at hand. But he met with no other affront from *Apollyon*, quite through this Valley.

     Christian goes on his Journey with his Sword drawn in his hand.

   Now at the end of this Valley, was another, called the Valley of the *Shadow of Death*, and *Christian* must needs go through it, because the way to the Cœlestial City lay through the midst of it: Now this Valley is 10 a very solitary place. The Prophet *Jeremiah* thus describes it, *A Wilderness, a Land of desarts, and of Pits, a Land of drought, and of the shadow of death, a Land that no Man* (but a Christian) *passeth through, and where no man dwelt.*

    Jer. 2. 6.

   Now here *Christian* was worse put to it then in his fight with *Apollyon*, as by the sequel you shall see.

   I saw then in my Dream, that when *Christian* was got to the Borders of the Shadow of Death, there met him two Men, *Children of them that brought up an 20 *evil report of the good Land, making haste to go back: to whom *Christian* spake as follows.

    The children of the Spies go back.
    Numb. 13.

   Chr. Whither are you going?

   Men. They said, Back, back; and would have you to do so too, if either life or peace is prized by you.

   Chr. Why? what's the matter? said Christian?

   Men. Matter! said they; we were going that way as you are going, and went as far as we durst; and indeed we were almost past coming back, for had we gone a little further, we had not been here to bring the news 30 to thee.

   Chr. But what have you met with? said Christian.

   Men. Why we were almost in the Valley of the shadow of Death, but that by good hap we looked before us, and saw the danger before we came to it.

    Psal. 44. 19.
    Psal. 107. 19.

   Chr. But what have you seen? said Christian.

---

7 marg. *The Valley of the Shadow of Death* add. 4: om. 7   18 to] unto 5, 6, 8, 9³, 9⁴: *unto* 10: *on* 11   20 hast 1   Numb. 13 *add*. 2 23 we *add*. 3   24 to *om*. 6, 8 *etc*.   too] to 8 *etc*.   32 Psal. 44. 29 || 7: Psal. 4. 19 || 4, 5, 6, 8, 9⁴ *etc*.: Psal. 23. 4 || 9³   Psal. 107. 10 || 1, 2: Psal. 117. 19 || 9⁴ *etc*.

Men. Seen! Why the Valley it self, which is as dark as pitch; we also saw there the Hobgoblins, Satyrs, and Dragons of the Pit: we heard also in that Valley a continual howling and yelling, as of a People under unutterable misery; who there sat bound in affliction and Irons: and over that Valley hangs the discouraging *Clouds of confusion, death also doth always spread his wings over it: in a word, it is every whit dreadful, being utterly without Order.

Ch. *Then said* Christian, *I perceive not yet, by what* 10 *you have said, but that *this is my way to the desired Haven.*

Men. Be it thy way, we will not chuse it for ours; so they parted, and *Christian* went on his way, but still with his Sword drawn in his hand, for fear lest he should be assaulted.

I saw then in my Dream, so far as this Valley reached, there was on the right hand a very deep Ditch; that Ditch is it into which the blind have led the blind in all Ages, and have both there miserably perished. Again, behold on the left hand, there was a very dangerous 20 Quagg, into which, if even a good Man falls, he can find no bottom for his foot to stand on: Into that Quagg *King* David *once did fall*, and had no doubt therein been smothered, had not He that is able, pluckt him out.

The path-way was here also exceeding narrow, and therefore good *Christian* was the more put to it; for when he sought in the dark to shun the ditch on the one hand, he was ready to tip over into the mire on the other; also when he sought to escape the mire, with- 30 out great carefulness he would be ready to fall into the ditch. Thus he went on, and I heard him here sigh bitterly: for, besides the dangers mentioned above, the path way was here so dark, that oft times when he lift up his foot to set forward, he knew not where, or upon what he should set it next.

Job 3. 5. ch. 10. 22.

Jer. 2. 6.

Psal. 69. 14.

---

7 Chap. 10. 2 ‖ 5 (6 *illegible*), 8 *etc.*   11 *disired* 3   *Heaven* 4, 5, 6, 8, 9⁴ *etc.*   14 least 3, 4, 5, 7   18 hath 11   21–22 he find 3: finds 4 *etc.*   22 that] this 10, 11   24 he 3   33 danger 3   35 set] go 10, 11   or] nor 9⁴ *etc.*

About the midst of this Valley, I perceived the mouth
of Hell to be, and it stood also hard by the way side:
Now thought *Christian*, what shall I do? And ever
and anon the flame and smoke would come out in such
abundance, with sparks and hideous noises, (things that
cared not for *Christians* Sword, as did *Apollyon* before)
that he was forced to put up his Sword, and betake
himself to another weapon called *All-prayer: so he * Ephes. 6.
cried in my hearing, *O Lord I beseech thee deliver my* 18.
                                                        * Psal. 116.
10 *Soul.* Thus he went on a great while, yet still the flames 4.
would be reaching towards him: also he heard doleful
voices, and rushings too and fro, so that sometimes he
thought he should be torn in pieces, or trodden down
like mire in the Streets. This frightful sight was seen,
and these dreadful noises were heard by him for several
miles together: and coming to a place, where he thought Christian *put*
he heard a company of *Fiends* coming forward to meet *to a stand, but*
                                                        for a while.
him, he stopt; and began to muse what he had best to
do. Somtimes he had half a thought to go back. Then
20 again he thought he might be half way through the
Valley; he remembred also how he had already vanquished many a danger: and that the danger of going
back might be much more, then for to go forward; so
he resolved to go on. Yet the *Fiends* seemed to come
nearer and nearer, but when they were come even
almost at him, he cried out with a most vehement voice,
I will walk in the strength of the Lord God; so they gave
back, and came no further.

One thing I would not let slip, I took notice that
30 now poor *Christian* was so confounded, that he did not
know his own voice: and thus I perceived it: Just when
he was come over against the mouth of the burning
Pit, one of the wicked ones got behind him, and stept
up softly to him, and whisperingly suggested many
grievous blasphemies to him, which he *verily thought * Christian
had proceeded from his own mind. This put *Christian* *made believe*
                                                        that he spake
more to it than any thing that he met with before, even *blasphemies,*
to think that he should now blaspheme him that he *when 'twas*
                                                        Satan that
                                                        suggested them
8 Ephess. 6. 18 ‖ 3, 4   9 Psal. 116. 3 ‖ 1–11   12 to 6, 8 *etc.* *into his mind.*
14 frighful 3   23 than 2   37 *then* 5, 6, 8

loved so much before; yet, could he have helped it, he would not have done it: but he had not the discretion neither to stop his ears, nor to know from whence those blasphemies came.

When *Christian* had travelled in this disconsolate condition some considerable time, he thought he heard the voice of a man, as going before him, saying, *Though I walk through the valley of the shaddow of death, I will fear none ill, for thou art with me.*

Then was he glad, and that for these reasons: 10

First, because he gathered from thence, that some who feared God were in this Valley as well as himself.

Secondly, For that he perceived, God was with them, though in that dark and dismal state; and why not, thought he, with me, though by reason of the impediment that attends this place, I cannot perceive it.

Thirdly, For that he hoped (could he over-take them) to have company by and by. So he went on, and called to him that was before, but he knew not what to answer; for that he also thought himself to be alone: And by 20 and by, the day broke; then said *Christian*, *He hath turned the shadow of death into the morning.*

Now morning being come, he looked back, not of desire to return, but to see, by the light of the day, what hazards he had gone through in the dark. So he saw more perfectly the Ditch that was on the one hand, and the Quag that was on the other; also how narrow the way was which lay betwixt them both; also now he saw the Hobgoblins, and Satyrs, and Dragons of the Pit, but all afar off; for after break of day, they came 30 not nigh; yet they were discovered to him, according to that which is written, *He discovereth deep things out of darkness, and bringeth out to light the shadow of death.*

Now was *Christian* much affected with his deliverance from all the dangers of his solitary way, which dangers, though he feared them more before, yet he

Psalm 23. 4.

Job 9. 10.

*Amos 5. 8.
Christian glad at break of day.

*Job. 12. 22.

---

1 could he] if he could 2   7 as *om.* 4, 5, 6, 8 *etc.*   20 *he ital.* 2, 3, 7   also *add.* 2   alone 1, 2, 4, 11 : *alone* 5, 6, 8–10 : also 3, 7 23 out of 7   25 thro 7   28 lay] led 3   now] how 3, 7 29 Hobgoblings 10, 11   Satyres 5, 6   32 Job 12. 22 *add.* 2

saw them more clearly now, because the light of the
day made them conspicuous to him; and about this
time the Sun was rising, and this was another mercy to
Christian: for you must note, that tho the first part of the
Valley of the shadow of Death was dangerous, *yet this ** The second
second part which he was yet to go, was, if possible, far *part of this
Valley very
more dangerous*: for from the place where he now stood, *dangerous.*
even to the end of the Valley, the way was all along set
so full of Snares, Traps, Gins, and Nets here, and so full
10 of Pits, Pitfalls, deep holes, and shelvings down there,
that had it now been dark, as it was when he came the
first part of the way, had he had a thousand souls, they
had in reason been cast away; but, as I said, just now the
Sun was rising. Then said he **His candle shineth on my* * Job 29. 3.
head, and by his light I go through darkness.*

In this light therefore he came to the end of the
Valley. Now I saw in my Dream, that at the end of
this Valley lay blood, bones, ashes, and mangled bodies
of men, even of Pilgrims that had gone this way
20 formerly: And while I was musing what should be the
reason, I espied a little before me a Cave, where two
Giants, *Pope* and *Pagan*, dwelt in old time, by whose
Power and Tyranny the Men whose bones, blood,
ashes, *&c.* lay there, were cruelly put to death. But
by this place *Christian* went without much danger,
whereat I somewhat wondered; but I have learnt since,
that *Pagan* has been dead many a day; and as for the
other, though he be yet alive, he is by reason of age,
and also of the many shrewd brushes that he met with
30 in his younger dayes, grown so crazy and stiff in his
joynts, that he can now do little more then sit in his
Caves mouth, grinning at Pilgrims as they go by, and
biting his nails, because he cannot come at them.

So I saw that *Christian* went on his way, yet at the
sight of the *old Man* that sat in the mouth of the *Cave*,
he could not tell what to think, specially because he
spake to him, though he could not go after him; saying,

5 marg. *The second . . . dangerous* add. 2   9 Gins] Guns 4
14 Job 29. 3 *om.* 6 (*possibly faded out*)   18 mingled 4, 5, 6, 8 *etc.*
24 cruelty 3   31 than 2, 8 *etc.*   36 especially 4, 5, 6, 8 *etc.*

You will never mend, till more of you be burned: but he
held his peace, and set a good face on't, and so went
by, and catcht no hurt. Then sang *Christian,*

> *O world of wonders! (I can say no less)*
> *That I should be preserv'd in that distress*
> *That I have met with here! O blessed bee*
> *That hand that from it hath delivered me!*
> *Dangers in darkness, Devils, Hell, and Sin,*
> *Did compass me, while I this Vale was in:*
> *Yea, Snares, and Pits, and Traps, and Nets did lie*   10
> *My path about, that worthless silly I*
> *Might have been catch't, intangled, and cast down:*
> *But since I live, let JESUS wear the Crown.*

Now as *Christian* went on his way, he came to a little
ascent, which was cast up on purpose, that Pilgrims
might see before them: up there therefore *Christian*
went, and looking forward, he saw *Faithful* before him,
upon his Journey. Then said *Christian* aloud, Ho, ho,
So-ho; stay, and I will be your Companion. At that
Faithful looked behind him, to whom *Christian* cried 20
again, Stay, stay, till I come up to you: but *Faithful*
answered, *No,* I am upon my life, and the Avenger of
Christian over- Blood is behind me. At this *Christian* was somwhat
takes Faithful. moved, and putting to all his strength, he quickly got
up with *Faithful,* and did also over-run him, so the *last
was first.* Then did *Christian* vain-gloriously smile, because he had gotten the start of his Brother: but not
Christians fall taking good heed to his feet, he suddenly stumbled and
makes Faithful fell, and could not rise again, until *Faithful* came up to
and he go
lovingly help him.   30
together. Then I saw in my Dream, they went very lovingly
on together; and had sweet discourse of all things that
had happened to them in their Pilgrimage: and thus
Christian began.

Chr. *My honoured and well beloved Brother* Faithful,
I am glad that I have overtaken you; and that God has so

---

15 asent 2   16 them? up there 2–6, 8: them up there, therefore
10, 11   24 too 2, 3, 7   33 hapned 7, 11

*tempered our spirits, that we can walk as Companions in
this so pleasant a path.*

Faith. I had thought dear friend, to have had your
company quite from our Town, but you did get the
start of me; wherefore I was forced to come thus much
of the way alone.

*Chr. How long did you stay in the City of Destruction,
before you set out after me on your Pilgrimage?*

Faith. Till I could stay no longer; for there was great
10 talk presently after you was gone out, that our City
would in short time with Fire from Heaven be burned
down to the ground.

Chr. What? Did your Neighbours talk so?

Faith. Yes, 'twas for a while in every bodies mouth.

*Chr. What, and did no more of them but you come out
to escape the danger?*

Their talk about the Countrey from whence they came.

Faith. Though there was, as I said, a great talk thereabout, yet I do not think they did firmly believe it. For
in the heat of the discourse, I heard some of them de-
20 ridingly speak of you, and of your desperate Journey,
(for so they called this your Pilgrimage) but I did
believe, and do still, that the end of our City will be
with Fire and Brimstone from above: and therefore I
have made mine escape.

Chr. Did you hear no talk of Neighbour Pliable?

Faith. Yes, *Christian,* I heard that he followed you
till he came at the Slough of *Dispond*; where, as some
said, he fell in; but he would not be known to have so
done: but I am sure he was soundly bedabled with
30 that kind of dirt.

Chr. And what said the Neighbours to him?

Faith. He hath since his going back been had greatly
in derision, and that among all sorts of People: some
do mock and despise him, and scarce will any set him
on work. He is now seven times worse then if he had
never gone out of the City.

How Plyable was accounted of when he got home.

*Chr. But why should they be so set against him, since
they also despise the way that he forsook?*

Faith. Oh, they say, Hang him; he is a Turn-Coat, he was not true to his profession: I think God has stired up even his enemies to hiss at him, and make him a

9. 18, 19. Proverb, because he hath forsaken the way.

Chr. *Had you no talk with him before you came out?*

Faith. I met him once in the Streets, but he leered away on the other side, as one ashamed of what he had done; so I spake not to him.

Chr. *Well, at my first setting out, I had hopes of that Man; but now I fear he will perish in the overthrow of the* 10

2 Pet. 2. 22. *City, *for it is happened to him according to the true Pro-*

The Dog and Sow. *verb, The Dog is turned to his Vomit again, and the Sow that was Washed to her wallowing in the mire.*

Faith. They are my fears of him too: But who can hinder that which will be?

Chr. Well Neighbour *Faithful* said *Christian*, let us leave him, and talk of things that more immediately concern our selves. *Tell me now, what you have met with in the way as you came; for I know you have met with some things, or else it may be writ for a wonder.* 20

Faith. I escaped the Slough that I perceive you fell into, and got up to the Gate without that danger; only

Faithfull I met with one whose name was *Wanton*, that had like

assaulted by Wanton. to have done me a mischief.

Gen. 39. 11, *Chr.* *'Twas well you escaped her Net;* *Joseph was*

12, 13. *hard put to it by her, and he escaped her as you did, but it had like to have cost him his life. But what did she do to you?*

Faith. You cannot think (but that you know somthing) what a flattering tongue she had, she lay at me hard to turn aside with her, promising me all manner 30 of content.

Chr. *Nay, she did not promise you the content of a good conscience.*

Faith. You know what I mean, all carnal and fleshly content.

1 he is Taurn-Coat 1: he is Turn-Coat 2, 3: a turn-coat 7: a turn-Coat 9[3]: a turn Coat 8, 9[4] *etc.*   4 Jer. 28. 19, 19 ‖ 9[4]: Jer. 28. 18, 19 ‖ 10, 11   11 hapned 11   2 Pet. 2. 22 *add.* 2: Pet. 2. 22 ‖ 10 marg.   *The Dog and Sow* 3 (blurred): rom. 11: *The Dog and the Sow* 7 16 Chr. *add.* 2   21 perceived 3   25 Gen. 39. 11, 12, 13 *add.* 2 34 what] that 3–7, 10, 11

Chr. *Thank God you have escaped her: The *abborred* * Prov. 22. 14.
of the Lord shall fall into her Ditch.

Faith. Nay, I know not whether I did wholly escape
her, or no.

Chr. *Why, I tro you did not consent to her desires?*

Faith. No, not to defile my self; for I remembred an
old writing that I had seen, which saith, *Her steps take* Prov. 5. 5.
hold of Hell. So I shut mine eyes, because I would not Job. 31. 1.
be bewitched with her looks: then she railed on me,
10 and I went my way.

Chr. *Did you meet with no other assault as you came?*

Faith. When I came to the foot of the Hill called *He is assaulted*
Difficulty, I met with a very aged Man, who asked me, *by Adam the*
first.
What I was, and whither bound? I told him that I was
a Pilgrim, going to the Cœlestial City: Then said the old
Man, *Thou lookest like an honest fellow; Wilt thou be con-*
tent to dwell with me, for the wages that I shall give thee?
Then I asked him his name, and where he dwelt? He
said his name was *Adam the first, and I dwell in the Town*
20 *of *Deceit.* I asked him then, What was his work? and * Eph. 4. 22.
what the wages that he would give? He told me,
That his work was *many delights; and his wages, that I*
should be his Heir at last. I further asked him, What
House he kept, and what other Servants he had? so he
told me, *That his House was maintained with all the*
dainties in the world, and that his Servants were those of
his own begetting. Then I asked how many children he
had, He said, that he had but three Daughters, *The*
*lust of the flesh, the lust of the eyes, and the pride of life, * 1 Joh. 2. 16.
30 and that I should marry them all, if I would. Then I
asked, how long time he would have me live with him?
And he told me, *As long as he lived himself.*

Chr. *Well, and what conclusion came the* Old Man,
and you to, at last?

Faith. Why, at first I found my self somewhat in-

1 *here* 3, 4, 7   Prov. 21. 14 || 6: Prov. 28. 14 || 8, 9³, 9⁴: Prov. 22:
24 || 10, 11   2 *her*] *the* 3   6 remember 8, 9³, 9⁴   7 said 3
10 my way] away 7   14 was] am 4; 5, 6, 8 *etc.*   19 *I dwell*]
do dwell 1: *that he dwelt* 4, 5, 6, 8 *etc.*   27–28 how . . . had] If
he had any children 1   29 *lust*] *lusts* 1, 2   *lust*] *lusts* 1–3   *pride*]
bride 9⁴   30 them; if 2   31 to live 8 *etc.*

clinable to go with the Man, for I thought he spake very fair; but looking in his forehead as I talked with him, I saw there written, *Put off the old Man with his deeds.*

Chr. *And how then?*

Faith. Then it came burning hot into my mind, whatever he said, and however he flattered, when he got me home to his House, he would sell me for a Slave. So I bid him forbear to talk, for I would not come near the door of his House. Then he reviled me, and told 10 me, that he would send such a one after me, that should make my way bitter to my soul: So I turned to go away from him: but just as I turned my self to go thence, I felt him take hold of my flesh, and give me such a deadly twitch back, that I thought he had pull'd part * Rom. 7. 24. of me after himself: This made me cry, **O wretched Man!* So I went on my way up the Hill.

Now when I had got about half way up, I looked behind me, and saw one coming after me, swift as the wind; so he overtook me just about the place where 20 the Settle stands.

Chr. *Just there, said* Christian, *did I sit down to rest me; but being overcome with sleep, I there lost this Roll out of my bosom.*

Faith. But good Brother hear me out: So soon as the Man over-took me, he was but a word and a blow: for down he knockt me, and laid me for dead. But when I was a little come to my self again, I asked him wherefore he served me so? he said, Because of my secret inclining to *Adam the first*; and with that, he 30 strook me another deadly blow on the brest, and beat me down backward; so I lay at his foot as dead as before. So when I came to my self again, I cried him mercy; but he said, I know not how to show mercy, and with that knockt me down again. He had doubtless made an end of me, but that one came by, and bid him forbear.

Chr. *Who was that, that bid him forbear?*

25 here 1, 2, 3: heare 4   31 stroke 6, 8: struck 9³ *etc.*   34 how *add.* 2   36 an end] a hand 1   38 *Who*] *What* 6, 8, 9³

Faith. I did not know him at first, but as he went by, I perceived the holes in his hands, and his side; then I concluded that he was our Lord. So I went up the Hill.

Chr. *That Man that overtook you, was* Moses,* *he spareth none, neither knoweth he how to shew mercy to those that transgress his Law.* _{* The temper of Moses.}

Faith. I know it very well, it was not the first time that he has met with me. 'Twas he that came to me 10 when I dwelt securely at home, and that told me, He would burn my house over my head, if I staid there.

Chr. *But did not you see the house that stood there on the top of that Hill on the side of which* Moses *met you?*

Faith. Yes, and the Lions too, before I came at it, but for the Lions, I think they were a sleep, for it was about Noon; and because I had so much of the day before me, I passed by the Porter, and came down the Hill.

Chr. *He told me indeed that he saw you go by, but I* 20 *wish you had called at the House; for they would have shewed you so many Rarities, that you would scarce have forgot them to the day of your death. But pray tell me, did you meet no body in the Valley of* Humility?

Faith. Yes, I met with one *Discontent,* who would willingly have perswaded me to go back again with him: his reason was, for that the Valley was altogether without *Honour;* he told me moreover, That there to go, was the way to disobey all my Friends, as Pride, Arrogancy, Self-conceit, worldly Glory, with others, 30 who he knew, as he said, would be very much offended, if I made such a Fool of my self, as to wade through this Valley. _{Faithful assaulted by Discontent.}

Chr. *Well, and how did you answer him?*

Faith. I told him, that although all these that he named might claim kindred of me, and that rightly, (for indeed they were my Relations, *according to the flesh*) yet since I became a Pilgrim, they have disowned me, _{Faithfuls answer to Discontent.}

---

2 and his] and in his 6, 8 *etc.*   5 marg. *temper* 1, 2, 7: *thmper* 3: *thunder* 4, 5: *Thunder* 6, 8 *etc.*   13 *the Hill* 3   35 Kindred]
hindred 2   me] men 3

as I also have rejected them; and therefore they were
to me now no more then if they had never been of my
Linage; I told him moreover, That as to this Valley,
he had quite mis-represented the thing: *for before
Honour is Humility, and a haughty spirit before a fall.*
Therefore said I, I had rather go through this Valley
to the Honour that was so accounted by the wisest,
then chuse that which he esteemed most worth our
affections.

Chr. *Met you with nothing else in that Valley?*   10

He is assaulted   Faith. Yes, I met with *Shame*, But of all the Men
with Shame. that I met with in my Pilgrimage, he, I think, bears
the wrong name: the other would be said nay, after a
little argumentation (and some what else) but this bold
faced *Shame* would never have done.

Chr. *Why, what did he say to you?*

Faith. What! why he objected against Religion it
self; he said it was a pitiful, low, sneaking business for
a man to mind Religion; he said that a tender conscience was an unmanly thing, and that for Man to   20
watch over his words and ways, so as to tye up himself
from that hectoring liberty, that the brave spirits of the
times accustom themselves unto, would make him the
Ridicule of the times. He objected also, that but few
1 Cor. 1. 26. of the Mighty, Rich, or Wise, were ever of my opinion;
ch. 3. 18. nor any of them neither, before they were perswaded
Phi. 3. 7, 8. to be Fools, and to be of a voluntary fondness, to venture the loss of all, *for no body else knows what.* He
* John 7. 48. moreover objected *the base and low estate and condition of those that were chiefly the Pilgrims; also their 30
ignorance of the times in which they lived, and want of
understanding in all natural Science. Yea, he did hold
me to it at that rate also, about a great many more
things then here I relate; as, that it was a *shame* to sit

1 as] and 4, 5, 6, 8 *etc.*   2 than 2 *etc.*   3 Lineage 3, 4, 7
8 worthy 3, 4, 7   11 marg. . . . *by* Shame 9⁴   13 after after 1
18 'twas 6, 8 *etc.*   23 him] me 1, *om.* 2   26 neither *add.* 2
27 Phil. 3. 7, 8 ‖ 1, 2: Phil. 3. 7, 9 ‖ 3, 4, 5, 7, 10, 11: Phil. 37. 9 ‖ 6,
8, 9⁴: Phil. 3. 8 ‖ 9³   28 *else* om. 4, 5, 6, 8, 9³, 10, 11   29
John 7. 48 *add.* 2   30–31 of the times; in which they lived, also
their ignorance, 1–11   32 did not hold 9⁴   34 set 9⁴

whining and mourning under a Sermon, and a *shame*
to come sighing and groaning home. That it was a
shame to ask my Neighbour forgiveness for petty faults,
or to make restitution where I had taken from any:
He said also that Religion made a man grow strange
to the great, because of a few vices (which he called by
finer names) and made him own and respect the base,
because of the same Religious fraternity. And is not
this, said he, a *shame?*

10   Chr. *And what did you say to him?*

    Faith. Say! I could not tell what to say at the first.
Yea, he put me so to it, that my blood came up in my
face, even this *Shame* fetch'd it up, and had almost beat
me quite off. But at last I began to consider, *That that * Luke 16. 15.
which is highly esteemed among Men, is had in abomination
with God.* And I thought again, this *Shame* tells me
what men are, but it tells me nothing what God, or the
Word of God is. And I thought moreover, That at the
day of doom, we shall not be doomed to death or life,
20 according to the hectoring spirits of the world; but
according to the Wisdom and Law of the Highest.
Therefore thought I, what God says, is best, though all
the men in the world are against it. Seeing then, that
God prefers his Religion, seeing God prefers a tender
Conscience, seeing they that make themselves Fools for
the Kingdom of Heaven, are wisest; and that the poor
man that loveth Christ, is richer then the greatest man
in the world that hates him; *Shame* depart, thou art an
enemy to my Salvation: shall I entertain thee against
30 my Soveraign Lord? How then shall I look him in the
face at his coming? Should I now be *ashamed* of his Mar. 8. 38.
ways and Servants, how can I expect the blessing? But
indeed this *Shame* was a bold Villain; I could scarce
shake him out of my company; yea, he would be haunting of me, and continually whispering me in the ear,
with some one or other of the infirmities that attend

4 have 3   6 he] is 5, 6, 8, 10, 11   11 at first 2 *etc.*   14
Luke 16. 15 *add.* 2   22 what God says, is best, is best 1, 2: what
God says is best indeed, is best 4, 5, 6, 8 *etc.*   23 the *om.* 4, 5, 6, 8 *etc.*
27 man *add.* 2   than 2   31 Mark 8. 3 ‖ 5, 9³⁻¹¹: *blurred* 6, 8

Religion: but at last I told him, Twas but in vain to attempt further in this business; for those things that he disdained, in those did I see most glory: And so at last I got past this *importunate* one:

And when I had shaken him off, then I began to sing.

The tryals that those men do meet withal
That are obedient to the Heavenly call,
Are manifold and suited to the flesh,
And come, and come, and come again afresh;
That now, or somtime else, we by them may 10
Be taken, overcome, and cast away.
O let the Pilgrims, let the Pilgrims then,
Be vigilant, and quit themselves like Men.

Chr. *I am glad, my Brother, that thou didst withstand this Villain so bravely; for of all, as thou sayst, I think he has the wrong name: for he is so bold as to follow us in the Streets, and to attempt to put us to* shame *before all men; that is, to make us* ashamed *of that which is good: but if he was not himself audacious, he would never attempt to do as he does, but let us still resist him: for notwithstanding all* 20 *his Bravadoes, he promoteth the Fool, and none else.* The Prov. 3. 35. Wise shall Inherit Glory, said *Solomon,* but shame shall be the promotion of Fools.

Faith. *I think we must cry to him for help against shame, that would have us be valiant for Truth upon the Earth.*

Chr. *You say true. But did you meet no body else in that Valley?*

Faith. No not I, for I had Sun-shine all the rest of the way, through that, and also through the Valley of the shadow of death. 30

Chr. *'Twas well for you, I am sure it fared far otherwise with me.* I had for a long season, as soon almost as I entred into that Valley, a dreadful Combat with that foul Fiend *Apollyon:* Yea, I thought verily he would have killed me; especially when he got me down, and crusht me under him, as if he would have crusht me to pieces. For as he threw me, my Sword flew out of my hand; nay he told me, *He was sure of me:* but *I cried to God, and he heard me, and delivered me out of all my troubles.* Then I entred into the Valley of the shadow of death, and had no light for almost half the way through it. I thought I should a been killed there, over, and over: but at last, day brake, and the Sun rise, and I went through that which was behind with far more ease and quiet.

Moreover, I saw in my Dream, that as they went on, *Faithful,* as he chanced to look on one side, saw a Man whose name is *Talkative,* walking at a distance besides them, (for in this place there was room enough for them all to walk). *He was a tall Man, and somthing more* Talkative *comely at a distance then at hand,* To this Man, *Faithful* described. addressed himself in this manner.

Faith. *Friend, Whither away? Are you going to the Heavenly Countrey?*

Talk. I am going to that same place.

Faith. *That is well: Then I hope we may have your good company.*

Talk. With a very good will, will I be your companion.

Faith. *Come on then, and let us go together, and let us* Faithful *and* *spend our time in discoursing of things that are profitable.* Talkative *enter* discourse.

Talk. To talk of things that are good, to me is very acceptable, with you or with any other; and I am glad that I have met with those that incline to so good a work. For to speak the truth, there are but few that care thus to spend their time (as they are in their travels) but chuse much rather to be speaking of things to no Talkatives profit, and this hath been a trouble to me. dislike of bad discourse.

Faith. *That is indeed a thing to be lamented; for what things so worthy of the use of the tongue and mouth of men on Earth, as are the things of the God of Heaven?*

---

1 crusht 1   7 have 2 *etc.*   8 broke 4, 5, 6, 8 *etc.*   rose 2 *etc.*
16 *than* 5, 6, 8 *etc.*   17 himselfe 4   20 that] the 3 *etc.*   21
That's 7   *may*] shall 4, 5, 6, 8 *etc.*   32 *marg.* Talkaive 1   35
thing 10, 11

Talk. I like you wonderful well, for your saying is full of conviction; and I will add, What thing so pleasant, and what so profitable, as to talk of the things of God?

What things so pleasant? (that is, if a man hath any delight in things that are wonderful) for instance: If a man doth delight to talk of the History or the Mystery of things; or if a man doth love to talk of Miracles, Wonders, or Signs, where shall he find things Recorded so delightful, and so sweetly penned, as in 10 the holy Scripture?

Faith. *That's true: but to be profited by such things in our talk, should be that which we design.*

Talk. That is it that I said; for to talk of such things is most profitable, for by so doing, a Man may get knowledge of many things; as of the vanity of earthly things, and the benefit of things above: (thus in general) but more particularly, By this a man may learn the necessity of the New-birth, the insufficiency of our Talkatives works, the need of Christs righteousness, &c. Besides, 20 *fine discourse.* by this a man may learn by *talk*, what it is to repent, to believe, to pray, to suffer, or the like: by this also a Man may learn what are the great promises & consolations of the Gospel, to his own comfort. Further, by this a Man may learn to refute false opinions, to vindicate the truth, and also to instruct the ignorant.

Faith. *All this is true, and glad am I to hear these things from you.*

Talk. Alas! the want of this is the cause that so few understand the need of faith, and the necessity of a 30 work of Grace in their Soul, in order to eternal life: but ignorantly live in the works of the Law, by which a man can by no means obtain the Kingdom of Heaven.

Faith. *But by your leave, Heavenly knowledge of these, is the gift of God; no man attaineth to them by humane industry, or only by the talk of them.*

1 sayings is 3: sayings are 4 *etc.*   2–3 is so pleasant 3   **13**
that which we] our chief 11   14 talk *ital.* 1   17 benefit] befit 1
18 particular 4, 5, 6, 8 *etc.*   21 learn, what 3   25 refuse 5, 6, 8 *etc.*
30–31 a work 1, 2, 4, 5, 6, 8 *etc.*: a works 3: the works 7   31 Souls 9[4]

Talk. All this I know very well. For a man can receive nothing except it be given him from Heaven; all is of Grace, not of works: I could give you an hundred Scriptures for the confirmation of this. *O brave Talkative.*

Faith. *Well then, said* Faithful; *what is that one thing, that we shall at this time found our discourse upon?*

Talk. What you will: I will talk of things heavenly, or things earthly; things Moral, or things Evangelical; things Sacred, or things Prophane; things past, 10 or things to come; things forraign, or things at home; things more Essential, or things Circumstantial: provided that all be done to our profit. *O brave Talkative.*

Faith. Now did *Faithful* begin to wonder; *and stepping to* Christian, *(for he walked all this while by himself) he said to him, (but softly) What a brave Companion have we got! Surely this man will make a very excellent Pilgrim.* *Faithful beguiled by Talkative.*

Chr. At this *Christian* modestly smiled, and said, This man with whom you are so taken, will beguile with this tongue of his, twenty of them that know him not. *Christian makes a discovery of Talkative, telling Faithful who he was.*

20   Faith. *Do you know him then?*

Chr. Know him! Yes, better then he knows himself.

Faith. *Pray what is he?*

Chr. His name is *Talkative*, he dwelleth in our Town; I wonder that you should be a stranger to him, only I consider that our Town is large.

Faith. *Whose Son is he? And whereabout doth he dwell?*

Chr. He is the Son of one *Saywell*, he dwelt in *Prating-row;* and he is known of all that are acquainted 30 with him, by the name of *Talkative* in *Prating-row*, and notwithstanding his fine tongue, he is but a sorry fellow.

Faith. *Well, he seems to be a very pretty man.*

Chr. That is, to them that have not through acquaintance with him, for he is best abroad, near home he is ugly enough: your saying, That he is a *pretty man*, brings to my mind what I have observed in the work of the Painter, whose Pictures shews best at a distance; but very near, more unpleasing.

---

1 this] that 4, 5, 6, 8 *etc.*   9 Prophanes 1   15 (*but softly*)]
but softly 4, 5, 6, 8 *etc.*   21 Yea 7   than 2   37 shew 2 *etc.*

Faith. *But I am ready to think you do but* jest, *because you* smiled.

Chr. God-forbid that I should *jest*, (though I smiled) in this matter, or that I should accuse any falsely; I will give you a further discovery of him: This man is for any company, and for any *talk*; as he *talketh now* with you, so will he *talk* when he is on the *Ale-bench*: And the more drink he hath in his crown, the more of these things he hath in his mouth: Religion hath no place in his heart, or house, or conversation; all he hath lieth 10 in his *tongue*, and his Religion is to make a noise *therewith*.

Faith. *Say you so! Then I am in this man greatly deceived.*

Chr. Deceived? you may be sure of it. Remember the Proverb, *They say and do not: but the Kingdom of God is not in word, but in power.* He *talketh* of Prayer, of Repentance, of Faith, and of the New-birth: but he knows but only to *talk* of them. I have been in his Family, and have observed him both at home and 20 abroad; and I know what I say of him is the truth. His house is as empty of Religion, *as the white of an Egg is of savour.* There is there, neither Prayer, nor sign of Repentance for sin: Yea, the bruit in his kind serves God far better than he. He is the very stain, reproach, and shame of Religion to all that know him; it can hardly have a good word in all that end of the Town where he dwells, through him. Thus say the common People that know him, *A* Saint *abroad, and a* Devil *at home*: His poor Family finds it so, he is such a *churl*, 30 such a railer at, and so unreasonable with his Servants, that they neither know how to do for, or speak to him. Men that have any dealings with him, say, 'tis better to deal with a *Turk* then with him, for fairer dealing they shall have at their hands. This *Talkative*, if it be possible, will go beyond them, defraud, beguile, and

Mat. 23.
1 *Cor.* 4. 20.
Talkative *talks, but does not.*

His house is empty of Religion.

He is a stain to Religion, Rom. 2. 24, 25.

The Proverb that goes of him.

Men shun to deal with him.

8 in] on 3, 7   crown, the more of these things he hath in his crown, the more 2   13 *am I* 2 etc.   16 1 Cor. 4. 2 ‖ 5, 6, 8 *etc.* 24 brute 10, 11: Bruit 7   32 or to speak 8 *etc.*   33 'its 4: it's 5, 10, 11   34 *Turk* rom. 1

over-reach them. Besides, he brings up his Sons to follow his steps; and if he findeth in any of them *a foolish timorousness*, (for so he calls the first appearance of a tender conscience) he calls them fools and blockheads; and by no means will imploy them in much, or speak to their commendations before others. For my part I am of opinion, that he has, by his wicked life, caused many to stumble and fall; and will be, if God prevent not, the ruine of many more.

10 Faith. *Well, my Brother, I am bound to believe you; not only because you say you know him, but also because like a Christian, you make your reports of men. For I cannot think that you speak these things of ill will, but because it is even so as you say.*

Chr. Had I known him no more than you, I might perhaps have thought of him as at the first you did: Yea, had he received this report, at *their* hands only, that are enemies to Religion, I should have thought it had been a slander: (A Lot that often falls from bad
20 mens mouths upon good mens names and professions:) But all these things, yea, and a great many more as bad, of my own knowledge I can prove him guilty of. Besides, good men are ashamed of him, they can neither call him *Brother* nor *Friend*: the very naming of him among them, makes them blush, if they know him.

Faith. *Well, I see that Saying, and Doing are two things, and hereafter I shall better observe this distinction.*

Chr. They are two things indeed, and are as diverse *The Carkass* as are the Soul and the Body: For as the Body without *of Religion.*
30 the Soul, is but a dead Carkass; so, *Saying*, if it be alone, is but a dead Carkass also. The Soul of Religion is the practick part: *Pure Religion and undefiled, before God* James 1. 27. *and the Father, is this, To visit the Fatherless and Widows* see ver. 22, *in their affliction, and to keep himself unspotted from the* 23, 24, 25, *World.* This *Talkative* is not aware of, he thinks that 26. *hearing* and *saying* will make a good Christian and thus he deceiveth his own Soul. Hearing is but as the sow-

6 commandations 3   17 *their* rom. 2   24 *Fiend* 4   32
see ver. 22, 23, 24, 25, 26 ‖ 1: *see ver.* 2, 3, 24, 25, 26 ‖ 2–5, 7, 10, 11:
see ver. 23, 24, 25, 26 ‖ 6, 8, 9³, 9⁴

ing of the Seed; talking is not sufficient to prove that fruit is indeed in the heart and life; and let us assure our selves, that at the day of Doom, men shall be judged *See Mat. 13.* according to their fruits. It will not be said then, *Did* *and ch. 25.* *you believe?* but, Were you *Doers*, or *Talkers* only? and accordingly shall they be judged. The end of the world is compared to our Harvest, and you know men at Harvest regard nothing but Fruit. Not that any thing can be accepted that is not of Faith: But I speak this to shew you how insignificant the profession of *Talkative* 10 will be at that day.

Lev. 11.   Faith. *This brings to my mind that of* Moses, *by which* *Deut. 14.* *he describeth the beast that is clean. He is such an one that* *parteth the Hoof, and cheweth the Cud: Not that parteth the* *Faithful con-* *Hoof only, or that cheweth the Cud only. The Hare cheweth* *vinced of the* *the Cud, but yet is unclean, because he parteth not the Hoof.* *badness of* *Talkative. And this truly resembleth* Talkative; *he cheweth the Cud,* *he seeketh knowledge, he cheweth upon the Word, but he* *divideth not the Hoof, he parteth not with the way of sinners;* *but as the Hare he retaineth the foot of a Dog, or Bear, and* 20 *therefore he is unclean.*

Chr. You have spoken, for ought I know, the true Gospel sense of those Texts; and I will add an other *1 Cor. 13. 1,* thing. *Paul* calleth some men, yea, and those great *2, 3 ch. 14. 7.* Talkers too, *sounding Brass, and Tinckling Cymbals*; that *Talkative, like* is, as he Expounds them in another place, *Things without* *to things that* *sound without* *life, giving sound.* Things without life, that is, without *life.* the true Faith and Grace of the Gospel; and conse- quently, things that shall never be placed in the King- dom of Heaven among those that are the Children of 30 life: Though their *sound* by their *talk*, be as if it were the *Tongue*, or voice of an Angel.

Faith. *Well, I was not so fond of his company at first,* *but I am as sick of it now. What shall we do to be rid* *of him?*

Chr. Take my advice, and do as I bid you, and you shall find that he will soon be sick of your Company too, except God shall touch his heart and turn it.

Faith. *What would you have me to do?*

Chr. Why, go to him, and enter into some serious discourse about *the power of Religion*: And ask him plainly (when he has approved of it, for that he will) whether this thing be set up in his Heart, House, or Conversation.

Faith. Then *Faithful* stept forward again, and said to *Talkative: Come, what chear? how is it now?*

Talk. Thank you, well. I thought we should have 10 had a great deal of *Talk* by this time.

Faith. Well, if you will, we will fall to it now; and since you left it with me to state the question, let it be this: How doth the saving Grace of God discover it self, when it is in the heart of man?

Talk. I perceive then that our talk must be *about the* power of things*; Well, 'tis a very good question, and I shall be willing to answer you. And take my answer in brief thus. First, *Where the Grace of God is in the heart, it causeth* there *a great out-cry against sin.* Secondly——

20   Faith. *Nay hold, let us consider of one at once: I think you should rather say, It showes it self by inclining the Soul to abhor its sin.*

Talk. Why, what difference is there between crying out against, and abhoring of sin?

Faith. *Oh! a great deal; a man may cry out against sin, of policy; but he cannot abhor it, but by vertue of a godly antipathy against it: I have heard many cry out against sin in the Pulpit, who yet can abide it well enough in the heart, and house, and conversation.* Josephs *Mistris cried out with 30 a loud voice, as if she had been very holy; but she would willingly, notwithstanding that, have committed uncleanness with him. Some cry out against sin, even as the Mother cries out against her Child in her lap, when she calleth it slut, and naughty Girl, and then falls to hugging and kissing it.*

Talk. You lie at the catch, I perceive.

Faith. *No not I, I am only for seting things right. But what is the second thing whereby you would prove a discovery of a work of grace in the heart?*

Talkatives *false discovery of a work of grace.*

To cry out *against sin, no sign of Grace.*

Gen. 39. 15.

12 *it*² add. 2   25 marg. *They cry out . . . 3: The crying out . . .* grace 11   28–29 *heart, house* 2   37 *would] will* 8 etc.

917.34   G

Talk. Great knowledge of Gospel Mysteries.

Great know-
ledge no sign
of grace.
1 Cor. 13. Faith. *This sign should have been first, but first or last, it is also false; Knowledge, great knowledge may be obtained in the mysteries of the Gospel, and yet no work of grace in the Soul. Yea, if a man have* all *knowledge, he may yet be nothing, and so consequently be no child of God. When Christ said,* Do you know all these things? *And the Disciples had answered,* Yes: *He addeth,* Blessed are ye if ye do them. *He doth not lay the blessing in the knowing of them, but in the doing of them. For there is a* 10 *knowledge that is not attended with doing:* He that knoweth his Masters will and doth it not. *A man may know like an Angel, and yet be no Christian: therefore your sign is not true. Indeed to know, is a thing that pleaseth Talkers and Boasters; but to do, is that which pleaseth God. Not that the heart can be good without knowledge; for without that the heart is naught: There is therefore knowledge,* *Knowledge and*
knowledge. *and knowledge. Knowledge that resteth in the bare speculation of things, and knowledge that is accompanied with the grace of faith and love, which puts a man upon doing even* 20 *the will of God from the heart: the first of these will serve the Talker, but without the other the true Christian is not* *True Know-*
ledge attended
with
endeavours. *content.* Give me understanding, and I shall keep thy Law, yea, I shall observe it with my whole heart, *Psal.* 119. 34.

Talk. You lie at the catch again, this is not for edification.

Faith. *Well, if you please propound another sign how this work of grace discovereth it self where it is.*

Talk. Not I, for I see we shall not agree.   30

Faith. *Well, if you will not, will you give me leave to do it?*

Talk. You may use your Liberty.

One good sign
of grace. Faith. *A work of grace in the soul discovereth it self, either to him that hath it, or to standers by.*

John 16. 8.   *To him that hath it, thus. It gives him conviction of sin,*

---

8 *added* 11   9 *if ye*] that 7   10 *knowing*] knowledge 7
11 *attended*] attained 1   12 doeth 8 *etc.*   14 *is not true*] is it not
true 3: it not true 2: of it is not true 4, 5, 6, 8 *etc.*   20 *put's* 4
24 shall I observe 9⁴ *etc.*   36 thus It gives 9⁴: thus it gives 10, 11

especially of the defilement of his nature, and the sin of — Rom. 7. 24.
unbelief, (for the sake of which he is sure to be damned, if — John 16. 9.
he findeth not mercy at Gods hand by faith in Jesus Christ.) — Mark 16. 16. Psal. 38. 18.
This sight and sense of things worketh in him sorrow and — Jer. 31. 19. Gal. 2. 16.
shame for sin; he findeth moreover revealed in him the — Acts 4. 12.
Saviour of the World, and the absolute necessity of closing — Matth. 5. 6. Rev. 21. 6.
with him, for life, at the which he findeth hungrings and
thirstings after him, to which hungrings, &c. the promise
is made. Now according to the strength or weakness of his
10 *Faith in his Saviour, so is his joy and peace, so is his love*
to holiness, so are his desires to know him more, and also to
serve him in this World. But though I say it discovereth it
self thus unto him; yet it is but seldom that he is able to
conclude that this is a work of Grace, because his corruptions
now, and his abused reason, makes his mind to mis-judge
in this matter; therefore in him that hath this work, there is
required a very sound Judgement, before he can with steddi-
ness conclude that this is a work of Grace.

To others it is thus discovered.

20 *1. By an experimental confession of his Faith in Christ.* — Rom. 10. 10.
2. By a life answerable to that confession, to wit, a life of — Phil. 1. 27. Matth. 5. 9.
holiness; heart-holiness, family-holiness (if he hath a Family) — John 24. 15.
and by Conversation-holiness in the world: which in the — Psal. 50. 20. Job 42. 5, 6.
general teacheth him, inwardly to abhor his sin, and himself — Ezek. 29. 43.
for that in secret, to suppress it in his Family, and to pro-
mote holiness in the World; not by talk only, as an Hypocrite
or Talkative *person may do: but by a practical Subjection in*
Faith, and Love, to the power of the word: And now Sir,
as to this brief description of the work of Grace, and also
30 *the discovery of it, if you have ought to object, object: if not,*
then give me leave to propound to you a second question.

Talk. Nay, my part is not now to object, but to hear, — *Another good*
let me therefore have your second question. — *sign of grace.*

Faith. It is this, *Do you experience the first part of this*
description of it? and doth your life and conversation testifie
the same? or standeth your Religion in Word, or in Tongue,

---

4 Gal. 2. 15 || 1–11   6 Rev. 1. 6 || 5, 6, 8 etc.   19 To . . .
discovered rom. 2 etc.   20 Phil. 8. 17 || 7   22 John 2 || 9³
Ps. 50. 23 || 1   34 the first] this first 2 etc.   36 in² om. 4,
5, 6, 8 etc.

and not in Deed *and* Truth: *pray, if you incline to answer me in this, say no more then you know the God above will say* Amen *to; and also, nothing but what your Conscience can justifie you in.* For, not he that commendeth himself is approved, but whom the Lord commendeth. *Besides, to say I am thus, and thus, when my Conversation, and all my Neighbours tell me, I lye, is great wickedness.*

Talkative not pleased with Faithfuls question. **Talk.** Then *Talkative* at first began to blush, but recovering himself, thus he replyed, You come now to Experience, to Conscience, and God: and to appeals to 10 him for justification of what is spoken: This kind of discourse I did not expect, nor am I disposed to give an answer to such questions, because, I count not my self bound thereto, unless you take upon you to be a *Catechizer*; and, though you should so do, yet I may refuse to make you my Judge: But I pray will you tell me, why you ask me such questions?

Faith. *Because I saw you forward to talk, and because I knew not that you had ought else but notion. Besides, to tell you all the truth, I have heard of you, that you are a* 20 *The reasons why Faithful put to him that question. Man whose Religion lies in talk, and that your conversation gives this your Mouth-profession the lye. They say You are a spot among Christians, and that Religion fareth the worse* *Faithfuls plain dealing to Talkative. for your ungodly conversation, that some already have stumbled at your wicked ways, and that more are in danger of being destroyed thereby; your Religion, and an Ale-house, and Covetousness, and uncleanness, and swearing, and lying, and vain Company-keeping, &c. will stand to- gether. The Proverb is true of you, which is said of a Whore; to wit, That she is a shame to all Women; so you* 30 *are a shame to all Professors.*

Talkative flings away from Faithful. **Talk.** Since you are ready to take up reports, and to judge so rashly as you do; I cannot but conclude you are some peevish, or melancholly man not fit to be dis- coursed with, and so adieu.

Chr. Then came up *Christian* and said to his Brother, I told you how it would happen, your words and his

2 *than* 2   10 appeals] appeal 2 *etc.*   19 *not* om. 2   22 marg. . . . *put him to* 8 *etc.*   29 *is²*] *it* 11   34 melancholick 5, 6, 8, 9³, 10, 11: melanchollick 9⁴

lusts could not agree; he had rather leave your company, then reform his life: but he is gone as I said, let
him go; the loss is no mans but his own, he has saved us *A good*
the trouble of going from him: for he continuing, as *riddance.*
I suppose he will do, as he is, he would have been but
a blot in our Company: besides, the Apostle says, *From
such withdraw thy self.*

Faith. *But I am glad we had this little discourse with
him, it may happen that he will think of it again; however,*
10 *I have dealt plainly with him; and so am clear of his blood,
if he perisheth.*

Chr. You did well to talk so plainly to him as you
did; there is but little of this faithful dealing with men
now a days, and that makes Religion so stink in the
nostrills of many, as it doth: for they are these *Talkative*
Fools, whose Religion is only in word, and are de-
bauched and vain in their Conversation, that (being so
much admitted into the Fellowship of the Godly) do
stumble the World, blemish Christianity, and grieve
20 the Sincere. I wish that all Men would deal with such,
as you have done, then should they either be made more
conformable to Religion, or the company of Saints
would be too hot for them. Then did Faithful say,

> *How* Talkative *at first lifts up his Plumes!*
> *How bravely doth he speak! how he presumes*
> *To drive down all before him! but so soon*
> *As* Faithful *talks of* Heartwork, *like the Moon*
> *That's past the full, into the wain he goes;*
> *And so will all, but he that* Heartwork *knows.*

30 Thus they went on talking of what they had seen
by the way; and so made that way easie, which would
otherwise, no doubt, have been tedious to them: for
now they went through a Wilderness.

Now when they were got almost quite out of this
Wilderness, *Faithful* chanced to cast his eye back, and

---

1 lust 10, 11   2 than 2   4–5 (as I suppose he will do) 2
14 so stink] to stink 1: to stink so 3   19 stumble] puzzle 2   **23**
Then . . . say, *add.* 3   28 *wane* 5 etc.   **34** Now when they
. . . a faithful Creator. (p. 88, l. 2) *add.* 2

espied one coming after them, and he knew him. Oh!
said *Faithful* to his Brother, who comes yonder? Then
Christian looked, and said, It is my good friend *Evangelist.* Ai, and my good friend too, said *Faithful;* for
'twas he that set me the way to the Gate. Now was

Evangelist *Evangelist* come up unto them, and thus saluted them.
overtakes   *Evan.* Peace be with you, dearly beloved, and, peace
them again. be to your helpers.

They are glad   Chr. *Welcome, welcome, my good* Evangelist, *the sight*
at the sight of *of thy countenance brings to my remembrance, thy ancient* 10
him. *kindness, and unwearied laboring for my eternal good.*

Faith. *And, a thousand times welcome, said good* Faithful; *Thy company, O sweet* Evangelist, *how desirable is it
to us, poor Pilgrims!*

Evan. Then, said *Evangelist*, How hath it fared with
you, my friends, since the time of our last parting?
what have you met with, and *how* have you behaved
your selves?

Chr. *Then* Christian, *and* Faithful *told him of all
things that had happened to them in the way; and* how, 20
and with what *difficulty they had arrived to that place.*

His exhorta-   *Evang.* Right glad am I, said *Evangelist*; not that
tion to them. you met with trials, but that you have been victors;
and for that you have (notwithstanding many weak-
nesses,) continued in the way to this very day.

I say, right glad am I of this thing, and that for
John 4. 36. mine own sake and yours; I have sowed, and you have
Gal. 6. 9. reaped, and the day is coming, when both he that
1 Cor. 9. 24,
25, 26, 27. sowed, and they that reaped shall rejoyce together; that
is, if you hold out: for, in due time ye shall reap, if you 30
faint not. The Crown is before you, and it is an incor-
Rev. 3. 11. ruptible one; so run that you may obtain it. Some there
be that set out for this Crown, and after they have gone
far for it, another comes in, and takes it from them;
hold fast therefore that you have, let no man take your
Crown; you are not yet out of the gun-shot of the
Devil: you have not resisted unto blood, striving against
sin: let the Kingdom be always before you, and believe

4 Ay 7   23 you have met 6, 8 *etc.*   29 1 Cor. 9. 24, 25,
29, 27 ‖ 9³   30 you²] ye 8 *etc.*   32 Rev. 3. 14 ‖ 4

stedfastly concerning things that are invisible. Let nothing that is on this side the other world get within you; and above all, look well to your own hearts, and to the lusts thereof; for they are deceitful above all things, and desperately wicked: set your faces like a flint, you have all power in Heaven and Earth on your side.

Chr. *Then *Christian thanked him for his exhortation, but told him withal, that they would have him speak farther to them for their help, the rest of the way; and the rather, for that they well knew that he was a Prophet, and could tell them of things that might happen unto them; and also how they might resist and overcome them. To which request Faithful also consented. So Evangelist began as followeth.* `* They do thank him for his exhortation.`

Evan.* My Sons, you have heard in the words of the truth of the Gospel, that you must through many tribulations enter into the Kingdom of Heaven. And again, that in every City, bonds and afflictions abide in you; and therefore you cannot expect that you should go long on your Pilgrimage without them, in some sort or other. You have found something of the truth of these testimonies upon you already, and more will immediately follow: for now, as you see, you are almost out of this Wilderness, and therefore you will soon come into a Town that you will by and by see before you: and in that Town you will be hardly beset with enemies, who will strain hard but they will kill you: and be you sure that one or both of you must seal the testimony which you hold, with blood: but be you faithful unto death, and the King will give you a Crown of life. *He that shall die there, although his death will be unnatural, and his pain perhaps great, he will yet have the better of his fellow; not only because he will be arrived at the Cœlestial City soonest, but because he will escape many miseries that the other will meet with in the rest of his Journey. But when you are come to the Town, and shall find fulfilled what I have here related, then remember your friend and quit your selves `* He predicteth what troubles they shall meet with in Vanity Fair, and encourageth them to stedfastness.` `* He whose lot it will be there to suffer, will have the better of his brother.`

6 in] on 2   10 marg. . . . exhortations 4, 5, 6, 8, 10, 11   18
in²] on 5, 6, 8 etc.   21 of¹] to 9³

like men; and commit the keeping of your souls to your God, as unto a faithful Creator.

Then I saw in my Dream, that when they were got out of the Wilderness, they presently saw a Town before them, and the name of that Town is *Vanity*; and at the Town there is a *Fair* kept called *Vanity-Fair*: It is kept all the year long, it beareth the name of *Vanity-Fair*, because the Town where tis kept, *is lighter then* Vanity; and also, because all that is there sold, or that cometh thither, is *Vanity*. As is the saying of the wise, 10 *All that cometh is vanity*.

Isa. 40. 17.
Eccles. 1.
ch. 2, 11, 17.

This Fair is no new erected business, but a thing of Ancient standing; I will shew you the original of it. Almost five thousand years agone, there were Pilgrims walking to the Cœlestial City, as these two honest persons are; and *Beelzebub*, *Apollyon*, and *Legion*, with their Companions, perceiving by the path that the Pilgrims made, that their way to the City lay through *this Town* of *Vanity*, they contrived here to set up a Fair; a Fair wherein should be sold of *all sorts of Vanity*, and 20 that it should last all the year long. Therefore at *this Fair* are all such Merchandize sold, as Houses, Lands, Trades, Places, Honours, Preferments, Titles, Countreys, Kingdoms, Lusts, Pleasures, and Delights of all sorts, as Whores, Bauds, Wives, Husbands, Children, Masters, Servants, Lives, Blood, Bodies, Souls, Silver, Gold, Pearls, Precious Stones, and what not.

The Antiquity
of this Fair.

The Merchan-
dise of this
Fair.

And moreover, at this Fair there is at all times to be seen Juglings, Cheats, Games, Plays, Fools, Apes, Knaves, and Rogues, and that of all sorts.   30

Here are to be seen too, and that for nothing, Thefts, Murders, Adultries, False-swearers, and that of a blood-red colour.

And as in other Fairs of less moment, there are the several Rows and Streets under their proper names, where such and such Wares are vended: So here like-

---

2 God in well doing, as 4, 5, 6, 8 *etc.*   6 it is 2   8 Isa. 40. 7 ‖11   Eccles. 1. 4 ch. 2. 11 ‖ 9³: Eccles. 1. 4 ch. 2. 11, 17 ‖ 8, 9⁴ 20 all sorts] every kind 2   31 too *add.* 2   34 the *om.* 4, 5, 6, 8 *etc.*   36 and such *om.* 5, 6, 8 *etc.*

wise, you have the proper Places, Rows, Streets, (*viz.*
Countreys, and Kingdoms) where the Wares of this
Fair are soonest to be found: Here is the *Britain* Row, *The Streets of*
the *French* Row, the *Italian* Row, the *Spanish* Row, the *this fair.*
German Row, where several sorts of Vanities are to be
sold. But as in other *fairs*, some one Commodity is as
the chief of all the *fair*, so the Ware of *Rome* and her
Merchandize is greatly promoted in *this fair*: Only
our *English* Nation, with some others, have taken a dis-
10 like thereat.

Now, as I said, the way to the Cœlestial City lyes just
thorow *this Town*, where this lusty Fair is kept; and
he that will go to the City, and yet not go thorow this
Town, must needs *go out of the World*. The Prince of
Princes himself, when here, went through *this Town* to 1 Cor. 5. 10.
his own Countrey, and that upon a *Fair-day* too: Yea, *Christ went through this*
and as I think it was *Beelzebub*, the chief Lord of this *Fair.*
Fair, that invited him to buy of his *Vanities*; yea, would Matth. 4. 8.
have made him Lord of the *Fair*, would he but have Luk. 4. 5, 6, 7.
20 done him Reverence as he went thorow the *Town*.
Yea, because he was such a person of Honour, *Beelzebub*
had him from *Street* to *Street*, and shewed him all the
Kingdoms of the World in a little time, that he might,
if possible alure that Blessed One, to *cheapen* and
buy some of his *Vanities*. But he had no mind to the *Christ bought*
Merchandize, and therefore left the *Town*; without *nothing in this Fair.*
laying out so much as one Farthing upon these *Vanities*.
This *Fair* therefore is an Ancient thing, of long standing, and a very great *Fair*.

30 Now these Pilgrims, as I said, must needs go thorow *The Pilgrims*
this *Fair*: Well, so they did; but behold, even as they *enter the Fair.*
entred into the *Fair*, all the people in the *Fair* were
moved, and the Town it self as it were in a Hubbub *The Fair in a*
about them; and that for several reasons: For, *hubbub about them.*

First, The Pilgrims were cloathed with such kind of *The first cause*
Raiment, as was diverse from the Raiment of any that *of the hubbub.*
traded in that *fair*. The people therefore of the *fair*

4 marg. *this*] the 4, 5, 6, 8 *etc.*   8 this Fare 5   14 must
ital. 1   16 too *ital*. 1   18 Matth. 4. 8 ‖ 1, 8, 9⁴: Matth. 7. 8 ‖
2–7, 10, 11: Matth. 4. 1 ‖ 9³   28 antient 4

made a great gazing upon them: Some said they were
Fools, some they were Bedlams, and some they are
Outlandish-men.

1 Cor. 2. 7, 8.   Secondly, And as they wondred at their Apparel,
The second so they did likewise at their Speech; for few could under-
cause of the stand what they said; they naturally spoke the Lan-
hubbub. guage of *Canaan*; But they that kept the *fair*, were the
men of this World: So that from one end of the *fair* to
the other, they seemed *Barbarians* each to the other.

Third cause of   Thirdly, But that which did not a little amuse the 10
the hubbub. Merchandizers, was, that these Pilgrims set very light
by all their Wares, they cared not so much as to look
upon them: and if they called upon them to buy, they
Psal. 119. 37. would put their fingers in their ears, and cry, *Turn away*
Phil. 3. 19, 20. *mine eyes from beholding vanity*; and look upwards, signi-
fying that their Trade and Traffick was in Heaven.

Fourth cause of   One chanced mockingly, beholding the carriages of
the hubbub. the men, to say unto them, What will ye buy? but they,
Prov. 23. 23. looking gravely upon him, said, *We buy the Truth*. At
that, there was an occasion taken to despise the men the 20
They are more; some mocking, some taunting, some speaking
mocked.
The fair in reproachfully, and some calling upon others to smite
a hubbub. them. At last things came to an hubbub, and great stir
in the *fair*; insomuch that all order was confounded.
Now was word presently brought to the *great one* of the
fair, who quickly came down, and deputed some of his
They are most trusty friends to take these men into examination,
examined. about whom the *fair* was almost overturned. So the
men were brought to examination; and they that sat
upon them, asked them whence they came, whither 30
they went, and what they did there in such an unusual
* They tell who Garb? **The men told them, that they were Pilgrims
they are and
whence they and Strangers in the world, and that they were going
came. to their own Countrey, which was the Heavenly *Jeru-*
Heb. 11. 13, *salem*; and that they had given none occasion to the
14, 15, 16.

2 are] were 8 *etc.*   4 marg. *The second*] 2d. 1   10 marg.
Third . . . hubbub add. 2: hubub 3   17 marg. *Fourth . . . hubbub* add.
2: hubub 3   22 marg. . . . *hubub* 3   27 those 2   30 whether 1
35 Heb. 11. 13, 14, 15, 16, *add.* 2: Heb. 11. 12, 13, 14, 15, 16 ‖ 5,
6, 8 *etc.*   none] no 2

men of the Town, nor yet to the Merchandizers, thus
to abuse them, and to let them in their Journey. Except
it was, for that, when one asked them what they would
buy, they said, they would *buy the Truth*. But they that *They are not*
were appointed to examine them, did not believe them *believed.*
to be any other then Bedlams and Mad, or else such
as came to put all things into a confusion in the *fair*.
Therefore they took them, and beat them, and be-
smeared them with dirt, and then put them into the *They are put*
10 Cage, that they might be made a Spectacle to all the *in the Cage.*
men of the *fair*. There therefore they lay for some
time, and were made the objects of any mans sport, or
malice, or revenge. The great one of the *fair* laughing *Their*
still at all that befel them. But the men being patient, *behaviour in the Cage.*
and not rendering railing for railing, but contrarywise
blessing, and giving good words for bad, and kindness
for injuries done: Some men in the *fair* that were more *The men of the*
observing, and less prejudiced then the rest, began *Fair do fall out among them-*
to check and blame the baser sort for their continual *selves about*
20 abuses done by them to the men: They therefore in *these two men.*
angry manner let fly at them again, counting them as
bad as the men in the Cage, and telling them that they
seemed confederates, and should be made partakers of
their misfortunes. The other replied, That for ought
they could see, the men were quiet, and sober, and
intended no body any harm; and that there were many
that Traded in their *fair*, that were more worthy to be
put into the Cage, yea, and Pillory too, then were the
men that they had abused. Thus, after divers words
30 had passed on both sides, (the men behaving themselves all the while very wisely, and soberly before
them) they fell to some Blows, among themselves, and
did harm one to another. Then were these two poor *They are made*
men brought before their Examiners again, and there *the Authors of this disturbance.*
charged as being guilty of the late Hubbub that had
been in the *fair*. So they beat them pitifully, and *They are led up*
hanged Irons upon them, and led them in Chaines up *and down the fair in Chaines, for a terror*

4 marg. *They are not in the cage* 11   6 than 2   18 prejudice *to others.*
3, 7   than 2   22 Cages 1   28 than 2   30–31 men themselves behaving themselves 1   32 among themselves *add.* 2

and down the *fair*, for an example and a terror to others, lest any should further speak in their behalf, or joyn themselves unto them. But *Christian and Faithful* behaved themselves yet more wisely, and received the ignominy and shame that was cast upon them, with so *Some of the men* much meekness and patience, that it won to their side *of the fair won* (though but few in comparison of the rest) several of *to them.* the men in the *fair*. This put the other party yet into a *Their adver-* greater rage, insomuch that they concluded the death *saries resolve* of these two men. Wherefore they threatned that the *to kill them.* Cage, nor Irons, should serve their turn, but that they should die, for the abuse they had done, and for deluding the men of the *fair*.

They are again Then were they remanded to the Cage again, until *put into the* further order should be taken with them. So they put *Cage and after brought to* them in, and made their feet fast in the Stocks. *Tryal.* Here also they called again to mind what they had heard from their faithful friend *Evangelist*, and was the more confirmed in their way and sufferings, by what he told them would happen to them. They also now comforted each other, that whose lot it was to suffer, even he should have the best on't; therefore each man secretly wished that he might have that preferment: but committing themselves to the All-wise dispose of him that ruleth all things, with much content they abode in the condition in which they were, until they should be otherwise disposed of.

Then a convenient time being appointed, they brought them forth to their Tryal in order to their Condemnation. When the time was come, they were brought before their Enemies and arraigned; the Judges name was Lord *Hategood*. Their Indictment was one and the same in substance, though somewhat varying in form; the Contents whereof was this.

Their Indict- *That they were enemies to, and disturbers of their Trade;* *ment.* *that they had made Commotions and Divisions in the Town,*

1 and a terror] and terror 2   2 should speak 2   5 ignominy] Ignomy 11   10–11 neither the Cage 11   17 Here also ... disposed of. (l. 27) *add.* 2   also] therefore 9⁴ *etc.*   18 were 5, 6, 8 *etc.*   21–22 suffer, that even 2

and had won a party to their own most dangerous Opinions,
in contempt of the Law of their Prince.

Then *Faithful* began to answer, That he had only set Faithfuls
himself against that which had set it self against him *answer for*
that is higher then the highest. And, said he, As for *himself.*
disturbance, I make none, being my self a man of
Peace; the Party that were won to us, were won, by
beholding our Truth and Innocence, and they are only
turned from the worse to the better. And as to the
10 King you talk of; since he is *Beelzebub*, the Enemy of
our Lord, I defie him and all his Angels.

Then Proclamation was made, that they that had
ought to say for their Lord the King against the
Prisoner at the Bar, should forthwith appear, and give
in their evidence. So there came in three Witnesses, to
wit, *Envy*, *Superstition*, *and Pickthank*. They was then
asked, If they knew the Prisoner at the Bar? and what
they had to say for their Lord the King against him.

Then stood forth *Envy, and said to this effect; My *Envy begins.*
20 Lord, I have known this man a long time, and will
attest upon my Oath before this honourable Bench,
That he is—

Judge. Hold, give him his Oath: So they sware him.
Then he said, My Lord, this man, notwithstanding his
plausible name, is one of the vilest men in our Countrey; He neither regardeth Prince nor People, Law nor
Custom; but doth all that he can to possess all men with
certain of his disloyal notions, which he in the general
calls Principles of Faith and Holiness. And in parti-
30 cular, I heard him once my self affirm, *That Christianity,*
and the Customs of our Town of Vanity, were Diametrically
opposite, and could not be reconciled. By which saying, my
Lord, he doth at once, not only condemn all our laud-
able doings, but us in the doing of them.

Judg. Then did the Judge say to him, Hast thou
any more to say?

Envy. My Lord, I could say much more, only I

5 than 2   7 Parties 2   16 were 2   19 *marg.* Envy
begins add. 3, om. 7   23 swear 3   29 Principle 3   35 to]
unto 11

would not be tedious to the Court. Yet if need be, when the other Gentlemen have given in their Evidence, rather then any thing shall be wanting that will dispatch him, I will enlarge my Testimony against him. So he was bid stand by. Then they called *Superstition*, and bid him look upon the Prisoner; they also asked, What he could say for their Lord the King against him? Then they sware him, so he began.

*Superstition *follows.*   *Super.** My Lord, I have no great acquaintance with this man, nor do I desire to have further knowledge 10 of him; However this I know, that he is a very pestilent fellow, from some discourse that the other day I had with him in this *Town*; for then talking with him, I heard him say, That our Religion was naught, and such by which a man could by no means please God: which sayings of his, my Lord, your Lordship very well knows, what necessarily thence will follow, *to wit*, That we still do worship in vain, are yet in our Sins, and finally shall be damned; and this is that which I have to say.   20

Then was *Pickthank* sworn, and bid say what he knew, in behalf of their Lord the King against the Prisoner at the Bar.

Pickthanks *Testimony.*   *Pick.* My Lord, and you Gentlemen all, This fellow I have known of a long time, and have heard him speak things that ought not to be spoke. For he hath railed on our noble Prince *Beelzebub*, and hath spoke con- *Sins are all* temptibly of his honourable Friends, whose names are *Lords and* the Lord *Old man*, the Lord *Carnal delight*, the Lord *Great ones.* *Luxurious*, the Lord *Desire of Vain-glory*, my old Lord 30 *Lechery*, Sir *Having Greedy*, with all the rest of our Nobility; and he hath said moreover, that if all men were of his mind, if possible, there is not one of these Noble-men should have any longer a being in this Town. Besides, he hath not been afraid to rail on you, my Lord, who are now appointed to be his Judge,

3 than 2   9 *marg.* Superstition *follows* add. 3, om. 7   **10** farther 3, 4, 5   14 nought 10, 11   16 saying 9⁴ *etc.*   **17** *two wit* 1   21 bid] did 10, 11   27–28 spoken contemptibly 8–10: spoken contemptible 11   32 noble Men 1

calling you an ungodly villain, with many other such like vilifying terms, with which he hath bespattered most of the Gentry of our Town. When this *Pickthank* had told his tale, the Judge directed his speech to the Prisoner at the Bar, saying, Thou Runagate, Heretick, and Traitor, hast thou heard what these honest Gentlemen have witnessed against thee.

Faith. *May I speak a few words in my own defence?*

Judg. Sirrah, Sirrah, thou deservest to live no longer, but to be slain immediately upon the place; yet that all men may see our gentleness towards thee, let us hear what thou hast to say.

Faith. 1. I say then in answer to what Mr. *Envy* hath spoken, I never said ought but this, *That what Rule, or Laws, or Custom, or People, were flat against the Word of God, are diametrically opposite to Christianity.* If I have said a miss in this, convince me of my errour, and I am ready here before you to make my recantation. Faithfuls defence of himself.

2. As to the second, to wit, Mr. *Superstition*, and his charge against me, I said only this, *That in the worship of God there is required a divine Faith; but there can be no divine Faith, without a divine Revelation of the will of God: therefore whatever is thrust into the worship of God, that is not agreeable to divine Revelation, cannot be done but by an humane Faith, which Faith will not profit to Eternal Life.*

3. As to what Mr. *Pickthank* hath said, I say, (avoiding terms, as that I am said to rail, and the like) That the Prince of this Town, with all the Rablement his Attendants, by this Gentleman named, are more fit for a being in Hell, then in this Town and Countrey; *and so the Lord have mercy upon me.*

Then the Judge called to the Jury (who all this while stood by, to hear and observe;) Gentlemen of the Jury, you see this man about whom so great an uproar hath been made in this Town: you have also heard what The Judge his speech to the Jury.

<hr>

1 Villian 1: Vilvain 7   2 with] by 1   11 hear] see 1, 2, 7
12 thou vile Runagate hast 4, 5, 6, 8 *etc.*   22 *to divine* 2   25
profit]: be profit 2   *be profitable* 5, 6, 8 *etc.*   30 Gentlemen 1
31 than 2

these worthy Gentlemen have witnessed against him; also you have heard his reply and confession: It lieth now in your brests to hang him, or save his life. But yet I think meet to instruct you into our Law.

Exod. 1. There was an Act made in the days of *Pharaoh* the Great, Servant to our Prince, That lest those of a contrary Religion should multiply and grow too strong for him, their Males should be thrown into the River. Dan. 3. There was also an Act made in the days of *Nebuchadnezzar* the Great, another of his Servants, That whoever would not fall down and worship his golden Image, should be thrown into a fiery Furnace. There was Dan. 6. also an Act made in the days of *Darius*, That who so, for some time, called upon any God but his, should be cast into the Lions Den. Now the substance of these Laws this Rebel has broken, not only in thought, (which is not to be born) but also in word and deed; which must therefore needs be intolerable.

For that of *Pharaoh*, his Law was made upon a supposition, to prevent mischief, no Crime being yet apparent; but here is a Crime apparent. For the second and third, you see he disputeth against our Religion; and for the Treason he hath confessed, he deserveth to die the death.

* *The Jury and their names.* Then went the Jury out, *whose names were Mr. *Blind-man*, Mr. *No-good*, Mr. *Malice*, Mr. *Love-lust*, Mr. *Live-loose*, Mr. *Heady*, Mr. *High-mind*, Mr. *Enmity*, Mr. *Lyar*, Mr. *Cruelty*, Mr. *Hate-light*, and Mr. *Implacable*, who every one gave in his private Verdict against him among themselves, and afterwards unanimously concluded to bring him in guilty before *Every ones* the Judge. And first Mr. *Blind-man*, the foreman, said, *private verdict.* *I see clearly that this man is an Heretick.* Then said Mr. *No-good*, *Away with such a fellow from the Earth.* *Ay,* said Mr. *Malice*, *for I hate the very looks of him.* Then

---

3 breasts 2, 3 : breast 5, 6, 8 *etc.*   4 into] in 8 *etc.*   14 time *om.* 3   his] him 2   19 a *om.* 4, 5, 6, 8 *etc.*   25 marg. *The Jury . . . names* add. 3, om. 7   26 Mr.²] M. 4   27 Mr.³] M. 3 31 conclude 8, 9³, 9⁴   32 marg. *Every . . . verdict* add. 3, om. 7 And first among themselves Mr. *Blindman* 4, 5, 6, 8 *etc.*

said Mr. *Love-lust*, *I could never indure him. Nor I*, said
Mr. *Live-loose*, *for he would always be condemning my
way. Hang him*, *hang him*, said Mr. *Heady*. *A sorry
Scrub*, said Mr. *High-mind*. *My heart riseth against him*,
said Mr. *Enmity*. *He is a Rogue*, said Mr. *Lyar*. *Hanging is too good for him*, said Mr. *Cruelty*. *Lets dispatch
him out of the way*, said Mr. *Hate-light*. Then said Mr.
Implacable, *Might I have all the World given me, I could
not be reconciled to him, therefore let us forthwith bring him
10 in guilty of death*:* And so they did, therefore he was
presently Condemned, To be had from the place where
he was, to the place from whence he came, and there
to be put to the most cruel death that could be invented.

 They therefore brought him out, to do with him
according to their Law; and first they Scourged him,
then they Buffetted him, then they Lanced his flesh
with Knives; after that they Stoned him with Stones,
then prickt him with their Swords, and last of all they
20 burned him to Ashes at the Stake. Thus came *Faithful*
to his end. *Now, I saw that there stood behind the
multitude, a Chariot and a couple of Horses, waiting for
Faithful, who (so soon as his adversaries had dispatched
him) was taken up into it, and straightway was carried
up through the Clouds, with sound of Trumpet, the
nearest way to the Cœlestial Gate. But as for *Christian*,
he had some respit, and was remanded back to prison;
so he there remained for a space: But he that over-rules
all things, having the power of their rage in his own
30 hand, so wrought it about, that *Christian* for that time
escaped them, and went his way.

 And as he went he Sang.

 *Well Faithful, *thou hast faithfully profest
 Unto thy Lord: with him thou shalt be blest;*

Marginal notes:

* *They conclude to bring him in guilty of death.*

The Cruel death of Faithful.

* *A Chariot and Horses wait to take away Faithful.*

Christian is still alive.

* *The Song that Christian made of Faithful after his death.*

---

10 marg. *They . . . death* add. 3, om. 7 17 Lanched 3: lanced 7:
lanched 9⁴ etc. 21 marg. *A Chariot . . . Faithful* add. 3, *om.* 7:
A Chariot om. 4 26 *marg.* Christian *is still alive*] Christian *still
a Prisoner* 4, 5, 6, 8 etc. 32 And . . . Sang. *add.* 3, *om.* 7: And
as he went he sang saying 4, 5, 6, 8 etc. 33 marg. *The Song
. . . death* add. 3, om. 7 34 him] *whom* 2

When Faithless *ones, with all their vain delights,*
Are crying out under their hellish plights.
Sing, Faithful, *sing; and let thy name survive;*
For though they kill'd thee, thou art yet alive.

Now I saw in my Dream, that *Christian* went not
forth alone, for there was one whose name was *Hopeful,*
(being made so by the beholding of *Christian* and *Faith-*
ful in their words and behaviour, in their sufferings at
the *fair*) who joyned himself unto him, and entring
into a brotherly covenant, told him that he would be
his Companion. Thus one died to make Testimony to
the Truth, and another rises out of his Ashes to be
a Companion with *Christian*. This *Hopeful* also told
Christian, that there were many more of the men in the
fair that would take their time and follow after.

So I saw that quickly after they were got out of the
fair, they overtook one that was going before them,
whose name was *By-ends*; so they said to him, What
Countrey-man, Sir? and how far go you this way? He
told them, That he came from the Town of *Fair-speech,*
and he was going to the Cœlestial City, (but told them
not his name.)

From *Fair-speech, said* Christian; *is there any that*
be good live there?

By-ends. Yes, said *By-ends,* I hope.

Chr. *Pray Sir, what may I call you? said Christian.*

By-ends. I am a Stranger to you, and you to me; if
you be going this way, I shall be glad of your Company;
if not, I must be content.

Chr. *This Town of* Fair-speech *said* Christian, *I have*
heard of it, and, as I remember, they say its a Wealthy
place.

By-ends. Yes, I will assure you that it is, and I have
very many Rich Kindred there.

Margin notes: Christian *has* another Com-*panion.* / *There is more* of the men of *the* fair *will* follow. / *They overtake* By-ends. / * Prov. 26. 25. / By-ends *loth to* tell his name.

5 my] may 1   7 so made 2 *etc.*   11 make] bear 4, 5, 6, 8 *etc.*   13 marg. . . . are . . . 4, 5, 6, 8 *etc.*   Christian in his Pilgrimage. This 4, 5, 6, 8 *etc.*   17 was *om.* 2, 7   21 Cælestial 3 23 Prov. 26. 25 *add.* 2   23–24 *that be good live*] *good that lives* 2 *etc.*   26 said Christian add. 3, om. 7   30 *said* Christian *add.* 3, *om.* 7   31 *it om.* 4, 5, 6, 8 *etc.*

Chr. *Pray who are your Kindred there, if a man may be so bold;*

By-ends. Almost the whole Town; and in particular, my Lord *Turn-about*, my Lord *Time-server*, my Lord *Fair-speech*, (from whose Ancestors that Town first took its name:) Also Mr. *Smooth-man*, Mr. *Facing-bothways*, Mr. *Any-thing*, and the Parson of our Parish, Mr. *Two-tongues*, was my Mothers own Brother by Father's side: And to tell you the Truth, I am become a Gentleman of 10 good Quality; yet my Great Grand-father was but a Water-man, looking one way, and Rowing another: and I got most of my estate by the same occupation.

Chr. *Are you a Married man?*

By-ends. Yes, and my Wife is a very Virtuous *The wife and* woman, the Daughter of a Virtuous woman: She was *Kindred of By-ends.* my Lady *Fainings* Daughter, therefore she came of a very Honourable Family, and is arrived to such a pitch of Breeding, that she knows how to carry it to all, even to Prince and Peasant. 'Tis true, we somewhat differ *Where By-ends* 20 in Religion from those of the stricter sort, yet but in *differs from others in* two small points: First, we never strive against Wind *Religion.* and Tide. Secondly, we are always most zealous when Religion goes in his Silver Slippers; we love much to walk with him in the Street, if the Sun shines, and the people applaud it.

Then *Christian* stept a little a toside to his fellow *Hopeful*, saying, It runs in my mind that this is one *By-ends*, of *Fair-speech*, and if it be he, we have as very a Knave in our company, as dwelleth in all these parts. 30 Then said *Hopeful, Ask him; methinks he should not be ashamed of his name.* So *Christian* came up with him again; and said, Sir, you talk as if you knew something more then all the world doth, and if I take not my mark amiss, I deem I have half a guess of you: Is not your name Mr. *By-ends* of *Fair-speech?*

By-ends. That is not my name, but indeed it is a

3–9 Almost ... side: And *add.* 2   9 the *add.* 2   become *add.*
3, *om.* 7   20 but yet 2, 7   25 it] him 4, 5, 6, 8 *etc.* (*see* p. 100,
ll. 24–25; p. 102, ll. 9–10)   26 a toside] atoside 2*etc.* : aside 4,
5, 6, 8 *etc.*   36 This 2

Nick-name that is given me by some that cannot abide me, and I must be content to bear it as a reproach, as other good men have born theirs before me.

How By-ends got his name. Chr. *But did you never give an occasion to men to call you by this name?*

By-ends. Never, never! The worst that ever I did to give them an occasion to give me this name, was, that I had alwayes the luck to jump in my Judgement with the present way of the times, whatever it was, and my chance was to get thereby; but it things are thus cast 10 upon me, let me count them a blessing, but let not the malicious load me therefore with reproach.

Chr. *I thought indeed that you was the man that I had heard of, and to tell you what I think, I fear this name belongs to you more properly then you are willing we should think it doth.*

He desires to keep Company with Christian. By-ends. Well, if you will thus imagine, I cannot help it. You shall find me a fair Company-keeper, if you will still admit me your associate.

Chr. *If you will go with us, you must go against Wind* 20 *and Tide, the which, I perceive, is against your opinion: You must also own Religion in his Rags, as well as when in his Silver Slippers, and stand by him too, when bound in Irons, as well as when he walketh the Streets with applause.*

By-ends. You must not impose, nor Lord it over my Faith; leave me to my liberty, and let me go with you.

Chr. *Not a step further, unless you will do in what I propound, as we.*

Then said *By-ends*, I shall never desert my old Prin- 30 ciples, since they are harmless and profitable. If I may not go with you, I must do as I did before you overtook me, even go by my self, until some overtake me that will be glad of my company.

Now I saw in my dream, that *Christian* and *Hopeful*, forsook him, and kept their distance before him, but one of them looking back, saw three men following

13 *were* 2   13–14 *I heard* 2   15 *than* 2   30 *marg.* By-ends *and* Christian *parts* 4, 7: By-ends . . . *part* 5, 6, 8 *etc.*   35 Now I . . . devouring fire? (p. 106, l. 20) *add.* 3   Now] Then 7

Mr. *By-ends*, and behold, as they came up with him,
he made them a very low *Conje*, and they also gave
him a *Complement*. The mens names were Mr. *Hold-
the-World*, Mr. *Mony-love*, and Mr. *Save-all*; men that
Mr. *By-ends*, had formerly bin acquainted with; for
in their minority they were Schoolfellows, and were
taught by one Mr. *Gripe-man*, a Schoolmaster in *Love-
gain*, which is a market town in the County of *Coveting*
in the North. This Schoolmaster taught them the art
10 of getting, either by violence, cousenage, flattery, lying
or by putting on a guise of Religion, and these four
Gentlemen had attained much of the art of their Master,
so that they could each of them have kept such a School
themselves.

Well when they had, as I said, thus saluted each
other, Mr. *Mony-love* said to Mr. *By-ends*, Who are they
upon the Road before us? for *Christian* and *Hopeful*
were yet within view.

By-ends. They are a couple of far countrey-men,
20 that after *their mode*, are going on Pilgrimage.

Mony-love. Alas, why did they not stay that we might
have had their good company, for *they*, and *we*, and *you*
Sir, I hope, are all going on Pilgrimage.

By-ends. We are so indeed, but the men before us,
are so ridged, and love so much their own notions, and
do also so lightly esteem the opinions of others; that
let a man be never so godly, yet if he jumps not with
them in all things, they thrust him quite out of their
company.

30 Mr. *Save-all*. That's bad; But we read of some, *that
are righteous over-much*, and such mens ridgedness prevails with them to judge and condemn all but themselves. But I pray what and how many, were the things
wherein you differed?

By-ends. Why they after their head-strong manner,

2 *Conjee* 5: *Congee* 6, 8 etc.   3 marg. *He has new Companions* 4 *etc.*
5 been 4 *etc.*   6 School-fellow 3   10 cosenage 7: cozenage
10, 11   19 *marg.* By-ends *Carracter of the* Pilgrims 4: By-ends
Character . . . 5 *etc.*   23 on a Pilgrimage 9⁴ *etc.*   25 rigid 4 *etc.*
26 other 4, 7   30 *Save-all,* that's 3   31 rigidness 4 *etc.*

conclude that it is duty to rush on their Journy *all* weathers, and I am for waiting for *Wind* and *Tide*. They are for hazzarding all for God, at a clap, and I am for taking *all* advantages to secure my life and estate. They are for holding *their notions*, though all other men are against them, but I am for Religion in what, and so far as the times, and my safety will bear it. They are for Religion, when in rags, and contempt, but I am for him when he walks in his golden slipers in the Sun-shine, and with applause. 10

Mr. *Hold-the-world*. Ai, and hold you there still, good Mr. *By-ends*, for, for my part, I can count him but a fool, that having the liberty to keep what he has, shall be so unwise as to lose it. Let us be wise *as Serpents*, 'tis best to make hay when the Sun shines; you see how the Bee lieth still all winter and bestirs her then only when she can have profit with pleasure. God sends sometimes Rain, and sometimes Sunshine; if they be such fools to go through the first, yet let us be content to take fair weather along with us. For my part I like 20 that Religion best, that will stand with the security of Gods good blessings unto us; for who can imagin that is ruled by his reason, since God has bestowed upon us the good things of this life, but that he would have us keep them for his sake. *Abraham* and *Solomon* grew rich in Religion. And *Job* saies, that a good man *shall lay up gold as dust*. He must not be such as the men before us, if they be as you have discribed them.

Mr. *Save-all*. I think that we are all agreed in this matter, and therefore there needs no more words 30 about it.

Mr. *Mony-love*. No, there needs no more words about this matter indeed, for he that believes neither Scripture nor reason (and you see we have both on our side) neither knows his own liberty, nor seeks his own safety.

---

6 are] be 10, 11   9 slippers 4 *etc.*   11 Ay 7, 9[4] *etc.*
12 for, *om.* 10, 11   13 having] leaving 3   14 as[1] *om.* 9[4] *etc.*
wise *ital.* 7   Serpents 4 *etc.*   15 'tis] 'its 4: it's 5 *etc.*   16 then
om. 4 *etc.*   27 *dust.* But he 4 *etc.*

Mr. *By-ends.* My Brethren, we are, as you see, going all on Pilgrimage, and for our better diversion from things that are bad, give me leave to propound unto you this question.

Suppose a man; a Minister, or a Tradesman, &c. should have an advantage lie before him to get the good blessings of this life. Yet so, as that he can by no means come by them, except, in appearance at least, he becomes extraordinary Zealous in some points of Religion, that he medled 10 *not with before, may he not use this means to attain his end, and yet be a right honest man?*

Mr. *Mony-love,* I see the bottom of your question, and with these Gentlemens good leave, I will endeavour to shape you an answer. And first to speak to your question, as it concerns a *Minister* himself. *Suppose a Minister, a worthy man, possessed but of a very small benefice, and has in his eye a greater, more fat, and plump by far; he has also now an opportunity of getting of it; yet so as by being more studious, by preaching more frequently, and zealously,* 20 *and because the temper of the people requires it, by altering of some of his principles, for my part I see no reason but a man may do this (provided he has a call.) Ai, and more a great deal besides, and yet be an honest man.* For why,

1. His desire of a greater benefice is lawful (this cannot be contradicted) since 'tis set before him by providence; so then, he may get it if he can, *making no question for conscience sake.*

2. Besides, his desire after that benefice, makes him more studious, a more zealous preacher, *&c.* and so 30 makes him a better man. Yea makes him better improve his parts, which is according to the mind of God.

3. Now as for his complying with the temper of his people, by disserting, to serve them, some of his principles, this argueth, 1. That he is of a self-denying temper. 2. Of a sweet and winning deportment. 3. And so more fit for the Ministerial function.

8 *in appearance, at least,* 4, 7: *in appearance at least,* 6, 8 etc.   **II**
man. 3–11   18 *of* [2] om. 7   20 *it* om. 7   22 *Ay* 7, 9[4] etc.
33 disserting 5, 9[3]: dissenting 3 *etc.* : deserting 1 [2]   34 safe denying 3: selfe-denying 4

4. I conclude then, that a Minister that changes a *small* for a *great*, should not for so doing, be judged as covetous, but rather, since he is improved in his parts and industry thereby, be counted as one that pursues his call, and the opportunity put into his hand to do good.

And now to the second part of the question which concerns the *Tradesman* you mentioned: suppose such an one to have but a poor imploy in the world, but by becoming Religious, he may mend his market, perhaps 10 get a rich wife, or more and far better customers to his shop. For my part I see no reason but that this may be lawfully done. For why,

1. To become religious is a vertue, by what means soever a man becomes so.

2. Nor is it unlawful to get a rich wife, or more custome to my shop.

3. Besides the man that gets these by becoming religious, gets that which is good, of them that are good, by becoming good himself; so then here is a good wife, 20 and good customers, and good gaine, and all these by becoming religious, which is good. Therefore to become religious to get all these is a good and profitable design.

This answer, thus made by this Mr. *Mony-love*, to Mr. *By-ends'* question, was highly applauded by them all; wherefore they concluded upon the whole, that it was most wholesome and advantagious. And because, as they thought, no man was able to contradict it, and because *Christian* and *Hopeful* was yet within call; they 30 joyfully agreed to assault them with the question as soon as they overtook them, and the rather because they had opposed Mr. *By-ends* before. So they called after them, and they stopt, and stood still till they came up to them, but they concluded as they went, that not *By-ends*, but old Mr. *Hold-the-world* should propound the

---

3 coveteous 3   4 industry, thereby be 10, 11   10 becomin 3
11 for 3, 4: far 5, 6, 8 *etc.*   26 Mr. *By-ends's* question 4, 10: Mr.
By-ends question 5–9⁴: Mr. *By-end's* question 11   30 were 5, 6,
8 *etc.*   31 joyfully] joyntly 4 *etc.*   35–36 *Mr. By-ends* 4 *etc.*

question to them, because, as they supposed, their answer to him would be without the remainder of that heat that was kindled betwixt Mr. *By-ends* and them, at their parting a little before.

So they came up to each other and after a short salutation, Mr. *Hold-the-world* propounded the question to *Christian* and his fellow, and bid them to answer it if they could.

Chr. Then said *Christian*, Even a babe in Religion
10 may answer ten thousand such questions. For if it be unlawful to follow Christ for loaves, as it is, *Joh.* 6. How much more abominable is it to make of him and religion a stalking horse to get and enjoy the world. Nor do we find any other than Heathens, Hypocrites, Devils and Witches that are of this opinion.

1. *Heathens*, for when *Hamor* and *Shechem* had a mind to the Daughter and Cattle of *Jacob*, and saw that there was no waies for them to come at them, but by becoming circumcised, they say to their companions;
20 If every male of us be circumcised, as they are circumcised, shall not their Cattle, and their substance, and every beast of theirs be ours? Their Daughters and their Cattle were that which they sought to obtain, and their Religion the stalking horse they made use of to come at them. Read the whole story, *Gen.* 34. 20, 21, 22, 23.

2. The Hypocritical Pharisees were also of this Religion, long prayers were their pretence, but to get widdows houses were their intent, and greater damnation
30 was from God their Judgment, *Luke* 20. 46, 47.

3. *Judas* the Devil was also of this Religion, he was religious for the bag, that he might be possessed of what was therein, but he was lost, cast away, and the very Son of perdition.

4. *Simon* the witch was of this Religion too, for he would have had the Holy Ghost, that he might have got money therewith, and his sentence from *Peters* mouth was according, *Act.* 8. 19, 20, 21, 22.

---

12 more is it abominable 8 *etc.*   **16** *Hamar* and *Sechem* 11
20 of it 3   **22** Daughter 3–9⁴ : Daughters 10, 11

5. Neither will it out of my mind, but that that man that takes up Religion for the world, will throw away Religion for the world; for so surely as *Judas* designed the world in becoming religious: so surely did he also sell Religion, and his Master for the same. To answer the question therefore affirmatively, as I perceive you have done, and to accept of as authentick such answer, is both Heathenish, Hypocritical and Devilish, and your reward will be according to your works. Then they stood stareing one upon another, but had not wherewith to answer *Christian*. *Hopeful* also approved of the soundness of *Christians* answer, so there was a great silence among them. Mr. *By-ends* and his company also staggered, and kept behind, that *Christian* and *Hopeful* might outgo them. Then said *Christian* to his fellow, if these men cannot stand before the sentence of men, what will they do with the sentence of God? & if they are mute when dealt with by vessels of clay, what will they do when they shall be rebuked by the flames of a devouring fire?

Then *Christian* and *Hopeful* outwent them again, and went till they came at a delicate Plain, called *Ease*, where they went with much content; but that Plain was but *narrow*, so they were quickly got over it. Now at the further side of that Plain, was a little Hill called *Lucre*, and in that *Hill* a *Silver-Mine*, which some of them that had formerly gone that way, because of the rarity of it, had turned aside to see; but going too near the brink of the pit, the ground being deceitful under them, broke, and they were slain; some also had been maimed there, and could not to their dying day be their own men again.

Then I saw in my Dream, that a little off the Road, over against the *Silver-Mine*, stood **Demas*, (*Gentle-man*-like) to call to Passengers to come and see: who said to *Christian* and his fellow; **Ho, turn aside hither, and I will shew you a thing.

The ease that Pilgrims have is but little in this life.

Lucre Hill *a dangerous Hill.*

* Demas *at the* Hill Lucre.

* *He calls to* Christian *and* Hopeful *to come to him.*

21 them again] him 1, 2   29 brink] brim 8 *etc.*   33 off] of 7
34 *marg.* Demas . . . Lucre *add.* 3   35 to² *om.* 5, 6, 8 *etc.*   36
marg. *He . . . him* add. 3

Chr. *What thing so deserving as to turn us out of the way?*

Dem. Here is a Silver-*Mine*, and some digging in it for Treasure; if you will come, with a little paines you may richly provide for your selves.

Hopef. Then said Hopeful, *Let us go see.* Hopeful

Chr. Not I, said *Christian*; I have heard of this place *tempted to go, but* Christian before now, and how many have there been slain; and *holds him back.* besides, that Treasure is a snare to those that seek it, for
10 it hindreth them in their Pilgrimage. Then *Christian* Hos. 4. 18. called to *Demas*, saying, *Is not the place dangerous? hath it not hindred many in their Pilgrimage?*

Dem. Not very dangerous, except to those that are careless: but withal, he *blushed* as he spake.

Chr. Then said *Christian* to *Hopeful*, Let us not stir a step, but still keep on our way.

Hope. *I will warrant you, when* By-ends *comes up, if he hath the same invitation as we, he will turn in thither to see.*
20 *Chr.* No doubt thereof, for his principles lead him that way, and a hundred to one but he dies there.

Dem. Then *Demas* called again, saying, But will you Christian not come over and see? *roundeth up* Demas.

Chr. Then *Christian* roundly answered, saying, *Demas*, Thou art an Enemy to the right ways of the Lord of this way, and hast been already condemned for thine 2 Tim. 4. 10. own turning aside, by one of his Majesties Judges; and why seekest thou to bring us into the like condemnation? Besides, if we at all turn aside, our Lord the King
30 will certainly hear thereof; and will there put us to shame, where we would stand with boldness before him.

Demas cried again, That he also was one of their fraternity; and that if they would tarry a little, he also himself would walk with them.

Chr. Then said *Christian*, What is thy name? is it not the same by the which I have called thee?

De. Yes, my name is *Demas*, I am the Son of *Abraham*.

1–2 *out of the way to see it* 9⁴ *etc.*   8 have there] there have
10, 11   36 the same] it 1

2 Kings 5. 20.
Mat. 26. 14, 15.
chap. 27. 1,
2, 3, 4, 5, 6. *Chr.* I know you, *Gehazi* was your Great Grand-father, and *Judas* your Father, and you have trod their steps. It is but a devilish prank that thou usest: Thy Father was hanged for a Traitor, and thou deservest no better reward. Assure thy self, that when we come to the King, we will do him word of this thy behaviour. Thus they went their way.

By-ends goes over to Demas. By this time *By-ends* and his companions was come again within sight, and they at the first beck went over to *Demas.* Now whether they fell into the Pit, by look-ing over the brink thereof, or whether they went down to dig, or whether they was smothered in the bottom, by the damps that commonly arise, of these things I am not certain: But this I observed, that they never was seen again in the way.

Then Sang Christian,

> *By-ends, and Silver-Demas, both agree;*
> *One calls, the other runs, that he may be*
> *A sharer in his Lucre: so these two*
> *Take up in this World, and no further go.*

They see a strange monu-ment. Now I saw, that just on the other side of this Plain, the Pilgrims came to a place where stood an old *Monument,* hard by the High-way-side, at the sight of which they were both concerned, because of the strangeness of the form therof; for it seemed to them as if it had been a *Woman* transformed into the shape of a Pillar: here therefore they stood looking, and looking upon it, but could not for a time tell what they should make thereof. At last *Hopeful* espied written above upon the head thereof, a Writing in an unusual hand; but he being no Scholar, called to *Christian* (for he was learned) to see if he could pick out the meaning: so he came, and after a little laying of Letters together, he found the same to be this, *Remember Lot's Wife.* So he read it

1 2 Kings 5. 10 ‖ 1   Chap. 27. 1, 2, 3, 4, 5 ‖ 1: chap. 27. 1, 2, 3, 5, 5 ‖ 2: ch. 27. 1, 2, 3, 5, 6 ‖ 3 *etc.*   8 and his companions *add.* 3 were 5, 6, 8 *etc.*   9–14 they] he 1, 2   12 were 5 *etc.*   14 were 5 *etc.*   16 Then Sang Christian, *add.* 2   19 *two*] *do* 3 21 Now I saw ... remember *Lot's* Wife (p. 110, l. 25) *add.* 2   marg. *They ... monument* add. 3

to his fellow; after which, they both concluded, that
that was the *Pillar of Salt into which *Lot's Wife* was *Gen. 19. 26.
turned for her looking back with a *covetous heart*, when
she was going from *Sodom* for safety. Which sudden
and amazing sight, gave them occasion of this discourse.

Chr. Ah my Brother, this is a seasonable sight, it
came opportunely to us after the invitation which *Demas* gave us to come over to view the Hill *Lucre*: and
10 had we gone over as he desired us, and as thou wast
inclining to do (my Brother) we had, for ought I know,
been made our selves a spectacle for those that shall
come after to behold.

Hope. I am sorry that I Was so foolish, and am made
to wonder that I am not now as *Lot's* Wife; for wherein
was the difference 'twixt her sin and mine? she only
looked back, and I had a desire to go see; let Grace
be adored, and let me be ashamed, that ever such a
thing should be in mine heart.

20 *Chr.* Let us take notice of what we see here, for our
help for time to come: *This* woman escaped one Judgment; for she fell not by the destruction of *Sodom*, yet
she was destroyed by another; as we see, she is turned
into a Pillar of Salt.

Hope. True, and she may be to us both *Caution*, and
Example; *Caution* that we should shun her sin, or a sign
of what judgment will overtake such as shall not be prevented by this caution: So *Korah, Dathan*, and *Abiram*,
with the two hundred and fifty men, that perished in
30 their sin, did also become *a sign, or example to others *Numb. 26.
to beware: but above all, I muse at one thing, to wit, 9, 10.
how *Demas* and his fellows can stand so confidently
yonder to look for that treasure, which this Woman,
but for looking behind her, after (for we read not that
she stept one foot out of the way) was turned into
a pillar of Salt; specially since the Judgment which

---

3 back *add.* 3   4 for safety *add.* 3   8–9 *Deman* 3, 7
11 inclined 6, 8 *etc.*   12 made our selves like this woman a spectacle
4, 5, 6, 8, 9³, 9⁴: made like this woman a spectacle 10, 11   28
Korah Dathan 3–11   30 their] the 7   Numb. 26. 19, 0 || 9³

overtook her, did make her an example, within sight of where they are: for they cannot chuse but see her, did they but lift up their eyes.

Chr. It is a thing to be wondered at, and it argueth that their heart is grown desperate in the case; and I cannot tell who to compare them to so fitly, as to them that pick Pockets in the presence of the Judge, or that will cut purses under the Gallows. It is said of the men of *Sodom, That they were sinners** exceedingly*, because they were sinners *before the Lord*; that is, in his eye- sight; and notwithstanding the kindnesses that he had shewed them, for the Land of *Sodom*, was now, like the *Garden of *Eden heretofore*. This therefore provoked him the more to jealousie, and made their plague as hot as the fire of the Lord out of Heaven could make it. And it is most rationally to be concluded, that such, even such as these are, that shall sin in the sight, yea, and that too in despite of such examples that are set continually before them, to caution them to the contrary, must be partakers of severest Judgments.

Hope. Doubtless thou hast said the truth, but what a mercy is it, that neither thou, but especially I, am not made, my self, this example: this ministreth occasion to us to thank God, to fear before him, and always to remember *Lot*'s Wife.

I saw then that they went on their way to a pleasant River, which *David the King* called the *River of God*; but, *John, The River of the water of life*. Now their way lay just upon the bank of the River: here therefore *Christian* and his Companion walked with great delight; they drank also of the water of the River, which was pleasant and enlivening to their weary Spirits: besides, on the banks of this River, on either side, were *green Trees*, that bore all manner of Fruit; and the leaves of the Trees were good for Medicine; with the Fruit of these Trees they were also much delighted; and the leaves they eat to prevent Surfeits, and other Diseases

*Gen. 13. 13.
*Vers. 10.

10

20

A River.
Psal. 65. 9.
Rev. 22.
Ezek. 47.

30

Trees by the River.
The Fruit and leaves of the trees.

5 hearts are 6, 8 *etc.*   the] that 5, 6, 8, *etc.*   17 are, they that
10, 11   34 that bore] therefore 2 : for 3   34–36 and ...
delighted *om.* 2 *etc.*

that are incident to those that heat their blood by *A Meadow in*
Travels. On either side of the River was also a Meadow, *which they lie*
down to sleep.
curiously beautified with Lilies; And it was green all Psal. 23. 2.
the year long. In this Meadow they lay down and slept, Isa. 14. 30.
for here they might *lie down safely.* When they awoke,
they gathered again of the Fruit of the Trees, and drank
again of the Water of the River: and then lay down
again to sleep. Thus they did several days and nights.
Then they sang,

10   *Behold ye how these Christal streams do glide*
    (To comfort Pilgrims) by the High-way side;
    The Meadows green, besides their fragrant smell,
    Yield dainties for them: And he that can tell
    What pleasant Fruit, yea Leaves, these Trees do yield,
    Will soon sell all, that he may buy this Field.

So when they were disposed to go on (for they were
not, as yet, at their Journeys end) they eat and drank,
and departed.

    Now I beheld in my Dream, that they had not
20journied far, but the River and the way, for a time,
parted. At which they were not a little sorry, yet they
durst not go out of the way. Now the way from the
River was rough, and their feet tender by reason of
their Travels; *So the soul of the Pilgrims was much dis-* Numb. 21. 4.
couraged, because of the way. Wherefore still as they
went on, they wished for better way. Now a little before
them, there was on the left hand of the Road, a *Meadow,*
and a Stile to go over into it, and that *Meadow* is called
By-Path-Meadow. Then said *Christian* to his fellow. If *By-Path-*
30this Meadow lieth along by our way side, lets go over into *Meadow.*
it. Then he went to the Stile to see, and behold a Path *One temptation*
does make way
lay along by the way on the other side of the fence. *for another.*
'Tis according to my wish, said *Christian,* here is the
easiest going; come good *Hopeful,* and let us go over. *Strong Chris-*
    Hope. *But how if this Path should lead us out of the way?* *tians may lead*
weak ones out
    Chr. That's not like, said the other; look, doth it not *of the way.*

    3 Ps. 22 || 1–11   5 Isa. 14. 13 || 6, 8 *etc.*   9 Then they
sang, *add.* 2   24 Travels] Trials 7   *Souls* 5, 6, 8 *etc.*   *were* 2, 3 *etc.*
34 lets us 1

go along by the way side? So *Hopeful*, being perswaded
by his fellow, went after him over the Stile. When they
were gone over, and were got into the Path, they found
it very easie for their feet; and withal, they looking
before them, espied a Man walking as they did, (and his
name was *Vain-confidence*) so they called after him, and
asked him whither that way led? he said, To the Cœlestial Gate.* Look, said *Christian*, did not I tell you so?
by this you may see we are right: so they followed, and
he went before them. But behold the night came on, 10
and it grew very dark; so that they that were behind,
lost the sight of him that went before.

He therefore that went before (*Vain-confidence* by
name) not seeing the way before him, fell into a deep
Pit, which was on purpose there made by the Prince of
those grounds, to catch *vain-glorious* fools withall; and
was dashed in pieces with his fall.

Now *Christian* and his fellow heard him fall. So they
called, to know the matter, but there was none to
answer, only they heard a groaning. Then said *Hopeful*, 20
Where are we now? Then was his fellow silent, as
mistrusting that he had led him out of the way. And
now it began to rain, and thunder, and lighten in a very
dreadful manner, and the water rose amain.

Then *Hopeful* groaned in himself, saying, *Oh that
I had kept on my way!*

Chr. Who could have thought that this path should
have led us out of the way?

Hope. *I was afraid on't at very first, and therefore gave
you that gentle caution. I would have spoke plainer, but* 30
that you are older then I.

Chr. Good Brother be not offended, I am sorry I
have brought thee out of the way, and that I have put
thee into such eminent danger; pray my Brother forgive me, I did not do it of an evil intent.

Hope. *Be comforted my Brother, for I forgive thee;
and believe too, that this shall be for our good.*

Marginal notes:

* *See what it is too suddenly to fall in with strangers.*

Isa. 9. 16.
A Pit to catch the vain-glorious in.

Reasoning between Christian and Hopeful.

Christians *repentance for leading of his Brother out of the way.*

8 marg. *See . . . strangers* add. 2   11 were] went 9⁴ etc.   27
would 7   31 *that* om. 10, 11   older] bolder 2   than 2 etc.
32 marg. . . . Bro- 1, 7

Chr. I am glad I have with me a merciful Brother:
but we must not stand thus, let's try to go back again.

Hope. *But good Brother let me go before.*

Chr. No, if you please let me go first; that if there
be any danger, I may be first therein, because by my
means we are both gone out of the way.

Hope. *No,* said Hopeful, *you shall not go first, for your
mind being troubled, may lead you out of the way again.*
Then for their encouragement, they heard the voice of
10 one, saying, *Let thine Heart be towards the High-way,*   Jer. 31. 21.
even the way that thou wentest, turn again. But by this   *They are in*
danger of
time the Waters were greatly risen, by reason of which,   *drowning as*
the way of going back was very dangerous. (Then I   *they go back.*
thought that it is easier going out of the way when we
are in, then going in, when we are out.) Yet they ad-
ventured to go back; but it was so dark, and the flood
was so high, that in their going back, they had like to
have been drowned nine or ten times.

Neither could they, with all the skill they had, get
20 again to the Stile that night. Wherefore, at last, light-
ing under a little shelter, they sat down there till the
day brake; but being weary, they fell asleep. Now there   *They sleep in*
the grounds
was not far from the place where they lay, a *Castle,*   *of Giant*
called *Doubting-Castle,* the owner whereof was *Giant*   Despair.
Despair, and it was in his grounds they now were sleeping; wherefore he getting up in the morning early, and
walking up and down in his Fields, caught *Christian*
and *Hopeful* asleep in his grounds. Then with a *grim*   *He finds them in*
and *surly* voice he bid them awake, and asked them   *his ground, and*
carries them to
30 whence they were? and what they did in his grounds?   Doubting
They told him, they were Pilgrims, and that they had   *Castle.*
lost their way. Then said the *Giant,* You have this
night trespassed on me, by trampling in, and lying on
my grounds, and therefore you must go along with me.
So they were forced to go, because he was stronger then
they. They also had but little to say, for they knew

10 Jer. 31. 21 ‖ 1: Jer. 31. 1 ‖ 2–11   13 *bracket om.* 2   15
than 2   18 drownded 9³   23 marg. *Giant* rom. 9⁴ *etc.*
25 now were] were now 10, 11   28 ground 3   35 than
2, 9³

917.84   I

The Grievous- themselves in a fault. The *Giant* therefore drove them
ness of their
Imprisonment. before him, and put them into his Castle, into a very
dark Dungeon, nasty and stinking to the spirit of these
two men: Here then they lay, from *Wednesday* morning
till *Saturday* night, without one bit of bread, or drop of
drink, or any light, or any to ask how they did. They
were therefore here in evil case, and were far from
Psal. 88. 18. friends and acquaintance. Now in this place, *Christian*
had double sorrow, because 'twas through his unadvised
haste that they were brought into this distress.   10

Now *Giant Despair* had a Wife, and her name was
Diffidence: so when he was gone to bed, he told his Wife
what he had done, to wit, that he had taken a couple of
Prisoners, and cast them into his *Dungeon*, for trespassing on his grounds. Then he asked her also what he
had best to do further to them. So she asked him what
they were, whence they came, and whither they were
bound; and he told her; Then she counselled him, that
when he arose in the morning, he should beat them
without any mercy: So when he arose, he getteth him 20
a grievous Crab-tree Cudgel, and goes down into the
Dungeon to them; and there, first falls to rateing of
them as if they were dogs, although they gave him
never a word of distaste; then he falls upon them, and
On Thursday beats them fearfully, in such sort, that they were not
Giant Despair
beats his able to help themselves, or to turn them upon the floor.
Prisoners. This done, he withdraws and leaves them, there to condole their misery, and to mourn under their distress:
so all that day they spent the time in nothing but sighs
and bitter lamentations. The next night she talking 30
with her Husband about them further, and understanding that they were yet alive, did advise him to
counsel them, to make away themselves: So when
morning was come, he goes to them in a surly manner,
as before, and perceiving them to be very sore with the

1 marg. *their* om. 7   3 spirits 6   5 Ps. 88. 18 || 1 : Psal.
88. 16. || 2–11   6 brink 3   or any light] or light 2 *etc.*   10
haste] counsel 4, 5, 6, 8 *etc.*   11 Now *Giant Despair* . . . in the
morning (p. 117, l. 36) *add.* 2   16 him *om.* 4, 5, 6, 8 *etc.*   22
rateing] beating 3, 7: rating 5, 6, 8 *etc.* (*see* l. 25)   24 then *add.* 3
35 as before *add.* 3

stripes that he had given them the day before; he told
them, that since they were never like to come out of
that place, their only way would be, forthwith to make
*an end of themselves, either with Knife, Halter or
Poison: For why, said he, should you chuse life, seeing
it is attended with so much bitterness. But they desired
him to let them go; with that he looked ugly upon
them, and rushing to them, had doubtless made an end
of them himself, but that he fell into one of his *fits;
10 (for he sometimes in Sun-shine weather fell into fits)
and lost (for a time) the use of his hand: wherefore he
withdrew, and left them, (as before) to consider what
to do. Then did the Prisoners consult between themselves, whether 'twas best to take his counsel or no:
and thus they began to discourse.

*On Friday *Giant* Despair *counsels them to* kill *themselves.*

* *The Giant* sometimes has *fits.*

    Chr. Brother, said *Christian*,* what shall we do? the
life that we now live is miserable: for my part, I know
not whether is best, to live thus, or to die out of hand?
**My soul chuseth strangling rather than life*; and the
20 Grave is more easie for me than this Dungeon: Shall
we be ruled by the Giant?

* Christian *crushed.*

* Job 7. 15.

    Hope. *Indeed our present condition is dreadful, and*
death would be far more welcome to me than thus *for ever*
to abide: but yet let us consider, the Lord of the Country to
which we are going, hath said, Thou shalt do no murther,
no not to another man's person; much more then are we for-
bidden to take his counsel to kill our selves. Besides, he that
kills another, can but commit murder upon his body; but for
one to kill himself, is to kill body and soul at once. And
30 *moreover, my Brother, thou talkest of ease in the Grave;*
but hast thou forgotten the Hell whither, for certain, the
murderers go? for no murderer hath eternal life, &c. And,
let us consider again, that all the Law is not in the hand
of Giant Despair: *Others, so far as I can understand, have*
been taken by him, as well as we; and yet have escaped out
of his hand: Who knows, but that God that made the world,
may cause that Giant Despair *may die; or that, at some*

* Hopeful *comforts him.*

9 them and himself 2   marg. *The Giant . . . fits* add. 3   10 in
Sun-shine weather *add.* 3: in sunshiny weather 8–11   16 *marg.*
Christian *crushed* add. 3   22 *marg.* Hopeful . . . *him* add. 3

time or other he may forget to lock us in; or, but he may in short time have another of his fits before us, and may lose the use of his limbs; and if ever that should come to pass again, for my part, I am resolved to pluck up the heart of a man, and to try my utmost to get from under his hand. I was a fool that I did not try to do it before, but however, my Brother, let's be patient, and endure a while; the time may come that may give us a happy release: but let us not be our own murderers. With these words, Hopeful, *at present did moderate the mind of his Brother; so they con-* 10 *tinued together (in the dark) that day, in their sad and doleful condition.*

Well, towards evening the Giant goes down into the Dungeon again, to see if his Prisoners had taken his counsel; but when he came there, he found them alive, and truly, alive was all: for now, what for want of Bread and Water, and by reason of the Wounds they received when he beat them, they could do little but breath: But, I say, he found them alive; at which he fell into a grievous rage, and told them, that seeing they had dis- 20 obeyed his counsel, it should be worse with them, than if they had never been born.

At this they trembled greatly, and I think that *Christian* fell into a Swound; but coming a little to himself again, they renewed their discourse about the *Giants* counsel; and whether yet they had best to take it or no.

* Christian *Now Christian again seemed to be for doing it, but still dejected. Hopeful made his second reply as followeth.*

* Hopeful Hope. *My Brother, said he, remembrest thou not how comforts him valiant thou hast been heretofore;* Apollyon *could not crush* 30
again, by calling thee, nor could all that thou didst hear, or see, or feel in the former things to Valley of the shadow of Death; what hardship, terror, and remembrance. amazement hast thou already gone through, and art thou now nothing but fear? Thou seest that I am in the Dungeon with thee, a far weaker man by nature than thou art: Also this Giant has wounded me as well as thee; and hath also cut off the Bread and Water from my mouth; and with thee*

1–2 *in a short* 6, 8 *etc.*   24 Swoun 7   27 *marg.* Christian
still dejected add. 3   29 *said he* rom. 10, 11   *marg.* Hopeful . . .
remembrance add. 3   34 *fears* 4, 5, 6, 8 *etc.*   37 *thee*] *that* 9⁴ *etc.*

I mourn without the light: but let's exercise a little more patience. Remember how thou playedst the man at Vanity-Fair, *and wast neither afraid of the Chain nor Cage; nor yet of bloody Death: wherefore let us (at least to avoid the shame, that becomes not a Christian to be found in) bear up with patience as well as we can.*

Now night being come again, and the *Giant* and his Wife being in bed, she asked him concerning the Prisoners, and if they had taken his counsel: To which he replied, They are sturdy Rogues, they chuse rather to bear all hardship, than to make away themselves. Then said she, Take them into the Castle-yard to morrow, and shew them the *Bones* and *Skulls* of those that thou hast already dispatch'd; and make them believe, e're a week comes to an end, thou also wilt tear them in pieces as thou hast done their fellows before them.

So when the morning was come, the *Giant* goes to them again, and takes them into the Castle-yard, and shews them, as his Wife had bidden him. *These, said he, were Pilgrims as you are, once, and they trespassed in my grounds, as you have done; and when I thought fit, I tore them in pieces; and so within ten days I will do you. Go get you down to your Den again; and with that he beat them all the way thither: they lay therefore all day on *Saturday* in a lamentable case, as before. Now when night was come, and when Mrs. *Diffidence*, and her Husband, the *Giant*, were got to bed, they began to renew their discourse of their Prisoners: and withal, the old *Giant* wondered, that he could neither by his blows, nor counsel, bring them to an end. And with that his Wife replied, I fear, said she, that they live in hope that some will come to relieve them, or that they have pick-locks about them; by the means of which they hope to escape. And, sayest thou so, my dear, said the *Giant*, I will therefore search them in the morning.

Well, on *Saturday* about midnight they began to

* On Saturday the Giant threatned, that shortly he would pull them in pieces.

2 *plaidst* 9⁴ *etc.*   3 *nor*¹] *or* 5, 6, 8 *etc.*   18 *Gyants* 9³
24 Go *om.* 6, 8 *etc.*   to] into 10, 11   25 thither: for they 2
26 a *om.* 7   33 hopes 10, 11

pray, and continued in Prayer till almost break of day.

Now a little before it was day, good *Christian*, as one half amazed, brake out in this passionate speech, *What a fool, quoth he, am I, thus to lie in a stinking Dungeon, when I may as well walk at liberty?* I have a *Key* in my bosom, called *Promise*, that will, (I am perswaded) open any Lock in *Doubting-Castle*. Then said *Hopeful*, That's good news; good Brother pluck it out of thy bosom, and try: Then *Christian* pulled it out of his bosom, and began to try at the Dungeon door, whose bolt (as he turned the Key) gave back, and the door flew open with ease, and *Christian* and *Hopeful* both came out. Then he went to the outward door, that leads into the *Castle yard*, and with his Key opened the door also. After he went to the *Iron* Gate, for that must be opened too, but that Lock went *damnable* hard, yet the Key did open it; then they thrust open the Gate to make their escape with speed; but that Gate, as it opened, made such a creaking, that it waked *Giant Despair*, who hastily rising to pursue his Prisoners, felt his Limbs to fail, for his fits took him again, so that he could by no means go after them. Then they went on, and came to the Kings high way again, and so were safe, because they were out of his Jurisdiction.

Now when they were gone over the Stile, they began to contrive with themselves what they should do at that Stile, to prevent those that should come after, from falling into the hands of *Giant Despair*. So they consented to erect there a *Pillar, and to engrave upon the side thereof; *Over this Stile is the way to* Doubting-Castle, *which is kept by* Giant Despair, *who despiseth the King of the Cœlestial Countrey, and seeks to destroy his holy Pilgrims.* Many therefore that followed after, read what was written, and escaped the danger. This done, they sang as follows.

Marginal notes:
A Key in Christians bosom, called Promise, opens any Lock in Doubting Castle.

** A Pillar erected by Christian and his fellow.*

11 Dungion   15 the] that 4, 5, 6, 8 *etc.*   20 cracking 3: craking 4, 5   21 persue 3   22 for ... again *add.* 3   24 again *om.* 3   28 shall 6, 8 *etc.*   30 *marg. A ... fellow* add.   31 thereof this Sentence, *Over* 4, 5, 6, 8 *etc.*   -*Castle* ital. 1, 2: *Doubting-Castle* ital. 3   33 *his*] *the* 4, 5, 6, 8 *etc.*

Out of the way we went, and then we found
What 'twas to tread upon forbidden ground:
And let them that come after have a care,
Lest heedlesness makes them, as we, to fare:
Lest they, for trespassing, his prisoners are,
Whose Castle's Doubting, and whose name's Despair.

They went then, till they came to the delectable *The delectable*
Mountains, which Mountains belong to the Lord of *mountains.*
that Hill of which we have spoken before; so they went
10 up to the Mountains, to behold the Gardens, and *They are re-*
Orchards, the Vineyards, and Fountains of water, where *freshed in the*
also they drank, and washed themselves, and did freely *mountains.*
eat of the Vineyards. Now there was on the tops of
these Mountains, Shepherds feeding their flocks, and
they stood by the high-way side. The Pilgrims therefore went to them, and leaning upon their staves, (as is
common with weary Pilgrims, when they stand to talk
with any by the way,) they asked, *Whose delectable* *Talk with*
Mountains are these? and whose be the sheep that feed *the Shepherds.*
20 upon them?

Shep. These Mountains are *Immanuels Land,* and
they are within sight of his City, and the sheep also are
his, and he laid down his life for them.   Joh. 10. 11.
Chr. *Is this the way to the Cælestial City?*
Shep. You are just in your way.
Chr. *How far is it thither?*
Shep. Too far for any, but those that *shall* get thither
indeed.
Chr. *Is the way safe, or dangerous?*
30 *Shep.* Safe for those for whom it is to be safe, *but*
transgressors shall fall therein.   Hos. 14. 9.
Chr. *Is there in this place any relief for Pilgrims that*
are weary and faint in the way?
Shep. The Lord of these Mountains hath given us Heb. 13. 1, 2.
a charge, *Not to be forgetful to entertain strangers:* Therefore the good of the place is before you.
I saw also in my Dream, that when the *Shepherds*

18 marg. *Talk . . . Shepherds* add. 3   23 John 10. 11 ‖ 1: om.
2 *etc.*   32 Pilgrims 3   36 is even before 1

perceived that they were way-fairing men, they also put questions to them, (to which they made answer as in other places) as, Whence came you? and, How got you into the way? and, By what means have you so persevered therein? For but few of them that begin to come hither, do shew their face on these Mountains. But when the Shepherds heard their answers, being pleased therewith, they looked very lovingly upon them; and said, *Welcome to the delectable Mountains.*

* *The Shep-herds welcome them.*

The Shepherds, I say, whose names were, *Know-* 10 *ledge, Experience, Watchful,* and *Sincere,* took them by the hand, and had them to their Tents, and made them partake of that which was ready at present. They said moreover, We would that you should stay here a while, to acquaint with us, and yet more to solace your selves with the good of these delectable Mountains. They then told them, That they were content to stay; and so they went to their rest that night, because it was very late.

The names of the Shepherds.

Then I saw in my Dream, that in the morning, the 20 Shepherds called up *Christian* and *Hopeful* to walk with them upon the Mountains: So they went forth with them, and walked a while, having a pleasant prospect on every side. Then said the Shepherds one to another, shall we shew these Pilgrims some *wonders? So when they had concluded to do it, they had them first to the top of an Hill, called *Errour,* which was very steep on the furthest side, and bid them look down to the bottom. So *Christian* and *Hopeful* lookt down, and saw at the bottom several men, dashed all to pieces by a fall 30 that they had from the top. Then said *Christian,* What meaneth this? The Shepherds answered; Have you not heard of them that were made to err, by hearkening to *Hymeneus,* and *Philetus,* as concerning the faith of the Resurrection of the Body? They answered, Yes.

* *They are sure wonders.*

The Mountain of Errour.

* *2 Tim. 2. 17, 18.*

9 marg. *The Shepherds ... them* add. 3　　　11 marg. *The names ...*
Shepherds add. 3　　　15 acquaint] be acquainted 2 *etc.*　　　16 these]
the 7　　　17 then *add.* 3　　　25 marg. *They ... wonders* add. 3
28 farthest 5, 6, 8 *etc.*　　　34 2 Tim. 2. 18, 19 *add.* 2: 2 Tim. 2. 17,
18 ‖ 4, 5, 6, 8 *etc.*: Tim. 2. 18, 19 ‖ 3, 7　　　35 yea, 5, 6, 8 *etc.*

Then said the Shepherds, Those that you see lie dashed
in pieces at the bottom of this Mountain, *are they*: and
they have continued to this day unburied (as you see)
for an example to others to take heed how they clamber
too high, or how they come too near the brink of this
Mountain.

Then I saw that they had them to the top of another
Mountain, and the name of that is *Caution; and bid * *Mount
them look a far off: Which when they did, they per- Caution.*
10 ceived, as they thought, several men walking up and
down among the Tombs that were there. And they
perceived that the men were blind, because they
stumbled sometimes upon the Tombs, and because
they could not get out from among them. Then said
Christian, What means this?

The Shepherds then answered, Did you not see a
little below these Mountains a *Stile* that led into
a Meadow on the left hand of this way? They answered, Yes. Then said the Shepherds, From that Stile
20 there goes a path that leads directly to *Doubting-Castle*,
which is kept by *Giant Despair*; and these men (pointing to them among the Tombs) came once on Pilgrimage, as you do now, even till they came to that
same *Stile*. And because the right way was rough in
that place, they chose to go out of it into that Meadow,
and there were taken by Giant *Despair*, and cast into
Doubting-Castle; where, after they had a while been kept
in the Dungeon, he at last did put out their eyes, and
led them among those Tombs, where he has left them
30 to wander to this very day, that the saying of the wise
Man might be fulfilled, *He that wandereth out of the way* Prov. 21.
of understanding, shall remain in the Congregation of the 16.
dead. Then *Christian* and *Hopeful* looked one upon
another, with tears gushing out; but yet said nothing
to the Shepherds.

Then I saw in my Dream, that the Shepherds had
them to another place, in a bottom, where was a door

4 to¹] for 7   8 marg. *Mount* Caution *om.* 2   15 *meant*
2, 3   17 led] lead 11   29 amongst the 9³   31 *marg.* Prov.
21. 26 ‖ 1–11   33 one upon] upon one 2 *etc.*

in the side of an Hill; and they opened the door, and
bid them look in. They looked in therefore, and saw
that within it was very dark, and smoaky; they also
thought that they heard there a lumbring noise as of
fire, and a cry of some tormented, and that they smelt
the scent of Brimstone. Then said *Christian, what
means this?* The Shepherds told them, saying, This is a
A by-way to By-way to Hell, a way that Hypocrites go in at; namely,
Hell. such as sell their Birthright, with *Esau*: such as sell their
Master, with *Judas*: such as blaspheme the Gospel, with 10
Alexander; and that lie, and dissemble, with *Ananias*
and *Saphira* his wife.

Hope. Then said *Hopeful* to the Shepherds, *I perceive that these had on them, even every one, a shew of
Pilgrimage as we have now; had they not?*

Shep. Yes, and held it a long time too.

*Hope. How far might they go on Pilgrimage in their
day, since they notwithstanding were thus miserably cast
away?*

Shep. Some further, and some not so far as these 20
Mountains.

Then said the Pilgrims one to another, *We had need
cry to the Strong for strength.*

Shep. Ay, and you will have need to use it when you
have it, too.

By this time the Pilgrims had a desire to go forwards,
and the Shepherds a desire they should; so they walked
together towards the end of the Mountains. Then said
the Shepherds one to another, Let us here shew to the
Pilgrims the Gates of the Cœlestial City, if they have 30
The Shep- skill to look through our *Perspective Glass. The Pil-
herds Per-* grims then lovingly accepted the motion: So they had
spective-Glass. them to the top of an high Hill called *Clear*, and gave
The Hill them their Glass to look. Then they essayed to look,
Clear. but the remembrance of that last thing that the Shep-
heards had shewed them, made their hands shake; by

1 an] a 6, 8 *etc.*   4 lumbring] rumbling 2   7 saying, om. 2
16 Yea 5, 6, 8 *etc.*   17 on in Pilgrimage 5, 6, 8 *etc.*   22–23 *need
to* cry 4, 5, 6, 8 *etc.*   31 marg. *The ... Glass* add. 2   33 marg.
The Hill Clear *add.* 3   34 assayed 2, 3   36 hand 1, 2

means of which impediment they could not look sted-
dily through the Glass; yet they thought they saw
something like the Gate, and also some of the Glory *The fruit of slavish fear.*
of the place. Then they went away and sang.

> *Thus by the* Shepherds, *Secrets are reveal'd,*
> *Which from all other men are kept conceal'd:*
> *Come to the* Shepherds *then, if you would see*
> *Things deep, things hid, and that mysterious be.*

When they were about to depart, one of the Shep-
10 herds gave them a *note of the way.* Another of them,
bid them *beware of the flatterer. The third *bid them take* ** A two fold Caution.*
heed that they sleep not upon the Inchanted Ground. And
the fourth, *bid them God speed.* So I awoke from my
Dream.

And I slept, and Dreamed again, and saw the same
two Pilgrims going down the Mountains along the
High-way towards the City. Now a little below these
Mountains, on the left hand, lieth the Countrey of *The Country*
Conceit; from which Countrey there comes into the way *of Conceit, out of which came*
20 in which the Pilgrims walked, a little crooked Lane. *Ignorance.*
Here therefore they met with a very brisk Lad, that
came out of that Countrey; and his name was *Ignorance.*
So *Christian* asked him, *From what parts he came? and*
whither he was going?

Ign. Sir, I was born in the Countrey that lieth off *Christian and*
there, a little on the left hand; and I am going to the *Ignorance hath some talk.*
Cœlestial City.

Chr. But how do you think to get in at the Gate, for
you may find some difficulty there?
30 *Ign.* As other good People do, said he.
Chr. But what have you to shew at that Gate, that may
cause that the Gate should be opened unto you?
Ign. I know my Lords will, and I have been a good
Liver, I pay every man his own; I Pray, Fast, pay Tithes,

3 marg....*fruits*...4, 7: *The fruits of servile fear* 5, 6, 8 *etc.*   4
Then...sang *add.* 3: Then...sang this Song 4, 5, 6, 8 *etc.*   11 *bid*²]
bed 7   marg. *A ... Caution add.* 2   13 *bad* 5, 6, 8 *etc.*   18
lieth in 2, 3   25 marg....*have* ...6, 8 *etc.*   30 do] doth 11
saith 4, 5, 6, 8 *etc.*   32 *unto*] *to* 2   33 I² *om.* 4, 5, 6, 8 *etc.*

and give Alms, and have left my Countrey, for whither I am going.

Chr. *But thou camest not in at the Wicket-gate, that is, at the head of this way: thou camest in hither through that same crooked Lane, and therefore I fear, however thou mayest think of thy self, when the reckoning day shall come, thou wilt have laid to thy charge, that thou art a Theif and a Robber, instead of getting admitance into the City.*

He saith to every one, that he is a fool.

Ignor. Gentlemen, ye be utter strangers to me, I know you not, be content to follow the Religion of your Countrey, and I will follow the Religion of mine. I hope all will be well. And as for the Gate that you talk of, all the world knows that that is a great way off of our Countrey. I cannot think that any man in all our parts doth so much as know the way to it; nor need they matter whether they do or no, since we have, as you see, a fine, pleasant, green Lane, that comes down from our Countrey the next way into it.

Pr. 26. 12.
Eccl. 10. 3.
How to carry it to a fool.

When *Christian* saw that the man was wise in his own conceit; he said to *Hopeful,* whisperingly. *There is more hopes of a fool then of him.* And said moreover, *When he that is a fool walketh by the way, his wisdom faileth him, and he saith to every one that he is a fool.* What, shall we talk further with him? or out-go him at present? and so leave him to think of what he hath heard already? and then stop again for him afterwards, and see if by degrees we can do any good of him? Then said *Hopeful,*

> *Let Ignorance a little while now muse*
> *On what is said, and let him not refuse*
> *Good counsel to imbrace, lest he remain*
> *Still ignorant of what's the chiefest gain.*
> *God saith, Those that no understanding have,*
> *(Although he made them) them he will not save.*

10

20

30

1 marg. *The ground of* Ignorance's *hope* add. 4, *om.* 7   8 *getting* add. 2   13 *of om.* 7   18 it] the way 4, 5, 6, 8 *etc.*   19 marg. Prov. 26. 12 ‖ 1, 8 *etc.*: Prov. 26. 11 ‖ 2–7   21 *than* 2   27 *of*] by 9⁴ *etc.*   27–28 Then . . . Hopeful add. 2   33 These 9⁴ *etc.*

Hope. He further added, It is not good, I think to say all to him at once, let us pass him by, if you will, and talk to him anon, *even as he is able to bear it.*

So they both went on, and *Ignorance* he came after. Now when they had passed him a little way, they entered into a very dark Lane, where they met a man Mat. 12. 45. whom seven Devils had bound with seven strong Cords, Prov. 5. 22. and were carrying of him back *to the door* that they saw in the side of the Hill. Now good *Christian* began 10 to tremble, and so did *Hopeful* his Companion: Yet as the Devils led away the man, *Christian* looked to see if he knew him, and he thought it might be one *Turn-* The destruc-*away* that dwelt in the *Town* of *Apostacy.* But he did *tion of one* Turn-away. not perfectly see his face, for he did hang his head like a Thief that is found: But being gone past, *Hopeful* looked after him, and espied on his back a Paper with this Inscription, *Wanton Professor, and damnable Apo-state.* Then said *Christian* to his Fellow, Now I call to Christian remembrance that which was told me of a thing that *telleth his* *Companion a* 20 happened to a good man hereabout. The name of the *story of* Little-man was *Little-Faith,* but a good man, and he dwelt in Faith. the Town of *Sincere.* The thing was this; at the entering in of this passage there comes down from *Broad-way-* Broad-way-*gate,* a Lane, called *Dead-mans Lane;* so called, because *gate.* Deadmans of the Murders that are commonly done there. And Lane. this *Little-Faith* going on Pilgrimage, as we do now, chanced to sit down there and slept. Now there hap-pened at that time, to come down that *Lane* from *Broad-way-gate,* three Sturdy Rogues; and their names 30 were *Faint-heart, Mistrust,* and *Guilt,* (three Brothers) and they espying *Little-faith* where he was, came gallop-ing up with speed: Now the good man was just awaked from his sleep, and was getting up to go on his Journey. So they came all up to him, and with threatning Lan- Little-Faith guage bid him *stand.* At this *Little faith* look'd as white *robbed by* Faint-heart, as a clout, and had neither power to *fight,* nor *flie.* Then Mistrust, *and* Guilt.

1 He further added *add.* 2   4 *Ignorance* rom. 1   8 a
carrying him 9⁴, 10: carrying him 11   9 in] on 2 *etc.*   28 that
Lane] the *Lane* 2, 4 *etc.*   29 Sturdy] hardy 7   32 awakned 7
34 came up all 2   36 or 10, 11

said *Faint-heart*, Deliver thy Purse; but he making
no haste to do it, (for he was loth to lose his Money)
Mistrust ran up to him, and thrusting his hand into his
Pocket, pull'd out thence a bag of Silver. Then he
cried out, Thieves, thieves. With that *Guilt* with a great
Club that was in his hand, strook *Little-Faith* on the
head, and with that blow fell'd him flat to the ground,
where he lay bleeding as one that would bleed to death.
All this while the Thieves stood by. But at last, they
hearing that some were upon the Road, and fearing 10
lest it should be one *Great-grace* that dwells in the City
of *Good-confidence*, they betook themselves to their heels,
and left this good man to shift for himself. Now after a
while, *Little-faith* came to himself, and getting up, made
shift to scrabble on his way. This was the story.

They got away his Silver, and knockt him down.

Hope. *But did they take from him all that ever he had?*

Chr. No: the place where his Jewels were, they
never ransackt, so those he kept still; but as I was
told, the good man was much afflicted for his loss. For
the Thieves got most of his spending Money. That 20
which they got not (as I said) were Jewels, also he had
a little odd Money left, but *scarce* enough to bring him
to his Journeys end; nay, (if I was not mis-informed)
he was forced to beg as he went, to keep himself alive,
(for his Jewels he might not sell.) But beg, and do
what he could, *he went* (as we say) *with many a hungry
belly* the most part of the rest of the way.

Little faith lost not his best things.

1 Pet. 4. 18.

Little-faith forced to beg to his Journeys end.

Hope. *But is it not a wonder they got not from him his
Certificate, by which he was to receive his admittance at
the Cœlestial gate?*   30

Chr. 'Tis a wonder, but they got not that; though
they mist it not through any good cunning of his, for
he being dismayed with their coming upon him, had
neither power nor skill to hide any thing; so 'twas more
by good Providence then by his Indeavour, that they
mist of *that good thing*.

He kept not his best things by his own cunning.

2 Tim. 1. 14.

6 struck 3   8 where] were 1, 3, 4   11 least 4, 10, 11
13–14 Now . . . and] who 10, 11   15 scrable 4, 7: scramble 5, 6,
8 etc.   17 were 3   31 'Tis . . . but] No, 1   32 they]
thy 1   35 than 2

Hope. *But it must needs be a comfort to him, that they got not this Jewel from him.*

Chr. It might have been great comfort to him, had 2 Pet. 1. 19.
he used it as he should; but they that told me the story,
said, That he made but little use of it all the rest of the
way; and that because of the dismay that he had in
their taking away his Money: indeed he forgot it a great
part of the rest of the Journey; and besides, when at
any time, it came into his mind, and he began to be
10 comforted therewith, then would fresh thoughts of his
loss come again upon him, and those thoughts would
swallow up all.

Hope. *Alas poor Man! this could not but be a great
grief unto him.*

Chr. Grief! Ay, a grief indeed! would it not *He is pitied*
been so to any of us, had we been used as he, to be *by both.*
Robbed and wounded too, and that in a strange place,
as he was? 'Tis a wonder he did not die with grief,
poor heart! I was told, that he scattered almost all the
20 rest of the way with nothing but doleful and bitter complaints. Telling also to all that over-took him, or that
he over-took in the way as he went, where he was
Robbed, and how; who they were that did it, and what
he lost; how he was wounded, and that he hardly
escaped with life.

Hope. *But 'tis a wonder that his necessities did not put
him upon* selling, *or pawning some of his Jewels, that he
might have wherewith to relieve himself in his Journey.*

Chr. Thou talkest like one, upon whose head is the *Christian*
30 Shell to this very day: For what should he *pawn* them? *snibbeth his*
or to whom should he sell them? In all that Countrey *fellow for*
 unadvised
where he was Robbed his Jewels were not accounted of, *speaking.*
nor did he want that relief which could from thence be
administred to him; besides, had his Jewels been
missing at the Gate of the Cœlestial City, he had (and
that he knew well enough) been excluded from an

2 *this Jewels* 2: *his Jewels* 3: *his Jewel* 10   3 2 Pet. 19 ‖ 1–11
6–7 in the taking away of his mony 7: in the taking away his money 9⁴ *etc.*
8 the²] his 2 *etc.*   15 a²] have 2 *etc.*   26 *necessity* 2   28 *therewith* 5, 6, 8–10

Inheritance there; and that would have been worse to him then the appearance, and villany of ten thousand Thieves.

Heb. 12. 16. Hope. *Why art thou so tart my Brother? Esau* sold his Birth-right, *and that for a mess of Pottage; and that Birth-right was his greatest Jewel: and if he, why might not* Little-Faith *do so too?*

A discourse about Esau and Little-Faith. Chr. *Esau* did sell his Birth-right indeed, and so do many besides; and by so doing, exclude themselves from the chief blessing, as also that *Caytiff* did. But you must put a difference betwixt *Esau* and *Little-Faith,* and also betwixt their Estates. *Esau's* Birth-right was Typical, but *Little-Faith's* Jewels were not so. *Esau's* belly was his God, but *Little-Faith's* belly was Esau was ruled by his lusts. Gen. 25. 32. not so. *Esau's* want lay in his fleshly appetite, *Little-Faith's* did not so. Besides, *Esau* could see no further then to the fulfilling of his lusts; *For I am at the point to dye,* said he, *and what good will this Birth-right do me?* But *Little-Faith,* though it was his lot to have but a *little faith,* was by his *little faith* kept from such extravagancies; and made to *see* and *prize* his Jewels more, Esau never had Faith. then to sell them, as *Esau* did his Birth-right. You read not any where that *Esau* had *Faith,* no not so much as a *little:* Therefore no marvel, if where the flesh only bears sway (as it will in that man where *no* Faith is to resist) if he sells his *Birth-right,* and his Soul and all, and that to the Devil of Hell; for it is with such, as it Jer. 2. 24. is with the Ass, *Who in her occasions cannot be turned away.* When their minds are set upon their Lusts, they Little-Faith could not live upon Esaus Pottage. will have them what ever they cost. But *Little-faith* was of another temper, his mind was on things Divine; his livelyhood was upon things that were Spiritual, and from above; Therefore to what end should he that is of such a temper sell his Jewels, (had there been any that would have bought them) to fill his mind with empty things? Will a man give a penny to fill his belly with A comparison between the Turtle-dove and the Crow. Hay? or can you perswade the *Turtle-dove* to live upon Carrion, like the *Crow?* Though *faithless* ones can for

2 than 2   17 than 2   Lust 11   19–20 a *littlefaith* 1
28 *marg.* Jer. 1. 24 ‖ 5, 6, 8 *etc.*   29 Lust 9⁴ *etc.*

carnal Lusts, pawn, or morgage, or sell what they have, and themselves out right to boot; yet they that have *faith, saving faith*, though but a *little* of it, cannot do so. Here therefore, my Brother, is thy mistake.

Hope. *I acknowledge it; but yet your severe reflection had almost made me angry.*

Chr. Why, I did but compare thee to some of the Birds that are of the brisker sort, who will run to and fro in untrodden paths with the shell upon their heads: 10 but pass by that, and consider the matter under debate, and all shall be well betwixt thee and me.

Hope. *But Christian, These three fellows, I am perswaded in my heart, are but a company of Cowards: would they have run else, think you, as they did, at the noise of one that was coming on the road? Why did not* Little-faith *pluck up a greater heart? He might, methinks, have stood one brush with them, and have yielded when there had been no remedy.* Hopeful swaggers.

Chr. That they are Cowards, many have said, but 20 few have found it so in the time of Trial. As for *a great heart, Little-faith* had none; and I perceive by thee, my Brother, hadst thou been the Man concerned, thou art but for a brush, and then to yield. And verily, since this is the height of thy Stomach, now they are at a distance from us, should they appear to thee, as they did to him, they might put thee to second thoughts. No great heart for God, where there is but little faith. We have more courage when out, then when we are in.

But consider again, they are but Journey-men Thieves, they serve under the King of the Bottomless pit; who, if need be, will come in to their aid himself, 30 and his voice is *as the roaring of a Lion.* I my self have been Ingaged as this *Little-faith* was, and I found it a terrible thing. These three Villains set upon me, and I beginning like a *Christian* to resist, they gave but a call and in came their Master: I would, as the saying is, have given my life for a penny; but that, as God would have it, I was cloathed with Armour of proof. 1 Pet. 5. 8. Christian tells his own experience in this case.

2 out-right 3: outright 6, 8 *etc.*   9 untrodden] troden 1 (corr. in Errata): trodden 2   16 *great* 1, 9³   24 heighth 3, 7 marg. *We have more courage when we are in* 7   30 Psal. 5. 8 || 1–6, 8 *etc.*: *Psal.* 8. 5 || 7

917.34   K

Ay, and yet, though I was so harnessed, I found it hard work to quit my self like a man; no man can tell what in that Combat attends us, but he that hath been in the Battle himself.

Hope. *Well, but they ran, you see, when they did but suppose that one* Great-Grace *was in the way.*

Chr. True, they often fled, both they and their Master, when *Great-grace* hath but appeared; and no marvel, for he is *the Kings Champion*: But I tro, you will put some difference between *Little-faith* and the Kings *Champion*; all the Kings Subjects are not his Champions: nor can they, when tried, do such feats of War as he. Is it meet to think that a little child should handle *Goliah* as *David* did? or that there should be the strength of an *Ox* in a *Wren*? Some are strong, some are weak, some have *great* faith, some have *little*: this man was one of the weak, and therefore he went to the walls.

The Kings Champion. [margin note]

Hope. *I would it had been* Great-Grace *for their sakes.*

Chr. If it had been he, he might have had his hands full: For I must tell you, that though *Great-Grace* is excellent good at his Weapons, and has, and can, so long as he keeps them at Swords point, do well enough with them: yet if they get within him, even *Faint-heart*, *Mistrust*, or the other, it shall go hard but they will throw up his heels. And when a man is down, you know, what can he do?

Who so looks well upon *Great-graces* face, shall see those Scars and Cuts there that shall easily give demonstration of what I say. Yea once I heard he should say, (and that when he was in the Combat) *We despaired even of life*: How did these sturdy Rogues and their Fellows make *David* groan, mourn, and roar? Yea *Heman* and *Hezekiah* too, though Champions in their day, were forced to bestir them, when by these assaulted; and yet, that notwithstanding, they had their Coats soundly brushed by them. *Peter* upon a time

---

1 harnessed] harmless 9⁴ (*catchword* correctly printed 'harnessed')
2 man²] Men 4, 5   7 have fled 3   30 heard that he 3   34
Haman 3, 4, 5, 7, 9³   36 yet, notwithstanding 2

would go try what he could do; but, though some do
say of him that he is the Prince of the Apostles, they
handled him so, that they made him at last afraid of
a sorry Girle.

Besides, their King is at their Whistle, he is never
out of hearing; and if at any time they be put to the
worst, he, if possible, comes in to help them: And, of
him it is said, *The Sword of him that layeth at him cannot* Job 41. 26.
hold: the Spear, the Dart, nor the Habergeon; he esteemeth
10 *Iron as Straw, and Brass as rotten Wood. The Arrow* Leviathans
cannot make him flie, Sling-stones are turned with him sturdiness.
into stubble, Darts are counted as stubble, he laugheth at
the shaking of a Spear. What can a man do in this case?
'Tis true, if a man could at every turn have *Jobs* Horse,
and had skill and courage to ride him, he might do
notable things. *For his neck is clothed with Thunder, he* The excellent
will not be afraid as the Grashoper, the glory of his Nostrils mettle that is in
is terrible, he paweth in the Valley, rejoyceth in his strength, Job's horse.
and goeth out to meet the armed men. He mocketh at fear,
20 *and is not affrighted, neither turneth back from the Sword.*
The Quiver rattleth against him, the glittering Spear, and
the shield. He swalloweth the ground with fierceness and
rage, neither believeth he that it is the sound of the Trumpet.
He saith among the Trumpets, Ha, ha; and he smelleth
the Battel a far off, the thundring of the Captains, and the
shoutings.
                                                    Job 39. 19.

But for such footmen as thee and I are, let us never
desire to meet with an enemy, nor vaunt as if we could
do better, when we hear of others that they have been
30 foiled, nor be tickled at the thoughts of our own manhood, for such commonly come by the worst when
tried. Witness *Peter*, of whom I made mention before.
He would swagger, Ay he would: He would, as his vain
mind prompted him to say, do better, and stand more
for his Master, then all men: But who so foiled, and
run down with these *Villains* as he?

5 Whistle] While 7   8 Job 41. 25 ‖ 7   9 *hold the Spear,*
1: *hold, the Spear,* 2, 7   17 marg. *metal* 3   36 with these
Villanies 2, 7: with these Villannies 3: with these Villainies 5: by these
Villains 6, 8, 9³, 9⁴: by those Villains 10, 11

When therefore we hear that such Robberies are done on the Kings High-way, two things become us to do: first to go out Harnessed, and to be sure *to take a Shield with us:* For it was for want of that, that he that laid so lustily at *Leviathan* could not make him yield. For indeed, if that be wanting, he fears us not at all. Therefore he that had skill, hath said, *Above all take* Ephes. 6. 16. *the Shield of Faith, wherewith ye shall be able to quench all the fiery darts of the wicked.*

'Tis good to have a Convoy. 'Tis good also that we desire of the King a Convoy, yea that he will go with us himself. This made *David* rejoyce when in the Valley of the shaddows of death; Exod. 33. 15. and *Moses* was rather for dying where he stood, then to Psal. 3. 5, 6, 7, 8. go one step without his God. O my Brother, if he will Psal. 27. 1, 2, 3. but go along with us, what need we be afraid of ten thousands that shall set themselves against us, but with- Isa. 10. 4. out him, *the proud helpers fall under the slain.*

I for my part have been in the fray before now, and though (through the goodness of him that is best) I am as you see alive: yet I cannot boast of my manhood. Glad shall I be, if I meet with no more such brunts, though I fear we are not got beyond all danger. How- ever, since the Lion and the Bear hath not as yet, devoured me, I hope God will also deliver us from the next uncircumcised *Philistine.* Then Sang *Christian.*

> *Poor* Little-Faith! *Hast been among the Thieves!*
> *Wast robb'd! Remember this, Who so believes*
> *And gets more faith, shall then a Victor be*
> *Over ten thousand, else scarce over three.*

So they went on, and *Ignorance* followed. They went then till they came at a place where they saw a *way* put A way and a way. it self into their *way,* and seemed withal, to lie as straight as the way which they should go; and here they knew not which of the two to take, for both seemed straight before them, therefore here they stood still to consider.

8 *the*] this 3   13 Exod. 35. 15 || 6: Exod. 32. 15 || 8 *etc.*   than 2
15 Psal. 27. 1, 2 || 8 *etc.*   17 Isa. 20. 4 || 6: Psa. 10. 4 || 9³   23
hath] have 3   25 *Philistines* 11   Then . . . *Christian add.* 3
28 *get* 2 *etc.*   Faith; *then shall you Victors be,* 2 *etc.*

And as they were thinking about the way, behold, a
man black of flesh, but covered with a very light Robe,
came to them, and asked them, why they stood there?
They answered, They were going to the Cœlestial City,
but knew not which of these ways to take. Follow me,
said the man, it is thither that I am going. So they
followed him in the way that but now came into the
road, which by degrees turned, and turned them so *Christian*
from the City that they desired to go to, that in little *and his fellow deluded.*
10 time their faces were turned away from it; yet they fol-
lowed him. But by and by, before they were aware, he
led them both within the compass of a Net, in which *They are taken*
they were both so entangled, that they knew not what *in a Net.*
to do; and with that, *the white robe fell off the black mans
back*: then they saw where they were. Wherefore there
they lay crying sometime, for they could not get themselves out.

    Chr. Then said *Christian* to his fellow, Now do I see *They bewail.*
my self in an errour. Did not the Shepherds bid us be- *their conditions.*
20 ware of the flatterers? As is the saying of the Wise
man, so we have found it this day: *A man that flattereth* Prov. 29.
his Neighbour, spreadeth a Net for his feet.

    Hope. They also gave us a note of directions about
the way, for our more sure finding thereof: but therein
we have also forgotten to read, and have not kept our
selves from the Paths of the destroyer. Here *David*
was wiser then wee; for saith he, *Concerning the works of
men, by the word of thy lips, I have kept me from the paths* Psal. 17. 4.
of the destroyer. Thus they lay bewailing themselves in
30 the Net. At last they espied a shining One coming
towards them, with a whip of small cord in his hand. *A shining one*
When he was come to the place where they were, he *comes to them with a whip*
asked them whence they came? and what they did *in his hand.*
there? They told him, That they were poor Pilgrims,
going to *Sion*, but were led out of their way by a black
man, cloathed in white; who bid us, said they, follow
him; for he was going thither too. Then said he with

2 marg. *The Flatterer finds them* add. 4, om. 7   **12** both *om.*
4, 5, 6, 8 *etc.*   **18** marg. . . . *condition* 3   **21** man]
men 3   Prov. 29. 6 ‖ 9³ *etc.*   **22** foot 5, 6: *Foot* 8 *etc.*

Prov. 29. 5. the Whip, it is *Flatterer*, a false Apostle, that hath trans-
Dan. 11. 32. formed himself into an Angel of Light. So he rent the
2 Cor. 11. 13, 14. Net and let the men out. Then said he to them, Follow
me, that I may set you in your way again; so he led
them back to the way, which they had left to follow the
They are *Flatterer*. Then he asked them, saying, Where did you
examined, and lie the last night? They said, with the Shepherds upon
convicted of the delectable Mountains. He asked them then, If they
forgetfulness. had not of them Shepherds *a note of direction for the
way?* They answered; Yes. But did you, said he, when 10
you was at a stand, pluck out and read your note?
They answered, No. He asked them why? They said
Deceivers fine they forgot. He asked moreover, If the Shepherds did
spoken. not bid them beware of the *Flatterer?* They answered,
Rom. 16. 18. Yes: But we did not imagine, said they, that this fine-
spoken man had been he.

Deut. 25. 2.   Then I saw in my Dream, that he commanded them
2 Chron. 6. 26, 27. to *lie down*; which when they did, he chastized them
Rev. 3, 19. sore, to teach them the good way wherein they should
They are walk; and as he chastized them, he said, *As many as I* 20
whipt, and sent love, *I rebuke and chasten; be zealous therefore, and repent.*
on their way. love, *I rebuke and chasten; be zealous therefore, and repent.*
This done, he bids them go on their way, and take good
heed to the other directions of the Shepherds. So they
thanked him for all his kindness, and went softly along
the right way, Singing.

> *Come hither, you that walk along the way;*
> *See how the Pilgrims fare, that go a stray!*
> *They catched are in an intangling Net,*
> *'Cause they good Counsel lightly did forget:*
> *'Tis true, they rescu'd were, but yet you see*   30
> *They're scourg'd to boot: Let this your caution be.*

Now after a while, they perceived afar off, one come-
ing softly and alone all along the High-way to meet
them. Then said *Christian* to his fellow, Yonder is a
man with his back toward *Sion*, and he is coming to
meet us.

1 is a *Flatterer* 10, 11   Prov. 29. 4 ‖ 4, 5, 6, 8 *etc.*   9 them]
those 10, 11   11 were 2 *etc.*   17 Deut. 25. 1 ‖ 5, 6, 8, 9³:
Dan. 25. 1 ‖ 9⁴, 10   24 all *ital.* 2 *etc.*   25 Singing *add.* 3
29 *Council* 8–10   *lightly*] *highly* 9⁴ *etc.*   31 *They'er* 3, 4: *They'r* 7

Hope. I see him, let us take heed to our selves now, lest he should prove a *Flatterer* also. So he drew nearer and nearer, and at last came up unto them. His name was *Atheist*, and he asked them whither they were going. *The* Atheist *meets them.*

Chr. *We are going to the Mount* Sion.

Then *Atheist* fell into a very great Laughter. *He Laughs at them.*

Chr. *What is the meaning of your Laughter?*

Atheist. I laugh to see what ignorant persons you 10 are, to take upon you so tedious a Journey; and yet are like to have nothing but your travel for your paines.

Chr. *Why man? Do you think we shall not be received?* *They reason together.*

Atheist. Received! There is no such place as you Dream of, in all this World.

Chr. *But there is in the World to come.*

Atheist. When I was at home in mine own Countrey, I heard as you now affirm, and from that hearing went out to see, and have been seeking this City this twenty Jer. 22. 13. Eccl. 10. 15. years: But find no more of it, then I did the first day 20 I set out.

Chr. *We have both heard and believe that there is such a place to be found.*

Atheist. Had not I, when at home, believed, I had not come thus far to seek: But finding none, (and yet *The* Atheist *takes up his content in this World.* I should, had there been such a place to be found, for I have gone to seek it further then you) I am going back again, and will seek to refresh my self with the things that I then cast away, for hopes of that, which I now see, is not.

30 Chr. Then said *Christian* to *Hopeful* his Fellow, *Is* Christian *proveth his Brother.* *it true which this man hath said?*

Hope. Take heed, he is one of the *Flatterers*; remem- Hopeful's *gracious answer.* ber what it hath cost us once already for our harkning to such kind of Fellows. What! no Mount *Sion?* Did 2 Cor. 5. 7. we not see from the delectable Mountains the Gate of the City? Also, are we not now to walk by Faith? *Let *A remembrance of former chastisements is an help against present temptations.*

4 whether 1   8 *What's* 8 etc.   19 than, 3
30 Fellow] Companion 10, 11   31 *has* 6, 8 etc. marg. . . . pro-
voketh . . . 10, 11   33 *has* 6, 8 etc.   harkening 2: huarkening 3:
hearkening 4, 8, 9³, 9⁴: hearkning 5, 6, 7, 10, 11   36 marg. *A re-*
membrance . . . *temptations* add. 2

us go on, said *Hopeful*, lest the man with the Whip overtakes us again.

You should have taught me that Lesson, which I will round you in the ears withal; *Cease, my Son, to hear the Instruction that causeth to err from the words of knowledge.* I say my Brother, cease to hear him, and let us believe to the saving of the Soul.

Chr. My Brother, I did not put the question to thee, for that I doubted of the Truth of our belief my self: But to prove thee, and to fetch from thee a fruit of the honesty of thy heart. As for *this man, I know that he is blinded by the god of this World: Let thee and I go on knowing that we have belief of the Truth, and no lie is of the Truth.*

Hope. Now do I rejoyce in hope of the glory of God: So they turned away from the man, and he, Laughing at them, went his way.

I saw then in my Dream, that they went till they came into a certain Countrey, whose Air naturally tended to make one drowsie, if he came a stranger into it. And here *Hopeful* began to be very dull and heavy of sleep, wherefore he said unto *Christian*, I do now begin to grow so drowsie, that I can scarcely hold up mine eyes; let us lie down here and take one Nap.

Chr. By no means, said the other, *lest sleeping, we never awake more.*

Hope. Why my Brother? sleep is sweet to the Labouring man; we may be refreshed if we take a Nap.

Chr. Do you not remember, that one of the Shepherds bid us beware of the Inchanted ground? He meant by that, that we should beware of sleeping; wherefore let us not sleep as do others, but let us watch and be sober.

Hope. I acknowledge my self in a fault, and had I been here alone, I had by sleeping run the danger of death. I see it is true that the wise man saith, *Two are better then one.* Hitherto hath thy Company been my mercy; *and thou shalt have a good reward for thy labour.*

Chr. Now then, said Christian, *to prevent drowsiness in this place, let us fall into good discourse.*

Prov. 19. 27.
Heb. 10. 39.

A fruit of an honest heart.

1 Joh. 2. 21.

They are come to the inchanted ground.

Hopeful begins to be drowsie.

Christian keeps him awake.

1 Thes. 5. 6.

He is thankful.

Eccl. 4. 9.

To prevent drowsiness, they fall to good discourse.

12 1 John 2. 11 ‖ 1–11   *God* 3   31 *others do* 7   32 a
add. 2   34 Eccles. 9. 8 ‖ 10, 11   35 *than* 2

Hope. With all my heart, said the other.

Chr. Where shall we begin?

Hope. Where God began with us. But do you begin if you please.

Good discourse prevents drowsiness.

When Saints do sleepy grow, let them come hither,
And hear how these two Pilgrims talk together:
Yea, let them learn of them, in any wise
Thus to keep ope their drowsie slumbring eyes.
Saints fellowship, if it be manag'd well,
10 *Keeps them awake, and that in spite of hell.*

The Dreamers note.

Chr. Then *Christian* began and said, *I will ask you a question.* How *came you to think at first of doing as you do now?

* *They begin at the beginning of their conversion.*

Hope. Do you mean, How came I at first to look after the good of my soul?

Chr. Yes, that is my meaning.

Hope. I continued a great while in the delight of those things which were seen, and sold at our *fair;* things which, as I believe now, would have (had I con-
20 tinued in them still) drownded me in perdition and destruction.

Chr. What things were they?

Hope. All the Treasures and Riches of the World. *Also I delighted much in Rioting, Revelling, Drink- ing, Swearing, Lying, Uncleanness, Sabbath-breaking, and what not, that tended to destroy the Soul. But I found at last, by hearing and considering of things that are Divine, which indeed I heard of you, as also of beloved *Faithful,* that was put to death for his Faith
30 and good-living in *Vanity-fair, That the end of these*

* *Hopeful's life before conversion.*

Rom. 6. 21, 22, 23. Ephes. 5, 6.

4 please.
　　Ch. *I will sing you first this Song.*
　　When . . . 4, 5, 6, 8, etc.
5 marg. *Index finger* add. 3, om. 7　　6 marg. *The Dreamer's note* add. 3　　8 *slumbring* 1, 10, 11: *slumering* 2: *slummering* 3: *slumbering* 7–9⁴　12 *of so doing as* 7: *of doing what* 8 etc.　marg. *They . . . con- version* add. 2　　19 *as om.* 2　　20 drowned 2, 3: drown'd 6, 8, 9³　22 *are* 10, 11　　24 *marg.* Hopeful's . . . *conversion* add. 2: om. 5, 6, 8 etc.

things is death. And that for these things sake the wrath of God cometh upon the children of disobedience.

Chr. And did you presently fall under the power of this conviction?

Hope. No,* I was not willing presently to know the evil of sin, nor the damnation that follows upon the commission of it, but endeavoured, when my mind at first began to be shaken with the word, to shut mine eyes against the light thereof.

* Hopeful *at first shuts his eyes against the light.*

Chr. But what was the cause of your carrying of it thus 10 *to the first workings of Gods blessed Spirit upon you?*

* *Reasons of his resisting of light.*

Hope. *The causes were, 1. I was ignorant that this was the work of God upon me. I never thought that by awaknings for sin, God at first begins the conversion of a sinner. 2. Sin was yet very sweet to my flesh, and I was loth to leave it. 3. I could not tell how to part with mine old Companions, their presence and actions were so desirable unto me. 4. The hours in which convictions were upon me, were such troublesome and such heart-affrighting hours that I could not bear, no not so 20 much as the remembrance of them upon my heart.

Chr. Then as it seems, sometimes you got rid of your trouble.

Hope. Yes verily, but it would come into my mind again; and then I should be as bad, nay worse then I was before.

Chr. Why, what was it that brought your sins to mind again?

Hope. Many things, As,

* *When he had lost his sense of sin, what brought it again.*

1. *If I did but meet a good man in the Streets; or, 30
2. If I have heard any read in the Bible; or,
3. If mine Head did begin to Ake; or,
4. If I were told that some of my Neighbours were sick; or,
5. If I heard the Bell Toull for some that were dead; or,

5 *marg.* Hopeful . . . *light* add. 2: . . . *shut* . . . 6, 8 *etc.*   12 marg.
Reasons . . . *light* add. 2: . . . *the resisting of light* 5, 6, 8, 9[4] *etc.*: . . . *his resisting the light* 7: . . . *the resisting light* 9[3]   25 then²] than 2
30 marg. *When* . . . *again* add. 2   33 If *add.* 2   35 Toull 1: toll 2,
4 *etc.*: tol 3

6. If I thought of dying my self; or,

7. If I heard that suddain death happened to others.

8. But especially, when I thought of my self, that I must quickly come to Judgement.

Chr. *And could you at any time with ease get off the guilt of sin when by any of these wayes it came upon you?*

Hope. No, not latterly, for then they got faster hold of my Conscience. And then, if I did but think of going
10 back to sin (though my mind was turned against it) it would be double torment to me.

Chr. *And how did you do then?*

Hope. I thought I must endeavour to mend my life, *When he could no longer shake off his guilt by sinful courses, then he endeavours to mend.* for else thought I, I am sure to be damned.

Chr. *And did you indeavour to mend?*

Hope. Yes, and fled from, not only my sins, but sinful Company too; and betook me to Religious Duties, as Praying, Reading, weeping for Sin, speaking Truth to my Neighbours, *&c.* These things I did, with many
20 others, too much here to relate.

Chr. *And did you think your self well then?*

Hope. Yes, for a while; but at the last my trouble *Then he thought himself well.* came tumbling upon me again, and that over the neck of all my Reformations.

Chr. *How came that about, since you was now Reformed?*

Hope. There were several things brought it upon *Reformation at last could not help, and why.* me, especially such sayings as these; *All our righteousnesses are as filthy rags, By the works of the Law no man* *Isa. 64. 6.* *Gal. 2. 16.*
30 *shall be justified. When you have done all things, say, We* *Luke 17. 10.* *are unprofitable:* with many more the like: From whence I began to reason with my self thus: If *all* my righteousnesses are filthy rags, if by the deeds of the Law, *no* man can be justified; And, if when we have done *all*, we are yet unprofitable: Then 'tis but a folly to think of heaven by the Law. I further thought thus:

8 latterly] heartily 2   9 of² *om.* 7   12 *do* om. 7   13 marg.
When . . . mend add. 2   15 *amend* 8 *etc.*   19 did 3   22 marg.
Then . . . well add. 2   25 *were* 2   27 marg. *Reformation . . . why*
add. 2   30 Gal. 2. 6 ∥ 5, 6, 8 *etc.*   31 the] such 2

*His being a
debtor by the
Law troubled
him.

*If a man runs an 100*l.* into the Shop-keepers debt, and after that shall pay for all that he shall fetch, yet his old debt stands still in the Book uncrossed; for the which the Shop-keeper may sue him, and cast him into Prison till he shall pay the debt.

Chr. *Well, and how did you apply this to your self?*

Hope. Why, I thought thus with my self; I have by my sins run a great way into Gods Book, and that my now reforming will not pay off that score; therefore I should think still under all my present amendments, But how shall I be freed from that damnation that I have brought my self in danger of by my former transgressions?

Chr. *A very good application: but pray go on.*

Hope. Another thing that hath troubled me, even

*His espying bad
things in his
best duties,
troubled him.*

since my late amendments, is, that if I look narrowly into the best of what I do now, I still see sin, new sin, mixing it self with the best of that I do. So that now I am forced to conclude, that notwithstanding my former fond conceits of my self and duties, I have committed sin enough in one duty to send me to Hell, though my former life had been faultless.

Chr. *And what did you do then?*

*This made him
break his mind
to Faithful,
who told him
the way to be
saved.*

Hope. Do! I could not tell what to do, till I brake my mind to *Faithful;* for he and I were well acquainted: And he told me, That unless I could obtain the righteousness of a man that never had sinned, neither mine own, nor all the righteousness of the World could save me.

Chr. *And did you think he spake true?*

Hope. Had he told me so when I was pleased and satisfied with mine own amendments, I had called him Fool for his pains: but now, since I see my own infirmity, and the sin that cleaves to my best performance, I have been forced to be of his opinion.

1 an 100l.] an hundred pound 3   100l. 8 *etc.*   marg. *His . . . him* add. 2   2–3 yet his . . . stand 3: yet if his . . . stand 4, 5, 6, 8, 9³, 9⁴: yet if this . . . stand 10, 11   4 the which] that 4, 5, 6, 8 *etc.* 10 think] sink 9⁴ *etc.*   16 marg. *His . . . him* add. 2   24 marg. *This . . . saved* add. 2   33 mine 6, 8 *etc.*

Chr. But did you think, when at first he suggested it to you, that there was such a man to be found, of whom it might justly be said, That he never committed sin?

Hope. I must confess the words at first sounded strangely, but after a little more talk and company with him, I had full conviction about it. At which he started at present.

Chr. And did you ask him what man this was, and how you must be justified by him?

Hope. Yes, and he told me it was the Lord Jesus, that dwelleth on the right hand of the most High: *And thus, said he, you must be justified by him, even by trusting to what he hath done by himself in the days of his flesh, and suffered when he did hang on the Tree. I asked him further, How that mans righteousness could be of that efficacy, to justifie another before God? And he told me, He was the mighty God, and did what he did, and died the death also, not for himself, but for me; to whom his doings, and the worthiness of them should be imputed, if I believed on him. Heb. 10.
Rom. 4.
Col. 1.
1 Pet. 1.
* A more particular discovery of the way to be saved.

Chr. And what did you do then?

Hope. I made my objections against my believing, for that I thought he was not willing to save me. He doubts of acceptation.

Chr. And what said *Faithful* to you then?

Hope. He bid me go to him and see: Then I said, It was presumption: but he said, No: for I was invited to come. *Then he gave me a Book of *Jesus* his inditing, to incourage me the more freely to come: And he said concerning that Book, That every jot and tittle there of stood firmer then Heaven and earth. Then I asked him, What I must do when I came? and he told me, I must intreat upon my knees with all my heart and soul, the Father to reveal him to me. Then I asked him further, How I must make my supplication to him? And he said, Go, and thou shalt find him upon a mercy-seat, where he sits all the year long, to give pardon and Mat. 11. 28.
* He is better instructed.
Mat. 24. 35.
Psal. 95. 6.
Dan. 6. 10.
Jer. 29, 12, 13.
Exod. 25. 22.
Lev. 16. 9.
Numb. 7.

---

4 marg. *At ... present* add. 2   8 *how*] *now* 3, 7   11 2 Pet. 1 ‖ 8, 9. Heb. 4. 16.
4, 5, 6, 8 etc.   12 marg. *A ... saved* add. 2   18 me] us
21 marg. *He ... acceptation* add. 2   25 but *om*. 2   26 marg. *He ... instructed* add. 2   29 than 2   Mat. 24. 25 ‖ 1–11   31 Dan. 7. 10 ‖ 8 etc.   34 Lev. 16 (*verse no. faded out*) 1, 5, 7: Lev. 16. 2 ‖ 6, 8 etc. 35 Numb. 7. 89 ‖ 1: Numb. 7. 8 ‖ 2 etc.   Heb. 4. 6 ‖ 1–11

forgiveness to them that come. I told him that I knew

* *He is bid to pray.* not what to say when I came: *and he bid me say to this effect, *God be merciful to me a sinner, and make me to know and believe in Jesus Christ; for I see that if his righteousness had not been, or I have not faith in that righteousness, I am utterly cast away: Lord, I have heard that thou art a merciful God, and hast ordained that thy Son Jesus Christ should be the Saviour of the world; and moreover, that thou art willing to bestow him upon such a poor sinner as I am, (and I am a sinner indeed) Lord take* 10 *therefore this opportunity, and magnifie thy grace in the Salvation of my soul, through thy Son Jesus Christ.* Amen.

Chr. *And did you do as you were bidden?*

Hope. Yes, over, and over, and over.

Chr. *And did the Father reveal his Son to you?*

He prays. Hope. Not at the first, nor second, nor third, nor fourth, nor fifth; no, nor at the sixth time neither.

Chr. *What did you do then?*

Hope. What! why I could not tell what to do.

Chr. *Had you not thoughts of leaving off praying?* 20

* He thought to leave off praying. Hope. *Yes, an hundred times, twice told.

Chr. *And what was the reason you did not?*

* He durst not leave off praying, and why. Hope. *I believed that that was true which had been told me, *to wit*, That without the righteousness of this Christ, all the World could not save me: And therefore thought I with my self, If I leave off, I die; and I can but die at the Throne of Grace. And withall, this came

Habb. 2. 3. into my mind, *If it tarry, wait for it, because it will surely come, and will not tarry.* So I continued Praying untill the Father shewed me his Son. 30

Chr. *And how was he revealed unto you?*

Hope. I did *not* see him with my bodily eyes, but

Ephes. 1. 18, 19. with the eyes of mine understanding; and thus it was. One day I was very sad, I think sader then at any one time in my life; and this sadness was through a fresh

---

2 marg. *He . . . pray* add. 2   **7** *hast*] *has* 9³   **15** *his*] *the* 10, 11

16 marg. *He prays* add. 2   **21** marg. *He . . . praying* add. 2   **23**

been] bin 7   marg. *He . . . why* add. 2   **28** Heb. 2. 3 ‖ 7   **33**

my 8 *etc.*   Eph. 1. 8, 19 ‖ 1   **34** than 2

sight of the greatness and vileness of my sins: And as *Christ is revealed to him, and how.* I was then looking for nothing but *Hell*, and the everlasting damnation of my Soul, suddenly, as I thought, I saw the Lord Jesus look down from Heaven upon me, and saying, *Believe on the Lord Jesus Christ, and thou shalt be saved.* Act. 16. 30, 31.

But I replyed, Lord, I am a great, a very great sinner; and he answered, *My grace is sufficient for thee.* Then 2 Cor. 12. 9. I said But Lord, what is believing? And then I saw 10 from that saying, [*He that cometh to me shall never* John 6. 35. *hunger, and he that believeth on me shall never thirst*] That believing and coming was all one, and that he that came, that is, run out in his heart and affections after Salvation by Christ, he indeed believed in Christ. Then the water stood in mine eyes, and I asked further, But Lord, may such a great sinner as I am, be indeed accepted of thee, and be saved by thee? And I heard him say, *And him that cometh to me, I will in no wise cast* John 6. 37. *out.* Then I said, But how, Lord, must I consider of 20 thee in my coming to thee, that my Faith may be placed aright upon thee? Then he said, *Christ Jesus came into* 1 Tim. 1. 15. *the World to save sinners. He is the end of the Law for* Rom. 10. 4. *righteousness to every one that believes. He died for our* chap. 4. *sins, and rose again for our justification: He loved us, and* Heb. 7. 24, 25. *washed us from our sins in his own blood: He is Mediator* between God and us. *He ever liveth to make intercession for us.* From all which I gathered, that I must look for righteousness in his person, and for satisfaction for my sins by his blood; that what he did in obedience to his Fathers 30 Law, and in submitting to the penalty thereof, was not for himself, but for him that will accept it for his Salvation, and be thankful. And now was my heart full of joy, mine eyes full of tears, and mine affections running over with love, to the Name, People, and Ways of Jesus Christ.

Chr. This was a Revelation of Christ to your soul indeed: But tell me particularly what effect this had upon your spirit?

1 marg. *Christ . . . how* add. 2   8 2 Cor. 12. 9 *om.* 6, 8 *etc.*
10 John 6. 25 ‖ 9³   13 ran 6, 8 *etc.*   18 John 6. 36 ‖ 1: John
6. 16 ‖ 2 *etc.*   26 betwixt 5, 6, 8 *etc.*

Hope. It made me see that all the World, notwith-standing all the righteousness thereof, is in a state of condemnation. It made me see that God the Father, though he be just, can justly justifie the coming sinner: It made me greatly ashamed of the vileness of my former life, and confounded me with the sence of mine own Ignorance; for there never came thought into mine heart before now, that shewed me so the beauty of Jesus Christ. It made me love a holy life, and long to do something for the Honour and Glory of the Name of the Lord Jesus. Yea I thought, that had I now a thousand gallons of blood in my body, I could spill it all for the sake of the Lord Jesus.

I then saw in my Dream, that *Hopeful* looked back and saw *Ignorance,* whom they had left behind, coming after. *Look,* said he, to *Christian, how far yonder Young-ster loitereth behind.*

Chr. Ay, Ay, I see him; he careth not for our Company.

Hope. *But I tro, it would not have hurt him, had he kept pace with us hitherto.*

Chr. That's true, but I warrant you he thinketh otherwise.

Hope. *That I think he doth, but however let us tarry* for him. So they did.

Then *Christian* said to him, *Come away man, why do you stay so behind?*

Ign. I take my pleasure in walking alone, even more a great deal then in Company, unless I like it the better.

Then said *Christian* to *Hopeful,* (but softly) *did I not tell you he cared not for our Company: But however, come up and let us talk away the time in this solitary place.* Then directing his Speech to *Ignorance,* he said, *Come, how do you? how stands it between God and your Soul now?*

Ignor. *I hope well, for I am always full of good motions, that come into my mind to comfort me as I walk.

Young Ignorance comes up again.

Their talk.

Ignorance's hope, and the ground of it.

Chr. *What good motions? pray tell us.*

Ignor. Why, I think of God and Heaven.

Chr. *So do the Devils, and damned Souls.*

Ignor. But I think of them, and desire them.

Chr. *So do many that are never like to come there:* The Soul of the Sluggard desires and hath nothing.

Ignor. But I think of them, and leave all for them.

Chr. *That I doubt, for leaving of all, is an hard matter, yea a harder matter then many are aware of. But why,* 10 *or by what, art thou perswaded that thou hast left all for God and Heaven?*

Ignor. My heart tells me so.

Chr. *The wise man sayes,* He that trusts his own heart is a fool. Prov. 28. 26.

Ignor. That is spoken of an evil heart, but mine is a good one.

Chr. *But how dost thou prove that?*

Ignor. It comforts me in the hopes of Heaven.

Chr. *That may be, through its deceitfulness, for a mans* 20 *heart may minister comfort to him in the hopes of that thing, for which he yet has no ground to hope.*

Ignor. But my heart and life agree together, and therefore my hope is well grounded.

Chr. *Who told thee that thy heart and life agrees together?*

Ignor. My heart tells me so.

Chr. *Ask my fellow if I be a Thief: Thy heart tells thee so! Except the word of God beareth witness in this matter, other Testimony is of no value.*

30 *Ignor.* But is it not a good heart that has good thoughts? And is not that a good life, that is according to Gods Commandments?

Chr. *Yes, that is a good heart that hath good thoughts, and that is a good life that is according to Gods Command-ments: But it is one thing indeed to have these, and another thing only to think so.*

Ignor. Pray, what count you good thoughts, and a life according to Gods Commandments?

13 Prov. 28. 29 ‖ 1–6, 8–11: *om.* 7   18 in hopes 2 *etc.*   24 *agree* 2 *etc.*

Chr. *There are good thoughts of divers kinds, some respecting our selves, some God, some Christ, and some other things.*

Ignor. What be good thoughts respecting our selves?

What are good thoughts. *Chr.* *Such as agree with the Word of God.*

Ignor. When does our thoughts of our selves, agree with the Word of God?

Chr. *When we pass the same Judgement upon our selves which the Word passes: To explain my self. The Word of* **Rom. 3.** *God saith of persons in a natural condition,* There is none 10 Righteous, there is none that doth good. *It saith also,* **Gen. 6. 5.** That every imagination of the heart of man is only evil, and that continually. *And again,* The imagination of mans heart is evil from his Youth. *Now then, when we think thus of our selves, having sense thereof, then are our thoughts good ones, because according to the Word of God.*

Ignor. I will never believe that my heart is thus bad.

Chr. *Therefore thou never hadst one good thought concerning thy self in thy life. But let me go on: As the Word passeth a Judgement upon our HEART, so it passeth a* 20 *Judgement upon our WAYS; and when our thoughts of our HEARTS and WAYS agree with the Judgement which the Word giveth of both, then are both good, because agreeing thereto.*

Ignor. Make out your meaning.

Psal. 125. 5. *Chr.* *Why, the Word of God saith, That mans ways* **Prov. 2. 15.** *are crooked ways, not good, but perverse: It saith, They are* **Rom. 3.** *naturally out of the good way, that they have not known it. Now when a man thus thinketh of his ways, I say when he doth sensibly, and with heart-humiliation thus think, then* 30 *hath he good thoughts of his own ways, because his thoughts now agree with the judgment of the Word of God.*

Ignor. What are good thoughts concerning God?

Chr. *Even (as I have said concerning ourselves) when our thoughts of God do agree with what the Word saith of him. And that is, when we think of his Being and Attributes as the Word hath taught: Of which I cannot now discourse at large. But to speak of him with reference*

5 marg. *What ... thoughts* add. 2   6 do 11   12 Gen. 6. 8 ‖
1–4, 7: Gen. 6. 2 ‖ 5, 6, 8 *etc.*   of a man 8 *etc.*   38 *with*] in 11

to us, Then *we have right thoughts of God, when we think that he knows us better then we know our selves, and can see sin in us, when, and where we can see none in our selves; when we think he knows our in-most thoughts, and that our heart, with all its depths is alwayes open unto his eyes: Also when we think that all our Righteousness stinks in his Nostrils, and that therefore he cannot abide to see us stand before him in any confidence, even of all our best performances.*

10 *Ignor.* Do you think that I am such a fool, as to think God can see no further then I? or that I would come to God in the best of my performances?

Chr. Why, how dost thou think in this matter?

Ignor. Why, to be short, I think I must believe in Christ for Justification.

Chr. How! think thou must believe in Christ, when thou seest not thy need of him! Thou neither seest thy original, nor actual infirmities, but hast such an opinion of thy self, and of what thou doest, as plainly renders thee to be one that 20 *did never see a necessity of Christs personal righteousness to justifie thee before God: How then dost thou say, I believe in Christ?*

Ignor. I believe well enough for all that.

Chr. How doest thou believe?

Ignor. I believe that Christ died for sinners, and that I shall be justified before God from the curse, through his gracious acceptance of my obedience to his Law: Or thus, Christ makes my Duties that are Religious, acceptable to his Father by vertue of his Merits; and 30 so shall I be justified.

Chr. Let me give an answer to this confession of thy faith.

1. *Thou believest with a* Fantastical *Faith, for this faith* The Faith of *is no where described in the* Word.   Ignorance.

2. *Thou believest with a* False *Faith, because it taketh Justification from the personal righteousness of Christ, and applies it to thy own.*

---

2 *than* 2, 9³   4 *we think*] *he thinks* 5, 6, 8, 9³: *he think* 4
6 *stincks* 4   8 *of*] *in* 8, 9³   11 *than* 2   12 *in the*] *i' th'* 9⁴ *etc.*
18 *or* 1   19 *dost* 7   21 *dost*] *durst* 9³: *doest* 9⁴ *etc.*   24 *dost* 2
31 *me*] *us* 6, 8, 9³: *us* 9⁴ *etc.*   32 marg. *The . . .* Ignorance *add.* 2

3. *This faith maketh not Christ a Justifier of thy person, but of thy actions; and of thy person for thy actions sake, which is false.*

4. *Therefore this faith is deceitful, even such as will leave thee under wrath, in the day of God Almighty. For true Justifying Faith puts the soul (as sensible of its lost condition by the Law) upon flying for refuge unto Christs righteousness: (which righteousness of his, is, not an act of grace, by which he maketh for Justification thy obedience accepted with God, but his personal obedience to the Law* 10 *in doing and suffering for us, what that required at our hands.) This righteousness, I say, true faith accepteth, under the skirt of which, the soul being shrouded, and by it presented as spotless before God, it is accepted, and acquit from condemnation.*

Ignor. What! would you have us trust to what Christ in his own person has done without us? This conceit would loosen the reines of our lust, and tollerate us to live as we list: For what matter how we live if we may be Justified by Christs personal righteousness from all, 20 when we believe it?

Chr. Ignorance *is thy name, and as thy name is, so art thou; even this thy answer demonstrateth what I say.* Ignorant *thou art of what Justifying righteousness is, and, as* Ignorant *how to secure thy Soul through the faith of it from the heavy wrath of God. Yea, thou also art* Ignorant *of the true effects of saving faith in this righteousness of Christ, which is, to bow and win over the heart to God in Christ, to love his Name, his Word, Ways and People, and not as thou* ignorantly *imaginest.* 30

Hope. Ask him if ever he had Christ revealed to him from Heaven?

Ignorance angles with them.

Ignor. What! you are a man for revelations! I believe that what both you, and all the rest of you say about that matter, is but the fruit of distracted braines.

Hope. Why man! Christ is so hid in God from the natural apprehensions of all flesh, that he cannot by any man be savingly known, unless God the Father reveals him to them.

Ignor. That is your faith, but not mine; yet mine I doubt not, is as good as yours: though I have not in my head so many whimzies as you. ^{He speaks reproachfully of what he knows not.}

Chr. Give me leave to put in a word: You ought not so slightly to speak of this matter: for this I will boldly affirm, (even as my good Companion hath done) that no man can know Jesus Christ but by the Revelation of
10 the Father: yea, and faith too, by which the soul layeth hold upon Christ (if it be right) must be wrought by the exceeding greatness of his mighty power, the working of which faith, I perceive, poor *Ignorance,* thou art ignorant of. Be awakened then, see thine own wretchedness, and flie to the Lord Jesus; and by his righteousness, which is the righteousness of God, (for he himself is God) thou shalt be delivered from condemnation. ^{Mat. 11. 27. 1 Cor. 12. 3. Eph. 1. 18, 19.}

Ignor. You go so fast, I cannot keep pace with you; do
20 *you go on before, I must stay a while behind.* ^{The talk broke up.}
Then they said,

Well Ignorance, *wilt thou yet foolish be,*
To slight good Counsel, ten times given thee?
And if thou yet refuse it, thou shalt know
Ere long the evil of thy doing so:
Remember man in time, stoop, do not fear,
Good Counsel taken well, saves; therefore hear:
But if thou yet shalt slight it, thou wilt be
The loser (Ignorance) *I'le warrant thee.*

30   Then *Christian* addressed thus himself to his fellow.
Chr. Well, come my good *Hopeful,* I perceive that thou and I must walk by our selves again.

So I saw in my Dream, that they went on a pace before, and *Ignorance* he came hobling after. Then said *Christian* to his Companion, *It pities me much for this poor man, it will certainly go ill with him at last.*

3 marg. *He . . . not* add. 2   8 Mat. 11. 18 || 1: Mat. 11. 28 ||
2 etc.   1 Co. 12. 3 || 1: 1 Cor. 11. 3 || *2 etc.*   21 Then they said
add. 2   27 *saves*] secures 7   29 Ignorance *ital.* 1   30 Then
. . . fellow *add.* 2

Hope. Alas, there are abundance in our Town in his condition; whole Families, yea, whole Streets, (and that of Pilgrims too) and if there be so many in our parts, how many, think you, must there be in the place where he was born?

Chr. Indeed the Word saith, He hath blinded their eyes, lest they should see, *&c. But now we are by our selves, what do you think of such men? Have they at no time, think you, convictions of sin, and so consequently fears that their state is dangerous?* 10

Hope. Nay, do you answer that question your self, for you are the elder man.

Chr. Then, I say, sometimes (as I think) they may, but they being naturally ignorant, understand not that such convictions tend to their good; and therefore they do desperately seek to stifle them, and presumptuously continue to flatter themselves in the way of their own hearts.

The good use of fear. *Hope.* I do believe as you say, that fear tends much to Mens good, and to make them right, at their beginning to go on Pilgrimage. 20

Job 28. 28. *Chr. Without all doubt it doth, if it be right: for so says the*
Psal. 111. 10. *Word,* The fear of the Lord is the beginning of Wisdom.
Prov. 1. 7.
ch. 9, 10. *Hope.* How will you describe right fear?

Right fear. *Chr. True, or right fear, is discovered by three things.*

1. By its rise. It is caused by saving convictions for sin.

2. It driveth the soul to lay fast hold of Christ for Salvation.

3. It begetteth and continueth in the soul a great reverence of God, his word, and ways, keeping it 30 tender, and making it afraid to turn from them, to the right hand, or to the left, to any thing that may dishonour God, break its peace, grieve the Spirit, or cause the enemy to speak reproachfully.

Hope. Well said, I believe you have said the truth. Are we now almost got past the Inchanted ground?

Chr. Why, are you weary of this discourse?

---

9 *fear* 11　　14 *ignorant* rom. 7　　21 Job 28. 29 ‖ 1–11
22 Prov. 17 ‖ 1–11　　24 marg. *Right fears* 4, 5, 6, 8 *etc.*　　**36**
Inchanced 3　　37 *are you*] *art thou* 11

Hope. No verily, but that I would know where we are.

Chr. We have not now above two Miles further to go Why ignorant persons stifle convictions.
thereon. But let us return to our matter. *Now the Ignorant*
know not that such convictions that tend to put them in fear, * 1. *In general.*
are for their good, and therefore they seek to stifle them.

Hope. How do they seek to stifle them?

Chr. *1. They think that those fears are wrought by * 2. *In parti-*
the Devil (though indeed they are wrought of God) and *cular.*
thinking so, they resist them, as things that directly
10 tend to their overthrow. 2. They also think that these
fears tend to the spoiling of their faith, (when alas for
them, poor men that they are! they have none at all)
and therefore they harden their hearts against them.
3. They presume they ought not to fear, and therefore,
in despite of them, wax presumptuously confident.
4. They see that these fears tend to take away from
them their pitiful old self-holiness, and therefore they
resist them with all their might.

Hope. I know something of this my self; for before
20 I knew my self it was so with me.

Chr. Well, we will leave at this time our Neighbour
Ignorance *by himself, and fall upon another profitable*
question.

Hope. With all my heart, but you shall still begin. *Talk about one Temporary.*

Chr. Well then, Did you not know about ten years ago;
one Temporary *in your parts, who was a forward man in*
Religion then?

Hope. Know him! Yes, he dwelt in *Graceless,* a Town
about two miles off of *Honesty,* and he dwelt next door *Where he dwelt.*
30 to one *Turn-back.*

Chr. Right, he dwelt under the same roof with him.
Well, that man was much awakened once; I believe that * He was towardly once.*
then he had some sight of his sins, and of the wages that was
due thereto.

Hope. I am of your mind, for (my house not being
above three miles from him) he would oft times come

2 marg. *Why . . . convictions* add. 2: . . . *conviction* 6   4 marg.
1. *In general* add. 2: *In general* 3–6, 8–11   7 marg. 2. *In particular*
add. 2: 2. *Particular* 6, 8 etc.   15 despight 7   16 those 2, 3
32 marg. *He . . . once* add. 2   33 *were* 11

to me, and that with many tears. Truly I pitied the man, and was not altogether without hope of him; but one may see, it is not every one that cries, *Lord, Lord.*

Chr. *He told me once, That he was resolved to go on Pilgrimage, as we do now; but all of a sudden he grew acquainted with one* Save-self, *and then he became a stranger to me.*

Hope. Now since we are talking about him, let us a little enquire into the reason of the suddain back-sliding of him and such others.

Chr. *It may be very profitable, but do you begin.*

Hope. Well then, there are in my judgement four reasons for it.

Reason, why towardly ones go back. 1. Though the Consciences of such men are awakened, yet their minds are not changed: therefore when the power of guilt weareth away, that which provoked them to be Religious, ceaseth. Wherefore they naturally turn to their own course again: even as we see the Dog that is sick of what he hath eaten, so long as his sickness prevails, he vomits and casts up all; not that he doth this of a free mind (if we may say a Dog has a mind) but because it troubleth his Stomach; but now when his sickness is over, and so his Stomach eased, his desires being not at all alienate from his vomit, he turns him about, and licks up all. And so it is true which is 2 Pet. 2. 22. written, *The Dog is turned to his own vomit again.* Thus, I say, being hot for Heaven, by virtue only of the sense and fear of the torments of Hell, as their sense of Hell, and the fears of damnation chills and cools, so their desires for Heaven and Salvation cool also. So then it comes to pass, that when their guilt and fear is gone, their desires for Heaven and Happiness die; and they return to their course again.

2*ly.* Another reason is, They have slavish fears that do over-master them. I speak now of the fears that they Prov. 29. 25. have of men: *For the fear of men bringeth a snare.* So

5 *do*] *go* 2   9 sudden 2, 3, 4, 7   14 marg. *Reason* ... *back* add. 2: *Reasons* ... 10, 11   16 provoketh 7, 9⁴ *etc.*   18 turn] return 11   24 alienated 9⁴ *etc.*   26 Thus] This 1, 2   30 for] of 9³

then, though they seem to be hot for Heaven, so long as the flames of Hell are about their ears, yet when that terrour is a little over, they betake themselves to second thoughts; namely, that 'tis good to be wise, and not to run (for they know not what) the hazard of loosing all; or at least, of bringing themselves into unavoidable and un-necessary troubles: and so they fall in with the world again.

3*ly.* The shame that attends Religion, lies also as a block in their way; they are proud and haughty, and Religion in their eye is low and contemptible: Therefore when they have lost their sense of Hell and wrath to come, they return again to their former course.

4*ly,* Guilt, and to meditate terrour, are grievous to them, they like not to see their misery before they come into it: Though perhaps the sight of it first, if they loved that sight, might make them flie whither the righteous flie and are safe; but because they do, as I hinted before, even shun the thoughts of guilt and terrour, therefore, when once they are rid of their awakenings about the terrors and wrath of God, they harden their hearts gladly, and chuse such ways as will harden them more and more.

Chr. You are pretty near the business, for the bottom of all is, for want of a change in their mind and will. And therefore they are but like the Fellon that standeth before the Judge, he quakes and trembles, and seems to repent most heartily; but the bottom of all is, the fear of the Halter, not of any detestation of the offence; as is evident, because, let but this man have his liberty, and he will be a Thief, and so a Rogue still; whereas, if his mind was changed, he would be otherwise.

Hope. Now I have shewed you the reasons of their going back, do you shew me the manner thereof.

Chr. So I will willingly.

1. They draw off their thoughts all that they may from the remembrance of God, Death, and Judgement to come.

How the Apostate goes back.

---

5 losing 2 *etc.*   26 *Felon* 8 *etc.*   29 *of* [1]] *that he hath* 4,
5, 6, 8 *etc.*   *offences* 4, 5, 6, 8 *etc.*   36 drew 9[4] *etc.*

2. Then they cast off by degrees private Duties, as Closet-Prayer, curbing their lusts, watching, sorrow for Sin, and the like.

3. Then they shun the company of lively and warm Christians.

4. After that, they grow cold to publick Duty, as Hearing, Reading, Godly Conference, and the like.

5. Then they begin to pick holes, as we say; in the Coats of some of the Godly, and that devilishly that they may have a seeming colour to throw Religion (for the sake of some infirmity they have spied in them) behind their backs.

6. Then they begin to adhere to, and associate themselves with carnal, loose, and wanton men.

7. Then they give way to carnal and wanton discourses in secret; and glad are they if they can see such things in any that are counted honest, that they may the more boldly do it through their example.

8. After this, they begin to play with little sins openly.

9. And then, being hardened, they shew themselves as they are. Thus being lanched again into the gulf of misery, unless a Miracle of Grace prevent it, they everlastingly perish in their own deceivings.

Now I saw in my Dream, that by this time the Pilgrims were got over the Inchanted Ground, and entering into the Country of *Beulah*, whose Air was very sweet and pleasant, the way lying directly through it, they solaced themselves there for a season. Yea, here they heard continually the singing of Birds, and saw every day the flowers appear in the earth: and heard the voice of the Turtle in the Land. In this Countrey the Sun shineth night and day; wherefore this was beyond the Valley of the *shadow of death*, and also out of the reach of Giant *Despair*; neither could they from this place so much as see *Doubting-Castle*. Here they were within sight of the City they were going to: also here met them some of the Inhabitants thereof. For in this Land the shining Ones commonly walked, because it

Isa. 62. 4.
Cant. 2. 10,
11, 12.

Angels.

27 Cant. 10, 11, 12 ‖ 7   in the 1

was upon the Borders of Heaven. In this Land also the contract between the Bride and the Bridgroom was renewed: Yea here, *as the Bridegroom rejoyceth over the* Isa. 62.5. *Bride, so did their God rejoyce over them.* Here they had ver. 8. no want of Corn and Wine; for in this place they met with abundance of what they had sought for in all their Pilgrimage. Here they heard voices from out of the City, loud voices, saying, *Say ye to the daughter of* Zion, *Behold thy Salvation cometh, behold his reward is with him.* ver. 11.
10 Here all the Inhabitants of the Countrey called them, ver. 12. *The holy People, the redeemed of the Lord, Sought out,* &c.

Now as they walked in this Land they had more rejoycing then in parts more remote from the Kingdom, to which they were bound; and drawing near to the City, they had yet a more perfect view thereof. It was builded of Pearls and Precious Stones, also the Street thereof was paved with Gold, so that by reason of the natural glory of the City, and the reflection of the Sunbeams upon it, *Christian*, with desire fell sick, *Hopeful*
20 also had a fit or two of the same Disease: Wherefore here they lay by it a while, crying out because of their pangs, *If you see my Beloved, tell him that I am sick of love.*

But being a little strengthned, and better able to bear their sickness, they walked on their way, and came yet nearer and nearer, where were Orchards, Vineyards, and Gardens, and their Gates opened into the Highway. Now as they came up to these places, behold the Gardener stood in the way; to whom the Pilgrims said, Whose goodly Vineyards and Gardens are these? He Deut. 23. 24.
30 answered, They are the Kings, and are planted here for his own delights, and also for the solace of Pilgrims, So the Gardiner had them into the Vineyards, and bid them refresh themselves with the Dainties; he also shewed them *there* the Kings Walks and the *Arbors* where he delighted to be: And here they tarried and slept.

Now I beheld in my Dream, that they talked more in their sleep at this time, then ever they did in all their

6 with *om.* 10, 11 for *add.* 2 7 Pilgrimages 2 8 voice 3
12 walked this 3, 7 13 than 2 17 were 11 38 than 2

Journey; and being in a muse there-about, the Gardiner said even to me, Wherefore musest thou at the matter? It is the nature of the fruit of the Grapes of these Vineyards to go down so sweetly, as to cause the lips of them that are asleep to speak.

So I saw that when they awoke, they addressed themselves to go up to the City. But, as I said, the reflections *Rev. 21. 18.* of the Sun upon the City, (for the City was pure Gold) was so extreamly glorious, that they could not, as yet, *2 Cor. 3. 18.* with open face behold it, but through an *Instrument* 10 made for that purpose. So I saw, that as they went on, there met them two men, in Raiment that shone like Gold, also their faces shone as the light.

These men asked the Pilgrims whence they came? and they told them; they also asked them, Where they had lodg'd, what difficulties, and dangers, what comforts and pleasures they had met in the way? and they told them. Then said the men that met them, You have but two difficulties more to meet with, and then you are in the City.   20

Christian then and his Companion asked the men to go along with them, so they told them they would; but, said they, you must obtain it by your own faith. So I saw in my Dream that they went on together till they came within sight of the Gate.

Death.   Now I further saw, that betwixt them and the Gate was a River, but there was no Bridge to go over; the River was very deep; at the sight therefore of this River, the Pilgrims were much stounded, but the men that went with them, said, You must go through, or you 30 cannot come at the Gate.

Death is not welcome to nature though by it we pass out of this World into glory. The Pilgrims then began to enquire if there was no other way to the Gate; to which they answered, Yes; but there hath not any, save two, to wit, *Enoch* and *Elijah*, been permitted to tread that path, since the foundation of the World, nor shall, untill the last *1 Cor. 15. 51, 52.* Trumpet shall sound. The Pilgrims then, especially

---

2 mater 3   8 Rev. 21. 28 ‖ 9⁴ *etc.*   10 2 Cor. 3. 18 ‖ 6:
1 Cor. 3. 18 ‖ 1–5, 7 *etc.*   12 shined 7   25 within] in 2
28 therefore] thereof 3   29 stun'd 2–9: stunned 10, 11

Christian, began to dispond in his mind, and looked this way and that, but no way could be found by them, by which they might escape the River. Then they asked the men if the Waters were all of a depth. They said no; yet they could not help them in that Case; for said they, *You shall find it deeper or shallower, as you believe in the King of the place.*

Angels help us not comfortably through death.

They then addressed themselves to the Water; and entring, *Christian* began to sink, and crying out to
10 his good friend *Hopeful*; he said, I sink in deep Waters, the Billows go over my head, all his Waves go over me, *Selah*.

Then said the other, Be of good chear, my Brother, I feel the bottom, and it is good. Then said *Christian*, Ah my friend, the sorrows of death have compassed me about, I shall not see the Land that flows with Milk and Honey. And with that, a great darkness and horror fell upon *Christian*, so that he could not see before him; also here he in great measure lost his senses, so that he
20 could neither remember nor orderly talk of any of those sweet refreshments that he had met with in the way of his Pilgrimage. But all the words that he spake, still tended to discover that he had horror of mind, and hearty fears that he should die in that River, and never obtain entrance in at the Gate: Here also, as they that stood by, perceived, he was much in the troublesome thoughts of the sins that he had committed, both since and before he began to be a Pilgrim. 'Twas also observed, that he was troubled with apparitions of Hob-
30 goblins and Evil Spirits, For ever and anon he would intimate so much by words. *Hopeful* therefore here had much adoe to keep his Brothers head above water, yea sometimes he would be quite gone down, and then ere a while he would rise up again half dead. *Hopeful* also would endeavour to comfort him, saying, Brother, I see the Gate, and men standing by it to receive us. But *Christian* would answer, 'Tis you, 'tis you they wait for, you have been *Hopeful* ever since I knew you: and so

Christians conflict at the hour of death.

15 hath 5, 6, 8 *etc.*   24 heart fears 8, 9⁴, 10: heart-fears 9³, 11
29–30 Hogoblins 1: Hopgoblins 4, 5, 6, 8, 9³

have you, said he to *Christian*. Ah Brother, said he, surely if I was right, he would now arise to help me; but for my sins he hath brought me into the snare, and hath left me. Then said *Hopeful*, My Brother, you have quite forgot the Text, where its said of the wicked, Psal. 73. *There is no band in their death, but their strength is firm,* 4, 5. *they are not troubled as other men, neither are they plagued like other men.* These troubles and distresses that you go through in these Waters, are no sign that God hath forsaken you, but are sent to try you, whether you will 10 call to mind that which heretofore you have received of his goodness, and live upon him in your distresses.

Then I saw in my Dream that *Christian* was as in a muse Christian a while; to whom also *Hopeful* added this word, *Be of* delivered from *good cheer, Jesus Christ maketh thee whole:* And with that, his fears in death. *Christian* brake out with a loud voice, Oh I see him Isa. 43. 2. again! and he tells me, *When thou passest through the waters, I will be with thee, and through the Rivers, they shall not overflow thee.* Then they both took courage, and the enemy was after that as still as a stone, until 20 they were gone over. *Christian* therefore presently found ground to stand upon; and so it followed that the rest of the River was but shallow. Thus they got over. Now upon the bank of the River, on the other side, they saw the two shining men again, who there waited for them. Wherefore being come up out of the The Angels do River, they saluted them, saying, *We are ministring* wait for them *Spirits, sent forth to minister for those that shall be Heirs of* so soon as they are passed out *Salvation.* Thus they went along towards the Gate, now of this world. you must note that the City stood upon a mighty hill, 30 but the Pilgrims went up that hill *with ease,* because they had these two men to lead them up by the Arms; They have put also they had left their *Mortal* Garments behind them off mortality. in the River: for though they went in with them, they came out without them. They therefore went up here with much agility and speed, though the foundation upon which the City was framed was higher then the

Clouds. They therefore went up through the Regions of the Air, sweetly talking as they went, being comforted, because they safely got over the River, and had such glorious Companions to attend them.

The talk that they had with the shining Ones, was about the glory of the place, who told them, that the beauty, and glory of it was inexpressible. There, said they, is the Mount *Sion*, the heavenly *Jerusalem*, the inumerable company of Angels, and the Spirits of Just Heb. 12. 22, 23, 24. Rev. 2. 7.
10 Men made perfect: You are going now, said they, to Rev. 3. 4. the Paradice of God, wherein you shall see the Tree of Life, and eat of the never-fading fruits thereof: And when you come there, you shall have white Robes given you, and your walk and talk shall be every day with the King, even all the days of eternity. There you shall not Rev. 21. 1. see again, such things as you saw when you were in the lower Region upon the earth, to wit, sorrow, sickness, affliction, and death, *for the former things are passed* Isa. 57. 1, 2. *away.* You are going now to *Abraham*, *to Isaac*, and Isa. 65. 14.
20 *Jacob*, and to the Prophets; men that God hath taken away from the evil to come, and that are now resting upon their Beds, each one walking in his rightousness. The men then asked, What must we do in the holy place? To whom it was answered, You must there receive the comfort of all your toil, and have joy for all your sorrow; you must reap what you have sown, even the fruit of all your Prayers and Tears, and sufferings for the King by the way. In that place you must wear Gal. 6. 7. Crowns of Gold, and enjoy the perpetual sight and
30 Visions of the *Holy One, for there you shall see him as he* 1 John 3. 2. *is.* There also you shall serve him continually with praise, with shouting and thanksgiving, whom you desired to serve in the World, though with much difficulty, because of the infirmity of your flesh. There your eyes shall be delighted with seeing, and your ears with hearing, the pleasant voice of the mighty One. There you shall enjoy your friends again, that are got thither before you; and there you shall with joy receive, even

every one that follows into the Holy place after you.
1 Thes. 4. 13. There also you shall be cloathed with Glory and
14, 15, 16. Majesty, and put into an equipage fit to ride out with
Jude 14.
Da. 7. 9, 10. the King of Glory. When he shall come with sound of
1 Cor. 6. 2, 3, Trumpet in the Clouds, as upon the wings of the Wind,
you shall come with him; and when he shall sit upon
the Throne of Judgement, you shall sit by him; yea,
and when he shall pass Sentence upon all the workers of
Iniquity, let them be Angels or Men, you also shall
have a voice in that Judgement, because they were his 10
and your Enemies. Also when he shall again return to
the City, you shall go too, with sound of Trumpet, and
be ever with him.

Now while they were thus drawing towards the Gate,
behold a company of the Heavenly Host came out to
meet them: To whom it was said, by the other two
shining Ones, These are the men that have loved our
Lord, when they were in the World, and that have left
all for his holy Name, and he hath sent us to fetch them,
and we have brought them thus far on their desired 20
Journey; that they may go in and look their Redeemer
in the face with joy. Then the Heavenly Host gave a
Rev. 19. great shout, saying, *Blessed are they that are called to the*
Marriage Supper of the Lamb.

There came out also at this time to meet them,
several of the Kings Trumpeters, cloathed in white and
shining Rayment, who with melodious noises, and loud,
made even the Heavens to eccho with their sound.
These Trumpeters saluted *Christian* and his Fellow
with ten thousand welcomes from the world: And this 30
they did with shouting, and sound of Trumpet.

This done, they compassed them round on every
side; some went before, some behind, and some on the
right hand, some on the left (as 'twere to guard them
through the upper Regions) continually sounding as
they went, with melodious noise, in notes on high; so
that the very sight was to them that could behold it, as
if Heaven it self was come down to meet them. Thus

25 There came out . . . joy be expressed (p. 161, l. 15) *add.* 2
34 it were 6, 8 *etc.*

therefore they walked on together, and as they walked,
ever and anon, these Trumpeters, even, with joyful
sound, would, by mixing their Musick, with looks and
gestures, still signifie to *Christian* and his Brother, how
welcome they were into their company, and with what
gladness they came to meet them: And now were these
two men, as 'twere, in Heaven, before they came at
it; being swallowed up with the sight of Angels, and
with hearing of their melodious notes. Here also they
10 had the City it self in view, and they thought they heard
all the Bells therein to ring, to welcome them thereto:
but above all, the warm and joyful thoughts that they
had about their own dwelling there, with such company, and that for ever and ever. Oh! by what tongue
or pen can their glorious joy be expressed: and thus
they came up to the Gate.

Now when they were come up to the Gate, there
was written over it, in Letters of Gold, *Blessed are they* Rev. 22. 14.
that do his commandments, that they may have right to the
20 *Tree of Life; and may enter in through the Gates into*
the City.

Then I saw in my Dream, that the shining men bid
them call at the Gate, the which when they did, some
from above looked over the Gate; to wit, *Enoch, Moses,*
and *Elijah, &c.* to whom it was said, These Pilgrims
are come from the City of *Destruction*, for the love that
they bear to the King of this place: and then the Pilgrims gave in unto them each man his Certificate,
which they had received in the beginning; those there-
30 fore were carried into the King, who when he had read
them, said, Where are the men? to whom it was answered, They are standing without the Gate. The King
then commanded to open the Gate; *That the righteous* Isa. 26. 2.
Nation, said he, *that keepeth Truth may enter in.*

Now I saw in my Dream, that these two men went
in at the Gate; and loe, as they entered, they were
transfigured, and they had Raiment put on that shone

7 too 2, 3   it were 6, 8 *etc.*   15 and thus] Thus 2   18 were 3
27 bare 11   30 in to 5, 6, 8 *etc.*   32 Gate, the *all edd.*
33 Isa. 27. 2 | 9³

like Gold. There was also that met them with Harps and Crowns, and gave them to them; The Harp to praise withal, and the Crowns in token of honor: Then I heard in my Dream, that all the Bells in the City Rang again for joy; and that it was said unto them, *Enter ye into the joy of your Lord.* I also heard the men themselves,

Rev. 5. 13, 14. that they sang with a loud voice, saying, *Blessing, Honour, Glory, and Power, be to him that sitteth upon the Throne, and to the Lamb for ever and ever.*

Now just as the Gates were opened to let in the men, I looked in after them; and behold, the City shone like the Sun, the Streets also were paved with Gold, and in them walked many men, with Crowns on their heads, Palms in their hands, and golden Harps to sing praises withall.

There were also of them that had wings, and they answered one another without intermission, saying, *Holy, Holy, Holy, is the Lord.* And after that, they shut up the Gates: which when I had seen, I wished my self among them.

Now while I was gazing upon all these things, I turned my head to look back, and saw *Ignorance* come up to the River side: but he soon got over, and that without half that difficulty which the other two men met with. For it happened, that there was then in that place one *Vain-hope* a Ferry-man, that with his Boat helped him over: so he, as the other I saw, did ascend the Hill to come up to the Gate, only he came alone; neither did any man meet him with the least incouragement. When he was come up to the Gate, he looked up to the writing that was above; and then began to knock, supposing that entrance should have been quickly administred to him: But he was asked by the men that lookt over the top of the Gate, Whence came you? and what would you have? He answered, I have eat and

2 Harps 6, 8, 9³, 9⁴: harps 10, 11   5 again *add.* 2   6 your] our 2   themselves say *add.* 2, *om.* 4, 5, 6, 8 *etc.*   13 head 9⁴, 10 17 intermission 4   19 myself 11   22 marg. *Ignorance comes up to the River* add. 4: om. 7   25 that²] the 2, 3, 7   27 marg. *Vain hope does ferry him over* add. 4: om. 7   34 come 8 *etc.*   35 would you] he would 3

drank in the presence of the King, and he has taught in our Streets. Then they asked him for his Certificate, that they might go in and shew it to the King. So he fumbled in his bosom for one, and found none. Then said they, Have you none? But the man answered never a word. So they told the King but he would not come down to see him; but commanded the two shining Ones that conducted *Christian* and *Hopeful* to the City to go out and take *Ignorance* and bind him hand and foot, and have him away. Then they took him up, and carried him through the air to the door that I saw in the side of the Hill, and put him in there. Then I saw that there was a way to Hell, even from the Gates of Heaven, as well as from the City of *Destruction*. So I awoke, and behold it was a Dream.

FINIS

13 away 1   15 beheld 9⁴ *etc*

The Conclusion

NOW Reader, I have told my Dream to thee;
   See if thou canst Interpret it to me;
Or to thy self, or Neighbour: but take heed
Of mis-interpreting: for that, instead
Of doing good, will but thy self abuse:
By mis-interpreting evil insues.
   Take heed also, that thou be not extream,
In playing with the out-side *of my Dream:*
Nor let my figure, or similitude,
Put thee into a laughter or a feud;   10
Leave this for Boys *and* Fools*; but as for thee,*
Do thou the substance of my matter see.
   Put by the Curtains, look within my Vail;
Turn up my Metaphors and do not fail:
There, if thou seekest them, such things to find,
As will be helpful to an honest mind.
   What of my dross *thou findest there, be bold*
To throw away, but yet preserve the Gold.
What if my Gold be wrapped up in Ore?
None throws away the Apple for the Core: 20
But if thou shalt cast all away as vain,
I know not but 'twill make me Dream again.

THE END

---

8 out-side *ital.* 2, 9⁴ *etc.*   11 *and* rom. 11   17 dross *ital.* 7
21 But . . . vain *ital.* 9⁴ *etc.*

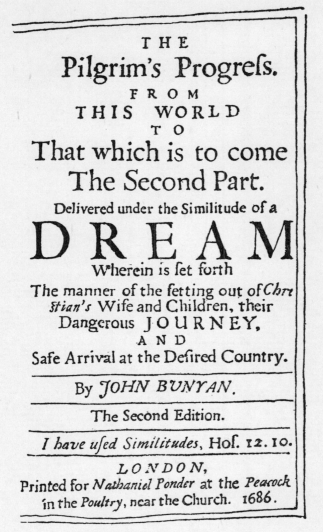

THE
Pilgrim's Progress.
FROM
THIS WORLD
TO
That which is to come
The Second Part.

Delivered under the Similitude of a

DREAM

Wherein is set forth
The manner of the setting out of *Christian's* Wife and Children, their
Dangerous JOURNEY,
AND
Safe Arrival at the Desired Country.

By *JOHN BUNYAN.*

The Second Edition.

I have used Similitudes, Hos. 12. 10.

LONDON,
Printed for *Nathaniel Ponder* at the *Peacock*
in the *Poultry*, near the Church. 1686.

THE
Authors Way of Sending forth
HIS
Second Part
OF THE
PILGRIM

GO, now my little Book, to every place,
Where my first Pilgrim has but shewn his Face,
Call at their door: If any say, who's there?
Then answer thou, Christiana is here.
If they bid thee come in, then enter thou
With all thy boys. And then, as thou know'st how,
Tell who they are, also from whence they came,
Perhaps they'l know them, by their looks, or name:
But if they should not, ask them yet again
10 If formerly they did not Entertain
One Christian a Pilgrim; If they say
They did: And was delighted in his way:
Then let them know that those related were
Unto him: Yea, his Wife and Children are.
  Tell them that they have left their House and Home,
Are turned Pilgrims, seek a World to come:
That they have met with hardships in the way,
That they do meet with troubles night and Day;
That they have trod on Serpents, fought with Devils,
20 Have also overcome a many evils.
Yea tell them also of the rest, who have
Of love to Pilgrimage been stout and brave
Defenders of that way, and how they still
Refuse this World, to do their Fathers will.
  Go, tell them also of those dainty things,

21 rest] next 1, 2

That Pilgrimage *unto the* Pilgrim *brings,*
Let them acquainted be, too, how they are
Beloved of their King, under his care;
What goodly Mansions *for them he Provides.*
Tho they meet with rough Winds, and swelling Tides,
How brave a calm they will enjoy at last,
Who to their Lord, and by his ways hold fast.

   Perhaps with heart and hand they will imbrace
Thee, as they did my firstling, and will Grace
Thee, and thy fellows with such chear and fair,   10
As shew will, they of Pilgrims *lovers are.*

1 *Object*

   But how if they will not believe of me
That I am truly thine, 'cause some there be
That Counterfeit the Pilgrim, and his name,
Seek by disguise to seem the very same.
And by that means have wrought themselves into
The Hands and Houses of I know not who.

Answer

'Tis true, some have of late, to Counterfeit
My *Pilgrim, to their own, my Title set;*
Yea others, half my Name and Title too;   20
Have stitched to their Book, to make them do;
But yet they by their Features *do declare*
Themselves not mine to be, whose ere they are.

   If such thou meetst with, then thine only way
Before them all, is, to say out thy say,
In thine own native Language, which no man
Now useth, nor with ease dissemble can.

   If after all, they still of you shall doubt,
Thinking that you like Gipsies *go about,*
In naughty-wise the Countrey to defile,   30
Or that you seek good People to beguile
With things unwarrantable: Send for me
And I will Testifie, you Pilgrims *be;*
Yea, I will Testifie that only you
My Pilgrims *are; And that alone will do.*

       8 *unbrace* 1

2 *Object*

But yet, perhaps, I may enquire for him,
Of those that wish him Damned life and limb,
What shall I do, when I at such a door,
For *Pilgrims* ask, and they shall rage the more?

Answer

Fright not thy self my Book, *for such* Bugbears
Are nothing else but ground for groundless fears,
My Pilgrims *Book has travel'd Sea and Land,*
Yet could I never come to understand,
That it was slighted, or turn'd out of Door
10 *By any Kingdom, were they Rich or Poor.*
   In France *and* Flanders *where men kill each other*
My Pilgrim *is esteem'd a Friend, a Brother.*
   In Holland *too, 'tis said, as I am told,*
My Pilgrim *is with some, worth more than Gold.*
   Highlanders, *and* Wild-Irish *can agree,*
My Pilgrim *should familiar with them be.*
   'Tis in New-England *under such advance,*
Receives there so much loving Countenance,
As to be Trim'd, new Cloth'd & Deckt with Gems,
20 *That it might shew its Features, and its Limbs,*
Yet more; so comely doth my Pilgrim *walk,*
That of him thousands daily Sing and talk.
   If you draw nearer home, it will appear
My Pilgrim *knows no ground of shame, or fear;*
City, and Countrey will him Entertain,
With welcome Pilgrim. *Yea, they can't refrain*
From smiling, if my Pilgrim *be but by,*
Or shews his head in any Company.
   Brave Galants do my Pilgrim *hug and love,*
30 *Esteem it much, yea value it above*
Things of a greater bulk, yea, with delight,
Say my Larks *leg is beter than a* Kite.
   Young Ladys, and young Gentle-women too,
Do no small kindness to my Pilgrim *shew;*
Their Cabinets, their Bosoms, and their Hearts

27 *smilling* 1

My Pilgrim *has, 'cause he to them imparts*
His pretty riddles in such wholsome straines
As yields them profit double to their paines
Of reading. Yea, I think I may be bold
To say some prize him far above their Gold.

    The very Children that do walk the street,
If they do but my holy Pilgrim *meet,*
Salute him will, will wish him well and say,
He is the only Stripling *of the Day.*

    They that have never seen him, yet admire   10
What they have heard of him, and much desire
To have his Company, and hear him tell
Those Pilgrim *storyes which he knows so well.*

    Yea, some who did not love him at the first,
But cal'd him Fool, *and* Noddy, *say they must*
Now they have seen & heard him, him commend,
And to those whom they love, they do him send.

    Wherefore my Second Part, *thou needst not be*
Afraid to shew thy Head: None can hurt thee,
That wish but well to him, that went before,   20
'Cause thou com'st after with a Second store,
Of things as good, as rich, as profitable,
For Young, for Old, for Stag'ring and for stable.

3 *Object*

But some there be that say he laughs too loud;
And some do say his Head is in a Cloud.
Some say, his Words and Storys are so dark,
They know not how, by them, to find his mark.

Answer

    One may (I think) say both his laughs & cryes,
May well be guest at by his watry Eyes.
Some things are of that Nature as to make   30
Ones fancie Checkle while his Heart doth ake,
When Jacob *saw his* Rachel *with the Sheep,*
He did at the same time both kiss and weep.

    Whereas some say a Cloud is in his Head,
That doth but shew how Wisdom's covered

With its own mantles: And to stir the mind
To a search after what it fain would find,
Things that seem to be hid in words obscure,
Do but the Godly mind the more alure;
To study what those Sayings should contain,
That speak to us in such a Cloudy strain.
    I also know, a dark Similitude
Will on the Fancie more it self intrude,
And will stick faster in the Heart and Head,
10 *Then things from Similies not borrowed.*
    Wherefore, my Book, let no discouragement
Hinder thy travels. Behold, thou art sent
To Friends, not foes: to Friends that will give place
To thee, thy Pilgrims, *and thy words imbrace.*
    Besides, what my first Pilgrim *left conceal'd,*
Thou my brave Second Pilgrim *hast reveal'd;*
What Christian *left lock't up and went his way,*
Sweet Christiana *opens with her Key.*

4 Object

But some love not the method of your first,
20 Romance they count it, throw't away as dust,
If I should meet with such, what should I say?
Must I slight them as they slight me, or nay?

Answer

My Christiana, *if with such thou meet,*
By all means in all Loving-wise, them greet;
Render them not reviling for revile:
But if they frown, I prethee on them smile.
Perhaps 'tis Nature, or some ill report
Has made them thus *dispise, or* thus *retort.*
    Some love no Cheese, some love no Fish, & some
30 *Love not their Friends, nor their own House or home;*
Some start at Pigg, slight Chicken, love not Fowl,
More then they love a Cuckoo or an Owl.
Leave such, my Christiana, *to their choice,*
And seek those, who to find thee will rejoyce;
By no means strive, but in all humble wise,

24 *all-means* 1 (Hunt.)   35 *all* om. 2

Present thee to them in thy Pilgrims *guise.*

Go then, my little Book and shew to all
That entertain, and bid thee welcome shall,
What thou shalt keep close, shut up from the rest,
And wish what thou shalt shew them may be blest
To them for good, may make them chuse to be
Pilgrims, better by far, then thee or me.

Go then, I say, tell all men who thou art,
Say, I am Christiana, *and my part*
Is now with my four Sons, to tell you what   10
It is for men to take a Pilgrims *lot.*

Go also tell them who, and what they be,
That now do go on Pilgrimage *with thee;*
Say, here's my neighbour Mercy, *she is one,*
That has long-time with me a Pilgrim *gone:*
Come see her in her Virgin *Face, and learn*
Twixt Idle ones, and Pilgrims *to discern.*
Yea let young Damsels learn of her to prize
The World which is to come, in any wise;
When little Tripping *Maidens follow God,*   20
And leave old doting Sinners to his Rod;
'Tis like those Days wherein the young ones cri'd
Hosanah to whom old ones did deride.

Next tell them of old Honest, *who you found*
With his white hairs treading the Pilgrims ground,
Yea, tell them how plain hearted this *man was,*
How after his good Lord he bare his Cross:
Perhaps with some gray Head this may prevail,
With Christ to fall in Love, and Sin bewail.

Tell them also how Master Fearing *went*   30
On Pilgrimage, and how the time he spent
In Solitariness, with Fears and Cries,
And how at last, he won the Joyful Prize.
He was *a good man, though much down in Spirit,*
He is *a good Man, and doth Life inherit.*

Tell them of Master Feeblemind *also,*
Who, not before, but still behind would go;
Show them also how he had like been slain,
And how one Great-Heart *did his life regain:*
This man was true of Heart, tho weak in grace,   40

One might true Godliness read in his Face.
   Then tell them of Master Ready-to-halt,
A Man with Crutches, but much without fault:
Tell them how Master Feeblemind, and he
Did love, and in Opinions much agree.
And let all know, tho weakness was their chance,
Yet sometimes one could Sing, the other Dance.
   Forget not Master Valiant-for-the-Truth,
That Man of courage, tho a very Youth.
10 Tell every one his Spirit was so stout,
No Man could ever make him face about,
And how Great-Heart, & he could not forbear
But put down Doubting Castle, slay Despair.
   Overlook not Master Despondancie.
Nor Much-a-fraid, his Daughter, tho they ly
Under such Mantles as may make them look
(With some) as if their God had them forsook.
They softly went, but sure, and at the end,
Found that the Lord of Pilgrims was their Friend.
20 When thou hast told the World of all these things,
Then turn about, my book, and touch these strings,
Which, if but touched will such Musick make,
They'l make a Cripple dance, a Gyant quake.
Those Riddles that lie couch't within thy breast,
Freely propound, expound: and for the rest
Of thy misterious lines, let them remain,
For those whose nimble Fancies shall them gain.
   Now may this little Book a blessing be,
To those that love this little Book and me,
30 And may its buyer have no cause to say,
His Money is but lost or thrown away.
Yea may this Second Pilgrim yield that Fruit,
As may with each good Pilgrims fancie sute,
And may it perswade some that go astray,
To turn their Foot and Heart to the right way.
      Is the Hearty Prayer
       of the Author
         JOHN BUNYAN

   22 *but* rom. 1, 2   **36** Heartly 1

THE
Pilgrims Progress
In the Similitude of a
DREAM

The Second Part

COurteous Companions, sometime since, to tell you my Dream that I had of *Christian* the Pilgrim, and of his dangerous Journey toward the Celestial Countrey; was pleasant to me, and profitable to you. I told you then also what I saw concerning his *Wife* and *Children*, and how unwilling they were to go with him on Pilgrimage: Insomuch that he was forced to go on his Progress without them, for he durst not run the danger of that destruction which he feared would come by staying with them, in the City of Destruction: Wherefore, as I then shewed you, he left them and departed.

Now it hath so happened, thorough the Multiplicity of Business, that I have been much hindred, and kept back from my wonted Travels into those Parts whence he went, and so could not till now obtain an opportunity to make further enquiry after whom he left behind, that I might give you an account of them. But having had some concerns that way of late, I went down again thitherward. Now, having taken up my Lodgings in a Wood about a mile off the Place, as I slept I dreamed again.

And as I was in my Dream, behold, an aged Gentleman came by where I lay; and because he was to go some part of the way that I was travelling, me thought I got up and went with him. So as we walked, and as

Travellers usually do, it was as if we fell into discourse, and our talk happened to be about *Christian* and his Travels: For thus I began with the Old-man.

Sir, said I, *what Town is that there below, that lieth on the left hand of our way?*

Then said Mr. *Sagasity*, for that was his name, it is the City of *Destruction*, a populous place, but possessed with a very ill conditioned, and idle sort of People.

I thought that was that City, quoth I, *I went once my 10 self through that Town, and therefore know that this report you give of it is true.*

Sag. Too true, I wish I could speak truth in speaking better of them that dwell therein.

Well, Sir, quoth I, *Then I perceive you to be a well meaning man: and so one that takes pleasure to hear and tell of that which is good; pray did you never hear what happened to a man sometime ago in this Town (whose name was* Christian*) that went on Pilgrimage up towards the higher Regions?*

20 *Sag.* Hear of him! Aye, and I also heard of the Molestations, Troubles, Wars, Captivities, Cries, Groans, Frights and Fears that he met with, and had in his Journey. Besides, I must tell you, all our Countrey rings of him, there are but few Houses that have heard of him and his doings, but have sought after and got the *Records* of his Pilgrimage; yea, I think I may say, that that his hazzardous Journey has got a many wel- wishers to his ways: For though when he was here, he was *Fool* in every mans mouth, yet now he is gone, he is 30 highly commended of all. For 'tis said he lives bravely where he is: Yea, many of them that are resolved never to run his hazzards, yet have their mouths water at his gains.

They may, quoth I *well think, if they think any thing that is true, that he liveth well where he is, for he now lives at and in the Fountain of Life, and has what he has without Labour and Sorrow, for there is no grief mixed therewith.*

Christians *are well spoken of when gone,* tho' called *Fools while they are here.*

Sag. Talk! The People talk strangely about him. Some say that he *now walks in White*, that he has a Chain of Gold about his Neck, that he has a Crown of Gold, beset with Pearls upon his Head: Others say, that the shining ones that sometimes shewed themselves to him in his Journey, are become his Companions, and that he is as familiar with them in the place where he is, as here one Neighbour is with another. Besides, 'tis confidently affirmed concerning him, that the King of the place where he is, has bestowed upon him already, a very rich and pleasant Dwelling at Court, and that he every day eateth and drinketh, and walketh, and talketh with him, and receiveth of the smiles and favours of him that is Judg of all there. Moreover, it is expected of some that his Prince, the Lord of that Countrey, will shortly come into *these* parts, and will know the reason, if they can give any, why his Neighbours set so little by him, and had him so much in derision when they perceived that he would be a Pilgrim. *For they say, that now he is so in the Affections of his Prince, and that his *Soveraign* is so much concerned with the *Indignities* that was cast upon *Christian* when he became a Pilgrim, that he will look upon all as if done unto himself; and no marvel, for 'twas for the love that he had to his Prince, that he ventured as he did.

I dare say, quoth I, *I am glad on't, I am glad for the poor mans sake, for now that he has rest from his labour, and for that he now reapeth the benefit of his Tears with Joy; and for that he is got beyond the Gun-shot of his Enemies, and is out of the reach of them that hate him. I also am glad for that a Rumour of these things is noised abroad in this Countrey; Who can tell but that it may work some good effect on some that are left behind? But, pray Sir, while it is fresh in my mind, do you hear any thing of his Wife and Children? poor hearts, I wonder in my mind what they do.*

Sag. Who! *Christiana*, and her Sons! *They are like to do as well as did *Christian* himself, for though they all plaid the Fool at the first, and would by no means be

Marginal notes:
Revel. 3. 4.
Chap. 6. 11.
Zech. 3. 7.
Luke 14. 15.
Jude 14, 15.
Christians King will take Christians part.
Luke 10. 16.
Revel. 14. 13.
Psal. 126. 5, 6.
Good tidings of Christians Wife and Children.

perswaded by either the tears or intreaties of *Christian*, yet second thoughts have wrought wonderfully with them, so they have packt up and are also gone after him.

Better, and better, quoth I, *But what! Wife and Children and all?*

Sag. 'Tis true, I can give you an account of the matter, for I was upon the spot at the instant, and was throughly acquainted with the whole affair.

Then, said I, *a man it seems may report it for a truth?*

10   *Sag.* You need not fear to affirm it, I mean that they are all gon on Pilgrimage, both the good Woman and her four Boys. And being we are, as I perceive, going some considerable way together, I will give you an account of the whole of the matter.

This *Christiana* (for that was her name from the day that she with her Children betook themselves to a *Pilgrims* Life,) after her Husband was gone *over the River*, *1 part pag.* and she could hear of him no more, her thoughts began 158. to work in her mind; First, for that she had lost her

20 Husband, and for that the loving bond of that Relation was utterly broken betwixt them. For you know, said he to me, nature can do no less but entertain the living with many a heavy Cogitation in the remembrance of the loss of loving Relations. This therefore of her Husband did cost her many a Tear. But this was not *Mark this, you* all, for *Christiana* did also begin to consider with her *that are Churles* self, whether her unbecoming behaviour towards her *to your godly* *Relations.* Husband, was not one cause that she saw him no more, and that in such sort he was taken away from her. And

30 upon this, came into her mind by *swarms*, all her unkind, unnatural, and ungodly Carriages to her dear Friend: Which also clogged her Conscience, and did load her with guilt. She was moreover much broken with recalling to remembrance the restless Groans, brinish Tears and self-bemoanings of her Husband, and how she did harden her heart against all his entreaties, and loving perswasions (of her and her Sons) to go with him, yea, there was not any thing that *Christian* either said to her, or did before her, all the

while that his burden did hang on his back, but it
returned upon her like a flash of lightning, and rent
1 part, pag. the Caul of her Heart in sunder. Specially that bitter
8. out-cry of his, *What shall I do to be saved*, did ring in
her ears most dolefully.

Then said she to her Children, Sons, we are all
undone. I have sinned away your Father, and he is
gone; he would have had us with him; but I would not
go my self; I also have hindred you of Life. With that
the Boys fell all into Tears, and cryed out to go after 10
their Father. Oh! Said *Christiana*, that it had been but
our lot to go with him, then had it fared well with us
beyond what 'tis like to do now. For tho' I formerly
foolishly imagin'd concerning the Troubles of your
Father, that they proceeded of a foolish fancy that he
had, or for that he was over run with Melancholy
Humours; yet now 'twill not out of my mind, but that
they sprang from another cause, to wit, for that the
James 1. 23, Light of Light was given him, by the help of which,
24, 25. as I perceive, he has escaped the Snares of Death. 20
Then they all wept again, and cryed out: Oh, Wo,
worth the day.

Christiana's   The next night *Christiana* had a Dream, and behold
Dream. she saw as if a broad Parchment was opened before her,
in which were recorded the sum of her ways, and the
times, as she thought, look'd *very black upon her*. Then
Luke 18. 13. she cryed out aloud in her sleep, Lord have mercy upon
me a Sinner, and the little Children heard her.

After this she thought she saw two very ill favoured
* *Mark this*, ones standing by her Bed-side, and saying, *What shall 30
this is the *we do with this Woman? For she cryes out for Mercy*
quintescence
of Hell. *waking and sleeping: If she be suffered to go on as she*
begins, we shall lose her as we have lost her Husband.
Wherefore we must by one way or other, seek to take
her off from the thoughts of what shall be hereafter:
else all the World cannot help it, but she will become
a Pilgrim.

Now she awoke in a great Sweat, also a trembling
was upon her, but after a while she fell to sleeping

3 marg. 1 *part page* 2, 3 ‖ 1, 2   30 marg. *Mark . . . Hell* add. 2

again. *And then she thought she saw *Christian* her Husband in a place of Bliss among many *Immortals*, with an *Harp* in his Hand, Standing and playing upon it before one that sate on a Throne with a Rainbow about his Head. She saw also as if he bowed his Head with his Face to the Pav'd-work that was under the Princes Feet, saying, *I heartily thank my Lord and King for bringing of me into this Place.* Then shouted a Company of them that stood round about, and harped with
10 their Harps: but no man living could tell what they said, but *Christian* and his Companions.

* *Help against Discouragement.*
Revel. 14. 2, 3.

Next Morning when she was up, had prayed to God, and talked with her Children a while, one knocked hard at the door; to whom she spake out saying, *If thou comest in Gods Name, come in.* So he said *Amen*, and opened the Door, and saluted her with *Peace be to this House.* *The which when he had done, he said, *Christiana*, knowest thou wherefore I am come? Then she blush'd and trembled, also her Heart began to wax
20 warm with desires to know whence he came, and what was his Errand to her. So he said unto her; my name is *Secret*, I dwell with those that are high. It is talked of where I dwell, as if thou had'st a desire to go thither; also there is a report that thou art aware of the evil thou hast formerly done to thy Husband in hardening of thy Heart against his way, and in keeping of these thy Babes in their Ignorance. *Christiana*, the merciful one has sent me to tell thee that he is a God ready to forgive, and that he taketh delight to multiply pardon to
30 offences. He also would have thee know that he inviteth thee to come into his presence, to his Table, and that he will feed thee with the Fat of his House, and with the Heritage of *Jacob* thy Father.

* *Convictions seconded with fresh Tidings of Gods readiness to Pardon.*

There is *Christian* thy Husband, *that was*, with Legions more his Companions, ever beholding that face that doth minister Life to beholders: and they will all be glad when they shall hear the sound of thy feet step over thy Fathers Threshold.

1 marg. *Help . . . Discouragement* add. 2   8 shooted 1   10 marg. Revel. 14. 2, 3 ‖ *om.* 2   17 marg. *Convictions . . . Pardon* add. 2

Christiana at this was greatly abashed in her self, and bowing her head to the ground, this *Visitor* proceeded and said, *Christiana*! Here is also a Letter for thee which I have brought from thy Husbands King. So she took it and opened it, but it smelt after the manner *Song* 1, 3. of the best Perfume, also it was Written in Letters of Gold. The Contents of the Letter was, *That the King would have her do as did* Christian *her Husband; For that was the way to come to his* City, *and to dwell in his* Christiana *Presence with* Joy, *forever*. At this the good Woman *quite overcome.* was quite overcome: So she cried out to her *Visitor*, *Sir, will you carry me and my children with you, that we also may go and Worship this King?*

Then said the Visitor, *Christiana! The bitter is before the sweet:* Thou must through Troubles, as did he that *Further* went before thee, enter this Celestial City. Wherefore *Instruction to* Christiana. I advise thee, to do as did *Christian* thy Husband: go to the *Wicket Gate* yonder, over the Plain, for that stands in the head of the way up which thou must go, and I wish thee all good speed. Also I advise that thou put this Letter in thy Bosome. That thou read therein to thy self and to thy Children, until you have got it by root-of-Heart. For it is one of the Songs that thou must Psal. 119. 54. Sing while thou art in this House of thy Pilgrimage. Also this thou must deliver in at the *further* Gate.

Now I saw in my Dream that this Old Gentleman, as he told me this Story, did himself seem to be greatly affected therewith. He moreover proceeded and said, So *Christiana* called her Sons together, and began thus * Christiana to Address her self unto them. *My Sons, I have, as *prays well for her Journey.* you may perceive, been of late under much exercise in my Soul about the Death of your Father; not for that I doubt at all of his Happiness: For I am satisfied now that he is well. I have also been much affected with the thoughts of mine own State and yours, which I verily believe is by nature miserable: My Carriages also to your Father in his distress, is a great load to my Con-

10 *marg.* Christiana . . . *overcome* add. 2   *for ever* 2   16
marg. *Further* . . . Christiana *add.* 2   30 *marg.* Christiana . . .
Journey add. 2

science. For I hardened both mine own heart and yours against him, and refused to go with him on Pilgrimage.

The thoughts of these things would now kill me outright; but that for a Dream which I had last night, and but that for the incouragement that this Stranger has given me this Morning. Come, my Children, let us pack up, and be gon to the Gate that leads to the Celestial Countrey, that we may see your Father, and be with him and his Companions in Peace according 10 to the Laws of that Land.

Then did her Children burst out into Tears for Joy that the Heart of their Mother was so inclined: So their *Visitor* bid them farewel: and they began to prepare to set out for their Journey.

But while they were thus about to be gon, two of the Women that were *Christiana's* Neighbours, came up to her House and knocked at her Dore. To whom she said as before. *If you come in Gods Name, come in.* *At this the Women were stun'd, for this kind of Language they 20 used not to hear, or to perceive to drop from the Lips of *Christiana.* Yet they came in; but behold they found the good Woman a preparing to be gon from her House.

* Christiana's *new language stunds her old Neighbours.*

So they began and said, *Neighbour, pray what is your meaning by this?*

Christiana answered and said to the eldest of them, whose name was Mrs. *Timorous,* I am preparing for a Journey (This *Timorous* was Daughter to him that met *Christian* upon the Hill *Difficulty*; and would a had him 30 gone back for fear of the Lyons.)

1 *Part, pag.* 43.

Timorous. For what Journey I pray you?

Chris. Even to go after my good Husband, and with that she fell aweeping.

Timo. I hope not so, good Neighbour, pray for your poor Childrens sake, do not so unwomanly cast away your self.

Timorous *comes to visit* Christiana, *with* Mercie *one of her Neighbours.*

Chris. Nay, my Children shall go with me; not one of them is willing to stay behind.

17 Door 2   18 *marg.* Christiana's . . . *Neighbours* add. 2
29 marg. 1 *Part, pag.* 63, 64 ‖ 1, 2   33 a weeping 2

Timo. I wonder in my very Heart, what, or who, has brought you into this mind.

Chris. Oh, Neighbour, knew you but as much as I do, I doubt not but that you would go with me.

Timo. Prithee what new knowledg hast thou got that so worketh off thy mind from thy Friends, and that tempteth thee to go no body knows where?

Chris. Then *Christiana* reply'd, I have been sorely afflicted since my Husbands departure from me; but *Death.* specially since he went *over the River.* But that which troubleth me most, is, my churlish Carriages to him when he was under his distress. Besides, I am *now,* as he was *then*; nothing will serve me but going on Pilgrimage. I was a dreamed last night, that I saw him. O that my Soul was with him. He dwelleth in the presence of the King of the Country, he sits and eats 2 Cor. 5. 1, with him at his Table, he is become a Companion of 2, 3, 4. *Immortals,* and has a House now given him to dwell in, to which, the best Palaces on Earth, if compared, seems to me to be but as a Dunghil. The Prince of the Place has also sent for me, with promise of entertainment if I shall come to him; his messenger was here even now, and has brought me a Letter, which Invites me to come. And with that she pluck'd out her Letter, and read it, and said to them, what now will you say to this?

Timo. Oh the madness that has possessed thee and thy Husband, to run your selves upon such difficulties! You have heard, I am sure, what your Husband did meet with, even in a manner at the first step, that he took on his way, 1 Part, pag. *as our Neighbour* Obstinate *yet can testifie; for he went* 14–16. *along with him, yea and* Plyable *too, until they, like* wise *men, were afraid to go any further. We also heard over and above, how he met with the Lyons, Appollion, the shadow of death, and many other things: Nor is the danger* The reasonings *he met with at* Vanity *fair to be forgotten by thee. For if* of the flesh. *he, tho' a man, was so hard put to it, what canst thou being but a poor Woman do? Consider also that these four sweet Babes are thy Children, thy Flesh and thy Bones. Where-*

---

14 a dreaming 1   30 marg. 1 *part, pag.* 9, 10, 11, 12, 13, 14 ‖ 1, 2
31 plyable 1   35 marg. *The . . . flesh* add. 2

*fore, though thou shouldest be so rash as to cast away thy
self: Yet for the sake of the Fruit of thy Body, keep thou
at home.*

But *Christiana* said unto her, tempt me not, my
Neighbour: I have now a price put into mine hand to
get gain, and I should be a Fool of the greatest size, if
I should have no heart to strike in with the opportunity.
And for that you tell me of all these Troubles that I am
like to meet with in the way, *they are so far off from
10 being to me a discouragement, that they shew I am in
the right. *The bitter must come before the sweet,* and that
also will make the sweet the sweeter. Wherefore, since
you came not to my House, *in Gods name,* as I said,
I pray you to be gon, and not to disquiet me further.

A pertinent reply to fleshly reasonings.

Then *Timorous* all to revil'd her, and said to her
Fellow, come Neighbour *Mercie,* lets leave her in her
own hands, since she scorns our Counsel and Company.
But *Mercie* was at a stand, and could not so readily
comply with her Neighbour: and that for a twofold
20 reason. First, her Bowels yearned over *Christiana*: so
she said with in her self, If my Neighbour will needs
be gon, I will go a little way with her, and help her.
Secondly, her Bowels yearned over her own Soul, (for
what *Christiana* had said, had taken some hold upon
her mind.) Wherefore she said within her self again,
I will yet have more talk with this *Christiana,* and if I
find Truth and Life in what she shall say, my self with
my Heart shall also go with her. Wherefore *Mercie*
began thus to reply to her Neighbour *Timorous.*

Mercies Bowels yearn over Christiana.

30 *Mercie.* Neighbour, *I did indeed come with you, to see*
Christiana *this Morning, and since she is, as you see, a
taking of her last farewel of her Country, I think to walk
this Sun-shine Morning, a little way with her to help her
on the way.* But she told her not of her second Reason,
but kept that to her self.

Timorous forsakes her; but Mercie cleaves to her.

Timo. Well, I see you have a mind to go a fooling
too; but take heed in time, and be wise: while we are
out of danger we are out; but when we are in, we are

9 marg. *A .. reasonings* add. 2   14 not to] do not 2   21
within 2

in. So Mrs. *Timorous* returned to her House, and

Timorous acquaints her Friends what the good Christiana intends to do. *Christiana* betook herself to her Journey. But when *Timorous* was got home to her House, she sends for some of her Neighbours, to wit, Mrs. *Bats-eyes*, Mrs. *Inconsiderate*, Mrs. *Light-mind*, and Mrs. *Know-nothing*. So when they were come to her House, she falls to telling of the story of *Christiana*, and of her intended Journey. And thus she began her Tale.

Timo. Neighbours, having had little to do this Morning, I went to give *Christiana* a Visit, and when 10 I came at the Door, I knocked, as you know 'tis our Custom: And she answered, *If you come in God's Name, come in.* So in I went, thinking all was well: But when I came in, I found her preparing her self to depart the Town, she and also her Children. So I asked her what was her meaning by that? and she told me in short, That she was now of a mind to go on Pilgrimage, as did her Husband. She told me also of a Dream that she had, and how the King of the Country where her Husband was, had sent her an inviting Letter to come 20 thither.

Mrs. Know-nothing. *Then said Mrs.* Know-nothing. *And what! do you think she will go?*

Timo. Aye, go she will, what ever come on't; and methinks I know it by this; for that which was my great Argument to perswade her to stay at home, (to wit, the Troubles she was like to meet with in the way) is one great Argument with her to put her forward on her Journey. For she told me in so many words, *The bitter goes before the sweet.* Yea, and for as much as it 30 so doth, it makes the sweet the sweeter.

Mrs. Bats-eyes. Mrs. *Bats-eyes.* Oh this blind and foolish Woman, said she, Will she not take warning by her Husband's Afflictions? For my part, I say if he was here again he would rest him content in a whole Skin, and never run so many hazards for nothing.

Mrs. Inconsiderate. Mrs. *Inconsiderate* also replied, saying, away with such Fantastical Fools from the Town; a good riddance, for my part I say, of her. Should she stay where she dwels, and retain this her mind, who could live quietly by her? for she will either be dumpish or un-neighbourly, or talk of such matters as no wise body can abide: Wherefore, for my part, I shall never be sorry for her departure; let her go, and let better come in her room: 'twas never a good World since these whimsical Fools dwelt in it.

Then Mrs. *Light-mind* added as followeth. Come put this kind of Talk away. I was Yesterday at Madam *Wantons*, where we were as merry as the Maids. For who do you think should be there, but I, and Mrs. *Love-the-flesh*, and three or four more, with Mr. *Lechery*, Mrs. *Filth*, and some others. So there we had Musick and dancing, and what else was meet to fill up the pleasure. And I dare say my Lady her self is an admirably well-bred Gentlewoman, and Mr. *Lechery* is as pretty a Fellow.

Mrs. Light-mind.

Madam Wanton, *she that had like to a bin too hard for* Faithful *in time past.*

1 part, pag. 68.

By this time *Christiana* was got on her way, and *Mercie* went along with her. So as they went, her Children being there also, *Christiana* began to discourse. And, *Mercie*, said *Christiana*, I take this as an unexpected favour, that thou shouldest set foot out of Doors with me to accompany me a little in my way.

Discourse *betwixt* Mercie *and good* Christiana.

Mercie. *Then said young* Mercie *(for she was but young,) If I thought it would be to purpose to go with you, I would never go near the Town any more.*

Mercie *inclines to go.*

Chris. Well *Mercie*, said *Christiana*, cast in thy Lot with me. I well know what will be the end of our Pilgrimage, my Husband is where he would not but be, for all the Gold in the *Spanish* Mines. Nor shalt thou be rejected, tho thou goest but upon *my Invitation*. The King, who hath sent for me and my Children, is one that delighteth in *Mercie*. Besides, if thou wilt, I will hire thee, and thou shalt go along with me as my servant. Yet we will have all things in common betwixt thee and me, only go along with me.

Christiana *would have her Neighbour with her.*

Mercie. *But how shall I be ascertained that I also shall*

Mercie *doubts of acceptance.*

18 marg. 1 *part, pag.* 111 ‖ 1, 2   34 *marg.* Christiana . . . *her* add. 2

be entertained? Had I but this hope from one that can tell, I would make no stick at all, but would go, being helped by him that can help, tho' the way was never so tedious.

Christiana
alures her to
the Gate which
is Christ, and
promiseth there
to enquire for
her.

Christiana. Well, loving *Mercie*, I will tell thee what thou shalt do, go with me to the *Wicket Gate*, and there I will further enquire for thee, and if there thou shalt not meet with incouragement, I will be content that thou shalt return to thy place. I also will pay thee for thy Kindness which thou shewest to me and my Children, in thy accompanying of us in our way as thou doest.   10

Mercie prays.

Mercie. Then will I go thither, and will take what shall follow, and the Lord grant that my Lot may there fall even as the King of Heaven shall have his heart upon me.

Christiana glad
of Mercie's
company.

Christiana then was glad at her heart, not only that she had a Companion, but also for that she had prevailed with this poor Maid to fall in love with her own Salvation. So they went on together, and *Mercie* began to weep. Then said *Christiana*, wherefore weepeth my Sister so?

Mercie grieves
for her carnal
Relations.

Mer. *Alas! said she, who can but lament that shall but* 20 *rightly consider what a State and Condition my poor Relations are in, that yet remain in our sinful Town: and that which makes my Grief the more heavy, is, because they have no Instructor, nor any to tell them what is to come.*

Christian's
Prayers were
answered for
his Relations
after he was
dead.

Chris. Bowels becometh Pilgrims. And thou dost for thy Friends, as my good *Christian* did for me when he left me; he mourned for that I would not heed nor regard him, but his Lord and ours did gather up his Tears and put them into his Bottle, and now both I, and thou, and these my sweet Babes, are reaping the 30 Fruit and Benefit of them. I hope, *Mercie*, these Tears

Psal. 126. 5, 6.

of thine will not be lost, for the truth hath said, *That they that sow in Tears shall reap in Joy, in singing. And he that goeth forth and weepeth, bearing precious seed, shall doubtless come again with rejoicing, bringing his Sheaves with him.*

1 *I this hope but from* 1: *but* om. 2   11 *marg.* Mercie *prays* add. 2   14 *marg.* Christiana . . . *company* add. 2   20 *marg.* Mercie . . . *Relations* add. 2   25 *marg.* Christian's . . . *dead* add. 2 Bowls 1

Then said *Mercie*,

> *Let the most blessed be my guide,*
> *If't be his blessed Will,*
> Unto *his Gate,* into *his Fould,*
> Up to *his Holy Hill.*

> *And let him never suffer me*
> *To swarve, or turn aside*
> *From his free grace, and Holy ways,*
> *What ere shall me betide.*

> *And let him gather them of mine,*
> *That I have left behind.*
> *Lord make them pray they may be thine,*
> *With all their heart and mind.*

Now my old Friend proceeded, and said, But when *Christiana* came up to the Slow of *Despond,* she began to be at a stand; for, said she, This is the place in which my dear Husband had like to a been smuthered with Mud. She perceived also, that notwithstanding the Command of the King to make this place for Pilgrims good; yet it was rather worse than formerly. So I asked if that was true? Yes, said the Old Gentleman, too true. For that many there be that pretend to be the Kings Labourers; and that say they are for mending the Kings High-way, that bring *Dirt* and *Dung* instead of Stones, and so marr, instead of mending. Here *Christiana* therefore, with her Boys, did make a stand: but said *Mercie,* *come let us venture, only let us be wary. Then they looked well to the *Steps,* and made a shift to get staggeringly over. Yet *Christiana* had like to a been in, and that not once nor twice. Now they had no sooner got over, but they thought they heard words that said unto them, *Blessed is she that believeth, for there shall be a performance of the things that have been told her from the Lord.*

Then they went on again; and said *Mercie* to *Chris-*

Marginal notes:
1 *Part, pag.* 14–16.

Their own Carnal Conclusions, instead of the word of life.

* Mercie *the boldest at the Slow of* Despond.

Luke 1. 45.

tiana, Had I as good ground to hope for a loving Reception at the *Wicket-Gate,* as you, I think no Slow of *Despond* would discourage me.

Well, said the other, you know *your sore,* and I know *mine*; and, good friend, we shall all have enough evil before we come at our Journeys end.

For can it be imagined, that the people that design to attain such excellent Glories *as we do,* and that are so envied that Happiness *as we are*; but that we shall meet with what Fears and Scares, with what Troubles 10 and Afflictions they can possibly assault us with, that hate us?

Prayer should be made with Consideration, and Fear: As well as in Faith and Hope. And now Mr. *Sagacity* left me to Dream out my Dream by my self. Wherefore me-thought I saw *Christiana,* and *Mercie* and the *Boys* go all of them up to the Gate. To which when they were come, they betook themselves to a short debate about *how* they must manage their calling at the Gate, and what should be said to him that did open to them. So it was concluded, since *Christiana* was the eldest, that she should knock 20 for entrance, and that she should speak to him that did *1 part, pag.* open, for the rest. So *Christiana* began to knock, and *25.* as her poor Husband did, she *knocked* and *knocked* again.

But instead of any that answered, they all thought that *The Dog, the Devil, an Enemy to Prayer.* they heard, as if a Dog came barking upon them. A Dog, and a great one too, and this made the Women and Children afraid. Nor durst they for a while dare to knock any more, for fear the *Mastiff* should fly upon ** Christiana and her companions perplexed about Prayer.* them. *Now therefore they were greatly tumbled up and down in their minds, and knew not what to do. 30 Knock they durst not, for fear of the Dog: go back they durst not, for fear that the Keeper of that Gate should espy them, as they so went, and should be offended with them. At last they thought of knocking again, and knocked more vehemently then they did at the first. Then said the Keeper of the Gate, who is there? So the *Dog* left off to bark, and he opened unto them.

Then *Christiana* made low obeysance, and said, Let

not our Lord be offended with his Handmaidens, for
that we have knocked at his Princely Gate. Then said
the Keeper, Whence come ye, and what is that you
would have?

Christiana answered, We are come from whence
Christian did come, and upon the same *Errand* as he;
to wit, to be, if it shall please you, graciously admitted
by this Gate, into the way that leads to the Celestial
City. And I answer, my Lord, in the next place, that
I am *Christiana*, once the Wife of *Christian*, that now
is gotten above.

With that the Keeper of the Gate did marvel, saying, *What! is she become now a Pilgrim, that but awhile
ago abhorred that Life?* Then she bowed her Head, and
said, yes; and so are these my sweet Babes also.

Then he took her by the hand, and led her in, and
said also, *Suffer the little Children to come unto me*, and
with that he shut up the Gate. This don, he called to
a Trumpeter that was above over the Gate, to entertain
Christiana with shouting and sound of Trumpet for joy.
So he obeyed and sounded, and filled the Air with his
melodious Notes.

How Christiana is entertained at the Gate. Luke 15. 7.

Now all this while, poor *Mercie* did stand without,
trembling and crying for fear that she was rejected.
But when *Christiana* had gotten admittance for her self
and her Boys: then she began to make Intercession
for *Mercy*.

Chris. *And she said, my Lord, I have a Companion of
mine that stands yet without, that is come hither upon the
same account as my self.* †*One that is much dejected in her
mind, for that she comes, as she thinks, without sending for,
whereas I was sent to, by my Husbands King, to come.*

†Christiana's Prayer for her friend Mercie.

Now *Mercie* began to be very impatient, for each
minute was as long to her as an Hour, wherefore she
prevented *Christiana* from a fuller interceding for her,
by knocking at the Gate her self. And she knocked
then so loud, that she made *Christiana* to start. Then

The delays make the hungring Soul the ferventer.

18 marg. *How . . . Gate* add. 2   21 Luke 15. 7 || *om.* 2   30
marg. Christiana's . . . Mercie *add.* 2   35 marg. *ferventer*] *fervant* 1
37 then *ital.* 1

said the Keeper of the Gate, Who is there? And said *Christiana*, It is my Friend.

• Mercie *faints.*   So he opened the Gate, and looked out; *but *Mercie* was fallen down without in a Swoon, for she fainted, and was afraid that no Gate should be opened to her.

Then he took her by the hand, and said, *Damsel*, I bid thee arise.

O Sir, said she, I am faint, there is scarce Life left
Jonah 2. 7. in me. But he answered, That one once said, *When my Soul fainted within me, I remembred the Lord, and my* 10 *prayer came in unto thee, into thy Holy Temple.* Fear not, but stand upon thy Feet, and tell me wherefore thou art come.

Mer. I am come, for *that*, unto which I was never
• The cause of invited, as my Friend *Christiana* was. *Hers* was from
her fainting. the King, and *mine* was but from *her:* Wherefore I fear I presume.

Did she desire thee to come with her to this Place?

Mer. Yes. And as my Lord sees, I am come. And if there is any Grace and forgiveness of Sins to spare, I be- 20 seech that I thy poor Handmaid may be partaker thereof.

Then he took her again by the Hand, and led her
• mark this. gently in, and said: *I pray for all them that believe on me, by what means soever they come unto me. Then said he to those that stood by: Fetch something, and give it *Mercie* to smell on, thereby to stay her fainting. So they fetcht her a *Bundle* of *Myrrh*, and a while after she was revived.

And now was *Christiana*, and her Boys, and *Mercie*, *received* of the Lord at the head of the way, and spoke 30 kindly unto by him.

Then said they yet further unto him, We are sorry for our Sins, and beg of our Lord his Pardon, and further information what we must do.

Song 1. 2.   I grant Pardon, said he, by word, and deed; by word
John 20. 20. in the promise of forgiveness: by deed in the way I obtained it. Take the first from my Lips with a kiss, and the other, as it shall be revealed.

3 *marg.* Mercie *faints* add. 2   15 marg. *The . . . fainting*
add. 2   23 marg. *mark this* add. 2

Now I saw in my Dream that he spake many good
words unto them, whereby they were greatly gladed.
He also had them up to the top of the Gate and shewed
them by what *deed* they were saved, and told them *Christ*
withall that that sight they would have again as they *Crucified seen afar off.*
went along in the way, to their comfort.

So he left them a while in a Summer-Parler below,
where they entred into talk by themselves. And thus
Christiana began, *O Lord! How glad am I, that we are * *Talk between the Christians.*
10 *got in hither!*

Mer. *So you well may; but I, of all have cause to leap
for joy.*

Chris. *I thought, one time, as I stood at the Gate (because
I had knocked and none did answer) that all our Labour
had been lost: Specially when that ugly Curr made such
a heavy barking against us.*

Mer. But my worst Fears was after I saw that you
was taken into his favour, and that I was left behind:
Now thought I, 'tis fulfiled which is Written, *Two* Mat. 24. 41.
20 *Women shall be Grinding together; the one shall be taken,
and the other left.* I had much ado to forbear crying out,
Undone, undone.

And afraid I was to knock any more; but when I
looked up, to what was Written over the Gate, I took
Courage. I also thought that I must either knock again 1 *Part, pag.*
or dye. So I knocked; but I cannot tell how, for my ²⁴⁻²⁵·
spirit now *struggled* betwixt life and death.

Chris. *Can you not tell how you knocked? I am sure* Christiana
your knocks were so earnest, that the very sound of them thinks her
30 *made me start. I thought I never heard such knocking in all* prays better
my Life. I thought you would a come in by violent hand, then she.
or a took the Kingdom by storm. Mat. 11. 12.

Mer. Alas, to be in my Case, who that so was, could
but a done so? You saw that the Door was shut upon
me, and that there was a most cruel *Dog* thereabout.
Who, I say, that was so faint hearted as I, that would
not a knocked with all their might? But pray what

9 marg. *Talk . . . Christians* add. 2   16 *against*] *at* 2
19 Written. 1, 2   25 marg. 1 *Part, pag.* 30 ‖ 1, 2   31
hands 1

said my Lord to my rudeness, was he not angry with me?

Chris. *When he heard your lumbring noise, he gave a wonderful Innocent smile. I believe what you did pleas'd him well enough, for he shewed no sign to the contrary. But I marvel in my heart why he keeps such a Dog; had I known that afore, I fear I should not have had heart enough to a ventured my self in this manner. But now we are in, we are in, and I am glad with all my heart.

Mer. I will ask if you please next time he comes 10 down, why he keeps such a filthy Cur in his Yard. I hope he will not take it amiss.

*Ay do, said the Children, and perswade him to hang him, for we are afraid that he will bite us when we go hence.

So at last he came down to them again, and *Mercie* fell to the Ground on her Face before him and worshipped, and said, Let my Lord accept of the Sacrifice of praise which I now offer unto him, with the calves of my Lips. 20

So he said to her, peace be to thee, stand up.

But she continued upon her Face and said, *Righteous art thou O Lord when I plead with thee, yet let me talk with thee of thy Judgments: †Wherefore dost thou keep so cruel a Dog in thy Yard, at the sight of which, such Women and Children as we, are ready to fly from thy Gate for fear?*

He answered, and said: *That Dog* has another Owner, he also is kept close in an other man's ground; only my Pilgrims hear his barking. He belongs to the Castle which you see there at a distance: but can come 30 up to the Walls of this Place. He has frighted many an honest Pilgrim from worse to better, by the great voice of his roaring. Indeed he that oweth him, doth not keep him of any good will to me or mine; but with intent to keep the Pilgrims from coming to me, and

that they may be afraid to knock at this Gate for
entrance. Sometimes also he has broken out and has
worried some that I love; but I take all at present
patiently: I also give my Pilgrims timely help, so they
are not delivered up to his power to do to them what
his Dogish nature would prompt him to. *But what! My *A Check to*
purchased one, I tro, hadst thou known never so much *the carnal fear*
before hand, thou wouldst not a bin afraid of a *Dog*. *of the Pilgrims.*

    The Beggers that go from Door to Door, will, rather then they
10 *will lose a supposed Alms, run the hazzard of the bauling,*
barking, and biting too of a Dog: and shall a Dog, a Dog in an
other Mans Yard: a Dog, whose barking I turn to the Profit
of Pilgrims, keep any from coming to me? I deliver them
from the *Lions*, their Darling from the power of the Dog.

    Mer. Then said *Mercie*, *I confess my Ignorance: I *Christians*
spake what I understood not: I acknowledg that thou doest *when wise*
all things well. *enough*
    Chris. Then *Christiana* began to talk of their Journey, *acquiesce in*
and to enquire after the way. So he fed them, and *the wisdom of*
their Lord.
20 washed their feet, and set them in the way of his Steps, *1 Part, pag.*
according as he had dealt with her Husband before. *27.*

    So I saw in my Dream, that they walkt on in their
way, and had the weather very comfortable to them.
    Then *Christiana* began to sing, saying,

        Bless't be the Day that I began
        A Pilgrim for to be;
        And blessed also be that man
        That thereto moved me.

        'Tis true, 'twas long ere I began
30   *To seek to live for ever:*
        But now I run fast as I can,
        'Tis better late then never.   Mat. 20. 6.

        Our Tears to joy, our fears to Faith
        Are turned, as we see:
        Thus our beginning, (as one saith,)
        Shews what our end will be.

6 marg. *A . . . Pilgrims* add. 2   12 another Mans-Yard 2
15 *marg.* Christians *. . . Lord* add. 2   16 *that* add. 2   19 marg.
1 *Part,* pag. 35 ‖ 1, 2

Now there was, on the other side of the Wall that fenced in the way up which *Christiana* and her Companions was to go, a *Garden; and that Garden belonged to him whose was that *Barking Dog*, of whom mention was made before. And some of the Fruit-Trees that grew in that Garden shot their Branches over the Wall, and being mellow, they that found them did gather them up and oft eat of them to their hurt. So *Christiana's* Boys, as Boys are apt to do, being pleas'd with the Trees, and with the Fruit that did hang thereon, did *Plash* them, and began to eat. Their mother did also chide them for so doing; but still the Boys went on.

Well, said she, my Sons, you Transgress, for that Fruit is none of ours: but she did not know that they did belong to the Enemy; Ile warrant you if she had, she would a been ready to die for fear. But that passed, and they went on their way. Now by that they were gon about two Bows-shot from the place that let them into the way: they espyed two very *ill-favoured ones* coming down a pace to meet them. With that *Christiana*, and *Mercie* her Friend, covered themselves with their Vails, and so kept on their Journey: The Children also went on before, so at last they met together. Then they that came down to meet them, came just up to the Women, as if they would imbrace them; but *Christiana* said, Stand back, or go peaceably by as you should. Yet these two, as men that are deaf, regarded not *Christiana's* words; but began to lay hands upon them; at that *Christiana* waxing very wroth, spurned at them with her feet. *Mercie* also, as well as she could, did what she could to shift them. *Christiana* again, said to them, Stand back and be gon, for we have no Money to loose being Pilgrims as ye see, and such too as live upon the Charity of our Friends.

Ill-fa. Then said one of the two of the Men, We make no assault upon you for Money; but are come out to tell you, that if you will but grant one small

The devils garden.

The Children eat of the Enemies Fruit.

Two ill favoured ones.

They assault Christiana.

The pilgrims struggle with them.

request which we shall ask, we will make Women of
you for ever.

Christ. Now *Christiana*, imagining what they should
mean, made answer again, *We will neither hear nor
regard, nor yield to what you shall ask. We are in haste,
cannot stay, our Business is a Business of Life and Death.*
So again she and her Companions made a fresh assay
to go past them. But they letted them in their way.

Ill-fa. And they said, we intend no hurt to your
10 lives, 'tis an other thing we would have.

Christ. Ay, quoth *Christiana*, you would have us
Body and Soul, for I know 'tis for that you are come;
but we will die rather upon the spot, then suffer our
selves to be brought into such Snares as shall hazzard
our well being hereafter. And with that they both
Shrieked out, and cryed Murder, Murder: and so put *She cryes out.*
themselves under those Laws that are provided for the Deut. 22. 25,
Protection of Women. But the men still made their 26, 27.
approach upon them, with design to prevail against
20 them: They therefore cryed out again.

*Now they being, as I said, not far from the Gate in * *'Tis good
at which they came, their voice was heard from where to cry out
they was, thither: Wherefore some of the House came when we are
 assaulted.*
out, and knowing that it was *Christiana*'s Tongue: they
made haste to her relief. But by that they was got
within sight of them, the Women was in a very great
scuffle, the Children also stood crying by. Then did *The* Reliever
he that came in for their relief, call out to the Ruffins *comes.*
saying, What is that thing that you do? Would you
30 make my Lords People to transgress? He also attempted to take them; but they did make their escape *The* Ill-ones
over the Wall into the Garden of the Man, to whom *fly to the devill
 for releif.*
the great Dog belonged, so the Dog became their Pro-
tector. This *Reliever* then came up to the Women, and
asked them how they did. So they answered, we thank
thy Prince, pretty well, only we have been somewhat
affrighted, we thank thee also for that thou camest in
to our help, for otherwise we had been overcome.

Reliever. So after a few more words, this *Reliever*
The Reliever talks to the Women. said as followeth: *I marvelled much when you was entertained at the Gate above, being ye knew that ye were but
weak Women, that you petitioned not the Lord there for
a Conductor: Then might you have avoided these Troubles,
and Dangers: For he would have granted you one.*

* *mark this.* *Christ.* *Alas said *Christiana*, we were so taken with
our present blessing, that Dangers to come were forgot-
ten by us; besides, who could have thought that so near
the Kings Palace there should have lurked such naughty 10
ones: indeed it had been well for us had we asked our
Lord for one; but since our Lord knew 'twould be for
our profit, I wonder he sent not one along with us.

We lose for want of asking for. Relie. *It is not always necessary to grant things not
asked for, lest by so doing they become of little esteem; but
when the want of a thing is felt, it then comes, under, in
the Eyes of him that feels it, that estimate, that properly is
its due, and so consequently will be thereafter used. Had
my Lord granted you a Conductor, you would not neither,
so have bewailed that oversight of yours in not asking for* 20
*one, as now you have occasion to do. So all things work
for good, and tend to make you more wary.*

Christ. Shall we go back again to my Lord, and
confess our folly and ask one?

*Relie. Your Confession of your folly, I will present him
with: To go back again, you need not. For in all places
where you shall come, you will find no want at all, for in
every of my Lord's Lodgings, which he has prepared for
the reception of his Pilgrims, there is sufficient to furnish
them against all attempts whatsoever. But, as I said, he* 30
*will be enquired of by them to do it for them: and 'tis a poor
thing that is not worth asking for.* When he had thus said,
Ezek. 36. 37. he went back to his place, and the Pilgrims went on their
way.

The mistake of Mercie. *Mer.* Then said *Mercie*, what a sudden blank is here?
I made account we had now been past all danger, and
that we should never see sorrow more.

Christiana's Guilt. *Christ.* Thy *Innocency*, my Sister, said *Christiana* to
Mercie, may excuse thee much; but as for me, my fault

7 marg. *mark this* add. 2   9 beside 2   20 *over sight* 2

is so much the greater, for that I saw this danger before I came out of the Doors, and yet did not provide for it where provision might a been had. I am therefore much to be blamed.

Mer. *Then said* Mercie, *how knew you this before you came from home? pray open to me this Riddle.*

Christ. Why, I will tell you. Before I set Foot out of Doors, one Night, as I lay in my Bed, I had a Dream about this. For methought I saw two men, as like these
10 as ever the World they could look, stand at my *Beds-feet*, plotting how they might prevent my Salvation. I will tell you their very words. They said, ('twas when I was in my Troubles,) *What shall we do with this* Christiana's *Woman? for she cries out waking and sleeping for forgive-* Dream *ness, If she be suffered to go on as she begins, we shall lose* repeated. *her as we have lost her Husband.* This you know might a made me take heed, and have provided when Provision might a been had.

Mer. Well, said *Mercie, as by this neglect, we have an* Mercie *makes*
20 *occasion ministred unto us to behold our own imperfections:* good use of *So our Lord has taken occasion thereby, to make manifest* their neglect *the Riches of his Grace. For he, as we see, has followed* of duty. *us with un-asked kindness, and has delivered us from their hands that were stronger then we, of his meer good pleasure.*

Thus now when they had talked away a little more time, they drew nigh to an House which stood in the way, which House was built for the relief of Pilgrims as you will find more fully related in the first part of 1 Part, *pag.* these Records of the *Pilgrims Progress.* So they drew 28.
30 on towards the House (the House of the Interpreter) and when they came to the Door, they heard a great talk in the House; they then gave ear, and heard, as *Talk in the* they thought, *Christiana* mentioned by name. For you *Interpreter's* must know that there went along, even before her, a *house about* talk of her and her Childrens going on Pilgrimage. *going on* And this thing was the more pleasing to them, because *pilgrimage.* they had heard that she was *Christian's* Wife; that Woman who was sometime ago so unwilling to hear of

---

19 *marg.* Mercie . . . *duty* add. 2   28 marg. 1 *Part, pag.* 36 ‖ 1, 2
32 marg. *Talk . . . pilgrimage* add. 2

going on Pilgrimage. Thus therefore they stood still
and heard the good people within commending her,
* She knocks who they little thought stood at the Door. *At last
at the Door. *Christiana* knocked as she had done at the Gate before.
Now when she had knocked, there came to the Door
The door is a young Damsel and opened the Door and looked, and
opened to them
by Innocent. behold two Women was there.

Damsel. *Then said the Damsel to them, With whom*
would you speak in this Place?

Christ. *Christiana* answered, we understand that this 10
is a priviledged place for those that are become Pilgrims, and we now at this Door are such: Wherefore
we pray that we may be partakers of that for which we
at this time are come; for the day, as thou seest, is very
far spent, and we are loth to night to go any further.

Damsel. Pray what may I call your name, that I may
tell it to my Lord within?

Christ. My name is *Christiana*, I was the Wife of
that Pilgrim that some years ago did Travel this way,
and these be his four Children. This Maiden also is 20
my Companion, and is going on Pilgrimage too.

Innocent. Then ran *Innocent* in (for that was her
name) and said to those within, Can you think who is
at the Door? There is *Christiana* and her Children,
and her Companion, all waiting for entertainment here.
* Joy in the *Then they leaped for Joy, and went and told their
house of the Master. So he came to the Door, and looking upon
Interpreter
that Christiana her, he said, *Art thou that* Christiana, *whom* Christian,
is turned *the Good-man, left behind him, when he betook himself to*
Pilgrim. *a Pilgrims Life?*
30

Christ. I am that Woman that was so hard-hearted
as to slight my Husbands Troubles, and that left him
to go on in his Journey alone, and these are his four
Children; but now I also am come, for I am convinced
that no way is right but this.

Mat. 21. 29. *Inter.* *Then is fulfilled that which also is written of the*
Man that said to his Son, go work to day in my Vineyard,

3 marg. *She . . . Door* add. 2   6 marg. *The . . .* Innocent *add.* 2
named *innocent* add. 2   20 also is] is also 2   26 marg.
Joy . . . Pilgrim add. 2

and he said to his Father, I will not; but afterwards repented and went.

Christ. Then said *Christiana*, So be it, *Amen*, God make it a true saying upon me, and grant that I may be found at the last, of him in peace without spot and blameless.

Inter. But why standest thou thus at the Door, come in thou Daughter of Abraham, *we was talking of thee but now: For tidings have come to us before, how thou art* 10 *become a Pilgrim. Come Children, come in; come Maiden, come in; so he had them all into the House.*

So when they were within, they were bidden sit down and rest them, the which when they had done, those that attended upon the Pilgrims in the House, came into the Room to see them. And one smiled, and another smiled, and they all smiled for Joy that *Chris-* *Old Saints* *tiana* was become a Pilgrim. They also looked upon *glad to see the young ones* the Boys, they stroked them over the Faces with the *walk in Gods* Hand, in token of their kind reception of them: they *ways.* 20 also carried it lovingly to *Mercie*, and bid them all welcome into their Masters House.

After a while, because Supper was not ready, *the ** *The Signi-* *Interpreter* took them into his *Significant* Rooms, and *ficant Rooms.* shewed them what *Christian, Christiana's* Husband had seen sometime before. Here therefore they saw the *Man* in the *Cage*, the man and his Dream, the man that cut his way thorough his Enemies, and the Picture of the biggest of them all: together with the rest of those things that were then so profitable to *Christian.*

30 This done, and after these things had been somewhat digested by *Christiana*, and her Company: the *Interpreter* takes them apart again: and has them first into a Room, *where was a man that could look no way but downwards, with a Muckrake in his hand. There stood* *The man with* *also one over his head with a Celestial Crown in his Hand,* *the Muck-rake* *and proffered to give him that Crown for his Muck-rake;* *expounded.* *but the man did neither look up, nor regard; but raked to himself the Straws, the small Sticks, and Dust of the Floar.*

Then said *Christiana, I perswade my self that I know*

11 *in to* 1   22 marg. *The Significant Rooms* add. 2   39 *knew* 1

somewhat the meaning of this: For this is a Figure of a man of this World: Is it not, good Sir?

Inter. Thou hast said the right, said he, and his *Muck-rake* doth show his Carnal mind. And whereas thou seest him rather give heed to rake up Straws and Sticks, and the Dust of the Floar, then to what he says that calls to him from above with the Celestial Crown in his Hand; it is to show, That Heaven is but as a Fable to some, and that things here are counted the only things substantial. Now whereas it was also 10 shewed thee, that the man could look no way but downwards: It is to let thee know that earthly things when they are with Power upon Mens minds, quite carry their hearts away from God.

Christiana's prayer against the Muck-rake. *Chris.* *Then said* Christiana, *O! deliver me from this* *Muck-rake.*

Inter. That Prayer said the *Interpreter*, has lain by Pro. 30. 8. till 'tis almost rusty: *Give me not Riches,* is scarce the Prayer of one of ten thousand. Straws, and Sticks, and Dust, with most, are the great things now looked after. 20

With that *Mercie*, and *Christiana* wept, and said, It is alass! too true.

When the *Interpreter* had shewed them this, he has them into the very best Room in the house, (a very brave Room it was) so he bid them look round about, and see if they could find any thing profitable there. Then they looked round and round: For there was nothing there to be seen but a very great *Spider* on the Wall: and that they overlook't.

Mer. *Then said* Mercie, *Sir, I see nothing; but* Chris- 30 tiana *held her peace.*

Inter. But said the *Interpreter*, look again: she therefore lookt again and said, Here is not any thing, but an *Of the Spider.* ugly *Spider*, who hangs by her Hands upon the Wall. Then said he, Is there but one *Spider* in all this spacious Room? Then the water stood in *Christiana*'s Eyes, for she was a Woman quick of apprehension: and she said, Yes Lord, there is more here then one. Yea, and

15 *marg.* Christiana's ... Muck-rake *add.* 2   18 *marg.* Pro. 30. 8.
om. 1 (Hunt.)   38 here more 1   than 2

Spiders whose Venom is far more destructive then that *Talk about* which is in her. The *Interpreter* then looked pleasantly *the Spider.* upon her, and said, Thou hast said the Truth. This made *Mercie* blush, and the Boys to cover their Faces. For they all began now to understand the Riddle.

Then said the *Interpreter* again, *The Spider taketh* Pro. 30. 28. *hold with her hands, as you see, and is in Kings Pallaces.* And wherefore is this recorded; but to show you, that how full of the Venome of Sin soever you be, yet you *The Inter-* 10 may by the hand of Faith lay hold of, and dwell in the *pretation.* best Room that belongs to the Kings House above?

Chris. I thought, said *Christiana,* of something of this; but I could not imagin it all. I thought that we were like *Spiders,* and that we looked like ugly Creatures, in what fine Room soever we were: But that by this *Spider,* this venomous and ill favoured Creature, we were to learn *how to act Faith,* that came not into my mind. And yet she has taken hold with her hands as I see, and dwells in the best Room in the House. 20 God has made nothing in vain.

Then they seemed all to be glad; but the water stood in their Eyes: Yet they looked one upon another, and also bowed before the *Interpreter.*

He had them then into another Room where was a Hen and Chickens, and bid them observe a while. So *Of the Hen* one of the Chickens went to the Trough to drink, and *and Chickens.* every time she drank she lift up her head and her eyes towards Heaven. See, said he, what this little Chick doth, and learn of her to acknowledge whence your 30 Mercies come, by receiving them with looking up. Yet again, said he, observe and look: So they gave heed, and perceived that the Hen did walk in a fourfold Method towards her Chickens. 1. She had a *common call,* and that she hath all day long. 2. She had a *special call,* and that she had but sometimes. 3. She had a *brooding note.* And 4. she had an *out-cry.*

Now, said he, compare this *Hen* to your King, and these Chickens to his Obedient ones. For answerable

1 marg. *Talk ... Spider* add. 2   9 marg. *The Interpretation* add. 2
25 Hen, Chickens *ital.* 2

to her, himself has his Methods, which he walketh in towards his People. By his common call, *he gives nothing,* by his special call, he always *has something to* Mat. 23. 37. *give,* he has also a brooding voice, *for them that are under his Wing.* And he has an out-cry, to give *the Alarm when he seeth the Enemy come.* I chose, my Darlings, to lead you into the Room where such things are, because you are Women, and they are easie for you.

Chris. And Sir, said *Christiana,* pray let us see some more: So he had them into the Slaughter-house, where 10 *Of the Butcher* was a *Butcher* a killing of a Sheep: And behold the *and the Sheep.* Sheep was quiet, and took her Death patiently. Then said the *Interpreter:* You must learn of this Sheep, to suffer: And to put up wrongs without murmurings and complaints. Behold how quietly she takes her Death, and without objecting she suffereth her Skin to be pulled over her Ears. Your King doth call you his Sheep.

Of the Garden. After this, he led them into his Garden, where was great variety of Flowers: and he said, do you see all 20 these? So *Christiana* said, yes. Then said he again, Behold the Flowers are divers in *Stature,* in *Quality,* and *Colour,* and *Smell,* and *Virtue,* and some are better then some: Also where the Gardiner has set them, there they stand, and quarrel not one with another.

Of the Field. Again he had them into his Field, which he had sowed with Wheat and Corn: but when they beheld, the tops of all was cut off, only the Straw remained. He said again, this Ground was Dunged, and Plowed, and Sowed; but what shall we do with the Crop? Then 30 said *Christiana,* burn some and make muck of the rest. Then said the *Interpreter* again, Fruit you see is that thing you look for, and for want of that you condemn it to the Fire, and to be trodden under foot of men: Beware that in this you condemn not your selves.

Of the Robbin Then, as they were coming in from abroad, they *and the* Spider. espied a little *Robbin* with a great *Spider* in his mouth. So the *Interpreter* said, look here. So they looked, and *Mercie* wondred; but *Christiana* said, what a disparagement is it to such a little pretty Bird as the *Robbin-red-* 40 *breast* is, he being also a Bird above many, that loveth to maintain a kind of Sociableness with man? I had thought they had lived upon crums of Bread, or upon other such harmless matter. I like him worse then I did.

The *Interpreter* then replied, This *Robbin* is an Emblem very apt to set forth some Professors by; for to sight they are as this *Robbin*, pretty of Note, Colour and Carriages, they seem also to have a very great Love for Professors that are sincere; and above all other to desire to sociate with, and to be in their Company, as if they could live upon the good Mans Crums. They pretend also that therefore it is, that they frequent the House of the Godly, and the appointments of the Lord: but when they are by themselves, *as the Robbin*, they can catch and gobble up *Spiders*, they can change their Diet, drink *Iniquity*, and swallow down *Sin* like Water.

So when they were come again into the House, because Supper as yet was not ready, *Christiana* again desired that the *Interpreter* would either *show* or *tell* of some other things that are Profitable. *Pray, and you will get at that which yet lies unrevealed.*

Then the *Interpreter* began and said, *The fatter the Sow is, the more she desires the Mire; the fatter the Ox is, the more gamesomly he goes to the Slaughter; and the more healthy the lusty man is, the more prone he is unto Evil.*

There is a desire in Women, to go neat and fine, and it is a comely thing to be adorned with that, that in Gods sight is of great price.

'Tis easier watching a night or two, then to sit up a whole year together: So 'tis easier for one to begin to profess well, then to hold out as he should to the end.

Every Ship-Master, when in a Storm, will willingly cast that over Board that is of the smallest value in the Vessel; but who will throw the best out first? none but he that feareth not God.

One leak will sink a Ship, and one Sin will destroy a Sinner.

He that forgets his Friend, is ungrateful unto him; but he that forgets his Saviour is unmerciful to himself.

He that lives in Sin, and looks for Happiness hereafter,

is like him that soweth Cockle, and thinks to fill his Barn with Wheat, or Barley.

If a man would live well, let him fetch his last day to him, and make it always his company-Keeper.

Whispering and change of thoughts, proves that Sin is in the World.

If the world which God sets light by, is counted a thing of that worth with men: what is Heaven which God commendeth?

If the Life that is attended with so many troubles, is so 10 *loth to be let go by us, What is the Life above?*

Every Body will cry up the Goodness of Men; but who is there that is, as he should, affected with the Goodness of God?

We seldom sit down to Meat; but we eat, and leave. So there is in Jesus Christ more Merit and Righteousness then the whole World has need of.

Of the Tree that is rotten at heart. When the *Interpreter* had done, he takes them out into his Garden again, and had them to a Tree whose inside was all rottten, and gone, and yet it grew and had 20 Leaves. Then said *Mercie*, what means this? This Tree, said he, whose *out-side* is fair, and whose *inside* is rotten; is it to which many may be compared that are in the Garden of God: Who with their mouths speak high in behalf of God, but indeed will do nothing for him: Whose Leaves are fair; but their heart Good for nothing, but to be *Tinder* for the Devils *Tinder-box.*

They are at Supper. Now Supper was ready, the Table spread, and all things set on the Board; so they sate down and did eat when one had given thanks. And the *Interpreter* did 30 usually entertain those that lodged with him with Musick at Meals, so the Minstrels played. There was also one that did Sing. And a very fine voice he had. His Song was this.

> *The Lord is only my support,*
> *And he that doth me feed:*
> *How can I then want any thing*
> *Whereof I stand in need?*

8 *which*] *that* 2   29 on Board 2   32 Ministrels 1, 2

When the Song and Musick was ended, the *Interpreter* asked *Christiana, what it was that at first did move her to betake her self to a Pilgrims Life?*

Christiana answered: *First,* the loss of my Husband *Talk at Supper.* came into my mind, at which I was heartily grieved: but all that was but natural Affection. Then after that, came the Troubles, and Pilgrimage of my Husband *A Repetition* into my mind, and also how like a Churl I had carried *of Christiana's* it to him as to that. So guilt took hold of my mind, *Experience.*
10 and would have drawn me into the *Pond*; but that opportunely I had a Dream of the well-being of my Husband, and a Letter sent me by the King of that Country where my Husband dwells, to come to him. The Dream and the Letter together so wrought upon my mind, that they forced me to this way.

Inter. *But met you with no opposition afore you set out of Doors?*

Chris. Yes, a Neighbour of mine, one Mrs. *Timerous.* (She was a kin to him that would have perswaded my
20 Husband to go back for fear of the Lions.) She allto-be-fooled me for, as she called it, my intended desperate adventure; she also urged what she could, to dishearten me to it, the hardships and Troubles that my Husband met with in the way; but all this I got over pretty well. But a Dream that I had, of two illlookt ones, that I thought did Plot how to make me miscarry in my Journey, that hath troubled me much: Yea, it still runs in my mind, and makes me afraid of every one that I meet, lest they should meet me to do me
30 a mischief, and to turn me out of the way. Yea, I may tell my Lord, tho' I would not have every body know it, that between this and the Gate by which we got into the way, we were both so sorely assaulted, that we were made to cry out Murder, and the two that made this assault upon us, were like the two that I saw in my Dream.

Then said the *Interpreter,* Thy beginning is good, *A question put* thy latter end shall greatly increase. So he addressed *to Mercie.* himself to *Mercie*: and said unto her, *And what moved thee to come hither sweet-heart?*

3 *her thus to* 2   7 Husbands 1   20–21 all-tobe-fooled 1

Mercie. Then *Mercie* blushed and trembled, and for a while continued silent.

Interpreter. *Then said he, be not afraid, only believe, and speak thy mind.*

Mercys
answer. *Mer.* So she began and said, Truly Sir, my want of Experience, is that that makes me covet to be in silence, and that also that fills me with fears of coming short at last. I cannot tell of Visions, and Dreams as my friend *Christiana* can; nor know I what it is to mourn for my refusing of the Counsel of those that were good 10 Relations.

Interpreter. *What was it then, dear-heart, that hath prevailed with thee to do as thou hast done?*

Mer. Why, when our friend here, was packing up to be gone from our Town, I and another went accidentally to see her. So we knocked at the Door and went in. When we were within, and seeing what she was doing, we asked what was her meaning. She said, she was sent for to go to her Husband, and then she up and told us, how she had seen him in a Dream, 20 dwelling in a curious place among *Immortals* wearing a Crown, playing upon a Harp, eating and drinking at his Princes Table, and singing Praises to him for bringing him thither, *&c.* Now methought, while she was telling these things unto us, my heart burned within me. And I said in my Heart, if this be true, I will leave my Father and my Mother, and the Land of my Nativity, and will, if I may, go along with *Christiana.*

So I asked her further of the truth of these things, and if she would let me go with her: For I saw now 30 that there was no dwelling, but with the danger of ruin, any longer in our Town. But yet I came away with a heavy heart, not for that I was unwilling to come away; but for that so many of my Relations were left behind. And I am come with all the desire of my heart, and will go if I may with *Christiana* unto her Husband and his King.

Inter. Thy setting out is good, for thou hast given Ruth 2. 11, 12. credit to the truth, Thou art a *Ruth*, who did for the

love that she bore to *Naomi*, and to the Lord her God,
leave Father and Mother, and the land of her Nativity
to come out, and go with a People that she knew not
heretofore. *The Lord recompence thy work, and a full
reward be given thee of the Lord God of* Israel, *under
whose Wings thou art come to trust.*

Now Supper was ended, and Preparations was *They address*
made for Bed, the Women were laid singly alone, *themselves*
and the Boys by themselves. Now when *Mercie* was *for bed.*
10 in Bed, she could not sleep for joy, for that now her
doubts of missing at last, were removed further from
her than ever they were before. So she lay blessing and *Mercy's good*
Praising God who had had such favour for her. *nights rest.*

In the Morning they arose with the *Sun*, and prepared themselves for their departure: But the *Interpreter* would have them tarry a while, for, said he, you
must orderly go from hence. Then said he to the
Damsel that at first opened unto them, Take them and
have them into the Garden, to the *Bath*, and there wash *The Bath*
20 them, and make them clean from the soil which they *Sanctification.*
have gathered by travelling. Then *Innocent* the Damsel
took them and had them into the Garden, and brought
them to the *Bath*, so she told them that there they must *They wash*
wash and be clean, for so her Master would have the *in it.*
Women to do that called at his House as they were
going on *Pilgrimage*. They then went in and washed,
yea they and the Boys and all, and they came out of
that *Bath* not only sweet, and clean; but also much
enlivened and strengthened in their Joynts: So when
30 they came in, they looked fairer a deal, then when they
went out to the washing.

When they were returned out of the Garden from
the *Bath*, the *Interpreter* took them and looked upon
them and said unto them, *fair as the Moon*. Then he
called for the *Seal* wherewith they used to be *Sealed* *They are*
that were washed in his *Bath*. So the *Seal* was brought, *sealed.*
and he set his Mark upon them, that they might be
known in the Places whither they were yet to go: Now

4 *and full* 2   7 marg. *They . . . bed* add. 2   12 *marg.*
Mercy's *. . . rest* add. 2   23 marg. *They . . . it* add. 2

the seal was the contents and sum of the Passover which the Children of *Israel* did eat when they came out from

Exo. 13. 8, the Land of *Egypt*: and the mark was set between their

9, 10. Eyes. This seal greatly added to their Beauty, for it was an Ornament to their Faces. It also added to their gravity, and made their Countenances more like them of Angels.

Then said the *Interpreter* again to the Damsel that waited upon these Women, Go into the Vestry and fetch out Garments for these People: So she went and 10 fetched out white Rayment, and laid it down before him; so he commanded them to put it on. *It was fine*

They are *Linnen, white and clean.* When the Women were thus
clothed. adorned they seemed to be a Terror one to the other, for that they could not see that glory each one on her self, which they could see in each other. Now therefore

True humility. they began to esteem each other better then themselves. For, You are fairer then I am, said one, and, You are more comely then I am, said another. The Children also stood amazed to see into what fashion they were brought. 20

The *Interpreter* then called for a *Man-servant* of his, one *Great-heart*, and bid him take *Sword*, and *Helmet* and *Shield*, and take these my Daughters, said he, and conduct them to the House called *Beautiful*, at which place they will rest next. So he took his Weapons, and went before them, and the *Interpreter* said, God speed. Those also that belonged to the Family sent them away with many a good wish. So they went on their way, and Sung.

This place has been our second Stage, 　30
Here we have heard and seen
Those good things that from Age to Age,
To others hid have been.
The Dunghil-raker, Spider, Hen,
The Chicken too to me
Hath taught a Lesson, let me then
Conformed to it be.

3 between] betwixt 2　　*marg.* Exo. 13. 8, 9, 10 *add.* 2　　14 other;
1, 2　　　　15 For that 1 : For 2　　　22 one *Great-heart* add. 2

The Butcher, Garden and the Field,
The Robbin *and his bait,*
Also the Rotten-tree doth yield
Me Argument of weight
 To move me for to watch and pray,
 To strive to be sincere,
 To take my Cross up day by day,
 And serve the Lord with fear.

Now I saw in my Dream that they went on, and *1 part pag.*
Great-heart went before them, so they went and came 38.
to the place where *Christians* Burthen fell off his Back,
and tumbled into a Sepulchre. Here then they made
a pause, and here also they blessed God. Now said
Christiana, it comes to my mind what was said to us at
the Gate, to wit, that we should have Pardon, by *Word*
and *Deed*; by word, that is, by the promise; by *Deed*,
to wit, in the way it was obtained. What the promise
is, of that I know something: But what is it to have
Pardon by deed, or in the way that it was obtained,
Mr. *Great-heart*, I suppose you know; wherefore if you
please let us hear you discourse thereof.

 Great-heart. Pardon by the deed done, is Pardon ob- *A comment*
tained by some one, for another that hath need there- *upon what*
of: Not by the Person pardoned, but in the way, *saith* *was said at*
the Gate, or
another, in which I have obtained it. So then to speak *a discourse*
to the question more large, The pardon that you and *of our being*
justified by
Mercie and these Boys have *attained*, was *obtained* by *Christ.*
another, to wit, by him that let you in at the Gate: And
he hath obtain'd it in this double way. He has performed Righteousness to cover you, and spilt blood to
wash you in.

 Chris. *But if he parts with his Righteousness to us:*
What will he have for himself?

 Great-heart. He has more Righteousness then you
have need of, or then he needeth himself.

 Chris. *Pray make that appear.*

 Great-heart. With all my heart, but first I must pre-
mise that he of whom we are now about to speak, is

one that has not his Fellow. He has two Natures in one Person, plain to be *distinguished, impossible* to be *divided.* Unto each of these Natures a Righteousness belongeth, and each Righteousness is essential to that Nature. So that one may as easily cause the Nature to be extinct, as to seperate its Justice or Righteousness from it. Of *these* Righteousnesses therefore, we are not made partakers so, as that they, or any of them, should be put upon us that we might be made just, and live thereby. Besides these there is a Righteousness which this Person has, as these two Natures are joyned in one. And this is not the Righteousness of the *Godhead*, as distinguished from the *Manhood*; nor the Righteousness of the *Manhood*, as distinguished from the *Godhead*; but a Righteousness which standeth in the Union of both Natures: and may properly be called, the Righteousness that is essential to his being prepared of God to the capacity of the Mediatory Office which he was to be intrusted with. If he parts with his first Righteousness, he parts with his *Godhead*; if he parts with his second Righteousness, he parts with the purity of his *Manhood*; if he parts with this third, he parts with that perfection that capacitates him to the Office of Mediation. He has therefore another Righteousness which standeth in *performance*, or obedience to a revealed Will: And that is it that he puts upon Sinners, and that by which their Sins are covered. Wherefore he saith, *as by one mans disobedience many were made Sinners: So* Rom. 5. 19. *by the obedience of one shall many be made Righteous.*

Chris. *But are the other Righteousnesses of no use to us?*

Great heart. Yes, for though they are essential to his Natures and Office, and so cannot be communicated unto another, yet it is by Virtue of them that the Righteousness that justifies, is for that purpose efficacious. The *Righteousness* of his *God-head* gives *Virtue* to his Obedience; the *Righteousness* of his *Manhood* giveth capability to his obedience to justifie, and the Righteousness that standeth in the Union of these two Natures to his Office, giveth Authority to

8 or *add.* 2

that Righteousness to do the work for which it is ordained.

So then, here is a Righteousness that Christ, as God, has no need of, for he is God without it: here is a Righteousness that Christ, as Man, has no need of to make him so, for he is perfect Man without it. Again, here is a Righteousness that Christ as God-man has no need of, for he is perfectly so without it. Here then is a Righteousness that Christ, as God, as Man, as God-man has no need of, with Reference to himself, and therefore he can spare it, a justifying Righteousness, that he for himself wanteth not, and therefore he giveth it away. Hence 'tis called the *gift of Righteousness*. This Righteousness, since Christ Jesus the Lord, has made Rom. 5. 17. himself under the Law, *must* be given away: For the Law doth not only bind him that is under it, *to do justly*; but to use Charity: Wherefore he *must*, he *ought* by the Law, if he hath two Coats, to give one to him that has none. Now our Lord hath indeed *two Coats*, one for himself, and one to spare: Wherefore he freely bestows one upon those that have none. And thus *Christiana*, and *Mercie*, and the rest of you that are here, doth your Pardon come by *deed*, or by the work of another man. Your Lord Christ is he that has worked, and given away what he wrought for to the next poor Beggar he meets.

But again, in order to Pardon by *deed*, there must something be paid to God as a price, as well as something prepared to cover us withal. Sin has delivered us up to the just Curse of a Righteous Law: Now from this Curse we must be justified by way of Redemption, a price being paid for the harms we have done, and this is by the Blood of your Lord: Who came and stood in your place, and stead, and died your Death for your Ro. 4. 24. Transgressions. Thus has he ransomed you from your Transgressions by Blood, and covered your poluted Gala. 3. 13. and deformed Souls with Righteousness: For the sake of which, God passeth by you, and will not hurt you, when he comes to Judge the World.

Chris. *This is brave. Now I see that there was some-* Christiana *affected with this way of Redemption.*

1 for] or 1 (of *in Errata*)   23 man? 1, 2   35 Gala. 13. 13 ‖ 1

thing to be learnt by our being pardoned by word *and* deed. *Good* Mercie, *let us labour to keep this in mind, and my Children do you remember it also. But, Sir, was not this it that made my good* Christians *Burden fall from off his Shoulder, and that made him give three leaps for Joy?*

* *How the Strings that bound Christians burden to him were cut.*

Great-heart. *Yes, 'twas the belief of this, that cut those Strings that could not be cut by other means, and 'twas to give him a proof of the Virtue of this, that he was suffered to carry his Burden to the Cross.

Chris. I thought so, for tho' my heart was lightful and 10 joyous before, yet it is ten times more lightsome and joyous now. And I am perswaded by what I have felt, tho' I have felt but little as yet, that if the most burdened Man in the World was here, and did see and believe, as I now do, 'twould make his heart the more merry and blithe.

How affection to Christ is begot in the Soul.

Great-heart. There is not only comfort, and the ease of a Burden brought to us, by the sight and Consideration of these; but an indeared Affection begot in us by it: For who can, if he doth but once think that Pardon comes, not only by promise, but thus; but be affected 20 with the way and means of his Redemption, and so with the man that hath wrought it for him?

1 *Part pag.* 38. *Cause of admiration.*

Chris. True, methinks it makes my Heart bleed to think that he should bleed for me. Oh! thou loving one, Oh! thou Blessed one. Thou deservest to have me, thou hast bought me: Thou deservest to have me all, thou hast paid for me ten thousand times more than I am worth. No marvel that this made the Water stand in my Husbands Eyes, and that it made him trudg so nimbly on, I am perswaded he wished me with him; but vile wretch, that I was, I let him come 30 all alone. O Mercie, that thy Father and Mother were here, yea, and Mrs. Timorous also. Nay I wish now with all my Heart, that here was Madam Wanton too. Surely, surely, their Hearts would be affected, nor could the fear of the one, nor the powerful Lusts of the other, prevail with them to go home again, and to refuse to become good Pilgrims.

Great-heart. You speak now in the warmth of your Affections, will it, think you, be always thus with you?

6 marg. *How . . . cut* add. 2   16 marg. *How . . . Soul* add. 2
23 marg. 1 *Part pag.* 54 ‖ 1, 2   24 marg. *Cause of admiration* add. 2

Besides, this is not communicated to every one, nor to *To be affected* every one that did see your Jesus bleed. There was that *with Christ and* stood by, and that saw the Blood run from his Heart *with what he has don is* to the Ground, and yet was so far off this, that instead *a thing special.* of lamenting, they laughed at him, and instead of becoming his Disciples, did harden their Hearts against him. So that all that you have, my Daughters, you have by a peculiar impression made by a Divine contemplating upon what I have spoken to you. Remember 10 that 'twas told you, that the *Hen* by her common call, gives no meat to her *Chickens*. This you have therefore by a special Grace.

Now I saw still in my Dream, that they went on *Simple and* until they were come to the place that *Simple*, and *Sloth* *Sloth and Presumption* and *Presumption* lay and slept in, when *Christian* went *hanged,* by on Pilgrimage. And behold they were hanged up in *and why.* Irons a little way off on the other-side.

Mercie. *Then said* Mercie *to him that was their Guide, and Conductor, What are those three men? and for what* 20 *are they hanged here?*

Great-heart. These three men, were Men of very bad Qualities, they had no mind to be Pilgrims themselves, and whosoever they could they hindred; they were for Sloth and Folly themselves, and whoever they could perswade with, they made so too, and withal taught them to presume that they should do well at last. They were asleep when *Christian* went by, and now you go by they are hanged.

Mercie. *But could they perswade any to be of their* 30 *Opinion?*

Great-heart. Yes, they turned several out of the way. There was *Slow-pace* that they perswaded to do as they. *Their Crimes.* They also prevailed with one *Short-wind*, with one *No-heart*, with one *Linger-after-lust*, and with one *Sleepy-* *Who they pre-* *head*, and with a young Woman her name was *Dull*, to *vailed upon to turn out* turn out of the way and become as they. Besides, they *of the way.* brought up an ill report of your Lord, perswading others that he was a task-Master. They also brought

1 nor] not 1   marg. *To . . . special* add. 2   15 slept] stept 1
24 *Sloth* 2   *Folly* 2   34 marg. *Who . . . way* add. 2   on 2

up an evil report of the good Land, saying, 'twas not half so good as some pretend it was: They also began to villifie his Servants, and to count the very best of them meddlesome, troublesome busie-Bodies: Further, they would call the Bread of God, *Husks*; the *Comforts* of his Children, *Fancies*, the Travel and Labour of Pilgrims, things to no purpose.

Chris. Nay, *said* Christiana, *if they were such, they shall never be bewailed by me, they have but what they deserve, and I think it is well that they hang so near the* 10 *High-way that others may see and take warning. But had it not been well if their Crimes had been ingraven in some Plate of Iron or Brass, and left here, even where they did their Mischiefs, for a caution to other bad Men?*

Great-heart. So it is, as you well may perceive if you will go a little to the Wall.

Mercie. No no, *let them hang and their Names Rot, and their Crimes live for ever against them; I think it a high favour that they were hanged afore we came hither, who knows else what they might a done to such poor Women* 20 *as we are?* Then she turned it into a Song, saying,

> *Now then, you three, hang there and be a Sign*
> *To all that shall against the Truth combine:*
> *And let him that comes after, fear this end,*
> *If unto Pilgrims he is not a Friend.*
> *And thou my Soul of all such men beware,*
> *That unto Holiness Opposers are.*

1 *Part pag.*
42. Thus they went on till they came at the foot of the Hill *Difficulty*. Where again their good Friend, Mr.
Ezek. 34. 18. *Great-heart*, took an occasion to tell them of what hap- 30 pened there when *Christian* himself went by. So he had 'Tis difficult them first to the Spring. *Lo*, saith he, *This is the Spring* getting of good *that* Christian *drank of*, before he went up this Hill, and Doctrine in then 'twas clear and good; but now 'tis Dirty with the *Times.* feet of some that are not desirous that Pilgrims here should quench their Thirst: Thereat *Mercie* said, *And why so envious tro?* But said their Guide, It will do, if taken up, and put into a Vessel that is sweet and good;

for then the Dirt will sink to the bottom, and the Water come out by it self more clear. Thus therefore *Christiana* and her Companions were compelled to do. They took it up, and put it into an Earthen-pot and so let it stand till the Dirt was gone to the bottom, and then they drank thereof.

Next he shewed them the two *by-ways* that were at the foot of the Hill, where *Formality* and *Hypocrisie*, lost themselves. And, said he, these are dangerous
10 Paths: Two were here cast away when *Christian* came by. *And although, as you see, these ways are since stopt up with *Chains, Posts* and a *Ditch*: Yet there are that will chuse to adventure here, rather then take the pains to go up this Hill.

By paths tho barred up will not keep all from going in them. 1 *Part pag.* 42.

Christiana. The way of Transgressors is hard. 'Tis a wonder that they can get into those ways, without danger of breaking their Necks.

Pro. 13. 15.

Great-heart. They will venture, yea, if at any time any of the Kings Servants doth happen to see them,
20 and doth call unto them, and tell them that *they* are in the wrong ways, and do bid them beware the danger. Then they will railingly return them answer and say, *As for the Word that thou hast spoken unto us in the name of the King, we will not hearken unto thee; but we will certainly do whatsoever thing goeth out of our own Mouths,* &c. Nay if you look a little farther, you shall see that these ways, are made cautionary enough, not only by these *Posts* and *Ditch* and *Chain*; but also by being hedged up. Yet they will chuse to go there.

Jer. 44. 16, 17.

30 *Christiana.* *They are Idle, they love not to take Pains, up-hill-way is unpleasant to them. So it is fulfilled unto them as it is Written, The way of the slothful man is a Hedg of Thorns. Yea, they will rather chuse to walk upon a Snare, then to go up this Hill, and the rest of this way to the City.*

The reason why some do chuse to go in by-waies. Pro. 15. 19.

Then they set forward and began to go up the Hill, and up the Hill they went; but before they got to the top, *Christiana* began to *Pant*, and said, I dare say this is a breathing Hill, no marvel if they that love their

The Hill puts the Pilgrims to it.

11 marg. *By . . . them* add. 2   14 marg. 1 *Part pag.* 62 || 1, 2
30 marg. *The . . . by-waies* add. 2

ease more than their Souls, chuse to themselves a smoother way. Then said *Mercie*, I must sit down, also the least of the Children began to cry. Come, come, *They sit in* said *Great-heart*, sit not down here, for a little above is *the* Arbour. the Princes *Arbour*. Then took he the little Boy by the Hand, and led him up thereto.

1 Part pag. When they were come to the *Arbour* they were very 42-43. willing to sit down, for they were all in a pelting heat. *Mat.* 11. 28. Then said *Mercie*, *How sweet is rest to them that Labour!* And how good is the Prince of Pilgrims, to provide 10 such resting places for them! Of *this Arbour* I have heard much; but I never saw it before. But here let us beware of sleeping: For as I have heard, for that it cost poor *Christian* dear.

The little Boys Then said Mr. *Great-heart* to the little ones, Come *answer to the* my pretty *Boys*, how do you do? what think you now *guide, and also* *to* Mercie. of going on Pilgrimage? Sir, said the least, I was almost beat out of heart; but I thank you for lending me a hand at my need. And I remember now what my Mother has told me, namely, That the way to Heaven 20 is as up a Ladder, and the way to Hell is as down a Hill. But I had rather go up the Ladder to Life, then down the Hill to Death.

Which is Then said *Mercie*, But the Proverb is, *To go down the* *hardest up Hill* *or down Hill?* Hill is easie: But *James* said (for that was his Name) The day is coming when in my Opinion, *going down Hill will be the hardest of all.* 'Tis a good Boy, said his Master, thou hast given her a right answer. Then *Mercie* smiled, but the little Boy did blush.

They refresh *Chris.* Come, said *Christiana*, will you eat a bit, a 30 *themselves.* little to sweeten your Mouths, while you sit here to rest your Legs? For I have here a piece of Pomgranate which Mr. *Interpreter* put in my Hand, just when I came out of his Doors; he gave me also a piece of an Honey-comb, and a little Bottle of Spirits. I thought he gave you something, said *Mercie*, because he called you a to-side. Yes, so he did, said the other, But *Mercie*, It shall still be as I said it should, when at first

7 marg. 1 *Part pag.* 62, 63 ‖ 1, 2   22 Laddar 2   24 marg.
Which . . . Hill? add. 2   32 peice 2

we came from home: Thou shalt be a sharer in all the good that I have, because thou so willingly didst become my Companion. Then she gave to them, and they did eat, both *Mercie*, and the Boys. And said *Christiana* to Mr. *Great-heart*, Sir will you do as we? But he answered, You are going on Pilgrimage, and presently I shall return; much good may what you have, do to you. At home I eat the same every day. Now when they had eaten and drank, and had chatted
10 a little longer, their guide said to them, The day wears away, if you think good, let us prepare to be going. So they got up to go, and the little Boys went before; but *Christiana* forgat to take her Bottle of Spirits with her, so she sent her little Boy back to fetch it. Then said *Mercie*, I think this is a *losing* Place. Here *Christian* lost his *Role*, and here *Christiana* left her Bottle behind her: Christiana
Sir, what is the cause of this? so their guide made *forgets her Bottle of*
answer and said, The cause is *sleep*, or *forgetfulness*; *Spirits.*
some *sleep*, when they should keep *awake*; and some
20 *forget*, when they should *remember*; and this is the very cause, why often at the resting places, some Pilgrims in some things come off losers. Pilgrims should watch Mark this.
and remember what they have already received under their greatest enjoyments: But for want of doing so, oft times their rejoicing ends in Tears, and their Sun-shine in a Cloud: Witness the story of *Christian* at this place. 1 part page
When they were come to the place where *Mistrust* 43.
and *Timorous* met *Christian* to perswade him to go back for fear of the Lions, they perceived as it were a Stage,
30 and before it towards the Road, a broad plate with a Copy of Verses Written thereon, and underneath, the reason of the raising up of that Stage in that place, rendered. The Verses were these.

> Let him that sees this Stage take heed,
> Unto his Heart and Tongue:
> Lest if he do not, here he speed
> As some have long agone.

16 *marg.* Christiana ... *Spirits* add. 2   26 marg. 1 *part page* 65 ||
1, 2

The words underneath the Verses were. *This Stage was built to punish such upon, who through* Timorousness, *or* Mistrust, *shall be afraid to go further on Pilgrimage. Also on this Stage both* Mistrust, *and* Timorous *were burned thorough the Tongue with an hot Iron, for endeavouring to hinder* Christian *in his Journey.*

Then said *Mercie.* This is much like to the saying of the beloved, *What shall be given unto thee? or what shall be done unto thee thou false Tongue? sharp Arrows of the mighty, with Coals of* Juniper.

Psal. 120. 3, 4.

So they went on till they came within sight of the Lions. Now Mr. *Great-heart* was a strong man, so he was not afraid of a Lion. But yet when they were come up to the place where the Lions were, the Boys that went before, were now glad to cringe behind, for they were afraid of the Lions, so they stept back and went behind. At this their guide smiled, and said, How now my Boys, do you love to go before when no danger doth approach, and love to come behind so soon as the Lions appear?

1 Part pag. 45. An Emblem of those that go on bravely, when there is no danger; but shrink when troubles come.

Now as they went up, Mr. *Great-heart* drew his Sword with intent to make a way for the Pilgrims in spite of the Lions. Then there appeared one, that it seems, had taken upon him to back the Lions. And he said to the Pilgrims guide, What is the cause of your coming hither? Now the name of that man was *Grim* or *Bloody man*, because of his slaying of Pilgrims, and he was of the race of the *Gyants.*

Of Grim *the Giant, and of his backing the Lions.*

Great-heart. Then said the *Pilgrims* guide, these Women and Children, are going on Pilgrimage, and this is the way they must go, and go it they shall in spite of thee and the Lions.

Grim. This is not their way, neither shall they go therein. I am come forth to withstand them, and to that end will back the Lions.

Now to say truth, by reason of the fierceness of the Lions, and of the *Grim*-Carriage of him that did back them, this way had of late lain much un-occupied, and was almost all grown over with Grass.

11 marg. 1 *Part pag.* 69 ‖ 1, 2   27 *Grim* or *add.* 2   34 with stand 2

Christiana. Then said *Christiana,* Tho' the High-ways have been unoccupied heretofore, and tho' the Travellers have been made in time past, to walk thorough by-Paths, it must not be so now I am risen, *Now I am Risen a Mother in* Israel.   Judg. 5. 6, 7.

Grim. Then he swore *by the Lions,* but it should; and therefore bid them turn aside, for they should not have passage there.

Great-heart. But their guide made first his Approach
10 unto *Grim,* and laid so heavily at him with his Sword, that he forced him to a retreat.

Grim. Then said he (that attempted to back the Lions) will you slay me upon mine own Ground?

Great-heart. 'Tis the Kings High-way that we are in, *A fight betwixt* and in this way it is that thou hast placed thy Lions; *Grim and* *Great-heart.* but these Women and these Children, tho' weak, shall hold on their way in spite of thy Lions. And with that he gave him again a down-right blow, and brought him upon his Knees. With this blow he also broke his
20 Helmet, and with the next he cut off an Arm. Then did the *Giant Roar* so hideously, that his Voice frighted the Women, and yet they were glad to see him lie *The Victory.* sprawling upon the Ground. Now the Lions were chained, and so of themselves could do nothing. Wherefore when old *Grim* that intended to back them was dead, Mr. *Great-heart* said to the Pilgrims, Come now and follow me, and no hurt shall happen to you from the Lions. They therefore went on; but the *They pass by* Women trembled as they passed by them, the Boys *the Lyons,*
30 also look't as if they would die; but they all got by without further hurt.

Now then they were within sight of the *Porters* *They come to the* Lodg, and they soon came up unto it; but they made *Porters Lodge.* the more haste after this to go thither, because 'tis dangerous travelling there in the Night. So when they were come to the Gate, the guide knocked, and the Porter cried, *who is there*; but as soon as the Guide had said *it is I,* he knew his Voice and came down. (For

14 marg. *A* ... Great-heart *add.* 2   22 marg. *The Victory* add. 2
28 marg. *They* ... *Lyons* add. 2   32 marg. *They* ... *Lodge* add. 2

the Guide had oft before that, came thither as a Conductor of Pilgrims) when he was came down, he opened the Gate, and seeing the Guide standing just before it (for he saw not the Women, for they were behind) he said unto him, How now Mr. *Great-heart*, what is your business here so late to Night? I have brought, said he, some Pilgrims hither, where by my Lords Commandment they must Lodg. I had been here some time ago, had I not been opposed by the Giant that did use to back the Lyons. But I after a long 10 and tedious combate with him, have cut him off, and have brought the Pilgrims hither in safety.

Great-heart attempts to go back.

Porter. *Will you not go in, and stay till Morning?*

Great-heart. No, I will return to my Lord to night.

The Pilgrims implore his company still.

Christiana. Oh Sir, I know not how to be willing you should leave us in our Pilgrimage, you have been so faithful, and so loving to us, you have fought so stoutly for us, you have been so hearty in counselling of us, that I shall never forget your favour towards us.

Mercie. Then said *Mercie*, O that we might have thy 20 Company to our Journeys end! How can such poor Women as we, hold out in a way so full of Troubles as this way is, without a Friend, and Defender?

James. Then said *James*, the youngest of the Boys, Pray Sir be perswaded to go with us and help us, because we are so weak, and the way so dangerous as it is.

Help lost for want of asking for.

Great-heart. I am at my Lords Commandment. If he shall allot me to be your Guide quite thorough, I will willingly wait upon you; but here you failed at first; 30 for when he bid me come thus far with you, then you should have begged me of him to have gon quite thorough with you, and he would have granted your request. However, at present I must withdraw, and so good *Christiana*, *Mercie*, and my brave Children, Adieu.

1 Part pag. 46–47. Christiana makes her self

Then the Porter, Mr. *Watchfull*, asked *Christiana* of her Country, and of her Kindred, and she said, *I came from the City of Destruction, I am a Widdow Woman,*

7 whereby 2   13 *marg.* Great-heart . . . *back* add. 2   15
marg. *The . . . still* add. 2   35 marg. 1 *Part pag.* 70 ‖ 1, 2   36
marg. Christiana . . . *damsel* add. 2

and my Husband is dead, his name was Christian *the* known to the
Pilgrim. How, said the Porter, was he your Husband? Porter, he tells
Yes, said she, and these are his Children: and this, it to a damsel.
pointing to *Mercie,* is one of my Towns-Women. Then
the Porter rang his Bell, as at such times he is wont, and
there came to the Door one of the Damsels, whose Name
was *Humble-mind.* And to her the Porter said, Go tell it
within that *Christiana* the Wife of *Christian* and her
Children are come hither on Pilgrimage. She went in
10 therefore and told it. But Oh what a Noise for gladness *Joy at the noise*
was there within, when the Damsel did but drop that *of the Pilgrims*
word out of her Mouth! *coming.*

So they came with haste to the Porter, for *Christiana*
stood still at the Door; then some of the most grave,
said unto her, *Come in* Christiana, *come in thou Wife of
that Good Man, come in thou Blessed Woman, come in with
all that are with thee.* So she went in, and they followed
her that were her Children, and her Companions. Now
when they were gone in, they were had into a very large
20 Room, where they were bidden to sit down: So they sat
down, and the chief of the House was called to see, and
welcome the Guests. Then they came in, and under- Christians *love*
standing who they were, did Salute each one with a kiss, *is kindled at*
and said, Welcome ye Vessels of the Grace of God, *the sight of*
welcome to us your Friends. *one another.*

Now because it was somewhat late, and because the
Pilgrims were weary with their Journey, and also made
faint with the sight of the Fight, and of the terrible
Lyons: Therefore they desired as soon as might be, to Exo. 12. 3, 8.
30 prepare to go to Rest. Nay, said those of the Family,
refresh your selves first with a Morsel of Meat. For
they had prepared for them a Lamb, with the accus- Joh. 1. 29.
tomed Sauce belonging thereto. For the Porter had
heard before of their coming, and had told it to them
within. So when they had Supped, and ended their
Prayer with a Psalm, they desired they might go to
rest. But let us, said *Christiana,* if we may be so bold 1 *Part pag.*
as to chuse, be in that Chamber that was my Husbands, 53.

7 *humble-mind* 1, 2   10 marg. *Joy . . . coming* add. 2   29 *marg.*
Exo. 12. 38 || 1, 2   37 marg. 1 *Part pag.* 82 || 1, 2

when he was here. So they had them up thither, and
they lay all in a Room. When they were at Rest,
Christiana and *Mercie* entred into discourse about things
that were convenient.

Chris. *Little did I think once, that when my Husband
went on Pilgrimage I should ever a followed.*

Mercie. And you as little thought of lying in his Bed,
and in his Chamber to Rest, as you do now.

*Christs Bosome
is for all
Pilgrims.*

Chris. *And much less did I ever think of seeing his Face
with Comfort, and of Worshipping the Lord the King with*   10
him, and yet now I believe I shall.

Mercie. Hark, don't you hear a Noise?

Musick.

Christiana. Yes, 'tis as I believe a Noise of Musick,
for Joy that we are here.

Mer. Wonderful! Musick in the House, Musick in
the Heart, and Musick also in Heaven, for joy that
we are here.

Thus they talked a while, and then betook themselves to sleep; so in the morning, when they were
awake, *Christiana* said to *Mercy*.   20

*Mercy did
laugh in her
sleep.*

Chris. *What was the matter that you did laugh in your
sleep to Night? I suppose you was in a Dream?*

Mercy. So I was, and a sweet Dream it was; but are
you sure I laughed?

Christiana. *Yes, you laughed heartily; But prethee*
Mercy *tell me thy Dream?*

*Mercy's
Dream.*

Mercy. I was a Dreamed that I sat all alone in a
Solitary place, and was bemoaning of the hardness of
my Heart. Now I had not sat there long, but methought many were gathered about me to see me, and   30
to hear what it was that I said. So they harkened, and
I went on bemoaning the hardness of my Heart. At
this, some of them laughed at me, some called me Fool,

*What her
dream was.*

and some began to thrust me about. With that, methought I looked up, and saw one coming with Wings
towards me. So he came directly to me, and said *Mercy*,
what aileth thee? Now when he had heard me make my
complaint; he said, *Peace be to thee:* he also wiped mine
Eyes with his Hankerchief, and *clad* me in *Silver* and

Gold; he put a Chain about my Neck, and Ear-rings in Ezek. 16. 8, mine Ears, and a beautiful Crown upon my Head. 9, 10, 11. Then he took me by my Hand, and said, *Mercy*, come after me. So he went up, and I followed, till we came at a Golden Gate. Then he knocked, and when they within had opened, the man went in and I followed him up to a Throne, upon which one sat, and he said to me, *welcome Daughter*. The place looked bright, and twinkling like the Stars, or rather like the *Sun*, and I thought
10 that I saw your Husband there, so I awoke from my Dream. But did I laugh?

Christiana. *Laugh! Ay, and well you might to see your self so well. For you must give me leave to tell you, that I believe it was a good Dream, and that as you have begun to find the first part true, so you shall find the second at last.* God speaks once, yea twice, yet man perceiveth Job 33. 14, it not. In a Dream, in a Vision of the Night, when deep 15. sleep falleth upon men, in slumbering upon the Bed. *We need not, when a-Bed, lie awake to talk with God; he*
20 *can visit us while we sleep, and cause us then to hear his Voice. Our Heart oft times wakes when we sleep, and God can speak to that, either by Words, by Proverbs, by Signs, and Similitudes, as well as if one was awake.*

Mercy. Well, I am glad of my Dream, for I hope ere *Mercy glad* long to see it fulfilled, to the making of me laugh again. *of her dream.*

Christiana. *I think it is now time to rise, and to know what we must do.*

Mercy. Pray, if they invite us to stay a while, let us willingly accept of the proffer. I am the willinger to
30 stay awhile here, to grow better acquainted with these Maids; methinks *Prudence, Piety* and *Charity*, have very comly and sober Countenances.

Chris. *We shall see what they will do.* So when they were up and ready, they came down. And they asked one another of their rest, and if it was Comfortable, or not?

Mer. *Very good, said* Mercy. *It was one of the best Nights Lodging that ever I had in my Life.*

Then said *Prudence*, and *Piety*, If you will be per- *They stay here some time.*

3 my] the 2   24 *marg.* Mercy . . . *dream* add. 2

swaded to stay here a while, you shall have what the House will afford.

Charity. *Ay, and that with a very good will, said* Charity. So they consented, and stayed there about a Month or above: And became very Profitable one to
Prudence another. And because *Prudence* would see how *Chris-*
desires to *tiana* had brought up her Children, she asked leave of
catechise
Christianas her to Catechise them: So she gave her free consent.
Children. Then she began at the youngest whose Name was *James*.

James Pru. *And she said, Come* James, *canst thou tell who* 10
Catechised. *made thee?*

Jam. God the Father, God the Son, and God the Holy-Ghost.

Pru. *Good Boy. And canst thou tell who saves thee?*

Jam. God the Father, God the Son, and God the Holy Ghost.

Pru. *Good Boy still. But how doth God the Father save thee?*

Jam. By his Grace.

Pru. *How doth God the Son save thee?* 20

Jam. By his Righteousness, Death, and Blood, and Life.

Pru. *And how doth God the Holy Ghost save thee?*

Jam. By his *Illumination,* by his *Renovation,* and by his *Preservation.*

Then said *Prudence* to *Christiana,* You are to be commended for thus bringing up your Children. I suppose I need not ask the rest these Questions, since the youngest of them can answer them so well. I will therefore now apply my self to the Youngest next. 30

Joseph *Prudence.* Then she said, Come *Joseph,* (for his
catechised. Name was *Joseph*) will you let me Catechise you?

Joseph. With all my Heart.

Pru. *What is Man?*

Joseph. A Reasonable Creature, so made by God, as my Brother said.

Pru. *What is supposed by this Word, saved?*

Joseph. That man by Sin has brought himself into a State of Captivity and Misery.

6 *marg.* Prudence ... *Children* add. 2

Pru. What is supposed by his being saved by the Trinity?

Joseph. That Sin is so great and mighty a Tyrant, that none can pull us out of its clutches but God, and that God is so good and loving to man, as to pull him indeed out of this Miserable State.

Pru. What is Gods design in saving of poor Men?

Joseph. The glorifying of his Name, of his Grace, and Justice, *&c.* And the everlasting Happiness of his Creature.

10   *Pru. Who are they that must be saved?*

Joseph. Those that accept of his Salvation.

Good Boy *Joseph,* thy Mother has taught thee well, and thou hast harkened to what she has said unto thee.

Then said *Prudence* to *Samuel,* who was the eldest but one.

Prudence. Come *Samuel,* are you willing that I should Catechise you also?

Samuel
Catechised.

Sam. Yes, forsooth, if you please.

Pru. What is Heaven?

20   *Sam.* A place, and State most blessed, because God dwelleth there.

Pru. What is Hell?

Sam. A Place and State most woful, because it is the dwelling place of Sin, the Devil, and Death.

Prudence. Why wouldest thou go to Heaven?

Sam. That I may see God, and serve him without weariness; that I may see Christ, and love him everlastingly; that I may have that fulness of the Holy Spirit in me, that I can by no means here enjoy.

30   *Pru. A very good Boy also, and one that has learned well.*

Then she addressed her self to the eldest, whose Name was *Mathew,* and she said to him, Come *Mathew,* shall I also Catechise you?

Mathew
Catechised.

Mat. With a very good will.

Pru. I ask then, if there was ever any thing that had a being, Antecedent to, or before God?

Mat. No, for God is Eternal, nor is there any thing excepting himself, that had a being until the beginning

20 place] palce 1: palace 2   29 enjoy] Joy 1

of the first day. *For in six days the Lord made Heaven and Earth, the Sea and all that in them is.*

Pru. *What do you think of the Bible?*

Mat. It is the Holy Word of God.

Pru. *Is there nothing Written therein, but what you understand?*

Mat. Yes, a great deal.

Pru. *What do you do when you meet with such places therein, that you do not understand?*

Mat. I think God is wiser then I. I pray also that he will please to let me know all therein that he knows will be for my good.

Pru. *How believe you as touching the Resurrection of the Dead?*

Mat. I believe they shall rise, the same that was buried: The same in *Nature*, tho' not in Corruption. And I believe this upon a double account. First, because God has promised it. Secondly, because he is able to perform it.

Prudences conclusion upon the Catechising of the Boys. Then said *Prudence* to the Boys, You must still harken to your Mother, for she can learn you more. You must also diligently give ear to what good talk you shall hear from others, for for your sakes do they speak good things. Observe also and that with carefulness, what the Heavens and the Earth do teach you; but especially be much in the Meditation of that Book that was the cause of your Fathers becoming a Pilgrim. I for my part, my Children, will teach you what I can while you are here, and shall be glad if you will ask me Questions that tend to Godly edifying.

Mercie has a sweet heart. Now by that these Pilgrims had been at this place a week, *Mercie* had a Visitor that pretended some good Will unto her, and his name was Mr. *Brisk*. A man of some breeding, and that pretended to Religion; but a man that stuck very close to the World. So he came once or twice, or more to *Mercie*, and offered love unto her. Now *Mercie* was of a fair Countenance, and therefore the more alluring.

Mercies temper. Her mind also was, to be always busying of her self

19 *marg.* Prudences . . . *Boys* add. 2   34 that] thut 1   close]
closs 1   38 *marg.* Mercies *temper* add. 2

in doing, for when she had nothing to do for her self, she would be making of Hose and Garments for others, and would bestow them upon them that had need. And Mr. *Brisk* not knowing where or how she disposed of what she made, seemed to be greatly taken, for that he found her never Idle. I will warrant her a good Huswife, quoth he to himself.

Mercie then revealed the business to the Maidens that were of the House, and enquired of them con-
10 cerning him: for they did know him better then she. So they told her that he was a very busie Young-Man, and one that pretended to Religion; but was as they feared, a stranger to the Power of that which was good.

Nay then, said Mercie, *I will look no more on him, for I purpose never to have a clog to my Soul.*

Prudence then replied, That there needed no great matter of discouragement to be given to him, her continuing so as she had began to do for the Poor, would quickly cool his Courage.

20 So the next time he comes, he finds her at her old work, a making of things for the Poor. Then said he, What always at it? Yes, said she, either for my self, or for others. And what canst thee *earn* a day, quoth he? I do these things, said she, *That I may be Rich in good Works, laying up in store a good Foundation against the time to come, that I may lay hold on Eternal Life:* Why prethee what dost thou with them? said he; Cloath the naked, said she. With that his Countenance fell. So he forbore to come at her again. And when he was
30 asked the reason why, he said, *That* Mercie *was a pretty lass; but troubled with ill Conditions.*

When he had left her, *Prudence* said, Did I not tell thee that Mr. *Brisk* would soon forsake thee? yea, he will raise up an ill report of thee: For notwithstanding his pretence to Religion, and his seeming love to *Mercie:* Yet *Mercie* and he are of tempers so different, that I believe they will never come together.

Mercie. *I might a had Husbands afore now, tho' I*

Mercie enquires of the Maids concerning Mr. Brisk.

Talk betwixt Mercie and Mr. Brisk.

1 Tim. 6. 17, 18, 19.

He forsakes her, and why.

Mercie *in the practice of Mercie rejected; While* Mercie *in the Name of Mercie is liked.*

8 marg. *Mercie . . .* Brisk *add.* 2   18 begun 2   21 marg.
Talk . . . Brisk *add.* 2   23 thee] thou 2

spake not of it to any; but they were such as did not like my Conditions, though never did any of them find fault with my Person: So they and I could not agree.

Prudence. *Mercie* in our days is little set by, any further then as to its Name: the Practice, which is set forth by thy Conditions, there are but few that can abide.

Mercie. *Well, said* Mercie, *if no body will have me, I will dye a Maid, or my Conditions shall be to me as a Husband. For I cannot change my Nature, and to have* 10 *one that lies cross to me in this, that I purpose never to* *admit of, as long as I live. I had a Sister named* Bountiful *that was married to one of these Churles; but he and she could never agree; but because my Sister was resolved to do as she had began, that is, to show Kindness to the Poor, therefore her Husband first cried her down at the Cross, and then turned her out of his Doors.*

Pru. And yet he was a Professor, I warrant you?

Mer. *Yes, such a one as he was, and of such as he, the World is now full; but I am for none of them all.* 20

*Now *Mathew* the eldest Son of *Christiana* fell Sick, and his Sickness was sore upon him, for he was much pained in his Bowels, so that he was with it, at times, pulled as 'twere both ends together. There dwelt also not far from thence, one Mr. *Skill,* an Antient, and well approved Physician. So *Christiana* desired it, and they sent for him, and he came. When he was entred the Room, and had a little observed the Boy, he concluded that he was sick of the Gripes. Then he said to his Mother, *What Diet has* Mathew *of late fed upon?* Diet, 30 said *Christiana,* nothing but that which is wholsome. *The Physician answered, *This Boy has been tampering with something which lies in his Maw undigested, and that will not away without means.* And I tell you he must be purged or else he will dye.

Samuel. *Then said *Samuel, Mother, Mother, what was that which my Brother did gather up and eat, so soon*

8 *marg.* Mercie's *resolution* add. 2   12 marg. *How . . . Husband* add. 2   21 *marg.* Mathew *. . . sick* add. 2   32 marg. *The . . . Judgment* add. 2   36 *marg.* Samuel *. . . eat* add. 2

as we were come from the Gate, that is at the head of this way? You know that there was an Orchard on the left hand, on the otherside of the Wall, and some of the Trees hung over the Wall, and my Brother did plash and did eat.

Christiana. True my Child, said *Christiana*, he did take thereof and did eat; naughty Boy as he was, I did chide him, and yet he would eat thereof.

Skill. I knew he had eaten something that was not whol-some Food. And that Food, to wit, that Fruit is even the
10 *most hurtful of all. It is the Fruit of* Belzebubs *Orchard. I do marvel that none did warn you of it; many have died thereof.*

Christiana. Then *Christiana* began to cry, and she said, O naughty Boy, and O careless Mother, what shall I do for my Son?

Skill. Come, do not be too much Dejected; the Boy may do well again; but he must purge and Vomit.

Christiana. Pray Sir try the utmost of your Skill with him whatever it costs.

20 *Skill. Nay, I hope I shall be reasonable:* So he made Heb. 10. 1, him a Purge; but it was too weak. 'Twas said, it was ², ³, ⁴· made of the Blood of a Goat, the Ashes of an Heifer, and with some of the Juice of Hyssop, &c. *When *Potion* Mr. *Skill* had seen that that Purge was too weak, he *prepared.* made him one to the purpose. 'Twas made *ex Carne* John 6. 54, *& Sanguine Christi.* (You know Physicians give strange 55, 56, 57· Mark 9. 49. Medicines to their Patients) and it was made up into The Lattine Pills with a Promise or two, and a proportionable *I borrow.* quantity of Salt. Now he was to take them three at Heb. 9. 14.
30 a time fasting in half a quarter of a Pint of the Tears of Repentance. When this potion was prepared, and brought to the Boy; *he was loth to take it, tho' torn *The boy loth* with the Gripes, as if he should be pulled in pieces. *to take the Physick.* *Come, come, said the Physician, you must take it.* It goes Zech. 12. 10. against my Stomach, said the Boy. *I must have you take it, said his Mother.* I shall Vomit it up again, said the Boy. Pray Sir, said *Christiana* to Mr. *Skill*, how does it taste? It has no ill taste, said the Doctor, and with

---

4 *plash*] *pluck* 2   22 an] a 2   23 marg. *Potion prepared* add. 2
27 marg. *Lattine*] *Latine* 2   32 marg. *The . . . Physick* add. 2

The Mother *tasts it, and* *perswades him.* that she touched one of the pills with the tip of her Tongue. Oh *Mathew*, said she, this potion is sweeter then Hony. If thou lovest thy Mother, if thou lovest thy Brothers, if thou lovest *Mercie*, if thou lovest thy Life, take it. So with much ado, after a short Prayer for the blessing of God upon it, he took it; and it wrought kindly with him. It caused him to Purge, it caused him to sleep, and rest quietly, it put him into a fine heat and breathing sweat, and did quite rid him of his Gripes.   10

A word of God in the hand of his Faith. So in little time he got up, and walked about with a Staff, and would go from Room to Room, and talk with *Prudence*, *Piety*, and *Charity* of his Distemper, and how he was healed.

Heb. 13. 11, 12, 13, 14, 15. So when the Boy was healed, *Christiana* asked Mr. *Skill*, saying, Sir, what will content you for your pains and care to and of my Child? And he said, you must pay the *Master of the Colledge* of Physicians, according to rules made, in that case, and provided.

Chris. *But Sir, said she, what is this Pill good for else?* 20

This Pill an Universal Remedy. *Skill.* It is an universal Pill, 'tis good against all the Diseases that Pilgrims are incident to, and when it is well prepared it will keep good, *time* out of *mind*.

Christiana. Pray Sir, make me up twelve Boxes of them: For if I can get these, I will never take other Physick.

Skill. These *Pills* are good to prevent Diseases, as well as to *cure* when one is Sick. Yea, I dare say it, and stand to it, that if a man will but use this Physick as 50. he should, *it will make him live for ever.* But, good *Christiana*, thou must give these Pills, *no other way*; 30

In a Glass of the Tears of Repentance. *but as I have prescribed: For if you do, they will do no good. So he gave unto *Christiana* Physick for her self, and her Boys, and for *Mercie*: and bid *Mathew* take heed how he eat any more *Green Plums*, and kist them and went his way.

It was told you before, That *Prudence* bid the Boys, that if at any time they would, they should ask her some Questions, that might be profitable, and she would say something to them.

1 marg. *The . . . him* add. 2

Mat. Then *Mathew* who had been sick, asked her, *Of Physick.*
Why for the most part Physick should be bitter to our
Palats?

Pru. To shew how unwelcome the word of God and
the Effects thereof are to a Carnal Heart.

Mathew. Why does Physick, if it does good, Purge, *Of the Effects*
and cause that we Vomit? *of Physick.*

Prudence. To shew that the Word when it works
effectually, cleanseth the Heart and Mind. For look
10 what the one doth to the Body, the other doth to the
Soul.

Mathew. What should we learn by seeing the Flame *Of Fire and*
of our Fire go upwards? and by seeing the Beams, and *of the Sun.*
sweet Influences of the Sun strike downwards?

Prudence. By the going up of the Fire, we are taught
to ascend to Heaven, by fervent and hot desires. And
by the Sun his sending his Heat, Beams, and sweet
Influences downwards; we are taught, that the Saviour
of the World, tho' high, reaches down with his Grace
20 and Love to us below.

Mathew. Where have the Clouds their Water? *Of the Clouds.*

Pru. Out of the Sea.

Mathew. What may we learn from that?

Pru. That Ministers should fetch their Doctrine
from God.

Mat. Why do they empty themselves upon the Earth?

Pru. To shew that Ministers should give out what
they know of God to the World.

Mat. Why is the Rainbow caused by the Sun? *Of the*
Rainbow.
30 *Prudence.* To shew that the Covenant of Gods Grace
is confirmed to us in Christ.

Mat. Why do the Springs come from the Sea to us,
thorough the Earth?

Prudence. To shew that the Grace of God comes to
us thorough the Body of Christ.

Mat. Why do some of the Springs rise out of the tops *Of the Springs.*
of high Hills?

Prudence. To shew that the Spirit of Grace shall
spring up in *some* that are Great and Mighty, as well
40 as in *many* that are Poor and low.

Of the Candle. Mat. *Why doth the Fire fasten upon the Candle-wick?*

Pru. To shew that unless Grace doth kindle upon the Heart, there will be no true Light of Life in us.

Mathew. *Why is the Wick and Tallow and all, spent to maintain the light of the Candle?*

Prudence. To shew that Body and Soul and all, should be at the Service of, and spend themselves to maintain in good Condition that Grace of God that is in us.

Of the Pelican. Mat. *Why doth the Pelican pierce her own Brest with* 10 *her Bill?*

Pru. To nourish her Young ones with her Blood, and thereby to shew that Christ the blessed, so loveth his Young, his People, as to save them from Death by his Blood.

Of the Cock. Mat. *What may one learn by hearing the Cock to Crow.*

Prudence. Learn to remember *Peter*'s Sin, and *Peter*'s Repentance. The Cocks crowing, shews also that day is coming on, let then the crowing of the Cock put thee in mind of that last and terrible Day of Judgment.   20

The weak may sometimes call the strong to Prayers. Now about this time their month was out, wherefore they signified to those of the House that 'twas convenient for them to up and be going. Then said *Joseph* to his Mother, It is convenient that you forget not to send to the House of Mr. *Interpreter*, to pray him to grant that Mr. *Great-heart* should be sent unto us, that he may be our Conductor the rest of our way. Good *Boy*, said she, I had almost forgot. So she drew up a Petition, and prayed Mr. *Watchful* the Porter to send it by some fit man to her good Friend Mr. *Interpreter*; 30 who when it was come, and he had seen the contents of the Petitions, said to the Messenger, Go tell them that I will send him.

They provide to be gone on their way. When the Family where *Christiana* was, saw that they had a purpose to go forward, they called the whole House together to give thanks to their King, for sending of them such profitable Guests as these. Which done, they said to *Christiana*, And shall we not shew thee something, according as our Custom is to do to

34 marg. *They . . . way* add. 2

Pilgrims, on which thou mayest meditate when thou art upon the way? So they took *Christiana*, her Children and *Mercy* into the Closet, and shewed them one of the *Apples* that *Eve* did eat of, and that she also did give *Eves Apple.* to her Husband, and that for the eating of which they both were turned out of Paradice, and asked her what *A sight of Sin* she thought that was? Then *Christiana* said, 'Tis *Food*, *is amazing.* or *Poyson*, I know not which; so they opened the matter *Ro. 7. 24.* to her, and she held up her hands and wondered. *Gen. 3. 6.*

10　Then they had her to a place, and shewed her *Jacob's Ladder*. Now at that time there were some Angels *Jacob's* ascending upon it. So *Christiana* looked and looked, *Ladder.* to see the Angels go up, and so did the rest of the *Gen. 28. 12.* Company. Then they were going into another place to shew them something else: But *James* said to his Mother, pray bid them stay here a little longer, for this is a curious sight. So they turned again, and stood *A sight of* feeding their Eyes with this *so pleasant a Prospect*. After *Christ is taking.* this they had them into a place where did hang up a 20 *Golden Anchor*, so they bid *Christiana* take it down; for, *Golden Anchor.* said they, you shall have it with you, for 'tis of absolute *Joh. 1. 51.* necessity that you should, that you may lay hold of that *Heb. 6. 12, 19.* within the vail, and stand stedfast, in case you should meet with turbulent weather: So they were glad thereof. Then they took them, and had them to the mount upon *Gen. 22.* which *Abraham* our Father, had offered up *Isaac* his *Of Abraham* Son, and shewed them the *Altar*, the *Wood*, the *Fire*, and *offering up* the *Knife*, for they remain to be seen to this very Day. *Isaac.* When they had seen it, they held up their hands and 30 blest themselves, and said, Oh! What a man, for love to his Master and for denial to himself, was *Abraham*: After they had shewed them all these things, *Prudence* took them into the Dining-Room, where stood a pair of *Prudences* Excellent Virginals, so she played upon them, and *Virginals.* turned what she had shewed them into this excellent Song, saying;

4 *marg.* Eves *Apple* add. 2　　11 *marg.* Jacob's *Ladder* add. 2　　20 marg. *Golden Anchor* add. 2　　22 *marg.* Heb. 6. 19, 12 ‖ 1, 2　　26 marg. *Of* . . . Isaac *add.* 2　　33 *marg.* Prudences *Virginals* add. 2

Eve's *Apple we have shewed you,*
Of that be you aware:
You have seen Jacobs *Ladder too,*
Upon which Angels are.

An Anchor you received have;
But let not these suffice,
Until with Abra'm *you have gave,*
Your best, a Sacrifice.

Mr. Great-
heart come Now about this time one knocked at the Door, So
again. the Porter opened, and behold Mr. *Great-heart* was 10
there; but when he was come in, what Joy was there?
For it came now fresh again into their minds, how but
a while ago he had slain old *Grim Bloody-man,* the Giant,
and had delivered them from the Lions.

He brings a Then said Mr. *Great-heart* to *Christiana,* and to
token from his *Mercie,* My Lord has sent each of you a Bottle of Wine,
Lord with him. and also some parched Corn, together with a couple of
Pomgranates. He has also sent the Boys some Figs,
and Raisins to refresh you in your way.

Then they addressed themselves to their Journey, 20
and *Prudence,* and *Piety* went along with them. When
they came at the Gate, *Christiana* asked the Porter, if
any of late went by. He said, No, only one some time
since: who also told me that of late there had been a
Robbery. great Robbery committed on the Kings High-way, as
you go: But he saith, the Thieves are taken, and will
shortly be Tryed for their Lives. Then *Christiana,* and
Mercie, was afraid; but *Mathew* said, Mother fear
nothing, as long as Mr. *Great-heart* is to go with us,
and to be our Conductor. 30

Christiana Then said *Christiana* to the Porter, Sir, I am much
takes her leave obliged to you for all the Kindnesses that you have
of the Porter. shewed me since I came hither, and also for that you
have been so loving and kind to my Children. I know
not how to gratifie your Kindness: Wherefore pray as
a token of my respects to you, accept of this small mite:

15 marg. *He . . . him* add. 2   25 marg. *Robbery* add. 2   31
marg. Christiana . . . Porter add. 2

So she put a Gold Angel in his Hand, and he made her
a low obeisance, and said, Let thy Garments be always *The Porters*
White, and let thy Head want no Ointment. Let *Mercie* *blessing.*
live and not die, and let not her Works be few. And
to the Boys he said, Do you fly Youthful lusts, and
follow after Godliness with them that are Grave, and
Wise, so shall you put Gladness into your Mothers
Heart, and obtain Praise of all that are sober minded.
So they thanked the Porter and departed.

10   Now I saw in my Dream, that they went forward
until they were come to the Brow of the Hill, where
Piety bethinking her self cryed out, *Alas!* I have forgot
what I intended to bestow upon *Christiana*, and her
Companions. I will go back and fetch it. So she ran,
and fetched it. While she was gone, *Christiana* thought
she heard in a Grove a little way off, on the Right-hand,
a most curious melodious Note, with Words much like
these,

20
> *Through all my Life thy favour is*
> *So frankly shew'd to me,*
> *That in thy House for evermore*
> *My dwelling place shall be.*

And listning still she thought she heard another
answer it, saying,

> *For why, the Lord our God is good,*
> *His Mercy is forever sure:*
> *His truth at all times firmly stood:*
> *And shall from Age to Age endure.*

So *Christiana* asked *Prudence*, what 'twas that made *Song 2. 11, 12.*
30 those curious Notes? They are, said she, our Countrey
Birds: They sing these Notes but seldom, except it be
at the Spring, when the Flowers appear, and the Sun
shines warm, and then you may hear them all day long.
I often, said she, go out to hear them, we also oft times
keep them tame in our House. They are very fine
Company for us when we are *Melancholy*, also they

make the Woods and Groves, and Solitary places, places desirous to be in.

Piety *bestoweth somthing on them at parting.* By this time *Piety* was come again, So she said to *Christiana*, Look here, I have brought thee a *Scheme* of all those things that thou hast seen at our House: Upon which thou mayest look when thou findest thy self forgetful, and call those things again to remembrance for thy Edification, and comfort.

1 *part pag.* 56. Now they began to go down the Hill into the Valley of *Humiliation*. It was a steep Hill, & the way was 10 slippery; but they were very careful, so they got down pretty well. When they were down in the Valley, *Piety* said to *Christiana*. This is the place where *Christian* your Husband met with the foul Fiend *Apollion*, and where they had that dreadful fight that they had. I know you cannot but have heard thereof. But be of good Courage, as long as you have here Mr. *Great-heart* to be your Guide and Conductor, we hope you will fare the better. So when these two had committed the Pilgrims unto the Conduct of their Guide, he went 20 forward, and they went after.

Mr. Great-heart *at the Valley of Humiliation.* *Great-heart*. Then said Mr. *Great-heart*, We need not be so afraid of this Valley: For here is nothing to hurt us, unless we procure it to our selves. 'Tis true, *Christian* did here meet with *Apollion*, with whom he also had a sore Combate; but that *frey*, was the fruit of those slips that he got in his going down the Hill. For 1 *part pag.* 56. they that get *slips there*, must look for *Combats here*. And hence it is that this Valley has got so hard a name. For the common people when they hear that some 30 frightful thing has befallen such an one in such a place, are of an Opinion that that place is haunted with some foul Fiend, or evil Spirit; when alas it is for the fruit of their doing, that such things do befal them there.

The reason why Christian *was so beset here.* This Valley of *Humiliation* is of it self as fruitful a place, as any the Crow flies over; and I am perswaded if we could hit upon it, we might find somewhere

3 *marg.* Piety . . . *parting* add. 2   9 *marg.* 1 *part pag.* 88 ‖ 1, 2
17 hear 2   22 *marg.* Mr. . . . *Humiliation* add. 2   28 marg.
1 *part pag.* 88 ‖ 1, 2   35 marg. *The . . . here* add. 2

here abouts something that might give us an Account why *Christian* was so hardly beset in this place.

Then *James* said to his Mother, Lo, yonder stands a Pillar, and it looks as if something was Written thereon: let us go and see what it is. So they went, and found there Written, *Let* Christian's *slips before he came hither, and the Battels that he met with in this place, be a warning to those that come after.* Lo, said their Guide, did not I tell you, that there was something here abouts

10 that would give Intimation of the reason why *Christian* was so hard beset in this place? Then turning himself to *Christiana*, he said: No disparagement to *Christian* more than to many others whose Hap and Lot his was. For 'tis easier going *up*, then *down this* Hill; and that can be said but of few Hills in all these parts of the World. But we will leave the good Man, he is at rest, he also had a brave Victory over his Enemy; let him grant that dwelleth above, that we fare no worse when we come to be tryed then he.

20 But we will come again to this Valley of *Humiliation*. It is the best, and most fruitful piece of Ground in all those parts. It is fat Ground, and as you see, consisteth much in Meddows: and if a man was to come here in the Summer-time, as we do now, if he knew not any thing before thereof, and if he also delighted himself in the sight of his Eyes, he might see that that would be delightful to him. Behold, how green this Valley is, also how beautified *with Lillies.* I have also known many labouring Men that have got good Estates in this

30 Valley of *Humiliation.* (For God resisteth the Proud; but gives *more, more* Grace to the Humble;) for indeed it is a very fruitful Soil, and doth bring forth by handfuls. Some also have wished that the next way to their Fathers House were here, that they might be troubled no more with either Hills or Mountains to go over; but the way is the way, and there's an end.

Now as they were going along and talking, they espied a Boy feeding his Fathers Sheep. The Boy was

Marginal notes:

A Pillar with an Inscription on it.

This Valley a brave place.

Song. 2. 1.

Jam. 4. 6.

1 Pet. 5. 5.

Men thrive in the Valley of Humiliation.

---

1 here about 2   11 hard] heard   15 part 1   20 marg.
This . . . place add. 2

in very mean Cloaths, but of a very fresh and well-favoured Countenance, and as he sate by himself he Sung. Hark, said Mr. *Great-heart*, to what the Shepherds Boy saith. So they hearkned, and he said,

> *He that is down, needs fear no fall,*
> *He that is low, no Pride:*
> *He that is humble, ever shall*
> *Have God to be his Guide.*

Philip. 4. 12, 13.

> *I am content with what I have,*
> *Little be it, or much:*
> *And, Lord, Contentment still I crave,*
> *Because thou savest such.*

Heb. 13. 5.

> *Fulness to such a burden is*
> *That go on Pilgrimage:*
> *Here little, and hereafter Bliss,*
> *Is best from Age to Age.*

Then said their *Guide*, Do you hear him? I will dare to say, that this Boy lives a merrier Life, and wears more of that Herb called *Hearts-ease* in his Bosom, then he that is clad in Silk and Velvet; but we will proceed in our Discourse.

Christ, when in the Flesh, had his Countrey-House in the Valley of Humiliation. In this Valley our Lord formerly had his *Countrey-House*, he loved much to be here; He loved also to walk these Medows, for he found the Air was pleasant: Besides here a man shall be free from the Noise, and from the hurryings of this Life; all States are full of Noise and Confusion, only the Valley of *Humiliation* is that empty and Solitary Place. Here a man shall not be so let and hindred in his Contemplation, as in other places he is apt to be. This is a Valley that no body walks in, but those that love a Pilgrims Life. And though *Christian* had the hard hap to meet here with *Apollion*, and to enter with him a brisk encounter: Yet I must Hos. 12. 4, 5. tell you, that in former times men have met with Angels here, have found Pearls here, and have in this place found the words of Life.

Did I say, our Lord had here in former Days his Countrey-house, and that he loved here to walk? I will

add, in this Place, and to the People that live and trace
these Grounds, he has left a yearly revenue to be faith- Mat. 11. 29.
fully payed them at certain Seasons, for their main-
tenance by the way, and for their further incouragement
to go on in their Pilgrimage.

Samuel. Now as they went on, *Samuel* said to Mr.
*Great-heart: Sir, I perceive that in this Valley, my Father
and* Apollyon *had their Battel; but whereabout was the
Fight, for I perceive this Valley is large?*

10 *Great-heart.* Your Father had that Battel with *Apol-* Forgetful-
lyon at a place yonder, before us, in a narrow Passage *Green.*
just beyond *Forgetful-Green.* And indeed that place is
the most dangerous place in all these Parts. For if at
any time the Pilgrims meet with any brunt, it is when
they forget what Favours they have received, and how
unworthy they are of them. This was the Place also
where others have been hard put to it. But more of the
place when we are come to it; for I perswade my self,
that to this day there remains either some sign of the
20 Battel, or some Monument to testifie that such a Battle
there was fought.

Mercie. Then said *Mercie,* I think I am as well in this Humility a
Valley, as I have been any where else in all our Journey: *sweet Grace.*
The place methinks suits with my Spirit. I love to be
in such places where there is no ratling with Coaches,
nor rumbling with Wheels: Methinks here one may
without much molestation be thinking what he is,
whence he came, what he has done, and to what the
King has called him: Here one may think, and break
30 at Heart, and melt in ones Spirit, until ones Eyes be- Song. 7. 4.
come like the *Fish Pools of Heshbon.* They that go Psal. 84.
rightly thorow this Valley of Baca make it a Well, 5, 6, 7.
the Rain that God sends down from Heaven upon them
that are here also *filleth the Pools.* This Valley is that Hos. 2. 15.
from whence also the King will give to his their Vineyards, and they that go through it, shall sing, (as
Christian did, for all he met with *Apollyon.*)

Great-heart. 'Tis true, said their Guide, I have gone An Experi-
ment of it.

6 Samuel¹, ²] Simon 1   16 was] is 2   28 to] lo 1   32
thorough 2   37 Christian] Christiana 1

thorough this Valley many a time, and never was better then when here.

I have also been a Conduct to several Pilgrims, and they have confessed the same; *To this man will I look, saith the King, even to him that is Poor, and of a contrite Spirit, and that trembles at my Word.*

Now they were come to the place where the afore *The place* mentioned Battel was fought. Then said the Guide to *where* *Christiana,* her Children, and *Mercie* : This is the place, *the Fiend did* on this Ground *Christian* stood, and up there came 10 *fight, some signs* *Apollyon* against him. And look, did not I tell you, here *of the Battel* . is some of your Husbands Blood upon these Stones to *remains.* this day: Behold also how here and there are yet to be seen upon the place, some of the Shivers of *Apollyon*'s Broken *Darts* : See also how they did beat the Ground with their Feet as they fought, to make good their Places against each other, how also with their by-blows they did split the very stones in pieces. Verily *Christian* did here play the Man, and shewed himself as stout, as could, had he been here, even *Hercules* him-20 self. When *Apollyon* was beat, he made his retreat to the next Valley, that is called The Valley of the shadow of Death, unto which we shall come anon.

A Monument Lo yonder also stands a Monument, on which is *of the Battel.* Engraven this Battle, and *Christian*'s Victory to his Fame throughout all Ages: So because it stood just on the way-side before them, they stept to it and read the Writing, which word for word was this;

> *Hard by, here was a Battle fought,*
> *Most strange, and yet most true.* 30
> Christian *and* Apollyon *sought*
> *Each other to subdue.*

A Monument
of Christians
Victory.

> *The Man so bravely play'd the Man,*
> *He made the* Fiend *to fly:*
> *Of which a Monument I stand,*
> *The same to testifie.*

1 *Part pag.* When they had passed by this place, they came upon
61.

the Borders of the shadow of Death, and this Valley
was longer then the other, a place also most strangely
haunted with evil things, as many are able to testifie:
But these Women and Children went the better
thorough it, because they had day-light, and because
Mr. *Great-heart* was their Conductor.

When they were entred upon this Valley, they *Groanings*
thought that they heard a groaning as of dead men: *heard.*
a very great groaning. They thought also they did hear
10 Words of Lamentation spoken, as of some in extream
Torment. These things made the Boys to quake, the
Women also looked pale and wan; but their Guide bid
them be of Good Comfort.

So they went on a little further, and they thought *The Ground*
that they felt the Ground begin to shake under them, *shakes.*
as if some hollow place was there; they heard also a kind
of a hissing as of Serpents; but nothing as yet appeared.
Then said the Boys, Are we not yet at the end of this
doleful place? But the Guide also bid them be of good
20 Courage, and look well to their Feet, lest haply, said
he, you be taken in some Snare.

Now *James* began to be Sick; but I think the cause *James sick*
thereof was Fear, so his Mother gave him some of that *with fear.*
Glass of Spirits that she had given her at the *Inter-*
preters House, and three of the Pills that Mr. *Skill* had
prepared, and the Boy began to revive. Thus they went
on till they came to about the middle of the Valley, and
then *Christiana* said, Methinks I see something yonder *The* Fiend
upon the Road before us, a thing of a shape such as *appears.*
30 I have not seen. Then said *Joseph*, Mother, what is it? *The Pilgrims*
An ugly thing, Child; an ugly thing, said she. But *are afraid.*
Mother, what is it like, said he? 'Tis like I cannot tell
what, said she. And now it was but a little way off.
Then said she, it is nigh.

Well, well, said Mr. *Great-heart*, let them that are *Great-heart*
most afraid keep close to me: So the *Fiend* came on, *incourages*
and the Conductor met it; but when it was just come *them.*
to him, it vanished to all their sights. Then remembred

25–26 that ... prepared *add.* 2   30 marg. *The ... afraid add.* 2
35 *marg.* Great-heart ... *them add.* 2

they what had been said sometime agoe. *Resist the Devil, and he will fly from you.*

They went therefore on, as being a little refreshed; but they had not gone far, before *Mercie* looking behind her, saw as she thought, something most like a Lion, and it came a great padding pace after; and it had a hollow Voice of Roaring, and at every Roar that it gave, it made all the Valley Eccho, and their Hearts to ake, save the Heart of him that was their Guide. So it came up, and Mr. *Great-heart* went behind, and put the Pil- 10 grims all before him. The Lion also came on apace, and Mr. *Great-heart* addressed himself to give him Battel. But when he saw that it was determined that resistance should be made, he also drew back and came no further.

A Lion.

1 Pet. 5. 8, 9.

Then they went on again, and their Conductor did go before them, till they came at a place where was cast up a pit, the whole breadth of the way, and before they could be prepared to go over that, a great mist and a darkness fell upon them, so that they could not see: 20 Then said the Pilgrims, Alass! now what shall we do? But their Guide made answer; Fear not, stand still and see what an end will he put to this also; so they stayed there because their Path was marr'd. They then also thought that they did hear more apparently the noise and rushing of the Enemies, the fire also and the smoke of the Pit was much easier to be discerned. Then said *Christiana* to *Mercie*, Now I see what my poor Husband went through. I have heard much of this place, but I never was here afore now; poor man, he went here all 30 alone in the night; he had night almost quite through the way, also these Fiends were busie about him, as if they would have torn him in pieces. Many have spoke of it, but none can tell what the Valley of the shadow of death should mean, until they come in it themselves. *The heart knows its own bitterness, and a stranger intermeddleth not with its Joy.* To be here is a fearful thing.

A pit and darkness.

Christiana now knows what her Husband felt.

Great-heart's Reply.

Greath. This is like doing business in great Waters, or like going down into the deep; this is like being in

38 *marg.* Great-heart's *Reply* add. 2

the heart of the Sea, and like going down to the Bottoms of the Mountains: Now it seems as if the Earth with its bars were about us for ever. *But let them that walk in darkness and have no light, trust in the name of the Lord, and stay upon their God.* For my part, as I have told you already, I have gone often through this Valley, and have been much harder put to it than now I am, and yet you see I am alive. I would not boast, for that I am not mine own Saviour. But I trust we shall have 10 a good deliverance. Come let us pray for light to him that can lighten our darkness, and that can rebuke, not only these, but all the Satans in Hell.

So they cryed and prayed, and God sent light and *They pray.* deliverance, for there was now no lett in their way, no not there, where but now they were stopt with a pit.

Yet they were not got through the Valley; so they went on still, and behold great stinks and loathsome smells, to the great annoyance of them. Then said *Mercie to* *Mercie* to *Christiana*, there is not such pleasant being *Christiana.* 20 here as at the *Gate*, or at the Interpreters, or at the House where we lay last.

O but, said one of the Boys, *it is not so bad to go* *One of the* *through here, as it is to* abide *here always, and for ought* *Boys Reply.* *I know, one reason why we must go this way to the House prepared for us, is, that our home might be made the sweeter to us.*

Well said, *Samuel,* quoth the *Guide,* thou hast now spoke like a man. Why, if ever I get out here again, said the *Boy,* I think I shall prize light and good way 30 better than ever I did in all my life. Then said the *Guide,* we shall be out by and by.

So on they went, and *Joseph* said, *Cannot we see to the end of this Valley as yet?* Then said the *Guide,* Look to your feet, for you shall presently be among the Snares. So they looked to their feet and went on; but they were troubled much with the Snares. Now when they were come among the Snares, they espyed a Man *Heedless is* cast into the Ditch on the left hand, with his flesh all *slain, and* *Takeheed* *preserved.*

18 *marg.* Mercie *to* Christiana *add.* 2   22 marg. One . . . Reply add. 2

rent and torn. Then said the *Guide*, that is one *Heed-less*, that was agoing this way; he has lain there a great while. There was one *Takeheed* with him, when he was taken and slain, but *he* escaped their hands. You cannot imagine how many are killed here about, and yet men are so foolishly venturous, as to set out lightly on Pilgrimage, and to come without a *Guide*. Poor *Christian*, it was a wonder that he here escaped, but he was beloved of his God, also he had a good heart of his own, or else he could never a-done it. Now they drew 10 towards the end of the way, and just there where *Christian* had seen the Cave when he went by, out thence came forth *Maull* a Gyant. This *Maull* did use to spoyl young Pilgrims with Sophistry, and he called *Great-heart* by his name, and said unto him, how many times have you been forbidden to do these things? Then said Mr. *Great-heart*, what things? What things, quoth the Gyant, you know what things; but I will put an end to your trade. But pray, said Mr. *Great-heart*, before we fall to it, let us understand wherefore we 20 must fight; (now the Women and Children stood trembling, and knew not what to do); quoth the Gyant, You rob the Countrey, and rob it with the worst of Thefts. These are but Generals, said Mr. *Great-heart*, come to particulars, man.

Then said the *Gyant*, thou practises the craft of a *Kidnapper*, thou gatherest up Women and Children, and carriest them into a strange Countrey, to the weaking of my Masters Kingdom. But now *Great-heart* replied, I am a Servant of the God of Heaven, my business is 30 to perswade sinners to Repentance, I am commanded to do my endeavour to turn Men, Women and Children, from darkness to light, and from the power of Satan to God, and if this be indeed the ground of thy quarrel, let us fall to it as soon as thou wilt.

Then the *Giant* came up, and Mr. *Great-heart* went to meet him, and as he went, he drew his *Sword*, but

1 Part pag. 65-66.
Maull a Gyant.
He quarrels with Great-heart.
God's Ministers counted as Kidnappers.
The Gyant and Mr. Great-heart must fight.

2 a going 2   5 hereabout 2   11 marg. 1 *Part pag.* 105, 106 || 1, 2   17 marg. *He* ... Great-heart *add.* 2   26 practisest 2   35 assoon 1   37 *Sword*] sword 2

the *Giant* had a *Club*: So without more ado they fell to it, and at the first blow the *Giant* stroke Mr. *Great-heart* down upon one of his knees; with that the Women, and Children cried out. So Mr. *Great-heart* recovering him- *Weak folks* self, laid about him in full lusty manner, and gave the *prayers do* *Giant* a wound in his arm; thus he fought for the space *sometimes help strong* of an hour to that height of heat, that the breath came *folks cries.* out of the *Giants* nostrils, as the heat doth out of a boiling Caldron.

10 Then they sat down to rest them, but Mr. *Great-heart* betook him to prayer; also the Women and Children did nothing but sigh and cry all the time that the Battle did last.

When they had rested them, and taken breath, they both fell to it again, and Mr. *Great-heart* with a full blow fetch't the *Giant* down to the ground. Nay hold, *The* Gyant and let me recover, quoth he. So Mr. *Great-heart* fairly *struck down.* let him get up; So to it they went again; and the *Giant* mist but little of all-to-breaking Mr. *Great-heart*'s Scull 20 with his Club.

Mr. *Great-heart* seeing that, runs to him in the full heat of his Spirit, and pierceth him under the fifth rib; with that the *Giant* began to faint, and could hold up his Club no longer. Then Mr. *Great-heart* seconded *He is slain,* his blow, and smit the head of the *Giant* from his *and his head* shoulders. Then the Women and Children rejoyced, *disposed of* and Mr. *Great-heart* also praised God, for the deliverance he had wrought.

When this was done, they amongst them erected a 30 Pillar, and fastned the *Gyant's* head thereon, and wrote underneath in letters that Passengers might read,

> *He that did wear this head, was one*
> *That Pilgrims did misuse;*
> *He stopt their way, he spared none,*
> *But did them all abuse;*
> *Until that I, Great-heart, arose,*
> *The Pilgrims Guide to be;*
> *Until that I did him oppose,*
> *That was their Enemy.*

22 pierced 2

1 Part pag. 66. Now I saw, that they went to the Ascent that was a little way off cast up to be a Prospect for Pilgrims. (That was the place from whence *Christian* had the first sight of *Faithful* his Brother.) Wherefore here they sat down, and rested, they also here did eat and drink, and make merry; for that they had gotten deliverance from this so dangerous an Enemy. As they sat thus and did eat, *Christiana* asked the *Guide, if he had caught no hurt in the battle.* Then said Mr. *Great-heart, No,* save a little on my flesh; yet that also shall be so far from being to 10 my determent, that it is at present a proof of my love 2 Cor. 4. to my Master and you, and shall be a means by Grace to encrease my reward at last.

Discourse of the fight. *But was you not afraid, good Sir, when you see him come with his Club?*

It is my duty, said he, to distrust mine own ability, that I may have reliance on him that is stronger then all. *But what did you think when he fetched you down to the ground at the first blow?* Why I thought, quoth he, that so my master himself was served, and yet he it was 20 that conquered at the last.

Mat. here admires Goodness. Mat. *When you all have thought what you please, I think God has been wonderful good unto us, both in bringing us out of this Valley, and in delivering us out of the hand of this Enemy; for my part I see no reason why we should distrust our God any more, since he has* now, *and in such a place as this, given us such testimony of his love as this.*

Old Honest asleep under an Oak. Then they got up and went forward; now a little before them stood an Oak, and under it when they came to it, they found an old *Pilgrim* fast asleep; they 30 knew that he was a *Pilgrim* by his *Cloths,* and his *Staff,* and his *Girdle.*

So the *Guide* Mr. *Great-heart* awaked him, and the old Gentleman, as he lift up his eyes cried out; What's the matter? who are you? and what is your business here?

Great. Come man be not so hot, here is none but Friends; yet the old man gets up and stands upon his guard, and will know of them what they were. Then said the

Guide, My name is *Great-heart*, I am the guide of these Pilgrims which are going to the Celestial Countrey.

Honest. Then said Mr. *Honest*, I cry you mercy; I feared that you had been of the Company of those that some time ago did rob *Little-faith* of his money; but now I look better about me, I perceive you are honester People. *One Saint sometimes takes another for his Enemy.*

Greath. Why what would, or could you adone, to helped your self, if we indeed had been of that Company? *A Talk between Great-heart and he.*

10 *Hon.* Done! Why I would a fought as long as breath had been in me; and had I so done, I am sure you could never have given me the worst on't, for a *Christian* can never be overcome, unless he shall yield of himself.

Greath. Well said, Father Honest, *quoth the Guide, for by this I know that thou art a Cock of the right kind, for thou hast said the Truth.*

Hon. And by this also I know that thou knowest what true Pilgrimage is; for all others do think that we are the soonest overcome of any.

20 *Greath. Well, now we are so happily met, pray let me crave your Name, and the name of the Place you came from?* *Whence Mr. Honest came.*

Hon. My Name I cannot, but I came from the Town of *Stupidity*; it lieth about four Degrees beyond the City of *Destruction*.

Greath. Oh! *Are you that Country-man then? I deem I have half a guess of you, your Name is old* Honesty, *is it not?* So the old Gentleman blushed, and said, Not Honesty in the *Abstract*, but *Honest* is my Name, and 30 I wish that my *Nature* shall agree to what I am called.

Hon. But Sir, said the old Gentleman, how could you guess that I am such a Man, since I came from such a place?

Greath. I had heard of you before, by my Master, for he knows all things that are done on the Earth: But I have often wondered that any should come from your place; for your Town is worse then is the City of Destruction *it self.* *Stupified ones are worse then those merely Carnal.*

Hon. Yes, we lie more off from the Sun, and so are more Cold and Sensless; but was a Man in a Mountain

8 marg. *Talk . . . he* add. 2   10 a] have 2

of Ice, yet if the Sun of Righteousness will arise upon him, his frozen Heart shall feel a Thaw; and thus it hath been with me.

Greath. I believe it, Father *Honest*, I believe it, for I know the thing is true.

Then the old Gentleman saluted all the Pilgrims with a holy Kiss of Charity, and asked them of their Names, and how they had fared since they set out on their Pilgrimage.

Old Honest and Christiana talk. *Christ.* Then said *Christiana*, My name I suppose you have heard of, good *Christian* was my Husband, 10 and these four were his Children. But can you think how the old Gentleman was taken, when she told him who she was! He skip'd, he smiled, and blessed them with a thousand good Wishes, saying,

Hon. *I have heard much of your Husband, and of his Travels and Wars which he underwent in his days. Be it spoken to your Comfort, the Name of your Husband rings all over these parts of the World; His Faith, his Courage, his Enduring, and his Sincerity under all, has made his* *He also talks with the Boys.* *name Famous.* Then he turned him to the Boys, and 20 asked them of their names, which they told him: And *Old Mr. Honest's Blessing on them.* then said he unto them, *Mathew*, be thou like *Mathew* the Publican, not in Vice, but Virtue. *Samuel*, said he, *Mat. 10. 3. Psal. 99. 6.* be thou like *Samuel* the Prophet, a Man of Faith and Prayer. *Joseph*, said he, be thou like *Joseph* in *Poti-* *Gen. 39.* *phar*'s House, Chast, and one that flies from Temptation. And, *James*, be thou like *James* the *Just*, and like *Acts.* *James* the brother of our Lord.

He blesseth Mercie. Then they told him of *Mercie*, and how she had left her Town and her Kindred to come along with *Chris-* 30 *tiana*, and with her Sons. At that the old *Honest* man said, *Mercie*, is thy Name? by *Mercie* shalt thou be sustained, and carried thorough all those Difficulties that shall assault thee in thy way; till thou come thither where thou shalt look the Fountain of Mercie in the Face with Comfort.

All this while the Guide Mr. *Great-heart*, was very much pleased, and smiled upon his Companion.

9 marg. *Old . . . talk* add. 2   12 them 1, 2   20 marg. *He . . . Boys* add. 2   29 marg. *He . . . Mercie* add. 2

Now as they walked along together, the Guide asked *Talk of one* the old Gentleman, *if he did not know one Mr.* Fearing, *Mr. Fearing.* *that came on Pilgrimage out of his Parts.*

Hon. Yes, very well, said he; he was a Man that had the Root of the Matter in him, but he was one of the most troublesome Pilgrims that ever I met with in all my days.

Greath. I perceive you knew him, for you have given a very right Character of him.

10   *Hon.* Knew him! I was a great Companion of his, I was with him most an end; when he first began to think of what would come upon us hereafter, I was with him.

Greath. I was his Guide from my Master's House, to the Gates of the Celestial City.

Hon. Then you knew him to be a troublesom one?

Greath. I did so, but I could very well bear it: for Men of my Calling are often times intrusted with the Conduct of such as he was.

20   *Hon.* Well then, pray let us hear a little of him, and how he managed himself under your Conduct.

Greath. Why he was always afraid that he should *Mr. Fearing's* come short of whither he had a desire to go. Every *troublesom* *Pilgrimage.* thing frightned him that he heard any body speak of, that had the least appearance of Opposition in it. I *His behaviour* heard that he lay roaring at the *Slow of Dispond,* for *at the* Slow of *Dispond.* above a Month together, nor durst he, for all he saw several go over before him, venture, tho they, many of them, offered to lend him their Hand. *He would not go* 30 *back again neither.* The Celestial City, he said he should die if he came not to it, and yet was dejected at every Difficulty, and stumbled at every Straw that any body cast in his way. Well, after he had layn at the *Slow of Dispond* a great while, as I have told you; one sunshine Morning, I do not know how, he ventured, and so got over. But when he was over, he would scarce believe it. He had, I think, a *Slow of Dispond* in his Mind, a *Slow* that he carried every where with him,

or else he could never have been as he was. So he came
up to the Gate, you know what I mean, that stands at
the head of this way, and there also he stood a good
His behavior while before he would adventure to knock. When the
at the Gate. Gate was opened he would give back, and give place
to others, and say that he was not worthy. For, for all
he gat before some to the Gate, yet many of them went
in before him. There the poor man would stand shaking and shrinking; I dare say it would have pitied ones
Heart to have seen him: *Nor would he go back again.* At 10
last he took the Hammer that hanged on the Gate in
his hand, and gave a small Rapp or two; then one
opened to him, but he shrunk back as before. He that
opened, stept out after him, and said, Thou trembling
one, what wantest thou? with that he fell to the Ground.
He that spoke to him wondered to see him so faint. So
he said to him, Peace be to thee; up, for I have set
open the Door to thee; come in, for thou art blest. With
that he gat up, and went in trembling, and when he
was in, he was ashamed to show his Face. Well, after 20
he had been entertained there a while, as you know
how the manner is, he was bid go on his way, and also
told the way he should take. So he came till he came
to our House, but as he behaved himself at the Gate,
His behavior so he did at my master the *Interpreters* Door. He lay
at the Inter- thereabout in the Cold a good while, before he would
preters Door. adventure to call; *Yet he would not go back.* And the
Nights were long and cold then. Nay he had a Note of
Necessity in his Bosom to my Master, to receive him,
and grant him the Comfort of his House, and also to 30
allow him a stout and valiant Conduct, because he was
himself so *Chickin-hearted* a Man; and yet for all that
he was afraid to call at the Door. So he lay up and down
there abouts, till, poor man, he was almost starved; yea
so great was his Dejection, that tho he saw several
others for knocking got in, yet he was afraid to venture.
At last, I think I looked out of the Window, and perceiving a man to be up and down about the Door, I
went out to him, and asked what he was; but poor man,

15 fell down 2   34 thereabouts 2

the water stood in his Eyes. So I perceived what he
wanted. I went therefore in, and told it in the House,
and we shewed the thing to our Lord; So he sent me
out again, to entreat him to come in, but I dare say
I had hard work to do it. At last he came in, and I will
say that for my Lord, he carried it wonderful lovingly
to him. There were but a few good bits at the Table, *How he was*
but some of it was laid upon his Trencher. Then he *entertained there.*
presented the *Note*, and my Lord looked thereon and
10 said, His desire should be granted. So when he had *He is a little*
bin there a good while, he seemed to get some Heart, *encouraged at the Interpreters*
and to be a little more Comfortable. For my Master, *house.*
you must know, is one of very tender Bowels, especially
to them that are afraid, wherefore he carried it so towards him, as might tend most to his Incouragement.
Well, when he had had a sight of the things of the
place, and was ready to take his Journey to go to the
City, my Lord, as he did to *Christian* before, gave him
a Bottle of Spirits, and some comfortable things to eat.
20 Thus we set forward, and I went before him; but the
man was but of few Words, only he would sigh aloud.

When we were come to where the three Fellows were *He was greatly*
hanged, he said, that he doubted that that would be his *afraid when he saw the Gibbit,*
end also. Only he seemed glad when he saw the Cross *Cheary when he*
and the Sepulcher. There I confess he desired to stay *saw the Cross.*
a little, to look; and he seemed for a while after to be a
little *Cheary*. When we came at the Hill *Difficulty*, he
made no stick at that, nor did he much fear the Lyons.
For you must know that his Trouble *was not about such*
30 *things as those*, his Fear was about his Acceptance at last.

I got him in at the House *Beautiful*, I think before *Dumpish at*
he was willing; also when he was in, I brought him *the house Beautiful.*
acquainted with the Damsels that were of the Place,
but he was ashamed to make himself much for Company, he desired much to be alone, yet he always loved
good talk, and often would get behind the *Screen* to
hear it; he also loved much to see *antient* things, and
to be *pondering* them in his Mind. He told me afterwards, that he loved to be in those two Houses from

10 marg. *He ... house* add. 2   24 Cross] *ital.* 2

which he came last, to wit, at the Gate, and that of the *Interpreters*, but that he durst not be so bold to ask.

He went down into, and was very Pleasant in the Valley of Humiliat. When we went also from the House *Beautiful*, down the Hill, into the Valley of *Humiliation*, he went down as well as ever I saw man in my Life, for he cared not how mean he was, so he might be happy at last. Yea, I think there was a kind of a Sympathy betwixt that Valley and him. For I never saw him better in all his Pilgrimage, then when he was in that Valley.

Lam. 3. 27, 28, 29. Here he would lie down, embrace the Ground, and kiss the very Flowers that grew in this Valley. He would now be up every Morning by break of Day, tracing, and walking to and fro in this Valley.

Much perplexed in the Valley of the Shadow of Death. But when he was come to the entrance of the Valley of the Shadow of Death, I thought I should have lost my Man; not for that he had any Inclination to go back, that he alwayes abhorred, but he was ready to dy for Fear. O, the *Hobgoblins* will have me, the *Hobgoblins* will have me, cried he; and I could not beat him out on't. He made such a noyse, and such an outcry here, that, had they but heard him, 'twas enough to encourage them to come and fall upon us.

But this I took very great notice of, that this Valley was as quiet while he went thorow it, as ever I knew it before or since. I suppose, those Enemies here, had now a special Check from our Lord, and a Command not to meddle until Mr. *Fearing* was pass'd over it.

It would be too tedious to tell you of all; we will therefore only mention a Passage or two more. When *His behaviour at Vanity-Fair.* he was come at *Vanity Fair*, I thought he would have fought with all the men in the Fair; I feared there we should both have been knock'd o'th Head, so hot was he against their Fooleries; upon the inchanted Ground, he also was very wakeful. But when he was come at the *River* where was no Bridge, there again he was in a heavy Case; now, now he said he should be drowned for ever, and so never see that Face with Comfort, that he had come so many miles to behold.

3 marg. *He went down into, and was very* add. 2   5 as well . . .
Life *ital.* 2   **13** too 2   **16** to go back *ital.* 2   28 only
add. 2   29 marg. *His . . . Fair add.* 2

And here also I took notice of what was very remarkable, the Water of that River was lower at this time, than ever I saw it in all my Life; so he went over at last, not much above wet-shod. When he was going up to the Gate, Mr. *Great-heart* began to take his Leave of him, and to wish him a good Reception above; So he said, *I shall, I shall.* Then parted we asunder, and I saw him no more.

His Boldness at last.

Honest. *Then it seems he was well at last.*

10 *Greath.* Yes, yes, I never had doubt about him, he was a man of a choice Spirit, only he was always kept very low, and that made his Life so burthensom to himself, and so troublesom to others. He was above many, tender of Sin; he was so afraid of doing Injuries to others, that he often would deny himself of that which was lawful, because he would not offend.

Psal. 88.

Rom. 14. 21.

1 Cor. 8. 13.

Hon. *But what should be the reason that such a good Man should be all his days so much in the dark?*

Greath. There are two sorts of Reasons for it; one 20 is, The wise God will have it so. Some must *Pipe*, and some must *Weep*: Now Mr. *Fearing* was one that play'd upon *this Base.* He and his fellows sound the *Sackbut,* whose Notes are more doleful than the Notes of other Musick are. Tho indeed some say, the Base is the ground of Musick. And for my part, I care not at all for that Profession that begins not in heaviness of Mind. The first string that the Musitian usually touches, *is the Base,* when he intends to put all in tune; God also plays upon this string first, when he sets the 30 Soul in tune for himself. Only here was the imperfection of Mr. *Fearing,* he could play upon no other Musick but this, till towards his latter end.

Reason why good men are so in the dark.

Mat. 11. 16, 17, 18.

I make bold to talk thus Metaphorically, for the ripening of the Wits of young Readers, and because in the Book of the Revelations, the Saved are compared to a company of Musicians that play upon their *Trumpets* and Harps, and sing their Songs before the Throne.

Revel. 8. 2.

Chap. 14. 2, 3.

Hon. *He was a very zealous man, as one may see by*

2 that River *ital.* 2   this *ital.* 2   4 wet-shod *ital.* 2   7 marg.
His . . . last add. 2   19 marg. *Reason . . . dark* add. 2

what Relation you have given of him. Difficulties, Lyons, or Vanity-Fair, he feared not at all: 'Twas only Sin, Death and Hell, *that was to him a Terror;* because he had some Doubts about his Interest in that Celestial Country.

Greath. You say right. *Those* were the things that were his Troublers, and they, as you have well observed, arose from the weakness of his Mind there about, not from weakness of Spirit as to the practical part of a Pilgrims Life. I dare believe, that as the Proverb is, he could have bit a Firebrand, had it stood 10 in his way: But the things with which he was oppressed, no man ever yet could shake off with ease.

Christiana. *Then said* Christiana, *This Relation of* Mr. Fearing *has done me good. I thought no body had been like me, but I see there was some Semblance 'twixt this good man and I, only we differed in two things. His Troubles were so great they brake out, but mine I kept within. His also lay so hard upon him, they made him that he could not knock at the Houses provided for Entertainment; but my Trouble was always such, as made me knock* 20 *the lowder.*

Mer. If I might also speak my Heart, I must say that something of him has also dwelt in me. For I have ever been more afraid of the Lake and the loss of a place in *Paradice*, then I have been of the loss of other things. Oh, thought I, may I have the Happiness to have a Habitation *there*, 'tis enough, though I part with all the World to win it.

Mat. *Then said* Mathew, *Fear was one thing that made me think that I was far from having that within me* 30 *that accompanies Salvation, but if it was so with such a good man as he, why may it not also go well with me?*

Jam. No fears, no Grace, said *James.* Though there is not always Grace where there is the fear of Hell; yet to be sure there is no Grace where there is no fear of God.

Greath. *Well said,* James, *thou hast hit the Mark, for*

the fear of God is the beginning of Wisdom; and to be sure
they that want the beginning, *have neither* middle *nor*
end. *But we will here conclude our Discourse of Mr.*
Fearing, *after we have sent after him this Farewel.*

> *Well, Master* Fearing, *thou didst fear*   Their Farewell
> *Thy God: And wast afraid*   about him.
> *Of doing any thing, while here,*
> *That would have thee betray'd.*
> *And didst thou fear the Lake and Pit?*
> *Would others did so too;*
> *For, as for them that want thy Wit,*
> *They do themselves undo.*

Now I saw, that they still went on in their Talk.
For after Mr. *Great-heart* had made an end with Mr.
Fearing, Mr. *Honest* began to tell them of another, but   Of Mr.
his Name was Mr. *Selfwil.* He pretended himself to   Self-will.
be a *Pilgrim*, said Mr. *Honest*; But I perswade my self,
he never came in at the Gate that stands at the head
of the way.

Greath. *Had you ever any talk with him about it?*

Hon. Yes, more then once or twice; but he would   Old Honest
always be like himself, *self-willed.* He neither cared for   had talked
man, nor Argument, nor yet Example; what his Mind   with him.
prompted him to, that he would do, and nothing else
could he be got to.

Greath. *Pray what Principles did he hold, for I suppose*
you can tell?

Hon. He held that a man might follow the Vices as   Self-will's
well as the Virtues of the Pilgrims, and that if he did   Opinions.
both, he should be certainly saved.

Greath. How! *If he had said, 'tis possible for the best*
to be guilty of the Vices, as well as to partake of the Virtues
of Pilgrims, he could not much a been blamed: For indeed
we are exempted from no Vice absolutely, but on condition
that we Watch and Strive. But this I perceive is not the
thing: But if I understand you right, your meaning is, that
he was of that Opinion, that it was allowable so to be.

5 marg. *Their . . . him* add. 2   21 marg. *Old . . . him* add. 2
33 *a*] *have* 2

Hon. Ai, ai, so I mean, and so he believed and practised.

Greath. *But what Ground had he for his so saying?*

Hon. Why, he said he had the Scripture for his Warrant.

Greath. *Prethee, Mr.* Honest, *present us with a few particulars.*

Hon. So I will. He said, to have to do with other mens Wives, had been practised by *David*, Gods Beloved, and therefore he could do it. He said, to have 10 more Women then one, was a thing that *Solomon* practised, and therefore he could do it. He said, that *Sarah* and the godly Midwives of *Egypt* lyed, and so did saved *Rahab*, and therefore he could do it. He said, that the Disciples went at the bidding of their Master, and took away the Owners *Ass*, and therefore he could do so too. He said, that *Jacob* got the Inheritance of his Father in a way of Guile and Dissimulation, and therefore he could do so too.

Greath. *High base! indeed, and you are sure he was of this Opinion?*   20

Hon. I have heard him plead for it, bring Scripture for it, bring Argument for it, *&c.*

Greath. *An Opinion that is not fit to be, with any Allowance, in the World.*

Hon. You must understand me rightly: He did not say that any man might do this; but, that those that had the Virtues of those that did such things, might also do the same.

Greath. *But what more false then such a Conclusion? For this is as much as to say, that because good men hereto-* 30 *fore have sinned of Infirmity, therefore he had allowance to do it of a presumptuous Mind. Or if because a Child, by the blast of the Wind, or for that it stumbled at a stone, fell down and so defiled it self in Myre, therefore he might wilfully ly down and wallow like a Bore therein. Who could a thought that any one could so far a bin blinded by the power of Lust? But what is written must be true: They*

1 Pet. 2. 8. *stumble at the Word, being disobedient, whereunto also they were appointed.*

36 *been* 2

His supposing that such may have the godly Mans Vir-
tues, who addict themselves to their Vices, is also a Delusion
as strong as the other. 'Tis just as if the Dog *should say,*
I have, or may have the Qualities *of the* Child, *because*
I lick up its stinking Excrements. To eat up the Sin of Gods Hos. 4. 8.
People, is no sign of one that is possessed with their Virtues.
Nor can I believe that one that is of this Opinion, can at
present have Faith or Love in him. But I know you have
made strong Objections against him, prethee what can he
10 *say for himself?*

Hon. Why, he says, To do this by way of Opinion,
seems abundance more honest, then to do it, and yet
hold contrary to it in Opinion.

Greath. A very wicked Answer, for tho to let loose the
Bridle to Lusts, while our Opinions are against such things,
is bad; yet to sin, and plead a Toleration so to do, is worse;
the one stumbles Beholders accidentally, the other pleads
them into the Snare.

Hon. There are many of this mans mind, that have
20 not this mans mouth, and *that* makes going on Pilgrimage of so little esteem as it is.

Greath. You have said the Truth, and it is to be
lamented. But he that feareth the King of Paradice, shall
come out of them all.

Christiana. There are strange Opinions in the World.
I know one that said 'twas time enough to repent when
they came to die.

Greath. Such are not over wise. That man would a bin
loath, might he have had a week to run twenty mile in for
30 *his Life, to have deferred that Journey to the last hour of*
that Week.

Hon. You say right, and yet the generality of them that
count themselves Pilgrims, do indeed do thus. I am, as
you see, an old Man, and have bin a Traveller in this Rode
many a day; and I have taken notice of many things.

I have seen some that have set out as if they would
drive all the World afore them. Who yet have in few
days, dyed as they in the Wilderness, and so never gat
sight of the promised Land.

28 *been* 2   34 been 2

I have seen some that have promised nothing at first setting out to be Pilgrims, and that one would a thought could not have lived a day, that have yet proved very good Pilgrims.

I have seen some that have run hastily forward, that again have after a little time, run just as fast back again.

I have seen some who have spoke very well of a Pilgrims Life at first, that after a while, have spoken as much against it.

I have heard some, when they first set out for Para-dice, say positively, there is such a place, who when they have been almost there, have come back again, and said there is none.

I have heard some vaunt what they would do in case they should be opposed, that have even at a false Alarm fled Faith, the Pilgrims way, and all.

Fresh News of trouble.   Now as they were thus in their way, there came one runing to meet them, and said, Gentlemen, and you of the weaker sort, if you love Life, shift for your selves, for the Robbers are before you.   20

1 Part p. 125–6.

Greatheart's Resolution.   *Greath.* Then said Mr. *Greatheart*, They be the three that set upon *Littlefaith* heretofore. Well, said he, we are ready for them; so they went on their way. Now they looked at every Turning when they should a met with the Villains. But whether they heard of Mr. *Greatheart*, or whether they had some other Game, they came not up to the Pilgrims.

Christiana wisheth for an Inn.   *Chris. Christiana* then wished for an Inn for her self and her Children, because they were weary. Then said Mr. *Honest*, There is one a little before us, where a very honourable Disciple, one *Gaius* dwells. So they all concluded to turn in thither; and the rather, because the old Gentleman gave him so good a Report. So when they came to the Door, they went in, not knocking for folks use not to knock at the Door of an Inn. Then they called for the Master of the House, and he came to them. *So they asked if they might lie there that Night?*

Rom. 16. 23.

Gaius.

They enter into his House.

Gaius. Yes Gentlemen, if you be true Men, for my House is for none but Pilgrims. Then was *Christiana*, *Mercie*, and the *Boys*, the more glad, for that the Inn-keeper was a lover of Pilgrims. So they called for Rooms; and he shewed them one for *Christiana*, and her Children, and *Mercy*, and another for Mr. *Great-heart* and the old Gentleman. Gaius Enter-tains them, and how.

Greath. *Then said Mr.* Great-heart, *good* Gaius, *what hast thou for Supper? for these Pilgrims have come far to* 10 *day, and are weary.*

Gaius. It is late, said *Gaius*; so we cannot con-veniently go out to seek Food; but such as we have you shall be welcome to, if that will content.

Greath. *We will be content with what thou hast in the House, for as much as I have proved thee; thou art never destitute of that which is convenient.*

Then he went down, and spake to the Cook, whose Name was *Taste-that-which-is-good*, to get ready Supper for so many Pilgrims. This done, he comes up again, 20 saying, come my good Friends, you are welcome to me, and I am glad that I have an House to entertain you; and while Supper is making ready, if you please, let us entertain one another with some good Discourse. So they all said, content. Gaius *his Cook.*

Gaius. *Then said* Gaius, *Whose Wife is this aged Matron? and whose Daughter is this young Damsel?* *Talk between* Gaius *and his Guests.*

Greath. The Woman is the Wife of one *Christian*, a Pilgrim of former times, and these are his four Chil-dren. The Maid is one of her Acquaintance; one that 30 she hath perswaded to come with her on Pilgrimage. The Boys take all after their Father, and covet to tread in his Steps. Yea, if they do but see any place where the old Pilgrim hath lain, or any print of his Foot, it ministreth Joy to their Hearts, and they covet to lie, or tread in the same. *Mark this.*

Gaius. Then said *Gaius*, is this *Christian*'s Wife, and are these *Christian*'s Children? I knew your Husband's Act. 11. 26. *Of* Christian's *Ancestors.*

1 *marg.* Gaius . . . *how* add. 2   17 *marg.* Gaius *his Cook* add. 2
25 marg. *Talk . . . Guests* add. 2   32 marg. *Mark this* add. 2   36 *marg.*
Act. 11. 26] Ps. 11. 26 || 1   37 marg. *Of . . . Ancestors* add. 2

Father, yea, also, his Fathers Father. Many have been good of this stock, their Ancestors dwelt first at *Antioch*. *Christian*'s Progenitors (I suppose you have heard your Husband talk of them) were very worthy men. They have above any that I know, shewed themselves men of great Virtue and Courage, for the Lord of the Pilgrims, his ways, and them that loved him. I have heard of many of your Husbands Relations that have stood Acts 7. 59, 60. all Tryals for the sake of the Truth. *Stephen* that was *Cha.* 12. 2. one of the first of the Family from whence your Hus- 10 band sprang, was knocked o'th' Head with Stones. *James*, an other of this Generation, was slain with the edge of the Sword. To say nothing of *Paul* and *Peter*, men antiently of the Family from whence your Husband came. There was *Ignatius*, who was cast to the Lyons. *Romanus*, whose Flesh was cut by pieces from his Bones; and *Policarp*, that played the man in the Fire. There was he that was hanged up in a Basket in the Sun, for the Wasps to eat; and he who they put into a Sack and cast him into the Sea, to be drowned. 20 'Twould be impossible, utterly to count up all of that Family that have suffered Injuries and Death, for the love of a Pilgrims Life. Nor can I, but be glad, to see that thy Husband has left behind him four such Boys as these. I hope they will bear up their Fathers Name, and tread in their Fathers Steps, and come to their Fathers End.

Greath. *Indeed Sir, they are likely Lads, they seem to chuse heartily their Fathers Ways.*

Advice to Christiana about her Boys. *Gaius.* That is it that I said, wherefore *Christians* Family is like still to spread abroad upon the face of 30 the Ground, and yet to be numerous upon the Face of the Earth. Wherefore let *Christiana* look out some Damsels for her Sons, to whom they may be Betrothed, *&c.* that the Name of their Father, and the House of his Progenitors may never be forgotten in the World.

Hon. *'Tis pity this Family should fall and be extinct.*

Gaius. Fall it cannot, but be diminished it may; but let *Christiana* take my Advice, and that's the way to uphold it.

12 another 2   **29** marg. *Advice . . . Boys* add. 2

And *Christiana*, said *This* Inn-keeper, I am glad to Mercie *and*
see thee and thy Friend *Mercie* together here, a lovely Matthew *Marry*.
Couple. And may I advise, take *Mercie* into a nearer
Relation to thee. If she will, let her be given to *Mathew*
thy eldest Son. 'Tis the way to preserve you a posterity
in the Earth. So this match was concluded, and in
process of time they were married. But more of that
hereafter.

    Gaius also proceeded, and said, I will now speak on
10 the behalf of Women, to take away their Reproach.
For as Death and the Curse came into the World by
a Woman, so also did Life and Health; *God sent forth* Gen. 3.
his Son, made of a Woman. Yea, to shew how much Gal. 4.
those that came after did abhor the Act of their Mother,
this Sex, in the old Testament, coveted Children, if *Why Women*
happily this or that Woman might be the Mother of *of old so*
the Saviour of the World. I will say again, that when *much desired Children.*
the Saviour was come, Women rejoyced in him, before Luke 2.
either Man or Angel. I read not that ever any man did
20 give unto Christ so much as one *Groat*, but the Women
followed him, and ministred to him of their Substance.
'Twas a Woman that washed his Feet with Tears, and Chap. 8. 2, 3.
a Woman that anointed his Body to the Burial. They chap. 7. 37, 50.
were Women that wept when he was going to the Joh. 11. 2.
Cross; And Women that followed him from the Cross, chap. 12. 3. Luk. 23. 27.
and that sat by his Sepulcher when he was buried. Matt. 27, 55,
They were Women that was first with him at his 56, 61. Luke 24.
Resurrection *morn*, and Women that brought Tidings 22, 23.
first to his Disciples that he was risen from the Dead.
30 Women therefore are highly favoured, and shew by these
things that they are sharers with us in the Grace of Life.

    Now the Cook sent up to signifie that Supper was *Supper ready.*
almost ready, and sent one to lay the Cloath, the
Trenshers, and to set the Salt and Bread in order.

    Then said *Mathew, The sight of this Cloath, and of
this Forerunner of the Supper, begetteth in me a greater
Appetite to my Food then I had before.*

1 *marg.* Mercie . . . *Marry* add. 2   14–15 Mother. This 1
Mother; this 2   20 *Groat*] Gorat 1   28 Tiding 1   32 marg.
Supper ready add. 2   36 *the*] *a* 1   37 *than* 2

What to be gathered from laying of the Board with the Cloath and Trenshers.

Gaius. So let all ministring Doctrines *to* thee in this Life, beget *in* thee a greater desire to sit at the Supper of the great King in his Kingdom; for all Preaching, Books, and Ordinances here, are but as the laying of the Trenshers, and as setting of Salt upon the Board, when compared with the Feast that our Lord will make for us when we come to his House.

Levit. 7. 32, 33, 34. Chap. 10. 14, 15. Psal. 25. 1. Heb. 13. 15.

So Supper came up, and first a *Heave-shoulder*, and a *Wave-breast* was set on the Table before them: To shew that they must begin their *Meal* with Prayer and 10 Praise to God. The *Heave-shoulder David* lifted his Heart up to God with, and with the *Wave-breast, where his heart lay*, with that he used to lean upon his Harp when he played. These two Dishes were very fresh and good, and they all eat heartily-well thereof.

Deut. 32. 14. Judg. 9. 13. Joh. 15. 1.

The next they brought up, was a Bottle of Wine, red as Blood. So *Gaius* said to them, Drink freely, this is the Juice of the true Vine, that makes glad the Heart of God and Man. So they drank and were merry.

1 Pet. 2. 1, 2.

The next was a Dish of Milk well crumbed. But *Gaius* 20 said, *Let the Boys have that, that they may grow thereby.*

A Dish of Milk. Of Honey and Butter.

Then they brought up in course a Dish of *Butter* and *Hony*. Then said *Gaius*, Eat freely of *this*, for this is good to chear up, and strengthen your Judgments and Understandings: This was our Lords Dish when he

Isa. 7. 15.

was a Child; *Butter and Hony shall he eat, that he may know to refuse the Evil, and choose the Good.*

A Dish of Apples.

Then they brought them up a Dish of Apples, and they were very good tasted Fruit. Then said *Mathew*, May we eat Apples, since they were such, by, and with 30 which the Serpent beguiled our first Mother? Then said *Gaius*,

Apples were they with *which we were beguil'd,*
Yet Sin, *not Apples hath our Souls defil'd.*
Apples forbid, if eat, corrupts the Blood:
To eat such, when commanded, does us good.
Drink of his Flagons then, thou, Church, his Dove,
And eat his *Apples, who art sick of Love.*

12 *where*] *when* 1 (corr. in Errata)

Then said *Mathew*, I made the Scruple, *because I a while since was sick with eating of Fruit.*

Gaius. Forbidden Fruit will make you sick, but not what our Lord has tolerated.

While they were thus talking, they were presented with an other Dish; and 'twas a dish of *Nuts.* Then said some at the Table, *Nuts* spoyl tender Teeth; especially the Teeth of Children. Which when *Gaius* heard, he said, Song 6. 11.
A dish of
Nuts.

10   *Hard* Texts *are* Nuts (*I will not call them* Cheaters,)
Whose Shells *do keep their* Kirnels *from the* Eaters.
Ope then the Shells, and you shall have the Meat,
They here are brought, for you to crack and eat.

Then were they very Merry, and sate at the Table a long time, talking of many things. Then said the old Gentleman, My good Landlord, while we are cracking your *Nuts,* if you please, do you open this Riddle.

A man there was, tho some did count him mad,
The more he cast away, the more he had. *A Riddle*
put forth by
old Honest.

20   Then they all gave good heed, wondring what good *Gaius* would say, so he sat still a while, and then thus replyed:

He that bestows his Goods upon the Poor, Gaius *opens it.*
Shall have as much again, and ten times more.

Then said *Joseph*, I dare say Sir, I did not think you could a found it out. Joseph
wonders.

Oh! said *Gaius*, I have bin trained up in this way a great while: Nothing teaches like Experience; I have learned of my Lord to be kind, & have found by experience that 30 I have gained thereby: *There is that scattereth, yet increaseth, and there is that withholdeth more then is meet, but it tendeth to Poverty. There is that maketh himself Rich, yet hath nothing; there is that maketh himself poor, yet hath great Riches.* Prov. 11. 24.
Chap. 13. 7.

Then *Samuel* whispered to *Christiana* his Mother,

18 marg. *put forth by old* Honest *add.* 2   23 *marg.* Gaius *opens it* add. 2   25 *marg.* Joseph *wonders* add. 2   27 been 2   35
Samuel] Simon 1

and said, Mother, this is a very good mans House, let us stay here a good while, and let my Brother *Matthew* be married here to *Mercy*, before we go any further.

The which *Gaius* the Host overhearing, said, *With a very good Will my Child.*

Mathew and Mercie are Married. So they stayed there more then a Month, and *Mercie* was given to *Mathew* to Wife.

While they stayed here, *Mercy* as her Custom was, would be making Coats and Garments to give to the Poor, by which she brought up a very good Report 10 upon the Pilgrims.

The boys go to Bed, the rest sit up. But to return again to our Story. After Supper, the Lads desired a Bed, for that they were weary with Travelling. Then *Gaius* called to shew them their Chamber, but said *Mercy*, I will have them to Bed. So she had them to Bed, and they slept well, but the rest sat up all Night. For *Gaius* and they were such sutable Company, that they could not tell how to part. Then after much talk of their Lord, themselves, and their Journey, Old Mr. *Honest,* he that put forth the Riddle 20 *Old Honest Nods.* to *Gaius,* began to *nod.* Then said *Great-heart,* What Sir, you begin to be drouzy, come rub up, now here's a *Riddle* for you. Then said Mr. *Honest,* let's hear it.

Then said Mr. *Great-heart,*

A Riddle.
> *He that will kill, must first be overcome:*
> *Who live abroad would, first must die at home.*

Huh, said Mr. *Honest,* it is a hard one, hard to expound, and harder to practise. But come Landlord, said he, I will, if you please, leave my part to you, do you expound it, and I will hear what you say.   30

No, said *Gaius,* 'twas put to you, and 'tis expected that you should answer it.

Then said the old Gentleman,

The Riddle opened.
> *He first by Grace must conquer'd be,*
> *That Sin would mortifie.*
> *And who, that lives, would convince me,*
> *Unto himself must die.*

6 *marg.* Mathew . . . *Married* add. 2   **12** marg. *The . . . up* add. 2
21 marg. *Old . . . Nods* add. 2   **34** marg. *The Riddle opened* add. 2

It is right, said *Gaius*; good Doctrine, and Experience teaches this. For first, until Grace displays it self, and overcomes the Soul with its Glory, it is altogether without Heart to oppose Sin. Besides, if Sin is Satan's Cords, by which the Soul lies bound, how should it make Resistance, before it is loosed from that Infirmity?

Secondly, Nor will any that knows either Reason or Grace, believe that such a man can be a living Monument of Grace, that is a Slave to his own Corruptions.

And now it comes in my mind, I will tell you a Story, worth the hearing. There were two Men that went on Pilgrimage, the one began when he was young, the other when he was old. The young man had strong Corruptions to grapple with, the old mans were decayed with the decays of Nature. The young man trod his steps as even as did the old one, and was every way as light as he; who now, or which of them had their Graces shining clearest, since both seemed to be alike? *A Question worth the minding.*

Honest. The young mans doubtless. For that which heads it against the greatest Opposition, gives best demonstration that it is strongest. Specially when it also holdeth pace with that that meets not with half so much: as to be sure old Age does not. *A Comparison.*

Besides, I have observed that old men have blessed themselves with this mistake; Namely, taking the decays of Nature for a gracious Conquest over Corruptions, and so have been apt to beguile themselves. Indeed old men that are gracious, are best able to give Advice to them that are young, because they have seen most of the emptiness of things. But yet, for an old and a young to set out both together, the young one has the advantage of the fairest discovery of a work of Grace within him, tho the old mans Corruptions are naturally the weakest. *A Mistake.*

Thus they sat talking till break of Day. Now when the Family was up, *Christiana* bid her Son *James* that he should read a Chapter; so he read the 53 of *Isaiah*. When he had done, Mr. *Honest* asked why it was said,

Another *That the Savior is said to come out of a dry ground, and*
Question. *also that he had no Form nor Comliness in him?*

Greath. Then said Mr. *Great-heart,* To the first I
answer, Because, the Church of the Jews, of which
Christ came, had then lost almost all the Sap and Spirit
of Religion. To the Second I say, The Words are
spoken in the Person of the Unbelievers, who because
they want *that* Eye that can see into our Princes Heart,
therefore they judg of him by the meanness of his
Outside.   10

Just like those that know not that precious Stones
are covered over with a homely *Crust*; who when they
have found one, because they know not what they have
found, cast it again away as men do a common Stone.

Well, said *Gaius,* Now you are here, and since, as
I know, Mr. *Great-heart* is good at his Weapons, if you
please, after we have refreshed our selves, we will walk
Gyant Slay- into the Fields, to see if we can do any good. About
good *assaulted* a mile from hence, there is one *Slaygood,* a *Gyant,* that
and slain. doth much annoy the Kings High-way in these parts. 20
And I know whereabout his Haunt is, he is Master of
a number of Thieves; 'twould be well if we could clear
these Parts of him.

So they consented and went, Mr. *Great-heart* with
his *Sword, Helmet* and *Shield*; and the rest with Spears
and Staves.

He is found When they came to the place where he was, they
with one found him with one *Feeble-mind* in his Hands, whom
Feeble-mind
in his hands. his Servants had brought unto him, having taken him
in the Way; now the Gyant was rifling of him, with 30
a purpose after that to pick his Bones. For he was of
the nature of *Flesh-eaters.*

Well, so soon as he saw Mr. *Great-heart,* and his
Friends, at the mouth of his Cave with their Weapons,
he demanded what they wanted?

Greath. We want thee; for we are come to revenge
the Quarrel of the many that thou hast slain of the
Pilgrims, when thou hast dragged them out of the
Kings High-way; wherefore come out of thy Cave. So

1 marg. *Another Question* add. 2   27 marg. *He . . . hands* add. 2

he armed himself and came out, and to a Battle they
went, and fought for above an Hour, and then stood
still to take Wind.

Slaygood. *Then said the Gyant, Why are you here on
my Ground?*

Greath. To revenge the Blood of Pilgrims, as I also
told thee before; so they went to it again, and the Gyant
made Mr. *Great-heart* give back, but he came up again,
and in the greatness of his Mind, he let fly with such
10 stoutness at the Gyants Head and Sides, that he made
him let his Weapon fall out of his Hand. So he smote
him, and slew him, and cut off his Head, and brought
it away to the *Inn.* He also took *Feeble-mind* the Pil- *One*
grim, and brought him with him to his Lodgings. *Feeble-mind*
When they were come home, they shewed his Head to *the Gyant.* *rescued from*
the Family, and then set it up as they had done others
before, for a Terror to those that should attempt to do
as he, hereafter.

Then they asked Mr. *Feeblemind* how he fell into
20 his hands?

Feeblem. Then said the poor man, I am a sickly man, *How Feeble-*
as you see, and because *Death* did usually once a day *mind came to*
knock at my Door, I thought I should never be well at *be a Pilgrim.*
home. So I betook my self to a Pilgrims life; and have
travelled hither from the Town of *Uncertain,* where I
and my Father were born. I am a man of no strength
at all, of Body, nor yet of Mind, but would, if I could,
tho I can but *craul,* spend my Life in the Pilgrims way.
When I came at the Gate that is at the head of the Way,
30 the Lord of that place did entertain me freely. Neither
objected he against my weakly Looks, nor against my
feeble Mind; but gave me such things that were necessary for my Journey, and bid me hope to the end.
When I came to the House of the *Interpreter,* I received
much Kindness there, and because the Hill *Difficulty*
was judged too hard for me, I was carried up that by
one of his Servants. Indeed I have found much Relief
from Pilgrims, tho none was willing to go so softly as
I am forced to do. Yet still as they came on, they bid

me be of good Chear, and said that it was the will of
their Lord, that Comfort should be given to the *feeble
minded*, and so went on their *own* pace. When I was
come up to *Assault-Lane*, then this *Gyant* met with me,
and bid me prepare for an *Incounter*; but alas, feeble
one that I was, I had more need of a *Cordial*. So he
came up and took me, I conceited he should not kill
me; also when he had got me into his Den, since I went
not with him *willingly*, I believed I should come out
alive again. For I have heard, that not any Pilgrim that 10
is taken Captive by violent Hands, if he keeps Heart-
whole towards his Master, is by the Laws of Providence
to die by the Hand of the Enemy. *Robbed*, I looked
to be, and Robbed to be sure I am; but I am as you
see escaped with Life, for the which I thank my King
as Author, and you as the Means. Other Brunts I also
look for, but this I have resolved on, to wit, to *run* when
I can, to *go* when I cannot *run*, and to *creep* when I cannot *go*. As to the main, I thank him that loves me, I am
fixed; my way is before me, my Mind is beyond the 20
River that has no Bridg, tho I am as you see, but of
a *feeble Mind*.

　　Hon. *Then said old Mr.* Honest, *Have not you some time
ago, been acquainted with one Mr.* Fearing, *a* Pilgrim?
　　Feeble. Acquainted with him; Yes. He came from
the Town of *Stupidity*, which lieth *four Degrees* to the
Northward of the City of *Destruction*, and as many off,
of where I was born; Yet we were well acquainted, for
indeed he was mine Uncle, my Fathers Brother; he and
I have been much of a Temper, he was a little shorter 30
then I, but yet we were much of a Complexion.

　　Hon. *I perceive you knew him, and I am apt to believe
also that you were related one to another; for you have his
whitely Look, a Cast like his with your Eye, and your
Speech is much alike.*

　　Feebl. Most have said so, that have known us both,
and besides, what I have read in him, I have for the
most part found in my self.

Margin notes:
1 Thess. 5. 14.
Mark this.
Mark this.
Mr. Fearing
Mr. Feeble-
mind's Uncle.
Feeble-mind
has some of
Mr. Fearing's
Features.

Gaius. *Come Sir, said good* Gaius, *be of good Chear,* Gaius Comforts him. *you are welcome to me, and to my House; and what thou hast a mind to, call for freely; and what thou would'st have my Servants do for thee, they will do it with a ready Mind.*

Feebl. Then said Mr. *Feeble-mind,* This is unex- Notice to be taken of Providence. pected Favour, and as the Sun shining out of a very dark Cloud. Did Gyant *Slay-good* intend me this Favour when he stop'd me, and resolved to let me go no further? Did he intend that after he had rifled my 10 Pockets, I should go to *Gaius mine Host?* Yet so it is.

Now, just as Mr. *Feeble-mind,* and *Gaius* was thus in Tidings how one Not-right was slain with a Thunder-bolt, and Mr. Feeble-mind's Comment upon it. talk; there comes one running, and called at the Door, and told, That about a Mile and an half off, there was one Mr. *Not-right* a Pilgrim, struck dead upon the place where he was, with a *Thunder-bolt.*

Feebl. Alas! said Mr. *Feeble-mind,* is he slain? he overtook me some days before I came so far as hither, and would be my Company-keeper. He also was with me when *Slay-good* the Gyant took me, but he was 20 nimble of his Heels, and escaped. But it seems, he escaped to die, and I was took to live.

What, one would think, doth seek to slay outright,
Oftimes, delivers from the saddest Plight.
That very Providence, *whose Face is* Death,
Doth oftimes, to the lowly, Life bequeath.
I taken was, he did escape and flee,
Hands Crost, gives Death to him, and Life to me.

Now about this time *Mathew* and *Mercie* was Married; also *Gaius* gave his Daughter *Phebe* to *James,* 30 *Mathew's* Brother, to Wife; after which time, they yet stayed above ten days at *Gaius's* House, spending their time, and the Seasons, like as Pilgrims use to do.

When they were to depart, *Gaius* made them a Feast, The Pilgrims prepare to go forward. and they did eat and drink, and were merry. Now the Hour was come that they must be gon, wherefore Mr. *Great-heart* called for a Reckoning. But *Gaius* told him, that at his House, it was not the Custom for *Pilgrims* to pay for their Entertainment. He boarded

5 marg. *Nootice* 2   25 *Life* 1, 2   28 were 2

Luke 10. 33, them by the year, but looked for his pay from the good
34, 35. *Samaritan,* who had promised him at his return, what-
How they greet soever Charge he was at with them, faithfully to repay
one another him. Then said Mr. *Great-heart* to him,
at parting.

3 John 6.   *Greath.* Beloved, thou dost faithfully, whatsoever thou
dost, to the Brethren and to Strangers, which have born
Witness of thy Charity before the Church. Whom if thou
(yet) bring forward on their Journey after a Godly sort,
thou shalt do well.

Gaius his last   Then *Gaius* took his leave of them all, and of his 10
kindness to Children, and particularly of Mr. *Feeble-mind.* He also
Feeble-mind. gave him something to drink by the way.

    Now Mr. *Feeblemind,* when they were going out of
the Door, made as if he intended to linger. The which,
when Mr. *Great-heart* espied, he said, come Mr. *Feeble-
mind,* pray do you go along with us, I will be your
Conductor, and you shall fare as the rest.

Feeble-mind   *Feebl. Alas, I want a sutable Companion, you are all*
for going lusty and strong, but I, as you see, am weak; I chuse there-
behind. fore rather to come behind, lest, by reason of my many 20
Infirmities, I should be both a Burthen to my self, and to
you. I am, as I said, a man of a weak and feeble Mind,
and shall be offended and made weak at that which others
can bear. I shall like no Laughing, I shall like no gay
His Excuse Attire, I shall like no unprofitable Questions. Nay, I am
for it. so weak a Man, as to be offended with that which others
have a liberty to do. I do not yet know all the Truth; I am
a very ignorant Christian-man; sometimes if I hear some
rejoyce in the Lord, it troubles me because I cannot do so
too. It is with me, as it is with a weak Man among the 30
strong, or as with a sick Man among the healthy, or as a
Job 12. 5. Lamp despised. (He that is ready to slip with his Feet, is
as a Lamp despised, in the Thought of him that is at ease.)
So that I know not what to do.

Great-heart's   *Greath.* But Brother, said Mr. *Great-heart.* I have
Commission. it in Commission, to comfort the *feeble minded,* and to
1 Thess. 5. 14. support the weak. You must needs go along with us;

5 *marg.* 1 John 5. 6 ‖ 1, 2   15–16 *Feeble-mind*] *Feeble* 1   18
marg. Feeble-mind . . . *behind* add. 2   25 marg. *His . . . it* add. 2
35 *marg.* Great-heart's *Commission* add. 2   36 *Commission* ital. 2

we will wait for you, we will lend you our help, we will Rom. 14.
deny our selves of some things, both *Opinionative* and 1 Cor. 8.
Chap. 9. 22.
Practical, for your sake; we will not enter into doubtful *A Christian*
Disputations before you, we will be made all things to *Spirit.*
you, rather then you shall be left behind.

Now, all this while they were at *Gaius*'s Door; and
behold as they were thus in the heat of their Discourse, Psa. 38. 17.
Mr. *Ready-to-hault* came by, with his *Crutches* in his Promises.
hand, and he also was going on Pilgrimage.

10   Feebl. *Then said Mr.* Feeble-mind *to him, Man! how* Feeble-mind
camest thou hither? I was but just now complaining that glad to see
Ready-to-hault
I had not a sutable Companion, but thou art according to come by.
my Wish. Welcome, welcome, good Mr. Ready-to-hault,
I hope thee and I may be some help.

Ready-to. I shall be glad of thy Company, said the
other; and good Mr. *Feeble-mind*, rather then we will
part, since we are thus happily met, I will lend thee
one of my Crutches.

Feebl. *Nay, said he, tho I thank thee for thy good Will,*
20 *I am not inclined to hault before I am Lame. How be it,*
I think when occasion is, it may help me against a Dog.

Ready-to. If either my *self*, or my *Crutches*, can do
thee a pleasure, we are both at thy Command, good
Mr. *Feeble-mind.*

Thus therefore they went on, Mr. *Great-heart* and
Mr. *Honest* went before, *Christiana* and her Children
went next, and Mr. *Feeble-mind* and Mr. *Ready-to-hault*
came behind with his Crutches. Then said Mr. *Honest,*

Hon. *Pray Sir, now we are upon the Road, tell us* New Talk.
30 *some profitable things of some that have gon on Pilgrimage*
before us.

Greath. With a good Will. I suppose you have
heard how *Christian* of old, did meet with *Apollyon* in
the Valley of *Humiliation*, and also what hard work he
had to go thorow the Valley of the Shadow of Death.
Also I think you cannot but have heard how *Faithful*
was put to it with *Madam Wanton*, with *Adam* the first, 1 Part *from*
pag. 68, to
pag. 74.

3 marg. *A ... Spirit* add. 2   5 be] he 2   10 *marg.* Feeble-
mind ... *by* add. 2   29 marg. *New Talk* add. 2   37 *marg.*
1 Part *from* pag. 111, to pag. 122 ‖ 1, 2

with one *Discontent*, and *Shame*; four as deceitful Villains, as a man can meet with upon the Road.

Hon. *Yes, I have heard of all this; but indeed, good* Faithful *was hardest put to it with* Shame, *he was an unwearied one.*

Greath. Ai, for as the Pilgrim well said, He of all men had the wrong Name.

Hon. *But pray Sir, where was it that* Christian *and* Faithful *met* Talkative? *that same was also a notable one.*

Greath. He was a confident Fool, yet many follow 10 his wayes.

Hon. *He had like to a beguiled* Faithful?

1 Part pag. 75, pag. 78, pag. 87, Greath. Ai, But *Christian* put him into a way quickly to find him out. Thus they went on till they came at the place where *Evangelist* met with *Christian* and *Faithful*, and prophecyed to them of what should befall them at Vanity-Fair.

Greath. Then said their Guide, Hereabouts did *Christian* and *Faithful* meet with *Evangelist*, who Prophesied to them of what Troubles they should meet 20 with at *Vanity-Fair*.

Hon. *Say you so! I dare say it was a hard Chapter that then he did read unto them.*

1 Part pag. 92 &c. Greath. 'Twas so, but he gave them Incouragement withall. But what do we talk of them, they were a couple of Lyon-like Men; they had set their Faces like Flint. Don't you remember how undaunted they were when they stood before the Judg?

Hon. *Well* Faithful, *bravely suffered!*

Greath. So he did, and as brave things came on't: 30 For *Hopeful* and some others, as the Story relates it, were Converted by his Death.

Hon. *Well, but pray go on; for you are well acquainted with things.*

1 Part pag. 98. Greath. Above all that *Christian* met with after he had passed throw *Vanity-Fair*, one *By-ends* was the arch one.

Hon. *By-ends; what was he?*

---

13 *marg.* 1 Part pag. 123. pag. 127. pag. 144 ‖ 1, 2   24 *marg.*
1 Part pag. 157, &c. ‖ 1, 2   35 *marg.* 1 Part pag. 167 ‖ 1, 2   36
throw] thorow 2

Greath. A very arch Fellow, a downright Hypocrite; one that would be Religious, which way ever the World went, but so cunning, that he would be sure neither to lose, nor suffer for it.

He had his *Mode* of Religion for every fresh occasion, and his Wife was as good at it as he. He would turn and change from Opinion to Opinion; yea, and plead for so doing too. But so far as I could learn, he came to an ill End with his *By-ends*, nor did I ever hear that any of his Children were ever of any Esteem with any that truly feared God.

Now by this time, they were come within sight of the Town of *Vanity*, where Vanity Fair is kept. So when they saw that they were so near the Town, they consulted with one another how they should pass thorow the Town, and some said one thing, and some another. At last Mr. *Greatheart* said, I have, as you may understand, often been a *Conductor* of Pilgrims thorow *this* Town; Now I am acquainted with one Mr. *Mnason*, a *Cyprusian* by Nation, an old Disciple, at whose House we may Lodg. If you think good, said he, we will turn in there. *They are come within sight of Vanity. Psa. 12. 2.*

They enter into one Mr. Mnasons to Lodg.

Content, said old *Honest*; Content, said *Christiana*; Content, said Mr. *Feeble-mind*; and so they said all. Now you must think it was *Even-tide*, by that they got to the outside of the Town, but Mr. *Great-heart* knew the way to the Old man's House. So thither they came; and he called at the Door, and the old Man within knew his Tongue so soon as ever he heard it; so he opened, and they all came in. Then said *Mnason* their Host, How far have ye come to day? So they said, From the House of *Gaius* our Friend. I promise you, said he, you have gone a good stitch, you may well be a-weary; sit down. So they sat down.

Greath. *Then said their Guide, Come what Chear Sirs, I dare say you are welcome to my Friend.*

Mna. I also, said Mr. *Mnason*, do bid you Welcome; and whatever you want, do but say, and we will do what we can to get it for you. *They are glad of entertainment.*

Hon. *Our great Want, a while since, was Harbor, and good Company, and now I hope we have both.*

14 Psa. 21. 16 ‖ 1, 2.

Mna. For Harbour, you see what it is, but for good Company, that will appear in the Tryal.

Greath. *Well, said Mr.* Great-heart, *will you have the Pilgrims up into their Lodging?*

Mna. I will, said Mr. *Mnason.* So he had them to their respective Places; and also shewed them a very fair Dining-Room, where they might be and sup together, until time was come to go to Rest.

Now when they were set in their places, and were a little cheary after their Journey, Mr. *Honest* asked his Land- 1 lord if there were any store of good People in the Town?

Mna. We have a few, for indeed they are but a few, when compared with them on the other side.

They desire to see some of the good People in the Town. *Hon.* *But how shall we do to see some of them? for the sight of good men to them that are going on Pilgrimage, is like to the appearing of the Moon and the Stars to them that are sailing upon the Seas.*

Mna. Then Mr. *Mnason* stamped with his Foot, and his Daughter *Grace* came up; so he said unto her, *Grace,* *Some sent for.* go you, tell my Friends, Mr. *Contrite,* Mr. *Holy-man,* 2 Mr. *Love-saint,* Mr. *Dare-not-ly,* and Mr. *Penitent;* that I have a Friend or two at my House, that have a mind this Evening to see them.

So *Grace* went to call them, and they came, and after Salutation made, they sat down together at the Table.

Then said Mr. *Mnason* their Landlord, My Neighbours, I have, as you see, a company of *Strangers* come to my House, they are *Pilgrims:* They come from afar, and are going to Mount *Sion.* But who, quoth he, do you think this is? pointing with his Finger to *Christiana.* 3 It is *Christiana,* the Wife of *Christian,* that famous Pilgrim, who with *Faithful* his brother were so shamefully handled in our Town. At that they stood amazed, saying, We little thought to see *Christiana,* when *Grace* came to call us, wherefore this is a very comfortable Surprize. Then they asked her of her welfare, and if these young men were her Husbands Sons. And when she had told them they were; they said, The King whom you love, and serve, make you as your Father, and bring you where he is in Peace. 4

Hon. Then Mr. *Honest (when they were all sat down)* asked Mr. Contrite *and the rest, in what posture their Town was at present?* *Some Talk betwixt Mr. Honest and Contrite.*

Cont. You may be sure we are full of Hurry, in Fair time. *'Tis hard keeping our Hearts and Spirits in any good Order, when we are in a cumbred condition. He *that lives in such a place as this is, and that has to do with such as we have, has need of an Item to caution him to take heed, every moment of the Day. ** The Fruit of Watchfulness.*

10 Hon. *But how are your Neighbors for quietness?*

Cont. They are much more moderate now then formerly. You know how *Christian* and *Faithful* were used at our Town; but of late, I say, they have been far more moderate. I think the Blood of *Faithful* lieth with load upon them till now; for since they burned him, they have been ashamed to burn any more: In *those* days we were afraid to walk the Streets, but *now* we can shew our Heads. *Then* the Name of a Professor was odious, *now*, specially in some parts of our Town (for you know 20 our Town is large) Religion is counted Honourable. *Persecution not so hot at Vanity Fair as formerly.*

Then said Mr. Contrite *to them, Pray how faireth it with you in your Pilgrimage, how stands the Country affected towards you?*

Hon. It happens to us, as it happeneth to Way-fairing men; sometimes our way is clean, sometimes foul; sometimes up-hill, sometimes down-hill; We are seldom at a Certainty. The Wind is not alwayes on our Backs, nor is every one a Friend that we meet with in the Way. We have met with some notable Rubs already; and 30 what are yet behind we know not, but for the most part we find it true, that has been talked of of old, *A good Man must suffer Trouble.*

Contrit. You talk of Rubs, what Rubs have you met withal?

Hon. Nay, ask Mr. *Great-heart* our Guide, for he can give the best Account of that.

Greath. We have been beset three or four times already: First *Christiana* and her Children were beset with two Ruffians, that they feared would a took away

5 marg. *The . . . Watchfulness* add. 2   16 *those* rom. 1

their Lives; We was beset with Gyant *Bloody-man*, Gyant *Maul*, and Gyant *Slay-good*. Indeed we did rather beset the last, then were beset of him: And thus it was. After we had been some time at the House of *Gaius*, *mine Host, and of the whole Church*, we were minded upon a time to take our Weapons with us, and go see if we could light upon any of those that were Enemies to Pilgrims; (for we heard that there was a notable one thereabouts.) Now *Gaius* knew his *Haunt* better than I, because he dwelt thereabout, so we looked and looked, till at last we discerned the mouth of his Cave; then we were glad and pluck'd up our Spirits. So we approached up to his *Den*, and lo when we came there, he had dragged by meer force into his Net, this *poor man*, Mr. *Feeble-mind*, and was about to bring him to his End. But when he saw us, supposing as we thought, he had had an other Prey, he left the poor man in his Hole, and came out. So we fell to it full sore, and he lustily laid about him; but in conclusion, he was brought down to the Ground, and his Head cut off, and set up by the Way side for a Terror to such as should after practise such Ungodliness. That I tell you the Truth, here is the man himself to affirm it, who was as a Lamb taken out of the Mouth of the Lyon.

Feebl. *Then said Mr.* Feeble-mind, *I found this true to my Cost, and Comfort; to my Cost, when he threatned to pick my Bones every moment; and to my Comfort, when I saw Mr.* Great-heart *and his Friends with their Weapons approach so near for my* Deliverance.

Mr. Holy- | Holym. Then said Mr. *Holy-man*, There are two man's *Speech.* things that they have need to be possessed with that go on Pilgrimage, *Courage* and an *unspotted Life*. If they have not *Courage*, they can never hold on their way; and if their Lives be *loose*, they will make the very Name of a *Pilgrim* stink.

Mr. Love- | Loves. Then said Mr. *Love-saint*; I hope this Caution is saint's *Speech.* not needful amongst you. But truly there are many that go upon the Road, that rather declare themselves Strangers to Pilgrimage, then Strangers and Pilgrims in the Earth.

Darenot. *Then said Mr.* Dare-not-ly, *'Tis true; they* Mr. Dare-not-
neither have the *Pilgrims* Weed, *nor the Pilgrims Courage;* ly *his Speech.*
they go not uprightly, but all awrie *with their Feet, one*
Shoo goes inward, *an other* outward, *and their Hosen out*
behind; there a *Rag,* and there a *Rent,* to the Disparagement of their Lord.

Penit. These things, said Mr. *Penitent,* they ought Mr. Penitent
to be troubled for, nor are the Pilgrims like to have *his Speech.*
that Grace put upon them and their pilgrims Progress,
10 as they desire, until the way is cleared of such Spots
and Blemishes.

Thus they sat talking and spending the time, until
Supper was set upon the Table. Unto which they went
and refreshed their weary Bodys, so they went to Rest.
Now they stayed in this Fair a great while, at the House
of this Mr. *Mnason,* who in process of time gave his
Daughter *Grace* unto *Samuel Christiana's* Son, to Wife,
and his Daughter *Martha* to *Joseph.*

The time, as I said, that they lay here, was long (for
20 it was not now as in former times.) Wherefore the
Pilgrims grew acquainted with many of the good people
of the Town, and did them what Service they could.
Mercie, as she was wont, laboured much for the Poor,
wherefore their Bellys and Backs blessed her, and she
was there an Ornament to her Profession. And to say
the truth, for *Grace, Phebe,* and *Martha,* they were all
of a very good Nature, and did much good in their
place. They were also all of them very Fruitful, so that
Christian's Name, as was said before, was like to live in
30 the World.

While they lay here, there came a *Monster* out of the A Monster.
Woods, and slew many of the People of the Town. It
would also carry away their Children, and teach them
to suck its Whelps. Now no man in the Town durst
so much as Face this *Monster;* but all Men fled when
they heard of the noise of his coming.

The *Monster* was like unto no one Beast upon the Rev. 17. 3.
Earth. Its Body was like a Dragon, and it had seven *His Shape.*
Heads and ten Horns, *It made great havock of Children,* His Nature.

4 *another* 2   17 *Samuel*] *Simon* 1   28 also all] all also 1

and yet it was governed by a Woman. This *Monster* propounded Conditions to men; and such men as loved their Lives more then their Souls, accepted of those Conditions. So they came under.

Now this Mr. *Great-heart*, together with these that came to visit the Pilgrims at Mr. *Mnason*'s House, entred into a Covenant to go and ingage this Beast, if perhaps they might deliver the People of this Town, from the Paws and Mouths of this so devouring a Serpent.

How he is Then did Mr. *Great-heart*, Mr. *Contrite*, Mr. *Holy-*
ingaged. man, Mr. *Dare-not-ly*, and *Mr. Penitent*, with their Weapons go forth to meet him. Now the *Monster* at first was very Rampant, and looked upon these Enemies with great Disdain, but they so be-labored him, being sturdy men at Arms, that they made him make a Retreat: so they came home to Mr. *Mnasons* House again.

The *Monster*, you must know, had his certain Seasons to come out in, and to make his Attempts upon the Children of the People of the Town, also these Seasons did these valiant Worthies watch him in, and did still continually assault him, in so much, that in process of time, he became not only wounded, but lame; also he has not made that havock of the Towns mens Children, as formerly he has done. And it is verily believed by some, that this Beast will die of his Wounds.

This therefore made Mr. *Great-heart* and his Fellows, of great Fame in this Town, so that many of the People that wanted their tast of things, yet had a Reverend Esteem and Respect for them. Upon this account therefore it was that these Pilgrims got not much hurt here. True, there were some of the baser sort that could see no more then a *Mole*, nor understand more then a Beast, these had no reverence for these men, nor took they notice of their Valour or Adventures.

Well, the time drew on that the Pilgrims must go on their way, wherefore they prepared for their Journey. They sent for their Friends, they conferred with them,

they had some time set apart therein to commit each
other to the Protection of their Prince. There was
again, that brought them of such things as they had,
that was fit for the weak, and the strong, for the Women,
and the men; and so *laded* them with such things as Act. 28. 10.
was necessary.

Then they set forwards on their way, and their
Friends accompanying them so far as was convenient;
they again committed each other to the Protection of
10 their King, and parted.

They therefore that were of the Pilgrims Company
went on, and Mr. *Great-heart* went before them; now
the Women and Children being weakly, they were
forced to go as they could bear, by this means Mr.
Ready-to-hault and Mr. *Feeble-mind* had more to sym-
pathize with their Condition.

When they were gone from the Towns-men, and
when their Friends had bid them farewel, they quickly
came to the place where *Faithful* was put to Death:
20 There therefore they made a stand, and thanked him
that had enabled him to bear his Cross so well, and the
rather, because they now found that they had a benefit
by such a manly Suffering as his was.

They went on therefore after this, a good way
further, talking of *Christian* and *Faithful*, and how
Hopeful joyned himself to *Christian* after that *Faithful*
was dead.

Now they were come up with the *Hill Lucre*, where 1 Part
the *Silver-mine* was, which took *Demas* off from his P. 106.
30 Pilgrimage, and into which, as some think, *By-ends* fell
and perished; wherefore they considered that. But
when they were come to the old Monument that stood
over against the *Hill Lucre*, to wit, to the Pillar of Salt
that stood also within view of *Sodom*, and its stinking
Lake; they marvelled, as did *Christian* before, that men
of that Knowledg and ripeness of Wit as they was,
should be so blinded as to turn aside here. Only they
considered again, that Nature is not affected with the
Harms that others have met with, specially if that thing

28 *marg.* 1 Part p. 185 ‖ 1: 285 ‖ 2

upon which they look, has an attracting Virtue upon the foolish Eye.

1 Part pag.
110. I saw now that they went on till they came at the River that was on this side of the delectable Mountains. To the River where the fine Trees grow on both sides, and whose Leaves, if taken inwardly, are good against *Psal. 23.* Surfits; where the Medows are green all the year long, and where they might lie down safely.

By this River side in the Medow, there were Cotes and Folds for Sheep, an House built for the *nourishing* 10 and bringing up of those Lambs, the Babes of those *Heb. 5. 2.* Women that go on Pilgrimage. Also there was here *Isa. 40. 11.* one that was intrusted with them, who could have compassion, and that could gather these Lambs with his Arm, and carry them in his Bosom, and that could gently lead those that were with young. Now to the Care of *this Man, Christiana* admonished her four Daughters to commit their little ones; that by these Waters they might be housed, harbored, suckered and *Jer. 23. 4.* nourished, and that none of them might *be lacking in* 20 *Ezek. 34. 11,* *time to come.* This man, if any of them go astray, or be *12, 13, 14,* *15, 16.* lost, he will bring them again, he will also bind up that which was broken, and will strengthen them that are sick. Here they will never want Meat, and Drink and Cloathing, here they will be kept from Thieves and Robbers, for this man will dye before one of those committed to his Trust, shall be lost. Besides, here they shall be sure to have good *Nurture* and Admonition, *John 10. 16.* and shall be taught to walk in right Paths, and that you know is a Favour of no small account. Also here, as 30 you see, are delicate *Waters,* pleasant *Medows,* dainty *Flowers,* variety of *Trees,* and such as bear *wholsom Fruit.* Fruit, not like that that *Matthew* eat of, that fell over the Wall out of *Belzebubs* Garden, but Fruit that procureth Health where there is none, and that continueth and increaseth it where it is.

So they were content to commit their little Ones to him; and that which was also an Incouragement to

3 *marg.* 1 Part pag. 189 ‖ 1, 2   28 besure 1   *Nurture]* *Nurtri-*
ture 1

them so to do, was, for that all this was to be at the
Charge of the King, and so was an Hospital to young
Children, and *Orphans.*

    Now they went on: And when they were come to *They being*
By-path Medow, to the Stile over which *Christian* went *come to By-path*
with his Fellow *Hopeful,* when they were taken by *mind to have*
Gyant-dispair, and put into *doubting*-Castle: They sat *a pluck with*
down and consulted what was best to be done, to wit, *1 Part, pag.*
now they were so strong, and had got such a man as *111, 113.*
10 Mr. *Great-heart* for their Conductor; whether they had
not best to make an Attempt upon the Gyant, demolish
his Castle, and if there were any Pilgrims in it, to set
them at liberty before they went any further. So one
said one thing, and an other said the contrary. One
questioned if it was lawful to go upon *unconsecrated*
Ground, an other said they might, provided their end
was good; but Mr. *Great-heart* said, Though that
Assertion offered last, cannot be universally true, yet
I have a Comandment to resist Sin, to overcome Evil,
20 to fight the good Fight of Faith. And I pray, with
whom should I fight this good Fight, if not with *Gyant-*
dispair? I will therefore attempt the taking away of
his Life, and the demolishing of *Doubting* Castle. Then
said he, who will go with me? Then said old *Honest,*
I will, And so will we too, said *Christian's* four Sons, *1 John 2.*
Mathew, Samuel, James and *Joseph,* for they were *13, 14.*
young men and strong.

    So they left the Women in the Road, and with them
Mr. *Feeble-mind,* and Mr. *Ready-to-halt,* with his
30 Crutches, to be their *Guard,* until they came back, for
in that place tho *Gyant-Dispair* dwelt so near, they *Isa. 11. 6.*
keeping in the Road, *A little Child might lead them.*

    So Mr. *Great-heart,* old *Honest,* and the four young
men, went to go up to *Doubting* Castle, to look for
Gyant-Dispair. When they came at the Castle Gate,
they knocked for Entrance with an unusual Noyse. At
that the old Gyant comes to the Gate, and *Diffidence*

7 Gyant *Despair* 2   **8** *marg.* 1 Part, pag. 191, 195 ‖ 1, 2   **14**
another 2   **16** another 2   **21–22** Gyant *Despair* 2   **26**
Samuel] *Simon* 1

his Wife follows. Then said he, Who, and what is he, that is so hardy, as after this manner to molest the *Gyant-Dispair*? Mr. *Great-heart* replyed, It is I, *Great-heart*, one of the King of the Celestial Countries Conductors of Pilgrims to their Place. And I demand of thee that thou open thy Gates for my Entrance, prepare thy self also to Fight, for I am come to take away thy Head, and to demolish *Doubting* Castle.

Despair *has overcome Angels.* Now *Gyant-Dispair*, because he was a *Gyant*, thought no man could overcome him, and again, thought he, since heretofore I have made a Conquest of Angels, shall *Great-heart* make me afraid? So he harnessed himself and went out. He had a Cap of Steel upon his Head, a Brestplate of Fire girded to him, and he came out in Iron Shoos, with a great Club in his Hand. Then these six men made up to him, and beset him behind and before; also when *Diffidence*, the *Gyantess*, came up to help him, old Mr. *Honest* cut her down at one Blow. Then they fought for their Lives, and *Gyant-Dispair* was brought down to the Ground, *but was very* Despair *is loth to die.* *loth to die.* He strugled hard, and had, as they say, as many Lives as a Cat, but *Great-heart* was his death, for he left him not till he had severed his head from his shoulders.

Doubting-Castle *demolished.* They they fell to demolishing *Doubting* Castle, and that you know might with ease be done, since *Gyant-Dispair* was dead. They were seven Days in destroying of that; and in it of Pilgrims, they found one Mr. *Dispondencie*, almost starved to Death, and one *Much-afraid* his Daughter; these two they saved alive. But it would a made you a wondered to have seen the dead Bodies that lay here and there in the Castle Yard, and how full of dead mens Bones the Dungeon was.

When Mr. *Great-heart* and his Companions had performed this Exploit, they took Mr. *Despondencie*, and his Daughter *Much-afraid*, into their Protection, for they were honest People, tho they were Prisoners in *Doubting* Castle, to that Tyrant *Gyant-Dispair*. They therefore I say, took with them the Head of the *Gyant* (for his Body they had buried under a heap of Stones) and down to the Road and to their Companions they came, and shewed them what they had done. Now when *Feeble-mind*, and *Ready-to-hault* saw that it was the Head of *Gyant-Dispair* indeed, they were very jocond and merry. Now *Christiana*, if need was, could play upon the *Vial*, and her Daughter *Mercie* upon the *Lute:* So, since they were so merry disposed, she plaid them a Lesson, and *Ready-to-halt* would Dance. So he took *Dispondencie*'s Daughter, named *Much-afraid*, by the Hand, and to dancing they went in the Road. True, he could not Dance without one Crutch in his Hand, but I promise you, he footed it well; also the Girl was to be commended, for she answered the Musick handsomely.

They have Musick and dancing for joy.

As for Mr. *Despondencie*, the Musick was not much to him, he was for feeding rather then dancing, for that he was almost starved. So *Christiana* gave him some of her bottle of Spirits for present Relief, and then prepared him something to eat; and in little time the old Gentleman came to himself, and began to be finely revived.

Now I saw in my Dream, when all these things were finished, Mr. *Great-heart* took the Head of *Gyant-Dispair*, and set it upon a Pole by the Highway side, right over against the Piller that *Christian* erected for a *Caution* to Pilgrims that came after, to take heed of entering into his Grounds.

Then he writ under it upon a *Marble* stone, these Verses following.

> *This is the* Head *of* him, *whose* Name *only*,
> *In former times, did* Pilgrims *terrify.*
> *His* Castle's *down, and* Diffidence *his Wife,*
> *Brave Master* Great-heart *has bereft of Life.*
> Dispondencie, *his Daughter* Much-afraid,
> Great-heart, *for them, also the Man has plaid.*
> *Who hereof doubts, if he'l but cast his Eye,*
> *Up hither, may his Scruples satisfy,*
> *This Head, also when doubting* Cripples *dance,*
> *Doth shew from Fears they have* Deliverance.

A Monument of Deliverance.

When these men had thus bravely shewed themselves

against *Doubting-Castle*, and had slain *Gyant-Dispair*, they went forward, and went on till they came to the *Delectable* Mountains, where *Christian* and *Hopeful* refreshed themselves with the Varieties of the Place. They also acquainted themselves with the Shepherds there, who welcomed them as they had done *Christian* before, unto the delectable Mountains.

Now the Shepherds seeing so great a train follow Mr. *Great-heart* (for with him they were well acquainted;) they said unto him, Good Sir, you have got 10 a goodly Company here; pray where did you find all these?

Then Mr. *Great-heart* replyed,

The Guides Speech to the Shepherds.

First here's Christiana *and her train,*
Her Sons, and her Sons Wives, who like the Wain
Keep by the Pole, and do by Compass stere,
From Sin to Grace, else they had not been here.
Next here's old Honest *come on Pilgrimage,*
Ready-to-halt too, who I dare ingage,
True hearted is, and so is Feeble-mind, 20
Who willing was, not to be left behind.
Dispondencie, *good-man, is coming after,*
And so also is Much-afraid, *his Daughter.*
May we have Entertainment here, or must
We further go? let's know whereon to trust.

Their Entertainment.
Matt. 25. 40.

Then said the Shepherds; This is a comfortable Company, you are welcome to us, for we have for the *Feeble*, as for the *Strong*; our Prince has an Eye to what is done to the least of these. Therefore Infirmity must not be a block to our Entertainment. So they had them 30 to the Palace Door, and then said unto them, Come in Mr. *Feeble-mind*, come in Mr. *Ready-to-halt*, come in Mr. *Dispondencie*, and Mrs. *Much-afraid* his Daughter. *These* Mr. *Great-heart*, said the Shepherds to the Guide, we call in by Name, for that they are most subject to draw back; but as for you, and the rest that are *strong*,

A Description of false Shepherds.
Ezek. 34. 21.

we leave you to your wonted Liberty. Then said Mr. *Great-heart*, This day I see that Grace doth shine in your Faces, and that you are my Lords Shepherds indeed; for that you have not *pushed* these Diseased neither with Side nor Shoulder, but have rather strewed their way into the Palace with Flowers, as you should.

So the Feeble and Weak went in, and Mr. *Greatheart*, and the rest did follow. When they were also set down, the Shepherds said to those of the weakest sort, What is it that you would have? For said they, all things must be managed here, to the supporting of the weak, as well as to the warning of the Unruly.

10   So they made them a Feast of things easy of Digestion, and that were pleasant to the Palate, and nourishing; the which when they had received, they went to their rest, each one respectively unto his proper place. When Morning was come, because the Mountains were high, and the day clear; and because it was the Custom of the Shepherds to shew to the Pilgrims, before their Departure, some Rarities; therefore after they were ready, and had refreshed themselves, the Shepherds took them out into the Fields, and shewed them 20 first, what they had shewed to *Christian* before.

Then they had them to some new places. The first ⟨Mount-Marvel.⟩ was to *Mount-Marvel*, where they looked, and behold a man at a Distance, *that tumbled the Hills about with* ⟨1 Part, pag. 130.⟩ *Words*. Then they asked the Shepherds what that should mean? So they told him, that that man was the Son of one *Great-grace*, of whom you read in the first part of the Records of the *Pilgrims Progress*. And he is set there to teach Pilgrims how to believe down, or to tumble out of their ways, what Difficulties they shall ⟨Mar. 11. 23, 24.⟩ 30 meet with, by faith. Then said Mr. *Great-heart*, I know him, he is a man above many.

Then they had them to another place, called *Mount-* ⟨Mount-Innocent.⟩ *Innocent*. And there they saw a man cloathed all in White; and two men, *Prejudice*, and *Ill-will*, continually casting Dirt upon him. Now behold the Dirt, whatsoever they cast at him, would in little time fall off again, and his Garment would look as clear as if no Dirt had been cast thereat.

Then said the Pilgrims what means this? The Shep-

23 *marg*. 1 Part, pag. 226 ‖ 1, 2

herds answered, This man is named *Godly-man*, and this Garment is to shew the Innocency of his Life. Now those that throw Dirt at him, are such as hate his *Well-doing*, but as you see the Dirt will not stick upon his Clothes, so it shall be with him that liveth truly Innocently in the World. Whoever they be that would make such men dirty, they labor all in vain; for God, by that a little time is spent, will cause that their *Innocence* shall break forth as the Light, and their Righteousness as the Noon day.   10

Mount-Charity. Then they took them, and had them to *Mount-Charity*, where they shewed them a man that had a bundle of Cloth lying before him, out of which he cut Coats and Garments, for the Poor that stood about him; yet his Bundle or Role of Cloth was never the less.

Then said they, what should this be? This is, said the Shepherds, to shew you, That he that has a Heart to give of his Labor to the Poor, shall never want wherewithal. He that watereth shall be watered himself. And the Cake that the Widdow gave to the Prophet, did 20 not cause that she had ever the less in her Barrel.

The Work of one Fool, and one Want-witt. They had them also to a place where they saw one *Fool*, and one *Want-wit*, washing of an *Ethiopian* with intention to make him white, but the more they washed him, the blacker he was. They then asked the Shepherds what that should mean. So they told them, saying, Thus shall it be with the vile Person; all means used to get such an one a good Name, shall in Conclusion tend but to make him more abominable. Thus it was with the *Pharises*, and so shall it be with all 30 Hypocrites.

1 Part, pag. 121-2. Mercie has a mind to see the hole in the Hill. Then said *Mercie* the Wife of *Mathew* to *Christiana* her Mother, Mother, I would, if it might be, see the Hole in the Hill; or that, commonly called, the *By-way* to Hell. So her Mother brake her mind to the Shepherds. Then they went to the Door; it was in the side of an Hill, and they opened it, and bid *Mercie* harken awhile. So she harkened, and heard one saying, *Cursed*

22 marg. *The* . . . Want-witt add. 2   *marg.* Want-witt *ital.* 2
32 *marg.* 1 Part, pag. 211 ‖ 1, 2

be my Father for holding of my Feet back from the way of
Peace and Life; and another said, *O that I had been torn*
in pieces before I had, to save my life, lost my Soul; and
another said, *If I were to live again, how would I deny*
my self rather then come to this place. Then there was
as if the very Earth had groaned, and quaked under
the Feet of this young Woman for fear; so she looked
white, and came trembling away, saying, Blessed be he
and she that is delivered from this Place.

10   Now when the Shepherds had shewed them all these
things, then they had them back to the Palace, and
entertained them with what the House would afford; But
Mercie being a young, and breeding Woman, Longed   *Mercie longeth,*
for something which she saw there, but was ashamed   *and for what.*
to ask. Her Mother-in-law then asked her what she
ailed, for she looked as one not well. Then said *Mercy,*
There is a Looking-glass hangs up in the Dining-room, off
of which I cannot take my mind; if therefore I have it
not, I think I shall Miscarry. Then said her Mother,
20 I will mention thy Wants to the Shepherds, and they
will not deny it thee. But she said, I am ashamed that
these men should know that I longed. Nay my Daughter, said she, it is no Shame, but a Virtue, to long for
such a thing as that; so *Mercie* said, Then Mother, if you
please, ask the Shepherds if they are willing to sell it.

Now the Glass was one of a thousand. It would
present a man, one way, with his own Feature exactly,
and turn it but an other way, and it would shew one   *It was the*
the very Face and Similitude of the Prince of Pilgrims   *Word of God.*
30 himself. Yea I have talked with them that can tell, and   Jam. 1. 23.
they have said, that they have seen the very Crown of
Thorns upon his Head, by looking in that Glass, they
have therein also seen the holes in his Hands, in his   1 Cor. 13. 12.
Feet, and his Side. Yea such an excellency is there in   2 Cor. 3. 18.
that Glass, that it will shew him to one where they have
a mind to see him; whether living or dead, whether in
Earth or Heaven, whether in a State of Humiliation,
or in his Exaltation, whether coming to Suffer, or
coming to Reign.

Christiana therefore went to the Shepherds apart.
I Part, pag. 120. (Now the Names of the Shepherds are *Knowledge*, *Experience*, *Watchful*, and *Sincere*), and said unto them, There is one of my Daughters a breeding Woman, that, I think doth long for some thing that she hath seen in this House, and she thinks she shall miscarry if she should by you be denied.

Experience. Call her, call her, She shall assuredly have
She doth what we can help her to. So they called her, and said
not lose her to her, *Mercie*, what is that thing thou wouldest have? 10
Longing. Then she blushed and said, The great Glass that hangs up in the Dining-room: So *Sincere* ran and fetched it, and with a joyful Consent it was given her. Then she bowed her Head, and gave Thanks, and said, By this I know that I have obtained Favour in your Eyes.

They also gave to the other young Women such things as they desired, and to their Husbands great Commendations, for that they joyned with Mr. *Great-heart* to the slaying of *Gyant-Dispair*, and the demolishing of *Doubting-Castle*.   20

How the Shep-   About *Christiana*'s Neck, the Shepherds put a Brace-
herds adorn let, and so they did about the Necks of her four
the Pilgrims. Daughters, also they put Ear-rings in their Ears, and Jewels on their Fore-heads.

When they were minded to go hence, they let them go in Peace, but gave not to them those certain Cautions which before was given to *Christian* and his Companion. The Reason was, for that these had *Great-*
I Part, pag. heart to be their Guide, who was one that was well
123. acquainted with things, and so could give them their 30 Cautions more seasonably, to wit, even then when the Danger was nigh the approaching.

What Cautions *Christian* and his Companions had
I Part, pag. received of the Shepherds, they had also lost, by that
133. the time was come that they had need to put them in practice. Wherefore here was the Advantage that this Company had over the other.

<hr/>

2 *marg.* I Part, pag. 207 ‖ 1, 2   21 *marg. How . . . Pilgrims*
add. 2   27 were 2   29 *marg.* I Part, pag. 213 ‖ 1, 2   34
marg. I Part, pag. 233 ‖ 1, 2

From hence they went on Singing, and they said,

Behold, how fitly are the Stages set!
For their Relief, that Pilgrims are become;
And how they us receive without one let,
That make the other Life our Mark and Home.
What Novelties they have, to us they give,
That we, tho Pilgrims, joyful Lives may live.
They do upon us too such things bestow,
That shew we Pilgrims are, where ere we go.

10 When they were gone from the Shepherds, they quickly came to the Place where *Christian* met with one *Turn-a-way*, that dwelt in the Town of *Apostacy*. Wherefore of him Mr. *Great-heart* their Guide did now put them in mind; saying, This is the place where *Christian* met with one *Turn-a-way*, who carried with him the Character of his Rebellion at his Back. And this I have to say concerning this man, He would harken to no Counsel, but once a falling, perswasion could not stop him. When he came to the place where 20 the Cross and the Sepulcher was, he did meet with one that did bid him *look there*, but he gnashed with his Teeth, and stamped, and said, he was resolved to go back to his own Town. Before he came to the Gate, he met with *Evangelist*, who offered to lay Hands on him, to turn him into the way again. But this *Turn-a-way* *resisted him*, and having done much *despite* unto him, he got away over the Wall, and so escaped his Hand.

1 Part, pag. 125.

How one Turn-a-way managed his Apostacy.

Heb. 10. 26, 27, 28, 29.

Then they went on, and just at the place where *Little-faith* formerly was Robbed, there stood a man 30 with his Sword drawn, and his Face all bloody. Then said Mr. *Great-heart*, What art thou? The man made Answer, saying, I am one whose Name is *Valiant-for-Truth*, I am a Pilgrim, and am going to the Celestial City. Now as I was in my way, there was three men did beset me, and propounded unto me these three things. 1. Whether I would become one of them? Or go back from whence I came? Or die upon the Place? To the first I answered, I had been a true Man a long

One Valiant-for-truth beset with Thieves.

Prov. 1. 10, 11, 12, 13, 14.

15 *marg.* 1 Part, pag. 216 || 1, 2   32 marg. *One . . . Thieves* add. 2

Season, and therefore, it could not be expected that I now should cast in my Lot with Thieves. Then they demanded what I would say to the Second. So I told them that the Place from whence I came, had I not found Incommodity there, I had not forsaken it at all, but finding it altogether unsutable to me, and very unprofitable for me, I forsook it for this Way. Then they asked me what I said to the third. And I told them, my Life cost more dear far, then that I should lightly give it away. Besides, you have nothing to do thus to put things to my Choice; wherefore at your Peril be it, if you meddle. Then these three, to wit, *Wild-head*, *Inconsiderate*, and *Pragmatick*, drew upon me, and I also drew upon them.

How he be-haved himself, and put them to flight.   So we fell to it, one against three, for the space of above three Hours. They have left upon me, as you see, some of the Marks of their Valour, and have also carried away with them some of mine. They are but just now gone. I suppose they might, as the saying is, hear your Horse dash, and so they betook them to flight.

Greath. *But here was great Odds, three against one.*

Valiant. 'Tis true, but *little* and *more*, are nothing to *Psal.* 27. 3. him that has the Truth on his side. *Though an Host should encamp against me, said one, My Heart shall not* Great-heart *fear. Tho War should rise against me, in this will I be* wonders at Confident, etc. Besides, said he, I have read in some his Valour. Records, that one man has fought an Army; and how many did *Sampson* slay with the Jaw Bone of an Ass?

Greath. *Then said the Guide, Why did you not cry out, that some might a came in for your Succour?*

Valiant. So I did, to my King, who I knew could hear, and afford invisible Help, and that was sufficient for me.

Has a mind to see his Sword, and spends his Judgment on it.   Greath. *Then said Great-heart to Mr.* Valiant-for-Truth, *Thou hast worthily behaved thy self; Let me see thy Sword*; so he shewed it him.

Isa. 2. 3.   When he had taken it in his Hand, and looked thereon a while, he said, Ha! *It is a right* Jerusalem *Blade.*

15 marg. *How . . . flight* add. 2   25 *marg.* Great-heart . . . *Valour* add. 2   28 Ass! 1, 2   30 *a-came* 2   34 marg. *Has . . . it* add. 2

Valiant. It is so. Let a man have one of *these Blades,* Ephes. 6. 12,
with a Hand to wield it, and skill to use it, and he may 13, 14, 15,
16, 17.
venture upon an Angel with it. He need not fear its Heb. 4. 12.
holding, if he can but tell how to lay on. Its Edges
will never blunt. It will cut *Flesh,* and *Bones,* and *Soul,*
and *Spirit,* and all.

Greath. *But you fought a great while, I wonder you
was not weary?*

Valiant. I fought till my Sword did cleave to my 2 Sam. 23. 10.
10 Hand, and when they were joyned together, as if a *The Word.*
Sword grew out of my Arm, and when the Blood run *The Faith.*
thorow my Fingers, then I fought with most Courage. *Blood.*

Greath. *Thou hast done well, thou hast resisted unto
Blood, striving against Sin. Thou shalt abide by us, come
in, and go out with us; for we are thy Companions.*

Then they took him and washed his Wounds, and
gave him of what they had, to refresh him, and so they
went on together. Now as they went on, because Mr.
Great-heart was delighted in him (for he loved one
20 greatly that he found to be a man of his Hands) and
because there was with his Company, them that was
feeble and weak; Therefore he questioned with him about
many things; as first, *What Country-man he was?* *What*

Valiant. I am of *Dark-land,* for there I was born, *Countrey man
Mr.* Valiant
was.
and there my Father and Mother are still.

Greath. *Dark-land,* said the Guide, *Doth not that ly
upon the same Coast with the City of* Destruction?

Valiant. Yes it doth. Now that which caused me to *How Mr.*
come on Pilgrimage, was this: We had one Mr. *Tell-* Valiant *came
to go on*
30 *true* came into our parts, and he told it about, what Pilgrimage.
Christian had done, that went from the City of *Destruction.* Namely, how he had forsaken his *Wife* and
Children, and had betaken himself to a *Pilgrims* Life.
It was also confidently reported how he had killed a
Serpent that did come out to resist him in his Journey,
and how he got thorow to whither he intended. It was
also told what Welcome he had at all his Lords Lodgings; specially when he came to the Gates of the
Celestial City. For there, said the man, He was

23 marg. *What . . . was* add. 2

received with sound of Trumpet, by a company of shining ones. He told it also, how all the Bells in the City did ring for Joy at his Reception, and what Golden Garments he was cloathed with; with many other things that now I shall forbear to relate. In a word, that man so told the Story of *Christian* and his Travels, that my Heart fell into a burning hast to be gone after him, nor could Father or Mother stay me, so I got from them, and am come thus far on my Way.

Greath. *You came in at the Gate, did you not?*   10

He begins right.
Valiant. Yes, yes. For the same man also told us, that all would be nothing if we did not begin to enter this way at the Gate.

Christian's Name famous.
Greath. *Look you, said the Guide to* Christiana, *The Pilgrimage of your Husband, and what he has gotten thereby, is spread abroad far and near.*

Valiant. Why, is this *Christian*'s Wife?

Greath. *Yes, that it is, and these are also her four Sons.*

Valiant. What! and going on Pilgrimage too?

Greath. *Yes verily, they are following after.*   20

He is much rejoyced to see Christian's Wife.
Valiant. It glads me at the Heart! Good man! How Joyful will he be, when he shall see them that would not go with him, yet to enter after him, in at the Gates into the City?

Greath. *Without doubt it will be a Comfort to him; for next to the Joy of seeing himself there, it will be a Joy to meet there his Wife and his Children.*

Whether we shall know one another when we come to Heaven.
Valiant. But now you are upon that, pray let me see your Opinion about it. Some make a question whether we shall know one another when we are there.   30

Greath. *Do they think they shall know themselves then? Or that they shall rejoyce to see themselves in that Bliss? and if they think they shall know and do these; Why not know others, and rejoyce in their Welfare also?*

Again, Since Relations are our second self, tho that State will be dissolved there, yet why may it not be rationally concluded that we shall be more glad to see them there, then to see they are wanting?

Valiant. Well, I perceive whereabouts you are as to

28 marg. *Whether . . . Heaven* add. 2

this. Have you any more things to ask me about my beginning to come on Pilgrimage?

Greath. Yes, Was your Father and Mother willing that you should become a Pilgrim?

Valiant. Oh, no. They used all means imaginable to perswade me to stay at Home.

Greath. Why, what could they say against it?

Valiant. They said it was an idle Life, and if I my self were not inclined to Sloath and Laziness, I would never countenance a Pilgrim's Condition. *The great stumbling-Blocks that by his Friends were laid in his way.*

Greath. And what did they say else?

Valiant. Why, They told me that it was a dangerous Way, yea the most dangerous Way in the World, said they, is that which the Pilgrims go.

Greath. Did they shew wherein this Way is so dangerous?

Valiant. Yes. And that in many Particulars.

Greath. Name some of them.

Valiant. They told me of the Slow of *Dispond*, where *Christian* was well nigh Smuthered. They told me that there were Archers standing ready in *Belzebub-Castle*, to shoot them that should knock at the *Wicket* Gate for Entrance. They told me also of the Wood, and dark Mountains, of the Hill *Difficulty*, of the Lyons, and also of the three Gyants, *Bloodyman*, *Maul*, and *Slay-good*. They said moreover, That there was a foul *Fiend* haunted the Valley of *Humiliation*, and that *Christian* was, by him, almost bereft of Life. Besides, said they, You must go over the *Valley of the Shadow of Death*, where the *Hobgoblins* are, where the Light is Darkness, where the Way is full of Snares, Pits, Traps and Ginns. They told me also of *Gyant Dispair*, of *Doubting Castle*, and of the *Ruins* that the Pilgrims met with there. Further, They said, I must go over the enchanted Ground, which was dangerous. And that after all this I should find a River, over which I should find no Bridg, and that that River did lie betwixt me and the Celestial Countrey. *The first Stumbling-Block.*

Greath. And was this all?

19 *Slough* of *Despond* 2

The Second   *Valiant.* No, They also told me that this way was full of *Deceivers*, and of Persons that laid await there, to turn good men out of the Path.

Greath. *But how did they make that out?*

The Third.   *Valiant.* They told me that Mr. *Worldly-wise-man* did there lie in wait to deceive. They also said that there was *Formality* and *Hypocrisie* continually on the Road. They said also that *By-ends*, *Talkative*, or *Demas*, would go near to gather me up; that the Flatterer would catch me in his Net, or that with greenheaded *Ignorance* 10 I would presume to go on to the Gate, from whence he always was sent back to the Hole that was in the side of the Hill, and made to go the By-way to Hell.

Greath. *I promise you, This was enough to discourage. But did they make an end here?*

The Fourth.   *Valiant.* No, stay. They told me also of many that had tryed that way of old, and that had gone a great way therein, to see if they could find something of the Glory there, that so many had so much talked of from time to time; and how they came back again, and be- 20 fooled themselves for setting a Foot out of Doors in that Path, to the Satisfaction of all the Country. And they named several that did so, as *Obstinate*, and *Plyable*, *Mistrust*, and *Timerous*, *Turn-a-way*, and old *Atheist*, with several more; who, they said, had, some of them, gone far to see if they could find, but not one of them found so much Advantage by going, as amounted *to the weight of a Fether.*

Greath. *Said they any thing more to discourage you?*

The Fifth.   *Valiant.* Yes, They told me of one Mr. *Fearing*, who 30 was a Pilgrim, and how *he* found this way so Solitary, that he never had comfortable Hour therein, also that Mr. *Dispondency* had like to been starved therein; Yea, and also, which I had almost forgot, that *Christian* himself, about whom there has been such a Noise, after all his Ventures for a Celestial Crown, was certainly drowned in the black River, and never went foot further, however it was smuthered up.

5 marg. *The Second* 1   16 marg. *The Third* 1   30 marg.
The Fourth 1

Greath. *And did none of these things discourage you?*

Valiant. No. They seemed but as so many Nothings to me.

Greath. *How came that about?*

Valiant. Why, I still believed what Mr. *Tell-True* had said, and that carried me beyond them all.

Greath. *Then this was your Victory, even your Faith?*

Valiant. It was so, I believed and therefore came out, got into the Way, fought all that set themselves against me, and by believing am come to this Place.

> *Who would true Valour see*
> *Let him come hither;*
> *One here will Constant be,*
> *Come Wind, come Weather.*
> *There's no* Discouragement,
> *Shall make him once* Relent,
> *His first avow'd* Intent,
> To be a Pilgrim.
>
> *Who so beset him round,*
> *With dismal* Storys,
> *Do but themselves Confound;*
> *His Strength the* more is.
> *No* Lyon *can him fright,*
> *He'l with a* Gyant *Fight,*
> *But he will have a right,*
> To be a Pilgrim.
>
> Hobgoblin, *nor foul* Fiend,
> *Can* daunt *his Spirit:*
> *He knows, he at the end,*
> Shall Life Inherit.
> *Then Fancies fly away,*
> *He'l fear not what men say,*
> *He'l labour Night and Day,*
> To be a Pilgrim.

By this time they were got to the *enchanted Ground*, where the Air naturally tended to make one *Drowzy.* And that place was all grown over with Bryers and

marg. 1 Part, pag. 237 ‖ 1, 2

How he got over these Stumbling-Blocks.

1 Part, pag. 136.

Thorns; excepting *here* and *there*, where was an *inchanted Arbor*, upon which, if a Man sits, or in which if a man sleeps, 'tis a question, say some, whether ever they shall rise or wake again in this World. Over this Forrest therefore they went, both one with an other, and Mr. *Great-heart* went before, for that he was the Guide, and Mr. *Valiant-for-truth*, he came behind, being there a Guard, for fear lest paradventure some *Fiend*, or *Dragon*, or *Gyant*, or *Thief*, should fall upon their Rere, and so do Mischief. They went on here each man with his Sword drawn in his Hand; for they knew it was a dangerous place. Also they cheared up one another as well as they could. *Feeble-mind*, Mr. *Great-heart* commanded should come up after him, and Mr. *Dispondency* was under the Eye of Mr. *Valiant*.

Now they had not gone far, but a great Mist and a darkness fell upon them all; so that they could scarce, for a great while, see the one the other. Wherefore they were forced for some time, to feel for one another, by Words; for they walked not by Sight.

But any one must think, that here was but sorry going for the best of them all, but how much worse for the Women and Children, who both of *Feet* and *Heart* were but tender. Yet so it was, that, thorow the incouraging Words of he that led in the Front, and of him that brought them up behind, they made a pretty good shift to wagg along.

The Way also was here very wearysom, thorow Dirt and Slabbiness. Nor was there on *all* this Ground, so much as one *Inn*, or *Victualling-House*, therein to refresh the feebler sort. Here therefore was *grunting*, and *puffing*, and *sighing*: While one tumbleth over a Bush, another sticks fast in the Dirt, and the Children, some of them, lost their Shoos in the Mire. While one crys out, I am down, and another, Ho, Where are you? and a third, The Bushes have got such fast hold on me, I think I cannot get away from them.

An Arbor *on the Inchanting Ground.* Then they came at an *Arbor*, warm, and promising much Refreshing to the Pilgrims; for it was finely wrought above-head, beautified with *Greens*, furnished

with *Benches*, and *Settles*. It also had in it a soft Couch
whereon the weary might lean. This, you must think,
all things considered, was tempting; for the Pilgrims
already began to be foyled with the badness of the way;
but there was not one of them that made so much as
a motion to stop there. Yea, for ought I could perceive,
they continually gave so good heed to the Advice of
their Guide, and he did so faithfully tell them of
Dangers, and of the *Nature* of Dangers when they were
10 at them, that usually when they were nearest to them,
they did most pluck up their Spirits, and hearten one
another to deny the Flesh. This *Arbor* was called *The* *The Name of*
sloathfuls Friend, on purpose to allure, if it might be, *the Arbor.*
some of the Pilgrims there, to take up their Rest when
weary.

I saw then in my Dream, that they went on in this *The way diffi-*
their *solitary* Ground, till they came to a place at which *cult to find.*
a man is apt to lose his Way. *Now*, tho when it was
light, their Guide could well enough tell how to miss
20 those ways that led wrong, yet in the dark he was put
to a stand: But he had in his Pocket a Map of all ways *The Guide has*
leading to, or from the Celestial City; wherefore he *a Map of all*
ways leading
strook a Light (for he never goes also without his *to or from*
Tinder-box) and takes a view of his Book or Map; *the City.*
which bids him be careful in that place to turn to the
right-hand-way. And had he not here been careful to
look in his Map, they had all, in probability, been
smuthered in the Mud, for just a little before them,
and that at the end of the cleanest Way too, was a Pit,
30 none knows how deep, full of nothing but Mud; there
made on purpose to destroy the Pilgrims in.

Then thought I with my self, who, that goeth on *God's Book.*
Pilgrimage, but would have one of these Maps about
him, that he may look when he is at a *stand*, which is
the way he must take?

They went on then in this *inchanted* Ground, till they *An Arbor and*
came to where was an other *Arbor*, and it was built by *two asleep*
therein.
the High-way-side. And in that *Arbor* there lay two
men whose Names were *Heedless* and *Too-bold*. These

37 another 2

two went thus far on Pilgrimage, but here being wearied with their Journy, they sat down to rest themselves, and so fell fast asleep. When the Pilgrims saw them, they stood still and shook their Heads; for they knew that the Sleepers were in a pitiful Case. Then they consulted what to do; whether to go on and leave them in their Sleep, or to step to them and try to awake *The Pilgrims* them. So they concluded to go to them and wake them; *try to wake* that is, if they could; but with this Caution, namely, to *them.* take heed that themselves did not sit down, nor imbrace 10 the offered Benefit of that *Arbor*.

So they went in and spake to the men, and called each by his Name, (for the Guide, it seems, did know them) but there was no Voice nor Answer. Then the Guide did shake them, and do what he could to disturb them. Then said one of them, *I will pay you when I take my Mony*; At which the Guide shook his Head. *I will fight so long as I can hold my Sword in my Hand*, said the other. At that, one of the Children laughed.

Their Then said *Christiana*, What is the meaning of this? 20 *Endeavour* The Guide said, *They talk in their Sleep*. If you strike *is fruitless.* them, beat them, or whatever else you do to them, they will answer you after this fashion; or as one of them said in old time, when the Waves of the Sea did beat upon him, and he slept as one upon the Mast of a Ship, Prov. 23. *When I awake I will seek it again*. You know when 34, 35. men talk in their Sleeps, they say any thing; but their Words are not governed, either by Faith or Reason. There is an *Incoherencie* in their Words *now*, as there was before betwixt their going on Pilgrimage, and 30 sitting down here. This then is the Mischief on't, when *heedless* ones go on Pilgrimage, 'tis twenty to one, but they are served thus. For this *inchanted* Ground is one of the last Refuges that the Enemy to Pilgrims has; wherefore it is as you see, placed almost at the end of the Way, and so it standeth against us with the more advantage. For when, thinks the Enemy, will these Fools be so desirous to sit down, as when they are weary; and when so like to be weary, as when almost at their Journys end? Therefore it is, I say, that the 40

inchanted Ground is placed so nigh to the Land *Beulah*,
and so neer the end of their Race. Wherefore let Pilgrims look to themselves, lest it happen to them as it
has done to these, that, as you see, are fallen asleep,
and none can wake them.

Then the Pilgrims desired with trembling to go forward, only they prayed their Guide to strike a Light,
that they might go the rest of their way by the help of
the light of a Lanthorn. So he strook a light, and they
went by the help of that thorow the rest of this way,
tho the Darkness was very great.

But the Children began to be sorely weary, and they
cryed out unto him that loveth Pilgrims, to make their
way more Comfortable. So by that they had gone a
little further, a Wind arose that drove away the Fog,
so the Air became more clear.

Yet they were not off (by much) of the *inchanted*
Ground; only now they could see one an other better,
and the way wherein they should walk.

Now when they were almost at the end of this
Ground, they perceived that a little before them, was
a *solemn* Noise, as of one that was much concerned.
So they went on and looked before them, and behold,
they saw, as they thought, *a Man upon his Knees*, with
Hands and Eyes lift up, and speaking, as they thought,
earnestly to one that was above. They drew nigh, but
could not tell what he said; so they went softly till he
had done. When he had done, he got up and began to
run towards the Celestial City. Then Mr. *Great-heart*
called after him, saying, So-ho, Friend, let us have your
Company, if you go, as I suppose you do, to the
Celestial City. So the man stoped, and they came up
to him. But as soon as Mr. *Honest* saw him, he said,
I know this man. Then said Mr. *Valiant-for-truth*,
Prethee who is it? 'Tis one, said he, that comes from
whereabouts I dwelt, his Name is *Stand-fast*, he is
certainly a right good Pilgrim.

So they came up one to another, and presently *Stand-fast* said to old *Honest*, Ho, Father *Honest*, are you

Side notes:

The light of the Word.

2 Pet. 1. 19.

The Children cry for weariness.

Standfast *upon his Knees in the Inchanted* Ground.

The Story of Standfast.

Talk betwixt him and Mr. Honest.

18 another 2   24 *marg.* Standfast ... *Ground* add. 2

there? Ai, said he, that I am, as sure as you are there. Right glad am I, said Mr. *Stand-fast*, that I have found you on this Road. And as glad am I, said the other, that I espied you upon your Knees. Then Mr. *Stand-fast* blushed, and said, But why, did you see me? Yes, that I did, quoth the other, and with my Heart was glad at the Sight. Why, what did you think, said *Stand-fast*? Think, said old *Honest*, what should I think? I thought we had an honest Man upon the Road, and therefore should have his Company by and by. If you thought not amiss, how happy am I? But if I be not as I should, I alone must bear it. That is true, said the other; but your fear doth further confirm me that things are right betwixt the Prince of Pilgrims and your Soul. For he saith, *Blessed is the Man that feareth always.*

They found him at Prayer.   *Valiant.* Well, But Brother, I pray thee tell us what was it that was the cause of thy being upon thy Knees, even now? Was it for that some special Mercy laid Obligations upon thee, or how?

What it was that fetched him upon his Knees.   *Stand.* Why we are as you see, upon the *inchanted* Ground, and as I was coming along, I was musing with my self of what a dangerous Road, the Road in this place was, and how many that had come even thus far on Pilgrimage, had here been stopt, and been destroyed. I thought also of the manner of the Death with which this place destroyeth Men. Those that die here, die of no violent Distemper; the Death which such die, is not grievous to them. For he that goeth away in a *Sleep*, begins that Journey with Desire and Pleasure. Yea, such acquiesce in the Will of that Disease.

Hon. *Then Mr.* Honest *Interrupting of him said, Did you see the two Men asleep in the Arbor?*

Stand. Ai, ai, I saw *Heedless*, and *Too-bold* there; and *Prov. 10. 7.* for ought I know, there they will ly till they Rot. But let me go on in my Tale: As I was thus Musing, as I said, there was one in very pleasant Attire, *but old*, that presented her self unto me, and offered me three things, to wit, her *Body*, her *Purse*, and her *Bed*. Now the Truth is, I was both a weary, and sleepy, I am also

as poor as a *Howlet*, and that, perhaps, the *Witch* knew.
Well, I repulsed her once and twice, but she put by
my Repulses, and smiled. Then I began to be angry,
but she mattered that nothing at all. Then she made
Offers again, and said, If I would be ruled by her, she
would make me great and happy. For, said she, I am
the Mistriss of the World, and men are made happy
by me. Then I asked her Name, and she told me it
was *Madam Bubble*. This set me further from her; but
10 she still followed me with Inticements. Then I betook
me, as you see, to my Knees, and with Hands lift up,
and crys, I pray'd to him that had said, he would help.
So just as you came up, the Gentlewoman went her
way. Then I continued to give thanks for this my great
Deliverance; for I verily believe she intended no good,
but rather sought to make stop of me in my Journey.

Madam Buble, *or this vain World.*

Hon. *Without doubt her Designs were bad. But stay,*
now you talk of her, methinks I either have seen her, or
have read some story of her.

20 *Standf.* Perhaps you have done both.

Hon. *Madam Buble! Is she not a tall comely Dame,*
something of a Swarthy Complexion?

Standf. Right, you hit it, she is just such an one.

Hon. *Doth she not speak very smoothly, and give you*
a Smile at the end of a Sentence?

Standf. You fall right upon it again, for these are
her very Actions.

Hon. *Doth she not wear a great Purse by her Side,*
and is not her Hand often in it fingering her Mony, as if
30 *that was her Hearts delight?*

Standf. 'Tis just so. Had she stood by all this while,
you could not more amply set her forth before me,
nor have better described her Features.

Hon. Then he that drew her Picture was a good
Limner, and he that wrote of her, said true.

Greath. This Woman is a *Witch*, and it is by Virtue
of her *Sorceries* that this Ground is *enchanted*; whoever
doth lay their Head down in *her Lap*, had as good lay
it down upon that Block over which the Ax doth hang;
40 and whoever lay their Eyes upon her Beauty, are

The World.

Jam. 4. 4. counted the Enemies of God. This is she that main-
1 John 2. 15. taineth in their Splendor, all those that are the Enemies
of Pilgrims. Yea, This is she that has bought off many
a man from a Pilgrims Life. She is a great *Gossiper*,
she is always, both she and her Daughters, at one
Pilgrim's Heels or other, now Commending, and then
preferring the excellencies of this Life. She is a bold and
impudent Slut; She will talk with any Man. She always
laugheth Poor Pilgrims to scorn, but highly commends
the Rich. If there be one cunning to get Mony in 10
a Place, she will speak well of him, from House to
House. She loveth Banqueting, and Feasting, mainly
well; she is always at one full Table or another. She has
given it out in some places, that she is a Goddess, and
therefore some do Worship her. She has her times and
open places of Feasting, and she will say and avow it,
that none can shew a Food comparable to hers. She promiseth to dwell with Childrens Children, if they will
but love and make much of her. She will cast out of her
Purse, Gold like Dust, in some places, and to some 20
Persons. She loves to be sought after, spoken well of,
and to ly in the Bosoms of Men. She is never weary of
commending of her Commodities, and she loves them
most that think best of her. She will promise to some
Crowns, and Kingdoms, if they will but take her
Advice, yet many has she brought to the Halter, and
ten thousand times more to Hell.

    Standf. *O! Said* Stand-fast, *What a Mercy is it that
I did resist her; for whither might she a drawn me?*

    Greath. Whither! Nay, none but God knows whither. 30
But in general to be sure, she would a drawn thee *into*
1 Tim. 6. 9. *many foolish and hurtful Lusts, which drown men in
Destruction and Perdition.*

    'Twas she that set *Absalom* against his Father, and
Jeroboam against his Master. 'Twas she that perswaded
Judas to sell his Lord, and that prevailed with *Demas*
to forsake the godly Pilgrims Life; none can tell of the
Mischief that she doth. She makes Variance betwixt
Rulers and Subjects, betwixt Parents and Children,

16–17 Feasting . . . Food] Cheating . . . Good 1, 2

'twixt Neighbor and Neighbor, 'twixt a Man and his Wife, 'twixt a Man and himself, 'twixt the Flesh and the Heart.

Wherefore good Master *Stand-fast*, be as your Name is, and when you have done all, *stand*.

At this Discourse there was among the Pilgrims a mixture of Joy and Trembling, but at length *they brake* out and Sang:

> *What Danger is the Pilgrim in,*
> *How many are his Foes,*
> *How many ways there are to Sin,*
> *No living Mortal knows.*
> *Some of the Ditch, shy are, yet can*
> *Lie tumbling in the Myre:*
> *Some tho they shun the Frying-pan,*
> *Do leap into the Fire.*

After this I beheld, until they were come into the Land of *Beulah*, where the Sun shineth Night and Day. Here, because they was weary, they betook themselves a while to Rest. And because this Country was common for Pilgrims, and because the Orchards and Vineyards that were here, belonged to the King of the Celestial Country; therefore they were licensed to make bold with any of his things.

But a little while soon refreshed them here, for the Bells did so ring, and the Trumpets continually sound so Melodiously, that they could not sleep, and yet they received as much refreshing, as if they had slept their Sleep never so soundly. Here also all the noise of them that walked the Streets, was, *More Pilgrims are come to Town*. And an other would answer, saying, And so many went over the Water, and were let in at the Golden Gates to Day. They would cry again, There is now a Legion of Shining ones, just come to Town; by which we know that there are more Pilgrims upon the Road, for here they come to wait for them and to comfort them after all their Sorrow. Then the Pilgrims

¹ Part, pag. ¹⁵⁴⁻⁵.

---

10 *Foes?* 1, 2   17 *marg.* 1 Part, pag. 270, 271 ‖ 1, 2

got up and walked to and fro: But how were their Ears
now filled with heavenly Noises, and their Eyes delighted with Celestial Visions? In this Land, they *heard*
nothing, *saw* nothing, *felt* nothing, *smelt* nothing, *tasted*
nothing, that was offensive to their Stomach or Mind;
only when they tasted of the Water of the River, over
which they were to go, they thought that tasted a little
Bitterish to the Palate, but it proved sweeter when
'twas down.

Death bitter to the Flesh, but sweet to the Soul.

In this place there was a Record kept of the Names
of them that had been Pilgrims of old, and a History of
all the famous Acts that they had done. It was here
also much discoursed how the *River* to some had had
its *flowings*, and what *ebbings* it has had while others
have gone over. It has been in a manner *dry* for some,
while it has overflowed its Banks for others.

Death has its Ebbings and Flowings like the Tide.

In this place, the Children of the Town would go
into the Kings Gardens and gather Nose-gaies for the
Pilgrims, and bring them to them with much affection.
Here also grew *Camphire*, with *Spicknard*, and *Saffron*,
Calamus, and *Cinamon*, with all its Trees of *Frank-
incense*, *Myrrhe*, and *Aloes*, with all *chief* Spices. With
these the Pilgrims Chambers were perfumed, while
they stayed here; and with these were their Bodys
anointed to prepare them to go over the *River* when the
time appointed was come.

Now, while they lay here, and waited for the good
Hour; there was a Noyse in the Town, that there was
a *Post* come from the Celestial City, with Matter of
great Importance, to one *Christiana*, the Wife of *Christian* the Pilgrim. So Enquiry was made for her, and
the House was found out where she was, so the Post
presented her with a Letter; the Contents whereof was,

A Messenger of Death sent to Christiana.

*Hail, Good Woman, I bring thee Tidings that the Master
calleth for thee, and expecteth that thou shouldest stand in his
Presence, in Cloaths of Immortality, within this ten Days.*

His Message.

When he had read this Letter to her, he gave her
therewith a *sure* Token that he was a true Messenger,
and was come to bid her make hast to be gone. The

How welcome is Death to them that have nothing to do but to dy.

22 Myrrhr 2

Token was, *An Arrow with a Point sharpened with Love,
let easily into her Heart, which by degrees wrought so
effectually with her, that at the time appointed she must
be gone.*

When *Christiana* saw that her time was come, and
that she was the first of this Company that was to go
over: She called for Mr. *Great-heart* her Guide, and
told him how Matters were. So he told her he was
heartily glad of the News, and could a been glad had
10 the Post came for him. Then she bid that he should
give Advice, how all things should be prepared for her
Journey.

So he told her, saying, Thus and thus it must be, and
we that Survive will accompany you to the Riverside.

Then she called for her Children, and gave them *her*
Blessing; and told them that she yet read with Comfort
the Mark that was set in their Foreheads, and was glad
to see them with her there, and that they had kept their
Garments so white. Lastly, She bequeathed to the Poor
20 that little she had, and commanded her Sons and her
Daughters to be ready against the Messenger should
come for them.

When she had spoken these Words to her Guide and
to her Children, she called for Mr. *Valiant-for-truth*,
and said unto him, Sir, You have in all places shewed
your self true-hearted, be Faithful unto Death, and my
King will give you a Crown of Life. I would also
intreat you to have an Eye to my Children, and if at
any time you see them faint, speak comfortably to them.
30 For my Daughters, my Sons Wives, they have been
Faithful, and a fulfilling of the Promise upon them,
will be their end. But she gave Mr. *Stand-fast* a Ring.
Then she called for old Mr. *Honest*, and said of him,
Behold an Israelite indeed, in whom is no Guile. Then
said *he*, I wish you a fair Day when you set out for
Mount *Sion*, and shall be glad to see that you go over
the River dry-shod. But she answered, Come *Wet*,
come *Dry*, I long to be gone; for however the Weather
is in my Journey, I shall have time enough when I come
40 there to sit down and rest me, and dry me.

To Mr. Ready-to-halt. Then came in that good Man Mr. *Ready-to-halt* to see her. So she said to him, Thy Travel hither has been with Dificulty, but that will make thy Rest the sweeter. But watch, and be ready, for at an Hour when you think not, the Messenger may come.

To Dispondencie, and his Daughter. After him, came in Mr. *Dispondencie*, and his Daughter *Much-a-fraid*. To whom she said, You ought with Thankfulness for ever, to remember your Deliverance from the Hands of Gyant *Dispair*, and out of *Doubting-Castle*. The effect of that Mercy is, that you are brought 10 with Safety hither. Be ye watchful, and cast away Fear; be sober, and hope to the End.

To Feeble-mind. Then she said to Mr. *Feeble-Mind*, Thou was delivered from the Mouth of Gyant *Slay-good*, that thou mightest live in the Light of the Living for ever, and see thy King with Comfort. Only I advise thee to repent thee of thy aptness to fear and doubt of his Goodness before he sends for thee, lest thou shouldest when he comes, be forced to stand before him for that Fault with Blushing. 20

Her last Day, and manner of Departure. Now the Day drew on that *Christiana* must be gone. So the Road was full of People to see her take her Journey. But behold all the Banks beyond the River were full of Horses and Chariots, which were come down from above to accompany her to the City-Gate. So she came forth and entered the *River* with a *Beck'n* of Fare well, to those that followed her to the River side. The last word she was heard to say here was, *I come Lord, to be with thee and bless thee*.

So her Children and Friends returned to their Place, 30 for that those that waited for *Christiana*, had carried her out of their Sight. So she went, and called, and entered in at the Gate with all the Ceremonies of Joy that her Husband *Christian* had done before her.

At her Departure her Children wept, but Mr. *Great-heart*, and Mr. *Valiant*, played upon the well tuned Cymbal and Harp for Joy. So all departed to their respective Places.

Ready-to-halt Summoned. In process of time there came a *Post* to the Town again, and his Business was with Mr. *Ready-to-halt*. So 40 he enquired him out, and said to him, I am come to thee in the Name of him whom thou hast Loved and Followed, tho upon *Crutches*. And my Message is to tell thee, that he expects thee at his Table to Sup with him in his Kingdom the next Day after *Easter*. Wherefore prepare thy self for this Journey.

Then he also gave him a Token that he was a true Messenger, saying, *I have broken thy golden Bowl*, and loosed *thy silver Cord*. | Eccles. 12. 6.

10 After this Mr. *Ready-to-halt* called for his Fellow Pilgrims, and told them, saying, I am sent for, and God shall surely visit you also. So he desired Mr. *Valiant* to make his *Will*. And because he had nothing to bequeath to them that should Survive him, but his *Crutches*, and his good *Wishes*, therefore thus he said: *These Crutches, I bequeath to my Son that shall tread in my Steps with an hundred warm Wishes that he may prove better then I have done.* | Promises. His Will.

Then he thanked Mr. *Great-heart*, for his Conduct, 20 and Kindness, and so addressed himself to his Journey. When he came at the brink of the River, he said, Now I shall have no more need of these *Crutches*, since yonder are Chariots and Horses for me to ride on. The last Words he was heard to say, was, *Welcome Life.* So he went his Way. | His last words.

After this, Mr. *Feeble-mind* had Tidings brought him, that the Post sounded his Horn at his Chamber Door. Then he came in and told him, saying, I am come to tell thee that the Master has need of thee, and 30 that in very little time thou must behold his Face in Brightness. And take this as a Token of the Truth of my Message. *Those that look out at the Windows shall be darkned.* | Feeble-mind Summoned. Eccles. 12. 3.

Then Mr. *Feeble-mind* called for his Friends, and told them what Errand had been brought unto him, and what Token he had received of the truth of the Message. Then he said, Since I have nothing to bequeath to any, to what purpose should I make a Will? As for my *feeble Mind*, that I will leave behind me, for | He makes no Will.

8 Eccles. 12. 16 ‖ 1, 2

that I shall have no need of that in the place whither I go; nor is it worth bestowing upon the poorest Pilgrim: Wherefore when I am gon, I desire, that you Mr. *Valiant*, would bury it in a Dunghil. This done, and the Day being come, in which he was to depart; he entered the *River* as the rest. His last Words were, *His last words.* *Hold out Faith and Patience.* So he went over to the other Side.

Mr. Dis- When Days, had many of them passed away: Mr. *pondencie's* *Dispondencie* was sent for. For a *Post* was come, and 10 *Summons.* brought this Message to him; *Trembling Man, These are to summon thee to be ready with thy King, by the next Lords Day, to shout for Joy for thy Deliverance from all thy Doubtings.*

And said the Messenger, That my Message is true, *Eccl. 12. 5.* take this for a Proof. So he gave him *The Grashopper* *His Daughter* *to be a Burthen unto him.* Now Mr. *Dispondencie*'s *goes too.* Daughter, whose Name was *Much-a-fraid*, said, when she heard what was done, that she would go with her Father. Then Mr. *Dispondencie* said to his Friends; My 20 self and my Daughter, you know what we have been, and how troublesomly we have behaved our selves in *His Will.* every Company. My Will and my Daughters is, that our *Disponds*, and slavish Fears, be by no man ever received, from the day of our Departure, for ever; For I know that after my Death they will offer themselves to others. For, to be plain with you, they are *Ghosts*, the which we entertained when we first began to be Pilgrims, and could never shake them off after. And they will walk about and seek Entertainment of the Pil- 30 grims, but for our Sakes, shut ye the Doors upon them.

When the time was come for them to depart, they went to the Brink of the *River*. The last Words of *His last words.* Mr. *Dispondencie*, were, *Farewel Night, welcome Day.* His Daughter went thorow the River singing, but none could understand what she said.

Mr. Honest Then it came to pass, a while after, that there was *Summoned.* a *Post* in the Town that enquired for Mr. *Honest*. So he came to the House where he was, and delivered to his Hand these Lines: *Thou art Commanded to be ready against this Day seven Night, to present thy self before thy Lord, at his Fathers House.* And for a Token that my Message is true, *All thy Daughters of Musick shall be* Eccl. 12. 4. *brought low.* Then Mr. *Honest* called for his Friends, and said unto them, I Die, but shall make no Will. As *He makes* for my Honesty, it shall go with me; let him that comes *no Will.* after be told of this. When the Day that he was to be gone, was come, he addressed himself to go over the 10 *River.* Now the *River* at that time overflowed the Banks in some places. But Mr. *Honest* in his Life time had spoken to one *Good-conscience* to meet him there, Good- the which he also did, and lent him his Hand, and so conscience helped him over. The last Words of Mr. *Honest* were, Honest *over* *Grace Reigns.* So he left the World. *the River.*

After this it was noised abroad that Mr. *Valiant-for-* Mr. Valiant *truth* was taken with a Summons, by the same *Post* as *Summoned.* the other; and had this for a Token that the Summons was true, *That his Pitcher was broken at the Fountain.* Eccl. 12. 6. 20 When he understood it, he called for his Friends, and told them of it. Then said he, I am going to my Fathers, and tho with great Difficulty I am got hither, yet now I do not repent me of all the Trouble I have been at to arrive where I am. *My Sword,* I give to him that shall His *Will.* succeed me in my Pilgrimage, and my *Courage* and *Skill,* to him that can get it. My *Marks* and *Scarrs* I carry with me, to be a witness for me, that I have fought his Battels, who now will be my Rewarder. When the Day that he must go hence, was come, 30 many accompanied him to the River side, into which, as he went, he said, *Death, where is thy Sting?* And as he went down deeper, he said, *Grave where is* His *last words.* *thy Victory?* So he passed over, and the Trumpets sounded for him on the other side.

Then there came forth a Summons for Mr. *Stand-* Mr. Stand-fast *fast,* (This Mr. *Stand-fast,* was he that the rest of the *is summoned.* Pilgrims found upon his Knees in the *inchanted* Ground.) For the *Post* brought it him open in his Hands. The Contents whereof were, *That he must pre-* 40 *pare for a change of Life, for his Master was not willing that he should be so far from him any longer.* At this Mr. *Stand-fast* was put into a Muse; Nay, said the Messenger, you need not doubt of the truth of my Message; for here is a Token of the Truth thereof, *Eccl. 12. 6.* *Thy Wheel is broken at the Cistern.* Then he called to *He calls for Mr. Great-Heart.* him Mr. *Great-heart,* who was their Guide, and said unto him, Sir, Altho it was not my hap to be much in *His Speech to him.* your good Company in the Days of my Pilgrimage, yet since the time I knew you, you have been profitable to me. When I came from home, I left behind me a Wife, 10 and five small Children. Let me entreat you, at your Return (for I know that you will go, and return to your Masters House, in Hopes that you may yet be a Conductor to more of the Holy Pilgrims,) that you send to my Family, and let them be acquainted with all that hath, and shall happen unto me. Tell them moreover, of my happy Arrival to this Place, and of the present late blessed *His Errand to his Family.* Condition that I am in. Tell them also of *Christian,* and of *Christiana* his Wife, and how *She* and her Children came after her Husband. Tell them also of what a happy 20 End she made, and whither she is gone. I have little or nothing to send to my Family, except it be Prayers, and Tears for them; of which it will suffice, if thou acquaint them, if paradventure they may prevail. When Mr. *Stand-fast* had thus set things in order, and the time being come for him to hast him away; he also went down to the River. Now there was a great Calm at that time in the River, wherefore Mr. *Stand-fast,* when he was about half way in, he stood a while and talked to his Companions that had waited upon him thither. And he said, 30

His last words. This River has been a Terror to many, yea the thoughts of it also have often frighted me. But now methinks I stand easie, my Foot is fixed upon that, *Jos. 3. 17.* upon which the Feet of the Priests that bare the Ark of the Covenant stood while *Israel* went over this *Jordan.* The Waters indeed are to the Palate bitter, and to the Stomack cold; yet the thoughts of what I am going to, and of the Conduct that waits for me on the other side, doth lie as a glowing Coal at my Heart.

I see my self now at the *end* of my Journey, my *toil-som* Days are ended. I am going now to see *that* Head that was Crowned with Thorns, and *that* Face that was spit upon, for me.

I have formerly lived by Hear-say, and Faith, but now I go where I shall live by sight, and shall be with him, in whose Company I delight my self.

I have loved to hear my Lord spoken of, and wher-ever I have seen the print of his Shooe in the Earth, there I have coveted to set my Foot too.

His Name has been to me as a *Civit-Box*, yea sweeter then all Perfumes. His Voice to me has been most sweet, and his Countenance, I have more desired then they that have most desired the Light of the Sun. His Word I did use to gather for my Food, and for Anti-dotes against my Faintings. He has held me, and I have kept me from mine Iniquities: Yea, my Steps hath he strengthened in his Way.

Now while he was thus in Discourse his Countenance changed, his *strong men* bowed under him, and after he had said, *Take me, for I come unto thee*, he ceased to be seen of them.

But glorious it was, to see how the open Region was filled with Horses and Chariots, with Trumpeters and Pipers, with Singers, and Players on stringed Instru-ments, to welcome the Pilgrims as they went up and followed one another in at the beautiful Gate of the City.

As for *Christian*'s Children, the four Boys that *Chris-tiana* brought with her, with their Wives and Children, I did not stay where I was, till they were gone over. Also since I came away, I heard one say, that they were yet alive, and so would be for the Increase of the Church in that Place where they were for a time.

Shall it be my Lot to go that way again, I may give those that desire it, an Account of what I here am silent about; mean time I bid my Reader *Adieu.*

FINIS

COMMENTARY

THE FIRST PART

The Author's Apology for his Book

In these prefatory verses Bunyan defends his allegorical method and the imaginative treatment of his theme from anticipated charges of frivolity on the part of his fellow Nonconformists. The defence of similitudes by reference to Scripture metaphors and parables is frequently found in earlier Puritan writings; cf. especially Richard Bernard, *The Faithfull Shepheard* (1609), pp. 65–66, and the Apology with which he concludes *The Isle of Man* (1626), pp. [321–31].

PAGE 1, ll. 7–8. *the Way and Race of Saints* The book referred to is probably *The Heavenly Footman* (second edition, 1698) which teaches the Christian 'so to run that he may obtain'; the words would apply less aptly to *The Strait Gate* (1676) which John Brown at first thought was the book mentioned (Brown, p. 247). Brown admitted the better claim of *The Heavenly Footman* in his fourth edition (1918).

l. 17. *ad infinitum* Cf. the marginal note 'the Lattine I borrow' on the phrase '*ex Carne et Sanguine Christi*', Part Two, p. 229, and *The Doctrine of the Law and Grace Unfolded (Works*, i. 495): 'I never went to school to Aristotle or Plato, but was brought up at my father's house in a very mean condition, among a company of poor countrymen.'

PAGE 2, l. 2. *Still as I pull'd, it came* Like flax on the distaff, when the spinner takes hold of an end and draws it towards her, twisting it between her finger and thumb to form a continuous thread.

PAGE 2, l. 9. *others said, Not so* On the bearing of these lines on the probable long delay between the composition of Part One and its publication see Introduction, p. xxx.

PAGE 3, l. 17. *His Gun, His Nets, his Lime-twigs, light and bell* See Strutt, *Sports and Pastimes of the People of England*, ed. V. Charles Cox (1903), p. 31.

PAGE 4, l. 10. *By Types, Shadows and Metaphors* Cf. Bernard, *Isle of Man*, *ut supra*, pp. [321–31].

l. 14. *by pins and loops* Exod. xxvi. 5, xxvii. 19.

ll. 15–16. Alluding to the Passover and various Levitical sacrifices. *By Calves*, Lev. xvi. 3, 14, 15, Heb. ix. 12, 19. *And Sheep*, Lev. i. 10, xxii. 19. *By Heifers*, Lev. xix. 2–9, Heb. ix. 13. *By Rams*, Exod. xxix. 15–32, Lev. v. 15–16. *By Birds*, Lev. xiv. 4–39. *And Herbs, and by the blood of Lambs*, Exod. xii. 7, 8. Cf. *Grace Abounding*, § 71.

l. 24. *bereave* Take, snatch away. *of our Souls*, sc. 'from our souls'. Milton, *Paradise Lost*, x. 918, and Wither, *Britains Remembrancer* (1622), 170: 'Have . . . (Like Iezabell) oppress'd and bereav'n The poore mans portion.'

PAGE 4, l. 34. (*Dark Figures, Allegories*) For Puritan advocacy of a figurative interpretation of the Bible in regard to certain books see William Perkins, *The Art of Prophecying* (*Workes*, Cambridge, 1609), p. 747, quoting Chrysostom, 'Parables must not be expounded according to the letter, lest many absurdities doe follow.'

PAGE 5, l. 8. *his lies in Silver Shrines* The silver shrines made for the Ephesian Diana, Acts xix. 24.

l. 15. 1 Tim. vi. 3, iv. 7.

PAGE 6, ll. 3–4. *Men* (*as high as Trees*) *will write Dialogue-wise* Refers to edifying books in dialogue form like Arthur Dent's popular *Plain Mans Path-way to Heaven* (first edition, 1601). The phrase in parenthesis suggests an allusion to an author's name in the form of a rebus, such as that on Bunyan's own name in the verses at the end of *The Holy War*, p. 431: 'nu Honey in a B', but remains obscure. Thomas Allestree (1638–1715) was the author of a treatise on death *Epaphroditus his Sickness* (1671) but no dialogue by him is known.

l. 10. *he that taught us first to Plow* Isa. xxviii. 24, 26: 'Doth the ploughman plow all day to sow? doth he open and break the clods of his ground? . . . For his God doth instruct him to discretion, and doth teach him also.'

l. 24. *the everlasting Prize* 1 Cor. ix. 24; *The Heavenly Footman* (*Works*), iii. 381 ff.

PAGE 7, l. 6. *they will stick like Burs* Tilley, B 724.

l. 17. *a man i' th' Clouds* A reference may be intended to Wilkins, *The First Book. The Discovery of a New World* or, *A Discourse tending to prove that 'tis probable there may be another habitable World in the Moon* (1640). Bunyan seems to be referring to this work in the prefatory verses to *The Holy War* when he speaks of those who confidently insinuate concerning the stars, 'That each of them is now the residence Of some brave Creatures', *H.W.* p. 187.

PAGE 8, l. 2. *a Denn* The marginal note 'The Gaol' added in the third edition makes explicit that this was Bunyan's place of imprisonment; also used of the dungeon in Doubting Castle, p. 117: 'Go get you down to your Den again.'

l. 7. *a great burden upon his Back* Cf. *The Doctrine of the Law and Grace Unfolded* (*Works*), i. 526; Geffrey Whitney, *A Choice of Emblemes, and other Devises* (1586), Book ii, p. 225, has an illustration showing a pilgrim with scrip and staff turning his back on a geographical globe and setting his face towards the rising sun: the words *Peregrinus Christianus loquitur* appear in the margin of the poem; Quarles, *Emblemes* (1635), Book IV, p. 2, in an emblem on the theme of the Christian pilgrimage through life says: 'Her [the world's] freedom is my Gaol.'

ll. 10–11. *what shall I do?* *Law and Grace* (*Works*), i. 543; *The Strait Gate* (*Works*), i. 364; Acts xvi. 31.

ll. 18–19. *your dear Friend*: Relative.

PAGE 9, l. 2. *his Relations* The word is used frequently for the family in Part Two, which supports retention of the original second-edition reading.

PAGE 10, l. 17. *yonder Wicket-gate* The Wicket-gate is anticipated in the little door in the hill of Bunyan's dream, *Grace Abounding*, §§ 53–54. 'The straitness of the gate is not to be understood carnally but mystically . . . not . . . as if the entrance into heaven was some little pinching wicket' (*The Strait Gate*, i. 366). Cf. Donne on Christ's 'Metaphors of narrow wayes and strait gates', *LXXX Sermons* (1640), xxvi. 259.

PAGE 11, ll. 33–34. *take a fancy by the end*   The image is from spinning as in p. 2, l. 2.

PAGE 12, l. 8. *Come with me Neighbour Pliable*   Pliable is addressed in the vocative; the third-edition alteration of 'me' to 'thy' made it doubtful whether Obstinate or Pliable was addressed; edd. 4–6 introduce the sentence with 'Nay, but do thou', but the ambiguity is not satisfactorily removed till the addition of a comma after 'Neighbour' in the eighth.

PAGE 14, l. 18. *a very Miry Slough*   See *G.A.* § 82: 'I found myself as on a miry Bog that shook if I did but stir.'

PAGE 16, l. 1. *this sixteen hundred years*   i.e. since the proclamation of Christ's gospel.

l. 13 marg. *The Promises*   In the Calvinist sense: Biblical texts announcing or foreshadowing salvation by faith.

l. 30. *they all turned their tales*   'At the last he shall turne his tayl', Coverdale, Ecclus. xvii. 23 (1535). The idiomatic phrase is not in Tilley.

The general experience behind Pliable's relapse is frequently discussed in Bunyan's minor works; see *A Holy Life the Beauty of Christianity* (*Works*), ii. 521.

PAGE 17 l. 3. *Mr. Worldly-Wiseman*   Some features of the latitudinarian attitude of Edward Fowler (*Design of Christianity*, 1671) which Bunyan wrote against in *A Defence of the Doctrine of Justification by Faith* have been incorporated in this portrait, which first appeared in the second edition. Fowler was vicar of Northill near Bedford and, having conformed to the Prayer Book, did not suffer in the ejections of 1662 (*Calamy Revised*, ed. A. G. Matthews, 1954, s.v. Edward Fowler); this as well as his doctrine seems to have occasioned Bunyan's hostility: 'I know you not by face, much less your personal practice; yet I have heard as if blood might pursue you, for your unstable weathercock spirit, which doubtless could not but stumble the weak, and give advantage to the adversary to speak vilifyingly of religion' (*A Defence of the Doctrine of Justification* (*Works*), ii. 313–14). Wiseman's description of the religion of the town of Morality stresses its material comfort (p. 19, l. 28: 'Provision is there also cheap and good . . .'). In *A Defence* Bunyan censures Fowler for what he considers his purely moral Christianity, and there are several hints for Wiseman: 'So then, although you talk of gospel positive laws and particularly that of coming to God by Christ; yet those which you call first principles of morals, are of higher concern with you, and more indispensible by far than this' (ii. 285); 'Yet if the principles from which he acts, be but the habit of soul, the purity (as he feigns) of his own nature; all this is nothing else but the old gentleman in his holiday clothes' (ii. 290); Mr. Legality who has skill to help men off with their burdens is spoken of as if he were a physician ('he hath skill to cure those that are somewhat crazed in

their wits'), and this recalls a medical metaphor in Fowler which occasions
Bunyan's particular indignation: 'Would that man be accounted any better
than a perfect idiot, who, being sorely hurt, should expect from his surgeon
perfect ease, when he will not permit him to apply any plaister for the healing
of his wound? Or that being deadly sick, should look that his physician should
deliver him from his pain, when he will not take any course he prescribes for
the removal of the distemper that is the cause of it?' (*Design of Christianity*,
p. 216).

PAGE 20, l. 1. *yonder high hill* The hill is Mount Sinai, standing for the
old law of Moses and its inevitable condemnation of the sinner, Rom. vii,
Heb. xii. 18–21.

l. 10. *lest the Hill should fall on his head* This recalls Bunyan's fear during
his Elstow days that the church tower might fall on him as he was watching
the ringers, an experience also connected with the terrors of the Mosaic law,
G.A. §§ 33–34.

PAGE 22, ll. 23–24. 1. *His turning thee out of the way.* 2. *His labouring to render
the Cross odious to thee.* 'Others again, when they see the cross to be approaching, they turn aside to the left hand, or to the right hand, and so think to get to
heaven another way', *The Heavenly Footman* (*Works*), iii. 388.

PAGE 23, l. 21. *the Son of the Bond woman which now is* A misunderstanding
of Gal. iv. 25: 'This Agar . . . answereth to Jerusalem which now is, and is in
bondage with her children.'

PAGE 25, l. 22. *he opened the Gate* Christian's acceptance at the Wicket-gate
indicates his admission into a community of believers corresponding to
Bunyan's first association with Gifford's church and to his vision of the door-
way through the mountain which separates him from its members: 'a narrow
gap, like a little doorway in the Wall, through which I attempted to pass;
Now the passage being very strait and narrow, I made many efforts to get in,
but all in Vain. . . . At last, with great striving, methought I at first did get in
my head, and after that, by a sideling striving my Shoulders and my whole
Body. Then I was exceeding glad, and went and sat down in the midst of
them, and so was comforted with the light and heat of their Sun', *G.A.* § 54.
In the following section it is explained that the mountain signifies the church
of the living God and the gap in the wall is Christ. This is why the person who
receives Christian at this important juncture is the merely allegorical Good
Will. Cf. 'There is the door of faith, the door which the grace of God hath
opened to the Gentiles. This door is Jesus Christ, as also himself doth testify,
saying "I am the door" etc.', *The Strait Gate* (*Works*), i. 365.

PAGE 26, l. 33. *no betterment 'twixt him and my self*: difference for the
better.

PAGE 27, ll. 33–34. *Butt down upon this*: issue or lead into another road. 'Bur-
leigh Street buts against Exeter Street', Stow, *Survey of London* (ed. Strype,
1754), II. vi. 4. 650/1. 'The remote parts of their Country . . . do both butt
and bound upon the Hill called *Hellgate hill*', *H.W.*, p. 409.

PAGE 28, ll. 18–19. *the house of the Interpreter*   Coming as it does immediately after Christian's reception at the Wicket-gate this episode would seem to correspond to that early stage of Bunyan's conversion when John Gifford interpreted his spiritual condition to him at his own house: 'But he invited me to his House, where I should hear him confer with others, about the dealings of God with their Souls, from all which I still received more Conviction, and from that time began to see something of the Vanity and inward Wretchedness of my wicked Heart . . .', *G.A.* § 77. There is also a piece of Biblical interpretation of an emblematic character in one of the additions Bunyan made to his autobiography at this point: 'I was almost made, about this time, to see something concerning the beasts that Moses counted clean and unclean. I thought those Beasts were types of Men; the *clean*, types of them that were the people of God; but the *unclean*, types of such as were the children of the wicked One. Now, I read that the clean *Chewed the cud*; that is, thought I, they show us we must feed upon the Word of God; They also *parted the Hoof*; I thought that signified we must part, if we would be saved, with the ways of ungodly men', *G.A.* § 71.

PAGE 29, ll. 2–3. *the Picture of a very grave Person*   The first emblematic picture in the Interpreter's House represents Evangelist ('the only Man, whom the Lord of the Place whither thou art going, hath authorized, to be thy Guide in all difficult places thou mayest meet with . . .'). Bunyan evokes the character of the ideal pastor, perhaps with particular reference to John Gifford, first minister of the Bedford independent church, who received him into its fellowship (*G.A.* §§ 78, 118).

There is a striking resemblance to the emblem of Whitney already referred to in connexion with the description of Christian at the beginning of the dream (*Emblemes*, book ii, p. 225). The frontispiece to Quarles's *Emblemes* (1635) depicts a man with a book in his hand representing the Scriptures; he has cast aside the World, signified by a globe or bauble; however, the figure is in a reclining position; another emblem in Quarles, book iv, No. 2, p. 190, has a pilgrim gazing up to heaven.

ll. 25–27. *the only Man, whom the Lord of the Place whither thou art going, hath authorized, to be thy Guide*   Cf. Quarles, *Emblemes* (1635), book iv, No. 2, p. 190.

> Where shall I seek a Guide? where shall I meet
>   Some lucky hand to lead my trembling paces?
> What trusty Lanterne will direct my feet
>   To scape the danger of these dang'rous places?
> What hopes have I to pass without a Guide?
> Where one gets safely through, a thousand fall beside.

ll. 33–34. *a very large Parlour that was full of dust*   A similar emblem is found in Antonius Wierix, *Cor Iesu amanti sacrum* (reproduced in Etienne Luzvic, *Le cœur dévot*, Douai, 1627): Jesus is depicted sweeping out a dusty room which is the human heart (*Jesus cor expurgans* is the motto); he is driving out a multitude of snakes and venomous creatures, while outside the heart-shaped chamber tiny cherubs seated on puffs of cloud are looking on. See Mario Praz, *Studies in Seventeenth Century Imagery* (Warburg Institute Studies iii,

1939), fig. 61; L. Alvin, *Catalogue raisonné de l'œuvre des trois frères Wierix* (Brussels, 1866), p. 260; and *The Times*, 29 November 1928. Imagery of the human heart before and after sanctification played an important part in Catholic emblem literature on the Continent; the plates were often reproduced in English Protestant emblem books, and the image is adapted in English religious poems like George Herbert's *Love unknown* (*Works*, ed. F. E. Hutchinson, Oxford, 1941, p. 129). See Roger Sharrock in *R.E.S.* xxi (1945), pp. 105–16, and Rosemary Freeman, *English Emblem Books* (1948), pp. 134–7, 164–7, 178.

PAGE 30, ll. 33–34. *Passion . . . Patience* Like the other tableaux in the Interpreter's House this suggests an emblem picture. Though no precise identification can be made, the two boys strongly recall the Cupid-like figures Amor and Anima employed in the Jesuit emblem books and in those of their English imitators such as Christopher Harvey (*Schola Cordis*, 1647); see Freeman, op. cit., pp. 164–7, 216–17.

PAGE 31, l. 2. *The Governour of them* 'The heir as long as he is a child . . . is under tutors and governors until the time appointed of the father', Gal. iv. 12.

l. 6. *Then I saw that one came to Passion*, etc. 'One of the not many instances of faulty allegory in the *Pilgrim's Progress*; that is, it is no allegory. The beholding "but a while" and the changing into "nothing but rags" is not legitimately imaginable. A longer time and more interlinks are requisite. It is a hybrid compost of usual images and generalized words. Yet perhaps these very defects are practically excellences in relation to the writer and readers of the *Pilgrim's Progress*', Coleridge, *Literary Remains* (1836–9), iii. 402.

PAGE 32, l. 20. *a Fire burning against a Wall* The fire of grace burning in the human heart is a common theme in the Jesuit devotional emblem books, and it could have become available to Bunyan through the work of Quarles, who had adapted the emblems in two such books (Hermannus Hugo, *Pia Desideria*, 1624, and the anonymous *Typus Mundi*, 1627). See also John Hall, *Emblems with Elegant Figures* (1658), p. 40, where the soul holds up a heart to heaven and it is filled from a chalice poured down from above, and Sharrock *ut supra*, pp. 110–11.

'*You are very hot for mercy, but I will cool you; this frame shall not last always: Many have been as hot as you, for a spurt; but I have quenched their Zeal*', *G.A.* § 111. Bunyan uses the image elsewhere in *Saved by Grace*, i. 351: '. . . those that will cast water themselves upon those sparkes, which Christ labours to kindle in them; because they will not be troubled with the light of them'. Coleridge admired the theological accuracy of this emblem of the Interpreter's House.

PAGE 33, ll. 21–22. *a man, of a very stout countenance* The man has 'an Helmet upon his Head': cf. Eph. vi. 17.

l. 33. *the Three* Those who walk on the roof of the palace are said to be clothed in gold and to be prepared to dress the Christian warrior 'with such Garments as they'; they seem to be the saints rather than the Trinity, and the alteration in the second edition to 'those' removes the confusion. It seems likely however that Bunyan had in mind Enoch, Moses, and Elijah, who walk 'on top of the gate' when Christian and Hopeful are received into the Holy City, p. 161, ll. 22 f.

PAGE 34, l. 8. *a Man in an Iron Cage*

> From Sense to Hope; then hopps from Hope to Doubt,
> From Doubt to dull Despaire; there, seeks about
> For desp'rate Freedome, and at ev'ry Grate,
> She wildly thrusts, and begs th' untimely date
> Of the unexpired thraldome, to release
> Th' afflicted Captive, that can find no peace;
> Thus am I coop'd within this fleshly Cage
> I weare my youth, and waste my weary Age.

Quarles, *Emblemes*, book v, No. 10, p. 281; the illustration shows a man in a cage and an angel outside; the quotation following the poem might help to fix a reader's mind on the subject of despair: 'O miserable condition of mankind, that has lost that for which he was created. Alas, what hath he lost? And what hath he found? He hath lost happiness for which he was made, and found misery for which he was not made, Anselm, *In Protolog.* cap. 1.' The figure of the apostate who is guilty of the sin against the Holy Ghost is common in the Puritan literature of exhortation. The man in the iron cage was identified by George Offor with John Child, a member of the Bedford congregation who conformed to the Church of England after 1660 and afterwards, in 1684, took his own life in a fit of remorse (Offor, *Works*, iii. 72, *A Relation of the Life and Death of John Child* (1710), pp. 63–122). During his lapse Child was visited by Benjamin Keach, a Mr. Collins, and a Mr. B., who may have been Bunyan. Child's name occurs in the Bedford *Church Book*, ff. 18–22; the last of these references suggests that his withdrawal from the congregation took place before the time of persecution had begun: '27th of ye 11th moneth (27 February 1658–9): Whereas our bro: Bunyan has spoken to bro: Childe to come and render a reason of his withdrawing to some of the brethren and he refuseth to do it unless he may come before the whole congregation; we are agreed to have notice given to him to come to the next Church meeting.'

The portrait of the reprobate is also influenced by the celebrated case of Francis Spira: *G.A.* § 164: 'every sentence in that book, every groan of that man, with all the rest of his actions in his dolours, as his tears, his prayers, his gnashing of teeth, his ringing of hands, his twining and twisting, and languishing and pining away under that mighty hand of God that was upon him, was as knives and daggers in my Soul.'

ll. 17–18. *a fair and flourishing Professor*:   One who makes open profession of religion; a Puritan usage: *O.E.D.* s.v. 3.b.

ll. 24–25. *I cannot get out; O now I cannot.*   'This was the burden of Spira's complaint, "I cannot do it! Oh! now I cannot do it!" ', *The Barren Fig-Tree, or the Doom and Downfall of the Fruitless Professor* (*Works*), iii. 582.

ll. 27–28. *I laid the reins upon the neck of my lusts*   Cf. the proverb 'to give one the reins (or bridle)', Tilley, B 671.

l. 35. *Ask him*   This is followed in the first edition by 'Nay, said *Christian,* pray Sir, do you', and the interrogation is carried out by the Interpreter. But this rather unnecessary piece of politeness on Christian's part spoils the sense of the situation, since the Interpreter should be presumed to understand his own 'significant rooms'. The change in the second edition which allows Christian to ask the questions is a clear improvement, and must be accepted as an author's revision.

PAGE 36, l. 10. *in my Dream* 'even in my childhood the Lord did scare and affright me with fearful dreams, and did terrifie me with dreadful visions: For often, after I had spent this and the other day in sin, I have in my bed been greatly afflicted, while asleep, with the apprehensions of Devils, and wicked Spirits, who still, as I then thought, laboured to draw me away with them', *G.A.* § 5.

ll. 10–11. *saw the Clouds rack at an unusual rate*: be driven before the wind: *O.E.D.* s.v. Rack, *v.* 1.

l. 22. *a Fiery flame* 'his throne was like the fiery flame, and his wheels as burning fire', Dan. vii. 9. This establishes the correctness of the first-edition reading.

PAGE 38, l. 2. *upon that place stood a Cross* 'I remember that one day, as I was travelling into the Country, and musing on the wickedness and blasphemy of my heart, and considering of the enmity that was in me to God, that Scripture came in my mind, *He hath made peace by the blood of his cross*, Col. i. 20. By which I was made to see, both again and again, that God and my Soul were friends by this Blood . . .', *G.A.* § 116. 'The cross is the standing way-mark by which all they that go to glory must pass by', *The Heavenly Footman (Works)*, iii. 386. This episode conforms closely to the Calvinist idea of Christ's sacrifice: Christian is released from his sins by having Christ's righteousness freely imputed to him, Calvin, *Institution*, ed. Pannier (Paris, 1936), iii. 64–65. 'O! when Jesus Christ did come to make himself a sacrifice, or to offer himself for sin you may understand that our sins were indeed charged to *purpose* upon him', *Law and Grace (Works)*, i. 529. 'He that is come to Christ has the advantage of him that is coming, in that he is eased of his burden', *Come and Welcome to Jesus Christ (Works)*, i. 264.

l. 17. *three shining ones* Since the first says '*Thy sins be forgiven*', not the second, three angels rather than the Trinity.

ll. 21–22. *a Roll with a Seal upon it* 'Now I had an evidence, as I thought, of my Salvation from Heaven, with many golden Seals thereon, all hanging in my sight', *G.A.* § 129.

PAGE 39, l. 3. *Presumption* On the danger of over-confidence in the Christian life see Baxter, *Saints Everlasting Rest* (11th edition, 1677), p. 318.

l. 15. *Every Fatt must stand upon his own bottom* Proverbial: *Oxford Dictionary of English Proverbs* (2nd edition, 1948), p. 675: Tilley, T 596: 'Every tub must stand on its own bottom.'

l. 25. *Formalist* 'Neither is the Formalist exempted from this number. He is a man that has lost all but the shell of religion', *The Strait Gate (Works)*, i. 388.

PAGE 40, ll. 11–12. *more then a thousand years* Perhaps a reference to the Decretals of Constantine.

PAGE 40, ll. 18–19. *so be we get into the way, what's matter which way we get in*
The mechanism of the allegory here, depending as it does almost on a pun, is
criticized by Coleridge: 'The allegory is clearly defective, inasmuch as the
"way" represents two diverse meanings: (1) the outward profession of Christianity, and (2) the inward and spiritual grace . . . the allegory degenerates
into a sort of pun, that is, in the two senses of the word "way" and thus
supplies Formalist and Hypocrisy with an argument which Christian cannot
fairly answer. . . . For the obvious and only proper answer is: "No! you are
not in the same 'way' with me though you are walking in the same road" ',
Coleridge on the Seventeenth Century, ed. R. F. Brinkley (Duke University
Press, 1955), pp. 479–80.

l. 35. *Ordinances*   The usual Puritan term for the sacraments.

l. 38. *the Coat that is on thy back*   The white dress of the elect just given
to Christian by the angels, Rev. xix. 8. Christian's reply develops the allegorical idea that it is his lord's coat, i.e. a livery, and that he will therefore be
recognized at the Celestial City.

PAGE 42, ll. 19–20. *a wide field full of dark Mountains*   'before your feet stumble upon the dark mountains', Jer. xiii. 16. 'There are heights that build themselves up in us, and exalt themselves to keep the knowledge of God from our
hearts. . . . These are the dark mountains at which we should certainly stumble
and fall, but for one who can leap and skip over them to our aid', *The Saints'
Knowledge of Christ's Love (Works)*, ii. 8. 'Field', a stretch of open country:
but the Biblical image remains indefinite in the mind of one who knew only
the flat Bedfordshire landscape.

l. 27 marg. *Award of grace*   The 'A' and 'w' are slightly spaced out in
the first edition, and as a consequence the phrase appears as 'A Ward of grace'
in the later editions; 'ward' could mean a place of protection, but it would
seem ill applied to the arbour where Christian loses his roll; it is better read
like this. Sturt's 'corrected edition' reads 'a *word* of grace'.

PAGE 43, ll. 8–9. *what's the matter you run the wrong way?*   Ellipsis of 'that'.

ll. 12–13. *we turned, and are going back again*   'But why go back again?
That is the next way to hell. Never go over hedge and ditch to hell', *The Strait
Gate (Works)*, i. 388.

ll. 14–15. *a couple of Lions*   The lions stand for persecution, civil and ecclesiastical. In Part Two they are backed by Giant Bloodyman, clearly a per-
secutor, and it is noteworthy that Mr. Fearing whose difficulties are spiritual
has no fear of them. Bunyan writes from prison to the Bedford brethren in
the preface to *G.A.*: '*I thank God upon every Remembrance of you, and rejoice
even while I stick between the Teeth of the Lions in the Wilderness.*' Cf. 'The
lions, the wicked people of the world that fear not God . . .', *A Treatise of the
Fear of God (Works)*, i. 469. Elsewhere lions are used as an image of the Law,
Strait Gate (Works), i. 368.

l. 29. *he felt, and found it not*   Christian's loss of his roll signifies his forgetting the tokens of his election and thus being led to entertain doubts about
his salvation. There is some correspondence to the long episode of temptation
to despair in *G.A.* which also succeeds effectual calling (§§ 132–235), but in
the allegory this material serves for a number of episodes, including the fight

with Apollyon which takes place on Forgetful-green, and the later imprisonment in Doubting Castle which ends when Christian remembers he has a key
to it (the promises of salvation already given to him).

PAGE 44, l. 1. *his foolish Fact*   *Fact*, a deed, an act. 'This *fact* was infamous',
1 *Hen. IV*, iv. 1.

PAGE 45, l. 11. *doleful Creatures*   'Their houses shall be full of all doleful
creatures', Isa. xiii. 21.

l. 17. *shift*   Put to flight.

ll. 21–22. *Palace . . . the name whereof was Beautiful*   The Palace Beautiful represents church-fellowship; it stands 'just by the High-way side', that
is to say, it is not necessary to salvation. It has been suggested that the House
Beautiful was inspired by Bunyan's knowledge of Houghton Manor House
near Houghton Conquest which he may have visited when assisting his father
on his rounds as a brazier. The house was built by Mary Sidney, Countess of
Pembroke, who employed Inigo Jones. In 1630 it came into the hands of the
Bruce family and became the residence of Christian, Countess of Devonshire.
In Bunyan's maturity it was owned by the Earl of Ailesbury, a collector,
whose connoisseurship might have prompted reference to 'the rarities of the
place', Charles H. Harper, *The Bunyan Country; Landmarks of the Pilgrim's
Progress* (1928), pp. 87–95.

l. 30. *The Lions were chained*   Refers to a period when the application of
penal laws against Nonconformists was relaxed; the strong autobiographical
element would help to fix it as the Commonwealth, when Bunyan himself was
first received into church-fellowship.

PAGE 46, l. 26. *my Evidence*   i.e. of election.

PAGE 47, ll. 16–17. *Prudence, Piety and Charity*   The fact that the principal
allegorical personages in the House Beautiful are women is a reminder of the
important role played by women in the early life and meetings of the Bedford
separatist church (*Church Book, passim*). 'Esther was had to the house of the
women to be purified, and so came to the king. God also hath appointed that
those who come into his royal presence should first go to the house of the
women, the church', *The Greatness of the Soul (Works)*, i. 145.

PAGE 49, l. 2. *Saw!*   This repetition of a key word just spoken by an inter-
locutor is a colloquial idiom for rendering emotional emphasis: it occurs very
frequently in Bunyan's conversations, e.g. *Badman*, pp. 48, 149.

PAGE 50, l. 35. *I have a Wife and four small Children*   At the time of his
imprisonment in 1661 Bunyan had 'four small children that cannot help
themselves' (*A Relation of My Imprisonment*, p. 129). These were born before
1658 to his first wife, who died in that year, and were looked after by his
second wife Elizabeth, who appealed to the magistrates on their behalf. The
whole of this conversation between Charity and Christian was added in the
second edition. Brown, pp. 20–21, 388–9.

PAGE 52, ll. 35–36. *He had stript himself of his glory that he might do this for
the Poor*   2 Cor. viii. 9, Phil. ii. 7.

PAGE 54, ll. 2–3. *had offered great affronts to his Person and proceedings*
Cf. *G.A.* § 158.

PAGE 54, l. 13. *Sword, Shield, Helmet, etc.* Eph. vi. 13–17, 1 Thess. v. 8: 'The sword of the Spirit, which is the word of God', 'the shield of faith', 'the helmet of the hope of salvation', 'the breastplate of righteousness', 'the feet shod with the preparation of the gospel of peace'; see also Deut. xxxiii. 25: 'Thy shoes shall be iron and brass.'

ll. 20–29. *Moses Rod, etc.* Exod. iv. 2–4, 17; vii. 10, 17. *Jael*: Judges iv. 21. *Gideon*: Judges vii. 16–22. *Shamgar*: Judges iii. 31. *Samson*: Judges xv. 15. *David*: 1 Sam. xvii. 49, 50. *The Man of Sin*: 2 Thess. ii. 3–8.

PAGE 55, ll. 4–5. *beautified with Woods, Vinyards, Fruits of all sorts* An Old Testament landscape; cf. Canticles vii. 12.

PAGE 56, l. 8. *a loaf of Bread*, etc. 'Two hundred loaves of bread, and an hundred bunches of raisins, and an hundred of summer fruits, and a bottle of wine', 2 Sam. xvi. 1.

l. 13. *Apollyon* Ἀπολλύων, the Destroyer. 'The angel of the bottomless pit, whose name in the Hebrew tongue is Abaddon, but in the Greek tongue hath his name Apollyon', Rev. ix. 11. 'Tho swor Ynor to King Ermin, Be Mahoun and be Apolyn' (*The Romance of Sir Beves of Hamtoun*, edited by William Turnbull (Maitland Club, 1838), 3815–16). 'Sin is the Apollyon, the destroyer', Jeremy Taylor, *Holy Dying* (1651), p. 25.

ll. 24–28. 'His feet were as the feet of a bear, and his mouth as the mouth of a lion', Rev. xiii. 2. 'His scales are his pride, shut up together as with a close seal', Job xli. 15 (of Leviathan, a type of Satan).

PAGE 58, l. 24. *Thou didst faint at first setting out . . .* The paragraph indicates the extent to which Apollyon represents spiritual evil and recalls the temptation to despair in *G.A.*

PAGE 59, ll. 7–8. *the Kings High-way* Num. xxi. 17. 'I go the king's highway, and that in which many have been saved', Jeremy Taylor, *The Whole Works* (1847–54), ix. 656.

l. 10. *strodled* This provincial and now archaic form of the frequentative was altered to 'stradled' in the editions subsequent to the first.

l. 14–PAGE 60, l. 18. The fight with Apollyon resembles the combats with giants or dragons in chivalric romance and offers several parallels with the popular chap-book romances which Bunyan admits having read in his unregenerate youth (*A Few Sighs from Hell, or the Groans of a Damned Soul, Works*, iii. 711). Apollyon is winged, covered with scales and breathing fire, like the Egyptian dragon with which St. George fights in Richard Johnson's *Seven Champions of Christendom* (1597). St. George when wounded is healed by the leaves of a miraculous tree, just as Christian is restored by leaves from the tree of life. When the sun rises Christian sees the valley strewn with the bones, ashes, and mangled bodies of former pilgrims: St. George likewise, after rescuing the princess, comes to a valley containing the whitened bones of dead knights. The Valley of the Shadow of Death resembles the Enchanted Vale in the story of St. George, or the Vale of Waking Spirits in that of St. Andrew. The length of the fight ('Above half a day') is another popular feature; Spenser's Red-Cross Knight fights for two days with the dragon (*Faerie Queene*, 1. xi), but this parallel may be explained by a common reliance on romance tradition on the part of Spenser and Bunyan (*The Seven Champions of Christendom*, i, chap. 7, etc.) (Harold Golder, 'Bunyan's Valley of the Shadow', *M.P.* (1929), xxvii. 55–72; 'Bunyan and Spenser', *P.M.L.A.* (1930), xlv. 216 ff.). But this romantic treatment cannot disguise the Pauline theme of spiritual conflict or obscure the intimate relation of the episode to Bunyan's own experience of temptation (*G.A.* §§ 132–74; the dialogue of Satan with the sinner disputing his allegiance is paralleled in *The Jerusalem Sinner Saved (Works)*, i. 79–80).

PAGE 59, l. 14. *a flaming Dart* 'The devil is that great and dogged leviathan, that "spreadeth sharp pointed things upon the mire". Job xl. 30. For be the spreading nature of our corruptions never so broad, he will find sharp pointed things enough to stick in the mire of them for our affliction; they are called *fiery darts*, and he has abundance of them with which he can and will sorely prick and wound our spirits', *The Saints' Knowledge of Christ's Love (Works)*, ii. 65. Benjamin Keach, a member of Bunyan's own sect, in his *The Glorious Lover* describes the temptation in the wilderness as a combat between a knight and a dragon; some of his feeble lines provide a close analogy with the detail of Christian's fight:

> He flung at him a very cruel Dart,
> And aym'd to hit him just upon the Heart . . .
> But the blest Lord did use his Sword so well
> That down the others weapons straight way fell.

Glorious Lover (ed. 1679; 1st ed., 1672), p. 32.

PAGE 60, ll. 31–32. *some of the leaves of the Tree of Life* Cf. *Faerie Queene*, i. xi. 46–48.

PAGE 61, l. 5. *affront from Apollyon* affront, hostile encounter. 'The proud Duessa, full of wrathfull spight And fiers disdaine, to be affronted so', *Faerie Queene*, i. viii. 13, after her Beast has been encountered by the Squire sword in hand.

ll. 19–20. *Children of them that brought up an evil report of the good Land* Num. xiii. 32: 'And they brought up an evil report of the land which they had searched unto the children of Israel, saying, The land, through which we have gone to search it, is a land that eateth up the inhabitants thereof; and all the people that we saw in it are men of a great stature.'

l. 26. *Matter!* Cf. note on p. 49, l. 2.

PAGE 62, ll. 1–2 *as dark as pitch* Physical darkness is used as an image of spiritual despair by Richard Sibbes, *Divine Meditations (Works*, Edinburgh, 1862), i. 212.

ll. 2–3. *Hobgoblins, Satyrs, and Dragons of the Pit* Isa. xiii. 21: 'Owls shall dwell there and satyrs shall dance there'; xxxiv. 14: '. . . the satyr shall cry to his fellow. . . .'

l. 17. *on the right hand a very deep Ditch* The ditch on the right hand is error in belief, that on the left surrender to outward sin (exemplified in David's surrender to concupiscence). Stebbing suggests antinomian disregard for the moral law, and on the other hand self-righteous reliance on works (*Works*, ed. Stebbing, i. 96).

l. 29. *to tip over into the mire* *The Journeys of Celia Fiennes*, edited by Christopher Morris (1947), p. 332: '... Bedfordshire which I entered at Astick ... but this was base way narrow and the lanes rooty and long'; p. 339: 'Thence to Hitching (Hitchin) most in lanes and deep land.'

PAGE 63, ll. 34–35. *whisperingly suggested many grievous blasphemies to him* '... whole floods of blasphemies, both against God, Christ and the Scriptures, was poured upon my spirit, to my great confusion and astonishment', *G.A.* § 97. 'Sometimes it would run in my thoughts, not so little as an hundred times together; *Sell him, sell him, sell him*', *G.A.* § 137. 'How many strange, hideous and amazing blasphemies have some, that are coming to Christ, had injected upon their souls against him', *Christ a Complete Saviour* (*Works*), i. 209. 'He brought me up also out of a horrible pit; a pit of noise of devils, and of my heart answering them with distrust and fear', *Saints' Knowledge of Christ's Love* (*Works*), ii. 7. And cf. *Jerusalem Sinner Saved* (*Works*), i. 80; *Come and Welcome to Jesus Christ* (*Works*), i. 250.

PAGE 64, ll. 8–9. *I will fear none ill*

> Yet though I walke in vaile of death
> Yet will I fear none ill.

Ps. xxiii in the metrical version of Sternhold and Hopkins.

l. 21. In the second, third, fourth, and seventh editions the scripture reference 'Amos 5. 8' occurs twice, immediately before and immediately after the marginal note 'Christian *glad at break of day*'. This repetition is due to the misplacing of the reference in the first edition. The other editions of the first group, instead of shifting it to its proper position five lines below, merely repeat it at that point.

PAGE 65, l. 9. *Snares, Traps, Gins* 'The wicked spirits have made and laid for us snares, pits, holes and what not, if peradventure by something we may be destroyed', *Saints' Knowledge of Christ's Love* (*Works*), ii. 8.

l. 25. *without much danger* This reference to the weakness of Roman Catholic power could hardly have been made after the Declaration of Indulgence of 1672 and probably not after the Treaty of Dover of 1670 and the ascendancy of the Cabal.

PAGE 66, ll. 22–23. *the Avenger of Blood* 'Whoso killeth his neighbour ignorantly, whom he hated not in time past ... he shall flee unto one of those cities, and live: lest the avenger of the blood pursue the slayer ...', Deut. xix. 4–6. Cf. *G.A.* § 211.

l. 25. *over-run him* outrun him.

PAGE 68, ll. 6–7. *he leered away* 'The tempter did leer and steal away from me', *G.A.* § 145. To look with downcast eye: hence, to steal away as if ashamed.

PAGE 69, l. 19. *Adam the first* 'The old man which is corrupt according to the lusts of deceit', Eph. iv. 22. The old man as an allegory of the carnal nature unrenewed by grace figures in many emblematic title-pages of Puritan books, e.g. John Downame, *The Christian Warfare* (1604).

PAGE 70, l. 8. *a slave* 'Whosoever committeth sin is the slave of sin', John viii. 34.

ll. 14–15. *a deadly twitch back* 'the flesh lusting against the Spirit, and the Spirit against the flesh', Gal. v. 17.

PAGE 71, l. 5. *Moses* The old man, symbol of subjection to sin and the old law, is identified with Moses who proclaimed the law.

l. 5 marg. The variant readings indicate the relationship of the editions. The first, second, and seventh have '*The temper of Moses*' the third misprints '*thmper*', and this gives rise to the correction '*The thunder of Moses*' in the fourth and fifth, which becomes '*The Thunder of Moses*' in the sixth, eighth, and subsequent editions.

ll. 15–17. *I think they were asleep . . . I passed by the Porter* The sleep of the lions betokens a lull in persecution. The fact that Faithful does not stay at the House Beautiful is a further proof that church-fellowship is not considered necessary to salvation.

PAGE 72, l. 22. *that hectoring liberty* 'But when huffing and hectoring must be looked upon as the only badges of gallantry and courage, what can recommend the exercise of patience against the disgrace of it?' South, *Sermons* (1744), x. 4.

ll. 28–32. The first edition reads as follows: 'He moreover objected the base and low estate and condition of those that were chiefly the Pilgrims of the times; in which they lived, also their ignorance, and want of understanding in all natural Science.' The apparently incorrect position of the semi-colon could be explained if the phrase 'also their ignorance', occurring at the end of a line in the manuscript copy, had been transposed by the printer, the original being 'also their ignorance of the times in which they lived'; the semi-colon was then moved from after 'Pilgrims' but without clearing up the confusion satisfactorily.

PAGE 74, l. 21. *bravadoes* boasts, brags, cf. ambuscado and similar seventeenth century formations with the Spanish masculine suffix.

l. 25. *valiant for Truth* Cf. the name of the character in the Second Part.

PAGE 77, l. 31. *notwithstanding his fine tongue, he is but a sorry fellow* 'The Pharisee at his approach hath his mouth full of something, yea of many fine things, whereby he strokes himself over the head, and in effect calls himself, and that in his presence, one of God's white boys', *The Pharisee and the Publican (Works)*, ii. 258. And cf. *G.A.* §§ 299–301: 'Just thus, I saw, it was and will be with them who have Gifts, but want saving-Grace', etc.

PAGE 78, ll. 21–23. The phrase has a proverbial ring though it is not recorded in Tilley.

l. 24. *bruit* In a number of early eighteenth-century editions this becomes 'Brewer'. Offor and Brown record that this error occurs in the twenty-second edition by J. Clarke (1728) which contains Sturt's engravings, but both the British Museum copies of this edition keep the reading 'bruit'.

ll. 29–30. *A Saint abroad and a Devil at home* Proverbial; Tilley, S 31.

l. 31. *so unreasonable with his Servants* 'Be not a lion in thy house, nor frantick among thy servants', Ecclus. iv. 30.

PAGE 80, l. 1. *talking is not sufficient* 'A prating tongue will not unlock the gates of heaven', *Strait Gate (Works)*, i. 388.

PAGE 80, l. 12. *that of Moses*, etc.   Bunyan's interpretation has patristic authority; and his special interest in this moralization of the Levitical rule is shown
by his devoting a section of *G.A.* to it, § 71. See Theodoret, *Quaestiones in
Leviticum*, Migne, *Patrologia Graeca*, lxxx. 313–17.

l. 25. *sounding Brass, and Tinckling Cymbals*   '. . . shall I be proud because
I am a sounding Brass? Is it so much to be *a Fiddle?*', *G.A.* § 301.

PAGE 81, l. 35. *You lie at the catch*   i.e. lie in wait to catch out in conversation. 'This is doing things, with an high hand, against the Lord our God,
and a taking him, as it were, at the catch. This is, as we say among men, to
seek to put a trick upon God . . .', *The Jerusalem Sinner Saved* (*Works*), i. 93.

PAGE 83, l. 1 marg.   The misprint 'from. 7. 24' for 'Rom. 7. 24' is found in
the Lenox copy of the tenth edition but not in the British Museum copy.
Its reappearance in the eleventh suggests that the compositor was working
from a copy of the tenth with sig. G in uncorrected state.

l. 4. *sight and sense of things*   Cf. *Saved by Grace*, i. 351; *infra*, p. 151,
l. 33. Bunyan uses 'sight of' for knowledge or consciousness where 'sight in'
would be more usual in the seventeenth century: cf. *O.E.D.* s.v. 12. b.

ll. 22–23. *heart-holiness, family-holiness . . . Conversation-holiness*   Similar
compound nouns are frequent in Puritan usage and are found in other
works by Bunyan: 'gospel-holiness', *A Defence of the Doctrine of Justification
by Faith* (*Works*), ii. 289, 291; 'soul-fellowship', *The Greatness of the Soul
and Unspeakableness of the Loss Thereof* (*Works*), i. 115; and cf. 'Heartwork',
p. 85, l. 27; also compound adjectives: 'heart-affecting, heart-sweetening, and
heart-changing glory', *Come and Welcome* (*Works*), i. 260; 'a soul-humbling,
a Christ-advancing, and a creature-emptying consideration', *Israel's Hope
Encouraged* (*Works*), i. 617. For parents' duties to children see *Christian
Behaviour* (*Works*), ii. 558–9. 'All holy conversation', 1 Peter iii. 11.

PAGE 84, l. 19. *ought else but notion*   'loose ranters, and light notionists',
Some Gospel Truths Opened (*Works*), ii. 133.

l. 34. *some peevish, or melancholly man*   'Peevish', moody or capricious.
'A peevish fellow is one who has . . . a natural incapacity for delight, and therefore disturbs all who are happier than himself', *Spectator*, No. 438.

PAGE 85, l. 19. *stumble the World*:   confuse, nonplus; *O.E.D.* s.v. 4. b.

l. 34–PAGE 88, l. 2.   The encounter with Evangelist in which he exhorts
Christian and Faithful to prepare to withstand the trials of Vanity Fair was
added in the second edition.

PAGE 86, ll. 7–8. *peace be to your helpers*   Adapted from the words of Amasai
to David, 1 Chron. xii. 18.

l. 32. *run that you may obtain it*   The text of *The Heavenly Footman*, iii.
381: 'there may be many that do run, yea, and run far too, who yet miss of
the crown that standeth at the end of the race.'

ll. 36–37. *gun-shot of the Devil*   Cf. p. 25, ll. 23–32.

PAGE 87, ll. 5–6. *set your faces like a flint*   Isa. i. 7. 'He . . . sets his face
like a flint to plead for me with God', *Work of Jesus Christ as an Advocate*,
i. 180. Tilley, F 18.

PAGE 88, l. 6. *Vanity-Fair* Bunyan probably draws on his experience of the great annual fair at Stourbridge near Cambridge; it had its own 'Court of Piepowder' (sc. *Pieds Pouldreux*, dusty feet) presided over by the mayor or his deputy. This was first suggested by Isaac James in his poetic version of the allegory (1815): 'The shops or booths are built in rows like streets, having each its name; as Garlick Row, Booksellers' Row, Cook Row, &c. Here are all sorts of traders, who sell by wholesale or retail; as goldsmiths' toymen, braziers, turners, milliners, haberdashers, hatters, mercers, drapers, pewterers, china warehouses, and, in a word, most trades that can be found in London. Here are also taverns, coffee-houses, and eating-houses, in great plenty. The chief diversions are puppets, rope-dancing, and music booths. To this Fair, people from Bedfordshire and the adjoining counties still resort. . . . These mercantile fairs were very injurious to morals; but not to the extent of debauchery and villany, which reign in our present annual fairs, near the metropolis and large cities.' 'Here is a court of justice always open from morning till night, where the mayor of Cambridge, or his deputy, sits as judge' (Nichols, *Bibliographia Topographica Britannica* (1790), v. 82).

l. 16. *Legion* Bunyan has in mind Mark v. 9 and must suppose the name to be one of the Scriptural appellations of the Devil.

PAGE 90, l. 3. *Outlandish-men*: foreigners. Neh. xii. 26.

ll. 6–7. *the Language of Canaan* See Isa. xix. 18.

l. 9. *Barbarians each to the other* 'If I know not the meaning of the voice, I shall be unto him that speaketh a barbarian, and he that speaketh shall be a barbarian unto me', 1 Cor. xiv. 11.

ll. 14–15. The story is recorded of 'Holy Hunt' of Hitchin, an acquaintance of Bunyan and like him a preaching mechanic, that when he passed the market-place where mountebanks were performing, one of them called out, 'Look there, Mr. Hunt.' Turning his head away he replied: 'Turn away my eyes from beholding vanity.'

PAGE 91, l. 4 marg. In all the editions previous to the eleventh the marginal note reads '*They are not believed*'. The eleventh has confused this with the next note: '*They are put in the Cage*' and produced as a result '*They are not in the Cage*'.

l. 21. *let fly at them* Cf. Ps. lxiv. 3, 'Who shoot out their arrows, even bitter words'.

ll. 22–23. *they seemed confederates, and should be made partakers of their misfortunes* In 1670 the town bailiffs of Bedford refused to assist in distraining the goods of Nonconformists and two of them were committed to jail by the justices. *A true and Impartiall Narrative of Some Illegal and Arbitrary Proceedings . . . in and near the Town of Bedford* (1670), p. 5.

PAGE 92, l. 32. *Lord Hategood* The character of the judge may be based on that of Sir John Kelynge, before whom Bunyan appeared at Quarter Sessions after his arrest, or on that of the judges who reviewed his case later at the Assize; but some touches of Hategood's speeches recall the reported style of Jeffreys in his harsh handling of Dissenters.

l. 32. *Their Indictment* i.e. there was some variation in the wording of the indictments of Christian and Faithful. The precise form of the indictment was of great importance in the seventeenth century because of the possibility of loop-holes for offenders. Sir Matthew Hale declared that 'More offenders escape by the over-easy ear given to indictments than by any other means', Holdsworth, *History of English Law*, iii (1923), 614–31.

PAGE 93, l. 16. *Pickthank*   A flatterer: 'smiling pickthanks and base news-mongers', *1 Henry IV*, III. ii. 25.

PAGE 95, l. 9. *Sirrah, Sirrah,*   The reiterated word or phrase seems to have been a particular trait of Jeffreys: 'Come you, what do you say for your-self, you old knave! come, speak up: what doth he say?', *Baxter MSS. in Dr. Williams's Library, Letters* iii. 208–11.

PAGE 97, ll. 11–12. *To be had from the place where he was*   This and the im-mediately subsequent torments of Faithful show how Bunyan has conflated the formulae and procedure of an English criminal trial with the accounts of martyrdoms he had read in Foxe: cf. especially that of Pomponius Algerius, *Acts and Monuments* (1632), ii. 180–3.

l. 22. *a Chariot and a couple of Horses*   Borrowed from the ascension of Elijah, 2 Kings ii. 11.

PAGE 98, l. 18. *By-ends*   'By-end', an object lying aside from the main one. 'Are there not many by-ends in duties?', Flavel, *Touchstone of Sincerity* (1679), p. 36; '. . . when a man doth a thing simply for the sake of him [God] or of the law that commands it, without respect to this by-end, or that desire of praise or vain-glory from others', *Fear of God*, i. 464. By-ends' character exposes shiftiness and hypocrisy rather than doctrinal error; but there are indications that Bunyan had the Established Church in mind: the case of conscience proposed by his friend Mony-love concerns 'a greater benefice', and he has family connexions with local aristocrats and with the parson of the parish. As with Worldly Wiseman and Ignorance there is some reminiscence of the controversy with Fowler (Tindall, pp. 60–64).

PAGE 99, ll. 1–12.   The kindred of By-ends were added in the second edition.

ll. 10–11. *a Water-man, looking one way, and rowing another*   A proverb frequently quoted in moral contexts, e.g. Samuel Adams, *A Spiritual Salve* (1630), p. 646: Tilley, W 143.

ll. 21–22. *we never strive against Wind and Tide*   'The wind sets always on my face; and the foaming rage of the sea of this world, and the proud and lofty waves thereof do continually beat upon the sides of the bark, or ship, that myself, my cause, and followers are in', *The Greatness of the Soul*, i. 107.

> Fear not, therefore, in her for to abide,
> She keeps her ground, come weather, wind, or tide.

A Discourse of the Building, Nature, Excellency, and Government of the House of God, ii. 579.

l. 24. *if the Sun shines*   'Where the sun shines there resort', Tilley, S 991.

PAGE 100, l. 35–PAGE 106, l. 20.   The discourse between By-ends and his three friends was added in the third edition and is the sole lengthy addition to appear later than the second.

PAGE 101, l. 4. *Mr. Save-all* symbolizes the Arminian belief in a universal salvation.

PAGE 102, l. 15. *to make hay when the Sun shines* John Ray, *A Collection of English Proverbs* (1670), p. 101; Tilley, H 235.

The whole passage, like others in the By-ends episode, recalls the account in *The Strait Gate* of 'the temporizing latitudinarian': 'He is a man that hath no God but his belly, nor any religion but that by which his belly is worshipped. His religion is always, like the times, turning this way and that, like the cock on the steeple; neither hath he any conscience but a benumbed and seared one, and is next door to a downright atheist', i. 389.

l. 26. *Job saies* Job xxii. 24, but the words are those of Eliphaz the Temanite.

PAGE 103, l. 5. *a Minister, or a Tradesman,* The argument to justify a prudent self-interest anticipates some of the stratagems of Mr. Badman, e.g. 'If he dealt with honest men (as with some honest men he did) then he would be as they; talk as they, seem to be sober as they, talk of Justice and Religion as they, and against Debauchery as they; yea, and would too seem to shew a dislike of them that said, did, or were otherwise than honest', *Badman*, p. 89.

l. 33. *disserting* The spelling 'dissertion' for 'desertion' is found in *G.A.* § 89 in the first edition, so there is evidence that Bunyan employed this form; 'altering of some of his principles' has just been spoken of, and the 'dissenting' of the third edition would make poor sense, while Bunyan does not seem elsewhere to use 'dissent' transitively.

PAGE 104, l. 11. *get a rich wife* As does Badman, *Badman*, pp. 70–74.

PAGE 105, l. 13. *religion a stalking horse* 'A fellow that makes religion his stalking-horse', Marston, *Malcontent*, iv. i. 226; Tilley, R 63.

l. 16. *Hamor and Shechem* Gen. xxxiv. The story is mentioned in the same passage in *Badman* dealing with his hypocritical wooing of a rich and pious girl: '*Hamor* and *Shechem*, and all the men of their City, for attempting to make God and Religion the stalking-Horse to get *Jacobs* daughters to wife, were together slain with the edge of the sword', p. 74.

ll. 31–32. *Judas . . . was religious for the bag* John vi. 70, 71. 'Judas's religion lay much in the bag, but his soul is now burning in hell', *Strait Gate*, i. 388.

l. 35. *Simon the witch* Simon Magus, Acts viii. 19. This masculine use was common and Bunyan would have met it in Foxe, *Acts and Monuments*, 'He is a witch asking counsel at soothsayers.' Though the reading remains unaltered in all the editions from the first to the eleventh, it appears as 'Simon the Wizard' in many of the modern ones.

PAGE 106, l. 37. *I will shew you a thing* From 1 Sam. xiv. 12.

PAGE 107, ll. 1–2. *as to turn us out of the way?* 'Woe unto them who wander from the way', *A Discourse of the Building of the House of God*, ii. 582.

l. 6. *Let us go see* '. . . temptations are gilded with sweet and fine pretences, that men shall be wiser, richer . . . and by such like things the fools are easily allured', *Exposition on the First Ten Chapters of Genesis*, ii. 431.

PAGE 107, l. 27. *by one of his Majesties Judges* The apostle Paul: 'Demas hath forsaken me, having loved this present world', 2 Tim. iv. 10.

PAGE 108, l. 21–PAGE 110, l. 25. The episode of Lot's wife was first introduced in the second edition. 'I have sometimes wondered at Lot in this particular; his wife looked behind her, and died immediately, but let what would become of her, Lot would not so much as look behind him to see her ... there was the mountain before him, and the fire and brimstone behind him; his life lay at stake, and he had lost it if he had but looked behind him. Do thou so run', *Heavenly Footman*, iii. 394.

PAGE 109, l. 2. *the Pillar of Salt* There was a popular superstition that the pillar of salt into which Lot's wife was transformed was still to be seen. Mandeville locates it 'at the right side of the Dead Sea' (*Travels*, chap. ix). Bunyan refers to this in *The Barren Fig-tree*, iii. 583: 'I have had a fancy, that Lot's wife, when she was turned into a pillar of salt, stood yet looking over her shoulder or else with her face towards Sodom; as the judgement caught her, so it bound her, and left her a monument of God's anger to after generations.'

PAGE 110, ll. 26–27. *a pleasant River* Their walk through the meadows by the river signifies a period of assurance of God's love and electing grace. As in the case of Bunyan's vision of his salvation in *G.A.* ('evidence of my Salvation from Heaven, with many golden Seals thereon') it immediately precedes a severe onset of spiritual despair, represented here by imprisonment in Doubting Castle.

PAGE 111, l. 3. *beautified with Lillies* Cf. 'beautified with Woods', p. 55, l. 4, and the same phrase as here used of the Valley of Humiliation in the Second Part, p. 237, l. 28, where the second and subsequent editions read 'beautiful'.

l. 29. *By-Path-Meadow* 'Get into the way . . . Beware of by-paths', *Heavenly Footman*, iii. 389.

PAGE 112, ll. 2–3. *When they were gone over . . .* The most plausible gloss on the whole episode would seem to be this: Christian persuades Hopeful to abandon a strict adherence to their vocation because of the temporal afflictions it brings upon them; he is attracted by some worldly advantages and comforts, and the pleasure he enjoys from these leads him to pursue them further (Vain-confidence); when remorse comes (the storm of thunder and rain) they both believe, quite wrongly, that they have committed the unpardonable sin and thus easily fall victims to Giant Despair, forgetting for a time the promises of election that have been made to them. The vain confidence, and the by-path, may to some extent also stand for spiritual pride, since the fate of Vain-confidence is similar to that of its victims as described elsewhere in Bunyan: e.g. 'If thou be prying over much into God's secret decrees, or let thy heart too much entertain questions about some nice foolish curiosities, thou mayest stumble and fall as many hundreds in England have done, both in Ranting and Quakery, to their own eternal overthrow', *Heavenly Footman*, iii. 385.

l. 31. *you are older then I* 'The strongest may sometimes be out of the way', marginal note in *A Confession of My Faith, and A Reason of My Practice in Worship*, ii. 610.

PAGE 113, l. 24. *Doubting-Castle* i.e. doubts as to whether they have been predestined for salvation, not a sceptical attitude to the dogmas of religion. The parallel in *G.A.* is when Bunyan fears that he has surrendered to the tempting voice bidding him 'Sell him, sell him' (Christ), §§ 140–1.

ll. 24–25. *Giant Despair* Though the treatment smacks of folk-tale and popular romance (see Harold Golder, 'Bunyan's Giant Despair', *J.E.G.P.* (1931), xxx. 361–78, who instances the dungeon episode in Emmanuel Ford's *Parismus* (12th ed., 1684, part 1, chaps. 20, 21)) the giant represents the delusion of guilt which plunged Bunyan and many other Puritans into the belief that they had committed the sin against the Holy Ghost, the sin unpardonable. There are numerous warnings against such delusions in seventeenth-century handbooks of pastoral theology, as well as examples of them in autobiographies. Thomas Collier, the chief contemporary theologian of the Particular Baptists, provides an example of the former:

> In this matter, to depart from the Faith, and to reject Christ crucified, and Salvation by him, is the unpardonable sin. . . .
> Many gracious souls trouble themselves about this sin, fearing themselves to be guilty thereof, through their ignorance of the sin what it is: all sin (it's true) is against the Holy Spirit, but the unpardonable sin, or sin unto death, consists especially in . . . a wilful departing from the Faith. . . . 2. A wilful and malicious opposing of the spirits workings. . . . *The Body of Divinity* (1674), pp. 210–11.

See also Baxter, *A Christian Directory: or, A Sum of Practical Theologie, and Cases of Conscience* (1673), p. 356: 'Directions against sinful Despair.' Among many illustrations in the collections of experience, as well as Bunyan's own, see *Spirituall Experience of sundry Beleevers* (1653), p. 145. In the minor works *Light for Them that Sit in Darkness* (1674) and *Saved by Grace* (1675) are particularly full of references to spiritual despair (*Works*, i. 352, 358, 435).

PAGE 114, l. 11–PAGE 117, l. 36. This expansion of the Doubting Castle episode to include the counsels of Mrs. Diffidence and the Giant's treatment of his prisoners was added in the second edition.

l. 22. *rateing* The seventh edition follows the third in reading 'beating', though this is what the Giant is said to do in the next sentence.

PAGE 115, ll. 4–5. *either with Knife, Halter or Poison* 'And albeit, saith Satan, thou prayest sometimes, yet is not thy heart possessed with a belief that God will not regard thee? yes, says the sinner. Why then despair and go hang thyself, saith the devil', *The Saints' Knowledge of Christ's Love*, ii. 37. Also for the common homiletic background, Spenser, *Faerie Queene*, book 1, canto ix, stanzas 36, 41, 50.

l. 9. *one of his fits* 'It [despair] hath its fittes after the manner of an ague', William Perkins, *Workes* (1612), i. 418, and see Harold Golder, *J.E.G.P.* xxx. 367.

ll. 20–21. *Shall we be ruled by the Giant?* Cf. *Christ a Complete Saviour*, i. 209.

l. 29. *to kill body and soul at once* 'murder, I say, and that of a high nature, even to have killed his own body and soul at once', *Justification by an Imputed Righteousness, or No Way to Heaven but by Jesus Christ*, i. 315.

PAGE 116, ll. 23–24. *Christian fell into a Swound*   For the pathological results of despair see *G.A.* §§ 163–5 and *The Jerusalem Sinner Saved*, i. 91–92; an account of the state by a later evangelical may be found in Cowper's *Hope*:

> Alas! how chang'd! Expressive of his mind
> His eyes are sunk, arms folded, head reclin'd;
> Those awful syllables, hell, death, and sin,
> Though whisper'd, plainly tell what works within.

Hope, 688–91, *Poetical Works* edited by William Benham (1924), p. 125.

PAGE 117, l. 24. *to your Den again*   For the use of *den* for prison see p. 1 and also the account of the captains of the army of Doubters in *The Holy War*: 'The third Captain was Captain *Damnation*, he was Captain over the *Grace-doubters*, his were the Red Colours, Mr. *No-life* bare them, and he had for his Scutcheon the Black-den', *H.W.*, p. 367.

PAGE 118, ll. 6–7. *a Key in my bosom, called Promise*   'The Scriptures also were wonderful things unto me; I saw that the truth and verity of them, were the Keys of the Kingdom of Heaven. . . . By this temptation I was made to see more into the Nature of the Promises than ever I was before . . . I was greatly holden off my former foolish practice, of putting by the word of promise when it came into my mind', *G.A.* §§ 246–9. The conclusion is that Bunyan and Christian were mistaken in believing they had abandoned Christ: they erred in not understanding how the promises of the covenant precluded any possibility of their repentance being rejected. See *R.E.S.* xxiv (1948), 105–6, 118–20; and for the key metaphor Mat. xvi. 19; Thomas Goodwin, *A Childe of Light Walking in Darkness* (1650), pp. 99, 124; William Perkins, *A Dialogue of the State of a Christian*, Works (Cambridge, 1612).

l. 13. *Christian and Hopeful both came out*   'Now did my Chains fall off my Legs indeed; I was loosed from my Affliction and Irons; my Temptation also fled away . . .', *G.A.* § 231.

l. 14. *he went to the outward door*   Much of the description of the escape is borrowed from the story of St. Peter's deliverance, Acts xii. 10.

l. 17. *damnable hard*   It seems better to take this as grim theological punning than simply as an unconscious lapse from the language of edification. See *R.E.S.* article cited above and Sir Charles Firth, *Essays Historical and Literary* (Oxford, 1938), p. 151.

PAGE 119, ll. 7–8. *the delectable Mountains*   Among the attempts to find a realistic topography for the pilgrimage, Leith Hill in Surrey has been implausibly suggested for this episode (Brown, pp. 269–70).

l. 21. *Immanuels Land*   The name of God used throughout *H.W.* and one associated among sectarian Puritans with millenarian hopes (e.g. John Canne, *Emanuel, or God with Us*, 1650, and cf. Tindall, p. 268); but what is indicated here is a period of peace and assurance, perhaps associated with the experience of a gathered church, and preceding a happy death, not the reign of the saints on earth.

PAGE 120, l. 15. *acquaint with us*   The active use of 'acquaint' in this sense was current into the eighteenth century; the second and subsequent editions have altered to 'be acquainted'.

l. 16. *the good* Cf. 1 Chron. xxix. 3: 'of mine own proper good'.

PAGE 121, ll. 10–11. *walking up and down among the Tombs* 'The man that wandereth out of the way of understanding shall remain in the congregation of the dead', Prov. xxi. 16. 'O the unthought of imaginations, frights, fears and terrors, that are affected by a thorough application of guilt, leading to desperation. *This is the man that hath his dwelling among the tombs, with the dead; that is always crying out, and cutting himself with stones*', *G.A.* § 187.

PAGE 122, l. 4. *lumbring* The word is applied to a noise in the first edition of the Second Part also, p. 192, l. 3. It seems likely that Bunyan thought it meant 'rumbling', less likely that a compositor transposed letters on two such similar occasions.

l. 11. *Alexander* The coppersmith who 'greatly withstood' St. Paul's words, 2 Tim. iv. 14, 15.

l. 31. *through our Perspective Glass*

> Such mountains round about this house do stand
> As one from thence may see the Holy Land.

House of God, ii. 579.

PAGE 123, ll. 13–14. *So I awoke from my Dream* This break in the dream does not correspond to any change in the character of the pilgrimage, and it is probable that it signifies Bunyan's release from prison, so that the final third of the First Part was written after he was at liberty. For the reasons why it seems more likely that this was after the twelve years' imprisonment terminated in 1672, and not after the second imprisonment conjecturally assigned to 1676–7, see Introduction, pp. xxix–xxxv (also Brown, 247–8; Talon, 317–18).

l. 21. *a very brisk Lad* An anticipation of the swaggering Mr. Brisk of the Second Part who courts Mercy (p. 226). 'A Brisk man—Pert—Knows nothing of himself . . . he has nothing in him that is properly his own but confidence', Samuel Butler, *Characters and Passages from Notebooks* (Cambridge, 1908), p. 201.

l. 22. *his name was Ignorance* 'There is also the wilfully ignorant professor, or him that is afraid to know more, for fear of the cross. He is for picking and choosing of truth, and loveth not to hasard his all for that worthy name by which he would be called. When he is at any time overset by arguments, or awakenings of conscience, he uses to heal all by—I was not brought up in this faith . . .', *Strait Gate*, i. 389; cf. also *The Pharisee and the Publican*, ii. 224. The sin of false security was a grave one in Puritan eyes: among many references in homilies and sermons this description of the hypocrite comes very close to Ignorance: '[he] likes Heauen well, but not the way to it . . . I thanke God, he might say, I am no Recusant, I come to Church, I heare good Sermons, and if any could tell me a better way to heauen, I would surely take it' (Thomas Taylor, *The Parable of the Sower and the Seed*, 1621, p. 172). He also bears some resemblance to Dent's Antilegon in *The Plain Mans Path-Way*; there is not enough specific suggestion of Quakerism and the Inner Light to bear out J. W. Draper's theory that this is what he stands for (*M.L.R.* xxii, 1927); see Maurice Hussey, 'Bunyan's Mr. Ignorance', *M.L.R.* xliv (1949), 483–9.

l. 34. *I Pray, Fast . . .* A deliberate echo of the Pharisee in the temple.

PAGE 125, ll. 35–36. *as white as a clout* Cf. *Hamlet*, ii. i. 81: 'Pale as his shirt, his knees knocking each other', Tilley, C 446.

PAGE 126, l. 15. *to scrabble on his way* This provincial frequentative form is found also in the description of Bunyan's own fears when a prisoner expecting death in *G.A.*, where there is a clear parallel to Little-Faith's experience: 'If I should make a scrabbling shift to clamber up the ladder, yet I should either with quaking, or other symptoms of faintings, give occasion to the enemy to reproach the way of God and his people' (§ 335). The word also occurs in the sense of 'scramble' in *G.A.* § 199, *Some Gospel Truths Opened*, ii. 203, *Law and Grace*, i. 546. The instance in A.V. 1 Sam. xxi. 13 has the sense 'scrawl', and Bunyan uses the word like this in *The Acceptable Sacrifice*, i. 707.

l. 17. *his Jewels* His saving faith; the money taken from him represents his assurances of faith. Works as the gift of Christ to the faithful are described as jewels in *Christ a Complete Saviour*, i. 215. Cf. 'O, I saw my Gold was in my Trunk at home! in Christ, my Lord and Saviour!', *G.A.* § 233.

PAGE 127, ll. 29–30. . . . *upon whose head is the Shell to this very day* Proverbial: to speak with arrogant self-assurance: 'This lap-wing runs away with the shell on his head', *Hamlet*, v. ii. 190. Tilley, L 69.

l. 30 marg. *snibbeth* rebukes, snubs.

PAGE 128, l. 10. *Caytiff* wretch (expressing pity as well as contempt).

ll. 12–13. *Esau's Birth-right was Typical*: symbolic, especially in the sense where an Old Testament episode is held to prefigure an occurrence in the New, or an article of Christian belief.

ll. 37–38. *Turtle-dove . . . Crow* The phrase suggests an unrecorded traditional proverb.

PAGE 129, l. 9. *untrodden paths* The first edition's 'troden' is corrected in the errata which appear in some copies; 'trodden', however, is preserved in the second edition, and is not corrected until the third.

l. 17. *one brush*: a short but smart encounter.

ll. 20–21. *As for a great heart* Bunyan can here be seen moving towards the conception of a character the very opposite of Little-faith, an assured and valiant leader of souls; as so often, the germ of the idea is in a word or phrase, which in this case leads to the Greatheart of the Second Part.

ll. 27–28. *Journey-men Thieves*: thieves serving under a master-thief.

l. 34. *in came their Master* Christian refers to his fight with Apollyon: but that fight is not preceded by an encounter with an embodied Faintheart, Mistrust, and Guilt; at the risk of reporting his own narrative wrongly Bunyan is pointing out that these qualities provided the psychological basis of Christian's proneness to attack.

PAGE 130, ll. 17–18. *one of the weak, and therefore he went to the walls* Proverbial: usually found with 'wall' in the singular, but the plural occurs in R.B., *Adagia Scotica, or a Collection of Scotch Proverbs and Proverbial Phrases* (1668), p. 51; Tilley, W 185.

l. 26. *throw up his heels* A metaphor from wrestling. 'Young Orlando that tripped the wrestler's heel', *As You Like It*, iii. ii. 207.

ll. 30–31. *he should say*: was reported to have said; 'should' serves as the auxiliary of the past tense in narrative or reported speech: 'when the priest Should ask . . .', *Taming of the Shrew*, iii. ii. 162.

l. 34. *Heman* The psalmist, grandson of the prophet Samuel, to whom Psalm lxxxviii is ascribed. This less familiar name is replaced in the third, fourth, fifth, and seventh editions, and in the ninth of 1683, by the more familiar one of Haman. Some later editors, suspicious at finding Haman transformed into a champion of the faith, have boldly cut the Gordian knot by substituting Mordecai. The change first occurs in an edition by D. Bunyan (1768) and among those who adopt it is Southey (1830).

PAGE 131, l. 4. *a sorry Girle* The maid to whom Peter denied Christ: Luke xxii. 56–57.

ll. 8–9. The first edition has no pointing after 'hold', thus making it a transitive verb with '*the Spear, the Dart, nor the Habergeon*' as objects. This is due to a misunderstanding (conceivably Bunyan's) of the Hebrew poetic parallelism which gives in the second half of the verse fresh subjects parallel to '*The Sword*'.

PAGE 132, l. 5. *Leviathan* looks back to the previous long quotation from Job xli (p. 131).

PAGE 133, ll. 1–2. *a man black of flesh* This incident of the Flatterer troubled the earlier commentators considerably and there is still no unanimity of interpretation. Joseph Ivimey held that the black man in light garments symbolized Antinomianism (see Offor's note in *Works*, iii. 150–1); William Mason in his edition (1780) says 'It is plain the author means self-righteousness'; among modern interpreters Professor Talon appears to follow Mason ('The Flatterer does not exist outside Christian himself; he is the presumption that lingers in his heart', Talon, p. 155), while Tindall considers that he stands for all false pastors (Tindall, p. 64). Working, as one must, from what is apparently the main scriptural suggestion for the passage, 'a false Apostle, that hath transformed himself into an angel of Light', where Bunyan is paraphrasing 2 Cor. xi. 13, 14, it seems that he is indeed, like the apostle, speaking of false ministers. But Paul, after mentioning false apostles, says that Satan himself is transformed into an angel of light, and in this episode the personification of the false pastor has become fused with the conception of the devil as a black man found in popular superstition and in the emblems. Rom. xvi. 18 referred to in the margin (p. 134, l. 14) supports this interpretation: 'mark them which cause divisions . . . and by good words and fair speeches deceive the hearts of the simple'. In the early seventies at the beginning of his pastorate Bunyan had much experience of false guides who attempted to divide the Bedford congregation and had to be combated and refuted; chief among these were Nehemiah Cox and John Child (*Church Book*, ff. 54, 55, 57, 58, 61, 71; Child challenged Bunyan to a disputation in 1676, and before committing suicide he confessed to Keach that he had needlessly provoked disputes). Cox's learning, exceptional among congregations of mechanics, enabled him to plead before the magistrates in Greek and Hebrew, so that one of them could declare, 'The cordwainer has wound you all up, gentlemen.' When Christian and Hopeful describe the flatterer as '*this fine-spoken man*' there may be an allusion to Cox's dangerous eloquence. See also Walter Wilson, *The History and Antiquities of Dissenting Churches and Meeting Houses in London, Westminster, and Southwark* (1808–1814), ii. 181–7; *Trans. Bapt. Hist. Soc.* i (1908–9), 248, ii (1910–11), 260; Benjamin Keach, *A Trumpet Blown in Zion* (1694), pp. 48–50.

PAGE 133, l. 12. *within the compass of a Net* The fowler's net is used as a symbol of the decoys of the devil in Emblem ii of *A Book for Boys and Girls*, iii. 749: 'Upon the Lark and the Fowler.'

PAGE 134, l. 18. *he chastized them* 'If his children forsake my law, and walk not in my judgments; If they break my statutes, and keep not my commandments; Then will I visit their transgression with the rod, and their iniquity with stripes', Ps. lxxxix. 30–32, quoted in *Law and Grace*, i. 553.

PAGE 135, l. 18 marg. *Jer. 22. 13*. This verse, given in all the editions one to eleven, is not relevant to the text; Offor suggested a slip for 'Jer. 22. 12', and the passage does seem to echo that and the preceding verse: 'He shall not return thither any more: but he shall die in the place whither they have led him captive, and shall see this land no more.'

PAGE 136, l. 4. *round you in the ears*: whisper; cf. *King John*, II. i. 566.

l. 29. *the Inchanted ground* represents a period of peace and toleration for the faithful when moral and spiritual effort might be relaxed; the verse in 1 Thessalonians quoted ('watch and be sober', &c.) is preceded by the passage: 'For when they shall say, Peace and safety; then sudden destruction cometh upon them.' The allusion would be to the time after the Declaration of Indulgence in 1672 when meeting-houses could legally be reopened.

PAGE 137, l. 3. *Where God began with us*. i.e. they are to discuss personal experiences of grace, as in the spiritual autobiographies and the testimonies of new converts before the gathered congregations. Hopeful's account closely follows the pattern of *G.A.* § 21. Bunyan's conversion was begun by seeing the poor women of the Bedford congregation 'sitting at a door in the Sun', *G.A.* § 37.

PAGE 138, l. 32. The Welsh Baptist Vavasor Powell describes how a severe toothache made him realize the greater agony of damnation, *The Life and Death of Mr. Vavasor Powell* (1671), p. 4.

PAGE 140, l. 21. *sin enough in one duty* 'For there is not a day, nor a duty; not a day that thou livest, nor a duty that thou dost, but will need that mercy should come after to take away thy iniquity', *The Saints' Privilege and Profit*, i. 679. Many of the later editions alter 'duty' to 'day'.

PAGE 143, l. 8. *My grace is sufficient for thee*. 'Wherefore, one day, as I was in a Meeting of God's People, full of sadness and terrour . . . these words did with great power suddainly break in upon me; *My Grace is sufficient for thee, my Grace is sufficient for thee, my Grace is sufficient for thee*, three times together', *G.A.* § 207. 'Also they know that they have an euerlasting righteousnes, which they wait for through hope, as a certain and sure possession laid up for them in heauen, euen when they feele the horrible terrours of sinne and death . . .', Luther, *Commentary on the Epistle to the Galatians* (Thomas Vautrollier, 1575), p. 233. In an earlier section of the autobiography Bunyan describes how he came across a tattered copy of the Elizabethan translation of Luther on Galatians, 'before all the Books that ever I have seen . . . most fit for a wounded Conscience', *G.A.* §§ 130–1.

l. 15. *the water stood in mine eyes* Cf. p. 121, l. 34, p. 200, l. 36.

PAGE 144, l. 4. *the coming sinner* 'Trouble not thyself, coming sinner', *Come and Welcome*, i. 286.

PAGE 145, l. 6. *The Soul of the Sluggard* Prov. xiii. 4.

l. 27. *Ask my fellow if I be a Thief* Proverbial; Tilley, F177, T121a.

PAGE 147, l. 32. *a* Fantastical *Faith* A faith seated merely in the fantasy or imagination.

PAGE 148, ll. 16 ff. Ignorance's argument bears some resemblance to those of Fowler contested by Bunyan in *A Defence of Justification*; see especially ii. 317, where the following statement of Fowler is examined: 'That such a reliance (as that of acting faith, first, on the merits of Christ for justification) is ordinarily to be found amongst unregenerate, and even the worst of men' (*Design of Christianity*, p. 223).

l. 35. *the fruit of distracted braines* The reasonable, somewhat complacently balanced tone of Fowler's work is again suggested.

PAGE 149, l. 35. *It pitties me much* Cf. 'it pitieth them to see her in the dust', Ps. cii. 14 (*Prayer Book*).

PAGE 150, l. 27. *lay fast hold of Christ* The phrase, like 'getting into', 'applying', 'coming', and others, belongs to the peculiar phraseology of conversion used by the Baptists and gathered churches. These expressions are ridiculed by South, *Sermons* (6th ed. 1727), iii. 165.

PAGE 151, l. 33. *sight of* See note on p. 83, l. 4.

PAGE 153, ll. 34 ff. *the manner thereof*, etc. This account of the gradual stages of backsliding is a reflection of pastoral experience. It recalls some of the troublesome church members whose cases are recorded in the *Church Book*: for instance, the 'ungodly' and 'dishonest' Richard Deane (f. 45), Edward Dent who was excommunicated for not paying his debts (f. 66), and John Wildman who wrote a 'vain and frothy letter' and spread slanders against Bunyan himself (f. 68).

PAGE 154, l. 27. *the Country of Beulah* 'Thou shalt be called Hephzi-bah (my delight is in her) and thy land Beulah (married)', Is. lxii. 4.

PAGE 155, ll. 15–16. *It was builded of Pearls*, etc. The description of the Holy City relies on the traditional sources, Is. liv. 11 and Rev. xxi. 10–27; Bunyan had already elaborated a full-scale allegorical interpretation of the city's materials in *The Holy City*, iii. 431–9, and was to mention them again in his poem *The Building of the House of God* (1688), ii. 578, 11, 'Of the beauty of the Church'.

Page 155, ll. 19, 22. *Christian, with desire fell sick* ... *If you see my Beloved, tell him that I am sick of love* Canticles v. 8.

Page 157, ll. 10–12. The sentence combines verbal echoes of Ps. xlii. 7 and lxxxviii. 7.

l. 17. *a great darkness and horror* The terror of death experienced by Christian is to be contrasted with the easy end of the reprobate Badman, *Badman*, pp. 166–79; 'God can pardon thy sins, and yet make them a bitter thing and a burden at death', *Paul's Departure and Crown*, i. 730.

Page 158, ll. 6–8. The quotation is from the Geneva Version. The application to the death of the wicked again anticipates Badman.

l. 20. *the enemy was after that as still as a stone* Exod. xv. 16.

Page 159, ll. 8 ff. Heb. xii. 22–24 was a favourite text of Bunyan; it was 'a blessed Scripture' which 'came bolting in' upon him in the final serene stage of his conversion, *G.A.* §§ 263–5.

Page 160, l. 25–Page 161, l. 16. These paragraphs on the angelic trumpeters were added in the second edition; signs of Bunyan's lively musical appreciation abound in both parts of the work.

Page 161, ll. 24–25. *Enoch, Moses, and Elijah* They are above looking over the gate (see also p. 162, l. 34) and therefore presumably on the roof of the palace. They must be the 'Three' who in the reading of the first edition walk on the roof in the vision of the New Jerusalem in the Interpreter's House. Mark ix. 5, Luke ix. 33.

Page 162, ll. 21 ff. Ignorance's being assisted over the river by Vain-hope symbolizes an easy death with full confidence of salvation, ll. 35 ff.

Page 164, ll. 21–22. The suggestion of these lines is that a second part was already being planned before the publication and success of the first.

THE SECOND PART
The Authors Way of Sending forth his Second Part

Page 167, l. 21. *rest* All the editions read 'next'; it seems likely that the copy was misread by the compositor: the sentence refers to the rest of the pilgrim characters apart from Christiana and her family, i.e. Honest, Ready-to-halt, and the others who are enumerated on pp. 172–3.

Page 168, ll. 4–5. Both editions agree in having a comma after 'Provides' and finishing the sentence with a full stop at 'Tides'. But the second line of the couplet clearly belongs to the next sentence, into which it introduces the metaphor of the storm at sea that is succeeded by a 'brave calm'; the clause in the first line of the couplet is controlled by 'Let them acquainted be' in l. 2. The transposition of the comma and stop effects the necessary change.

l. 9. *my firstling*: the First Part.

l. 14. *That Counterfeit the Pilgrim*, &c. Thomas Sherman, a General Baptist, had published under the initials T.S. *The Second Part of the Pilgrim's Progress* (Printed by T.H. over against the Poultry, 1682). He objected to

the levity and homeliness of Bunyan's manner and to the comparative absence
from the First Part of any attention to the organized life of the church; these
he attempted to remedy in an allegory composed in a stilted and affected style.
Bunyan alludes to T.S. as one (though he says 'some') who has set Bunyan's
title to his own book; he then goes on to mention those who have put out
spurious continuations bearing as well as the title of *The Pilgrim's Progress*
'half my name'. In 1688, the year of Bunyan's death, Nathaniel Ponder com-
plained 'Of certain ballad sellers about Newgate and on London Bridge, who
have put the first two letters of the Author's name and his effigies to their
rhimes and ridiculous books, suggesting to the world as if they were his'
(Brown, p. 435). Examples would be *The Pilgrams Guide* and *The Progress
of the Christian Pilgrim*, published respectively for and by J. Blare at the
Looking Glass on London Bridge (1705); but such works may have been in
existence before 1684, quite apart from surreptitious editions of the genuine
work and copies made up from parts of different editions (Harrison, pp. 76–
77; *T.C.* iii. 435).

l. 26. *thine own native Language* See Introduction, p. cx, on Bunyan's
recognition of the uniqueness of his own colloquial manner; it would stand
out particularly sharply against the affectations of T.S.

ll. 29–30. Cf. another gipsy simile drawn from country lore in *G.A.* § 103.

PAGE 169, ll. 11–17. *France . . . Flanders . . . Highlanders, and Wild-Irish
. . . New-England* The earliest surviving translations into French, Dutch, and
Gaelic, and the first American edition are as follows: *Voyage d'un Chrestien
vers l'Eternité* (Amsterdam, 1685); *Eens Christens Reyse na de Eeuwigheyt*
(Amsterdam, 1682); *The Pilgrim's Progress* (Boston, 1681). Though no
Gaelic version has survived prior to Bunyan's death there is a Welsh one:
Taith y Pererin (London, 1687).

l. 19. *As to be Trim'd, new Cloth'd & Deckt with Gems*: referring to
splendidly bound copies of the first American editions.

l. 29. *Brave Galants* Bunyan had a friend at court in the person of
Dr. John Owen, who when Charles II marvelled at his going to hear the tinker
preach, declared, 'Had I the tinker's abilities, please your Majesty, I would
most gladly relinquish my learning' (William Orme in *Works of Owen*, 1826,
i. 305). The interest of politer readers is shown in a reference by Anthony
Wood in his life of Edward Fowler to Bunyan's 'several useful and practical
Books' (*Athenae Oxonienses*, 1721, ii. 1030) and perhaps in a mythical
anecdote related by Tom Brown in his *Letters from the Dead to the Living*
(*Amusements Serious and Comical and Other Works*, ed. by Arthur Hayward,
1927, p. 399).

l. 32. Proverbial: 'A lark's leg is worth more than a kite's body', Tilley,
L 186.

PAGE 170, l. 31. *Checkle*: laugh, chuckle.

ll. 32–33. 'It came to pass, when Jacob saw Rachel the daughter of Laban
his mother's brother, and the sheep of Laban . . . that Jacob kissed Rachel
and lifted up his voice and wept', Gen. xxix. 10, 11.

PAGE 171, ll. 15–18. The promise here held out that allegories concealed in
the First Part will be revealed by the Second is not fulfilled.

PAGE 171, ll. 31 f. Cf. *Merchant of Venice*, IV. i. 46.

PAGE 172, ll. 22–23. Matt. xxi. 15, 16.
l. 23. *deride*: intransitive: *O.E.D.* s.v. † 2.

PAGE 173, l. 27. i.e. shall gain their meaning.

PAGE 174, ll. 13–14. *Multiplicity of Business* As well as the duties of his pastorate, which entailed periodic visits to the daughter churches of Bedford at Kempston, Malden, Cotten End, Edworth, and Gamlingay, in the period between the publication of the First and Second Parts (1678–84) Bunyan published seven books (including *Badman* and *The Holy War*) and one shorter treatise (Harrison, 40–48).

PAGE 175, l. 6. *Mr. Sagasity* The narrative device of a dialogue in which one participant is seeking information is also employed in *Badman*. Sagacity is the leisurely narrator, like Wiseman in *Badman*; the method can be traced back to Dent's *Plain Mans Path-Way*, where the sagacious narrator is Theologus. Here Bunyan soon abandons it.

PAGE 176, ll. 15–16. *will shortly come into these parts* i.e. at the Day of Judgement.

PAGE 177, l. 12. *being we are* Not a colloquialism, but good prose usage; cf. Pearson, *Exposition of the Creed* (1669), p. 163: 'Being these and the like accidents and affections cannot come from the same nature'.
l. 23. *Cogitation* Longer and more literary words, though few in number, appear occasionally in *H.W.* and the Second Part of *P.P.*; cf. 'Courteous Companions' at the beginning, p. 174, l. 1.
l. 24. *Relations* Cf. Part One, p. 9, l. 2, and p. 206, l. 11.
l. 32. *clogged her Conscience*: impeded, obstructed: *O.E.D.* s.v. 36.

PAGE 178, l. 3. *the Caul of her Heart* A Hebrew idiom transmitted by the Authorized Version and the Geneva Version.
ll. 21–22. *Wo, worth the day* Ezek. xxx. 2.

PAGE 179, ll. 10–11. *no man living could tell what they said* 'no man could learn that song but the hundred and forty and four thousand', Rev. xiv. 3.
l. 20. *warm with desires* Cf. Canticles v. 8, and the language of Part One, p. 155, l. 19.

PAGE 180, l. 23. *root-of-Heart* The phrase is the result of a confusion of 'by rote' and 'by heart'.

PAGE 181, l. 19 marg. *stunds* Cf. 'stounded', p. 156, l. 29; *G.A.*, 3rd ed., § 12.
l. 23. *So they began* As in Part One the account of the interfering entreaties of the neighbours is paralleled in *Seasonable Counsel, or Advice to Sufferers*, which was published in the same year as the Second Part: 'Now also come kindred, and relations, and acquaintance; some chide, some cry, some argue, some threaten, some promise, some flatter, and some do all, to befool him for so unadvised an act as to cast away himself, and to bring his wife and children to beggary for such a thing as religion' (ii. 733).

PAGE 182, l. 14. *I was a dreamed* Impersonal verb, apparently formed from the past participle with its prefix *y-* as in *a-been*; 'I was a-dreamed I over-heard a ghost', Fielding, *Pasquin* (1736), IV. i.

PAGE 183, l. 6. *a Fool of the greatest size* Cf. 'malice of as great a size', *Henry VIII*, v. i. 134–5.

l. 11. *The bitter must come before the sweet* Tilley, S 1035.

l. 20. *her Bowels yearned* 1 Kings iii. 26: 'For her bowels yearned upon her son'.

l. 33. *Sun-shine Morning* Cf. 'sunshine holiday', Milton, *Comus*, 959.

PAGE 185, l. 3. *dumpish*: melancholy.

l. 16. *I dare say* i.e. I have no hesitation in saying.

l. 34. *one that delighteth in Mercie* The kind of pun referred to by Coleridge in another passage as breaking the consistency of the allegory (note on p. 40, ll. 18–19).

PAGE 186, l. 25. *Bowels* i.e. compassion.

PAGE 187, l. 20. *rather worse than formerly* The deterioration of the Slough is due to the ill counsels of false or unreliable ministers ('that pretend to be the Kings Labourers'); the allegory is aimed at the Strict Baptists of London who had differed from Bunyan on the essentials of church-membership and whose views would have been likely to exclude and to terrify a Mr. Fearing or a Mr. Ready-to-Halt.

PAGE 188, ll. 4–5. *you know your sore and I know mine* Proverbial: not in Tilley or the *Oxford Dictionary of Proverbs*.

l. 25. *a Dog* Psal. xxii. 20.

PAGE 190, l. 9. *That one* It is possible that 'That Jon.' (Jonah) in the manu-script copy was thus read by the compositor owing to the similarity of forms of capital 'O' and 'J' in the English hand.

ll. 15–16. *Hers was from the King, and mine was but from her* Mercy is not conscious of a special call, but has imitated the convert Christiana; a major instance of the more liberal and socially minded theology of the Second Part, which also does something to comply with the strictures of T.S. Cf. *Come and Welcome*, i. 247–53.

ll. 36–38. *by deed in the way I obtained it . . . as it shall be revealed* i.e. by the sight of the Cross from a distance mentioned below. For the theo-logical meaning see Greatheart's explanation, p. 209, ll. 22 ff.

PAGE 191, l. 24. *what was Written over the Gate* 'Knock and it shall be opened unto you', p. 25, l. 6.

PAGE 192, l. 3. *lumbring* See note on p. 122, l. 4.

PAGE 193, ll. 2–3. *has worried some that I love* An obvious theological pun; cf. 'damnably hard', First Part, p. 118, l. 15.

ll. 25 ff. *Bless't be the day that I began*, &c. This and the other lyrics with which the Second Part is interspersed are metrically derivative from Sternhold and Hopkins's version of the Psalms. Bunyan's object in including them was to promote the claims of congregational singing. The Open-Communion churches were divided on this point: Keach, for instance, was in favour of it, and Bunyan's universal love of music leaves no doubt where his sympathies would lie; but there were many who felt that singing was not conducive to worship: there was controversy on this point in the Bedford church in 1674 and subsequently, and hymns were not finally permitted until 1691. (*Church Book*, pp. 55, 75, 76, 77; 'The songs sung in the temple were new, or such as were compiled after the manner of repeated mercies, that the church of God had received, or were to receive. And answerable to this, is the church to sing now new songs, with new hearts', *Solomon's Temple Spiritualized*, iii. 496; *Trans. Bapt. Hist. Soc.* vi (1918–19), 277; Robert Barclay, *The Inner Life of the Religious Societies of the Commonwealth* (1876), pp. 451–8.)

PAGE 194, l. 11. *Plash*: beat down, bend down; the boys reached up and pulled down the branches in order to take the apples; altered to 'pluck' in the second and subsequent editions.

PAGE 195, l. 28. *Ruffins*: demons, devils; *O.E.D.* cites Brome, *Joviall Crew* (*Works*, 1873), iii. 389: 'I sweare by the Ruffin, that we are assaulted by a quire Cuffin.'

PAGE 199, l. 28. *the biggest of them all* The picture of Evangelist, the first emblem of the Interpreter's House in the First Part, who is 'one of a thousand'.

l. 34. *with a Muckrake* This memorable image takes its inspiration from traditional usage concerning avarice: Arthur Dent's Theologus speaks of 'the gripple muck-rakers' (*Plain Mans Path-Way*, ed. 1617, p. 91), and the metaphor is found in Quarles among other analogies with the two episodes in the Interpreter's House:

> Let not thy nobler thoughts be always raking
> The world's base Dunghill.

Emblemes, Book II. 2.

PAGE 200, l. 28. *a very great Spider* An emblem of the sinner defiled by his sin but nevertheless possessing faith and therefore able to receive divine mercy; 'The spider taketh hold with her hands, and is in kings' palaces', Prov. xxx. 28. A favourite image of Bunyan: 'The Sinner and the Spider' (*A Book for Boys and Girls*, Emblem XVIII. iii. 752–4) is the longest and most interesting of the poems in his own emblem-book and contains the following lines:

> I am a Spider, yet I can possess
> The palace of a King, where happiness
> So much abounds. Nor when I doe go thither
> Do they ask what, or whence, I come, or whither?
> Thou art worse than a Spider, but take hold
> On Christ the Door, thou shalt not be controul'd.
> By him do thou the heavenly palace enter,
> None chide thee will for this thy brave adventure.

In *Light for them that Sit in Darkness* (1675), i. 435, the image is used differently to symbolize the tempter who entangles the sinner in his web. The text in Proverbs is again referred to in *The Resurrection of the Dead*, ii. 111.

This emblem is particularly characteristic of the coarse vigour of Bunyan's homiletic, and has been attacked by Alfred Noyes on the score of inhumanity (*The Opalescent Parrot*, 1929, pp. 90–91). The use of the spider as a symbol for spiritual ugliness comes close to Swift's treatment in *The Battle of the Books* (ed. A. C. Guthkelch and D. Nichol Smith, Oxford, 1958, p. 234). Cf. also Tillotson, *Works*, ed. Thomas Birch (1820), iii. 420.

PAGE 201, l. 32. *did walk*: behave, conduct herself.

ll. 33–36. 'Common call, the invitations; brooding voice, the promises; outcry, the warnings of the gospel' (Joseph Ivimey, *The Pilgrim's Progress. A New Edition* (1821), p. 297).

PAGE 202, ll. 19–25. 'When Christians stand every one in their places, and do the work of their relations, then they are like the flowers in the garden, that stand and grow where the gardener hath planted them, and then they shall both honour the garden in which they are planted, and the gardener that hath so disposed of them. From the hyssop in the wall, to the cedar in Lebanon, their fruit is their glory', *Christian Behaviour*, ii. 550.

> See how the Flow'rs, as at Parade,
> Under their Colours stand displaid:
> Each Regiment in order grows,
> That of the Tulip, Pinke, and Rose.

Andrew Marvell, 'Upon Appleton House', *Poems*, ed. H. M. Margoliouth, i. 68.

PAGE 203, ll. 21–24. Cf. the proverb 'Likely lies in the mire and unlikely gets over', *Oxford Dictionary of English Proverbs* (1948), p. 369; Tilley, L 292.

ll. 28–29. '*Tis easier watching a night or two, then to sit up a whole year together* Not in Tilley.

l. 35. *One leak will sink a Ship* Tilley, L 147.

PAGE 204, ll. 3–4. *If a man would live well*, &c. Cf. 'As a man lives, so shall he die', *Oxford Dictionary of Proverbs* (1948), p. 377.

l. 19. *a Tree* . . . The fair tree rotten at the heart is the hypocritical lapsed professor, dealt with at length in a sermon treatise of eleven years earlier, *The Barren Fig-tree* (1673), iii. 561–85. It is described again in the first emblem of *A Book for Boys and Girls*, iii. 748–9. As with the satirical portraits of minor characters, the background of Bunyan's preoccupation with this theme is provided by his pastoral responsibility.

PAGE 205, l. 10. *into the Pond* Presumably refers to the Slough of Despond, but her reception of the letter precedes her setting out and crossing the Slough.

PAGE 206, ll. 26–28. The wording anticipates the comparison of Mercy to Ruth made by the Interpreter below, l. 39.

PAGE 207, l. 19 marg. *The Bath Sanctification* This representation of adult baptism by immersion is a concession to the peculiar opinions of the Open-Communion separatist congregations; there is no such stress on doctrinal features apart from the main Calvinist tradition in Part One, several in the Second Part. As against the Strict Baptists, Bunyan and those like him administered baptism not as a necessary condition of initiation into church-membership but as an optional outward sign of adherence.

PAGE 207, l. 34. *fair as the Moon* Cant. vi. 10.

l. 36. *the Seal* Of election, Eph. i. 13.

PAGE 208, ll. 13–20. Baxter agrees with Bunyan's eschatology both in believing that the saints will know their friends in heaven and recognize their perfections, and in his belief in an immediate beatific vision. (*Saints Everlasting Rest* (1677), pp. 82–84.)

ll. 22–23. *take Sword, and Helmet and Shield* Greatheart is a minister of Christ armed with 'the whole armour of God' of Eph. i. 13.

PAGE 209, ll. 15–16. *Pardon, by Word and Deed* The discourse of Greatheart to Christiana on pardon by the imputed righteousness of Christ continues to p. 211, l. 38. The theological argument is developed more fully elsewhere by Bunyan, especially in *Law and Grace* and *Of Justification by Imputed Righteousness*.

PAGE 211, ll. 3–4. *here is a Righteousness that Christ, as God, has no need of* Cf. *Law and Grace*, i. 545.

l. 18. *two Coats* Luke iii. 11.

PAGE 214, l. 34. *but now 'tis Dirty* 'This river is pure, is clear, is pure and clear as crystal. Is the doctrine offered unto thee so? or is it muddy, and mixed with the doctrines of men? Look, man, and see if the foot of the worshippers of Bel be not there and if the waters be not fouled thereby. What water is fouled is not the water of life, or at least not the water of life in its clearness', *The Water of Life*, iii. 559.

l. 37. *why so envious tro?* 'Tro' or 'trow' is the interrogative particle formed from 'trow ye'. 'What could you have done to him, tro?', Richardson, *Pamela* (1741), i. 57.

PAGE 215, l. 12. *Chains, Posts and a Ditch*: probably refer to the persecution of Roman Catholics after the Popish Plot.

l. 38. *a breathing Hill*: a hill which causes them to pant.

PAGE 216, l. 8. *pelting*: excessive.

ll. 20–23. 'A straight stair is like the ladder that leads to the gallows. They are turning stairs that lead to the heavenly mansion, stay not at their foot, but go up them, and up them, and up them, till you come to heaven.' *Solomon's Temple Spiritualized*, iii. 483.

ll. 32–33. *Pomgranate* Deut. viii. 8, Cant. iv. 13.

PAGE 217, l. 13. *forgat to take her Bottle of Spirits* The allegory means that periods of spiritual consolation and confidence are liable to bring in the end forgetfulness of the need for effort and of the promises of grace.

PAGE 218, l. 24. *to back the Lions*: to support, encourage them.

l. 27. *Grim or Bloody man* represents the civil power which puts into effect the penal laws against Nonconformists. When Faithful passed, the lions were asleep (a suspension of prosecutions). The renewed outbreak of persecution alluded to is that of 1681–4: cf. below: 'this way had of late lain much un-occupied, and was almost all grown over with Grass'.

Page 221, ll. 33–34. *the Porter had heard before of their coming* This is inconsistent with p. 220, ll. 5–12, where the Porter is surprised by the arrival of Great-heart and his party.

l. 38. *that Chamber that was my Husbands*—the name of which was Peace.

Page 222, l. 13. *a Noise of Musick* A concert, or a company of musicians; 'see if thou canst find Sneak's noise', 2 *Henry IV*, II. iv. 11; 'that melodious noise', Milton, *At a Solemn Musick*, 18.

l. 27. *a Dreamed* Cf. note on p. 182, l. 14.

Page 224, ll. 4–5. *about a Month or above* The leisurely progress of the pilgrimage in the Second Part, with long halts at the houses of resort along the way, has been commented on, particularly by Ronald A. Knox, *Essays in Satire* (1928), p. 206: 'Christian goes on a pilgrimage, Christiana on a walking tour.'

Page 226, l. 20. *learn you more* Teach: still a correct though old-fashioned form in Bunyan's time and one he would have met with in the Authorized Version: 'O learn me true understanding and knowledge', Ps. cxix. 66.

l. 32. *Mr. Brisk* The word often carries a pejorative, rakish connotation in Restoration usage, implying 'flashy' or 'fast'; *O.E.D.* instances Etheredge, *Man of Mode*: 'He has been, as the sparkish word is, Brisk Upon the Ladies already.'

Page 227, l. 31. *ill Conditions*: bad qualities.

Page 228, ll. 13–14. *he and she could never agree* The situation of the Puritan wife with an unregenerate husband is dealt with more fully in *Badman*, pp. 74–81.

l. 16. *cried her down at the Cross* Alludes to the custom by which a husband could publicly disown his wife's debts at the market cross. According to Offor the custom was current till a late period in Bedfordshire (*Works*, iii. 201).

l. 21. *Mathew . . . fell Sick* The apples stolen from Belzebub's orchard disagree with him: an obvious allegory of original sin. Cf. *Exposition of Genesis*, ii. 429.

l. 33. *his Maw* Cf. Deut. xviii. 3.

Page 229, l. 22. *the Blood of a Goat, etc.* The sin-offering of the old law.

ll. 25–26. *ex Carne & Sanguine Christi* The borrowed Latin imitates the jargon of a medical prescription; such medical metaphors are frequent in *The Water of Life*, for instance 'Bunyan's bill of his Master's Water of Life' in the Preface, iii. 539.

l. 28. *Pills* There is an allusion to 'Mathew's Pills', a well-known patent remedy of the time; their virtues are described in a puff by the originator, Richard Mathew, *The Unlearned Alchymist His Antidote, or, A more full and ample Explanation of the Use, Virtue and Benefit of my* PILL (1662); like the medicine with which Mathew is treated this contemporary nostrum was 'a corrector of all Vegetative poysons' and had to be taken in a liquid; it was also efficacious against 'Pains, Aches, gripings' (p. A2, p. 109). See my note in *N. & Q.*, New Series, i (1954), 246–7.

PAGE 230, l. 21. *an universal Pill* The same claim is made by Mathew, *The Unlearned Alchymist*, p. 107. Cf. '. . . as men, in their bills for conviction to readers, do give an account to the country of the persons cured, and the diseases that have been removed by liquors and preparations, they have made for that end . . . so could I give you accounts of numberless numbers that have not only been made to live, *but to live for ever*, by drinking of this water, this pure water of life. . . . No disease comes amiss to it; it cures blindness, deafness, dumbness' (*The Water of Life*, iii. 539–40, 558).

PAGE 232, l. 1. *the Candle-wick*

> Man's like a candle in a candlestick,
> Made up of tallow and a little wick;
> And as the candle when it is not lighted,
> So is he who is in his sins benighted.
> Nor can a man his soul with grace inspire,
> More than can candles set themselves on fire.
> Candles receive their light from what they are not;
> Men grace from Him for whom at first they care not.

A Book for Boys and Girls, Emblem xiv, 'Meditations upon a Candle' (iii. 751).

The stages of human life are represented by a candle that gradually burns down in the emblem series of Quarles, *Hieroglyphikes of the Life of Man* (1638).

l. 10. *the Pelican pierce her own Brest* Bunyan follows the traditional mystical interpretation of what was still accepted as a fact of natural history in his time: 'Some will have a Scar in the Brest, from a wound of her own making there, to feed (as is reported) her young with her own bloud; an action which ordinarily suggests devout fancies', *A Short Relation of the River Nile* (1673), p. 30.

PAGE 233, ll. 33–34. *a pair of Excellent Virginals* 'A pair' is used in the sense of 'a set'.

PAGE 235, l. 1. *a Gold Angel* Earlier called the angel-noble, and named from the device on the obverse of St. Michael transfixing the dragon, it was a new issue of the noble, introduced in March 1465: it became the standard professional fee (6s. 8d.). See George C. Brooke, *English Coins from the Seventh Century to the Present Day* (3rd ed. rev. 1950), pp. 148–9.

l. 2. *Let thy Garments*, &c. Quoted from Eccl. ix. 8.

ll. 3–4. *Let Mercy live*, &c. Adapted from Moses' prayer for Reuben, Deut. xxxiii. 6.

ll. 19 ff. *Through all my Life*, etc. This stanza is from Thomas Sternhold's version of Ps. xxiii. 6, and the following stanza is from the same version of Ps. c. 5.

ll. 29 ff.
> Such mountains round about this house do stand
> As one from thence may see the holy land.
> Her fields are fertile, do abound with corn,
> The lilies fair, her vallies do adorn.

> The birds that do come hither every spring,
> For birds, they are the very best that sing.
>   Her friends, her neighbours too, do call her blest;
> Angels do here go by, turn in and rest.
>   The road to paradise lies by her gate,
> Here pilgrims do themselves accommodate
> With bed and board, and do such stories tell
> As do for truth and profit all excel.
>   Nor doth the porter here say any nay,
> That hither would turn in, that here would stay.
> *This house is rent-free; here the man may dwell*
> *That loves his landlord, rules his passions well.*

House of God, ii. 579.

PAGE 236, ll. 26–27. *the fruit of those slips that he got in his going down the hill* The implication that Christian failed to achieve perfect humility is to be attributed to Bunyan's awareness of his own tendency to succumb to pride. Once again the spiritual pilgrimage of Christian is used as a vehicle, for 'I have also, while found in this blessed Work of Christ, been often tempted to pride and liftings up of Heart; . . . it hath been my every days portion to be let into the evil of my own heart' (*G.A.* § 297). 'The truth is, as himself sometimes acknowledged, he always needed the thorn in the flesh, and God in mercy sent it him, lest, under his extraordinary circumstances, he should be exalted above measure' (George Cokayne, Bunyan's intimate friend, in his preface to the posthumously published *The Acceptable Sacrifice* (1689), i. 686).

PAGE 237, l. 22. *fat Ground*: rich ground: 'fat pasture and good', 1 Chron. iv. 40.

PAGE 238, l. 29. *let and hindred* '. . . through our sins and wickedness we are sore let and hindered in running the race that is set before us', Collect for the Fourth Sunday in Advent.

PAGE 239, l. 12. *Forgetful-Green* 'Forgetfulness . . . makes things nothing; . . . it makes us as if things had never been . . . It is marvellous to see how some men are captivated with this forgetfulness', *A Holy Life the Beauty of Christianity*, ii. 522.

PAGE 240, ll. 17–18. *by-blows*: blows which glanced past them without hitting them.

PAGE 241, ll. 7 f. The whole scene, like the parallel episode in the First Part, is reminiscent of the temptations in *G.A.* Cf. also *Come and Welcome*, i. 286.

PAGE 242, ll. 19–20. *a great mist and a darkness* 'first, all my comfort was taken from me, then darkness siezed upon me', *G.A.* § 97.

PAGE 243, ll. 2–3. *the Earth with its bars* Jonah ii. 6.

ll. 34–35. *the Snares* 'As for me, my feet had almost gone, my steps had well nigh slipped', Ps. lxxiii. 2.

PAGE 244, l. 13. *Maull a Gyant* The second of the giants encountered by the Pilgrims represents the Roman Church: he 'did use to spoyl young

Pilgrims with Sophistry', the common charge against the Jesuits and other Catholic apologists; he charges Great-heart with weakening his master's kingdom' a reference to proselytizing and to the foreign allegiance of Roman Catholics; the latter was a familiar topic in the age of the Popish Plot and the Exclusion Bill (Sir Charles Firth, *Essays Historical and Literary*, Oxford, 1938, p. 146).

Bunyan used the giant's name once more, as a symbol for Satan's assaults on the confidence of the penitent, in a treatise published in the last year of his life but possibly written not long after the Second Part, *The Jerusalem Sinner Saved* (1688), i. 96: 'The tempted, wherever he dwells, always thinks himself the biggest sinner. . . . This is Satan's master argument. . . . I say this is his maul, his club, his master-piece.'

PAGE 245, l. 18. *let him get up* In the seventeenth-century metrical version of the romance of Guy of Warwick, Guy, during his fight with Colebrand, allows the giant to refresh himself with water when he is weary.

PAGE 246, ll. 9–10. *a little on my flesh* The remains of concupiscence persisting in the regenerate: Baxter, *Saints Everlasting Rest* (11th ed., 1677), pp. 274–5.

PAGE 247, l. 3. *Then said Mr. Honest* A slip of Bunyan's: he has not yet been introduced.

ll. 38 ff. Cf. *G.A.* §§ 53–55.

PAGE 249, l. 2. *Mr. Fearing* The first of the group of pilgrims illustrating Christians with tender and scrupulous consciences, Feeble-mind, Ready-to-halt, &c. Bunyan writes when the liberal principles of the Bedford church regarding inter-communion were being actively promoted without respect to inessentials of doctrine or practice; the link with Cokayne's independent congregation in London was strengthened, and sister Joan Cooke, who had gone from Bedford to live in London, was permitted to join any congregation she thought good 'for her edification and the furtherance of her faith' (*Church Book*, p. 71, 30 March 1682).

l. 5. *the Root of the Matter in him* Proverbial; not in Tilley.

l. 10. *Knew him!* Cf. p. 61, l. 26.

l. 11. *most an end*: continually.

PAGE 250, l. 11. *the Hammer that hanged on the Gate* Frequently used as a substitute for a knocker.

PAGE 251, l. 30. *his Fear was about his Acceptance at last* The same is the case with all the major temptations related in *G.A.*

PAGE 253, ll. 5–6. *Mr. Great-heart began to take his Leave of him* By an oversight Great-heart is made to speak of himself in the third person.

PAGE 254, l. 10. *he could have bit a Firebrand* Proverbial: not in Tilley.

PAGE 255, ll. 28–30. Self-will's attempt to justify immorality by Biblical precedents corresponds to the ideas of the Ranters, who held that the elect could not be condemned for sin and, in some cases, that it was necessary to emphasize the difference between the two covenants of grace and works by the unbridled indulgence of the flesh. During the Commonwealth such opinions were held by Abiezer Coppe and put into practice by his disciple Lawrence Clarkson, who 'ran through all the sects' and experienced the whole gamut of the religious revolution of his time. He gives an account of his career in *The Lost Sheep Found* (1660). See Norman Cohn, *The Pursuit of the Millennium* (1957), pp. 315–72. Bunyan had as a young man a friend who shocked him by Ranters' opinions, *G.A.* §§ 44–45.

PAGE 258, l. 31. *Gaius*: 'the host of himself and of the whole church', Rom. xvi. 23. The Third Epistle of John is written to one of the same name, 'the well beloved Gaius', commending him for his hospitality to Christians.

PAGE 259, l. 36 marg. *Act 11. 26*   It looks as if 'Ps.', the first-edition reading, was the result of confusion between 'A' and 'Ps' in the copy.

PAGE 260, l. 2. *first at Antioch*   'And the disciples were called Christians first in Antioch', Acts xi. 26. The Scripture reference in the margin is placed eight lines below its proper place in all the editions.

ll. 15–17. *Ignatius…Romanus…Policarp*   The martyrdoms of Ignatius and Romanus are also described in *Come and Welcome*, i. 295–6, and reference is there given to his source: Foxe, *Acts and Monuments* (1632), i. 52, 116. Ignatius, the disciple of St. John, was Bishop of Antioch, condemned by the Emperor Trajan to be taken to Rome and given to the wild beasts, 20 Dec. A.D. 107. There were two martyrs of the name of Romanus: one of Rome, baptized by St. Lawrence, who perished in the Decian persecution, A.D. 255; the other a deacon of Antioch who was put to death by Diocletian. 'The raging Emperor' suggests that it was probably the latter whom Bunyan had in mind. Polycarp, Bishop of Smyrna, also a disciple of St. John, was martyred at Smyrna, A.D. 169.

l. 18. *he that was hanged up in a Basket*   This martyr was Marcus of Arethusa; the story is related in *Come and Welcome, ut supra*: 'What did Marcus Arethusius see in Christ, when after his enemies had cut his flesh, anointed it with honey, and hanged him up in a basket for flies and bees to feed on, he would not give, to uphold idolatry, one halfpenny to save his life? P. 128' (i.e. of Foxe, ed. of 1632).

l. 36. *fall*: become extinct, lapse: *O.E.D.* iii. 23. d.

PAGE 261, ll. 9–10. *on the behalf of Women*   A tribute to the part played by women in the Bedford church. In the original list of members there are ninety-five women out of a total of 142 members, *Church Book*. By 1683 their prestige was such that Bunyan had to contend with a demand for separate prayer-meetings for women; in *A Case of Conscience Resolved* (1683) he summarily rejected their proposal; after this rebuff he may well have felt in writing the Second Part that the devotion of the female members of his congregation required some recognition.

PAGE 262, ll. 8–9. *a Heave-shoulder and a Wave-breast*   'And the right shoulder shall ye give unto the priest for an heave offering of the sacrifices of your peace offerings. . . . For the wave breast and the heave shoulder have I taken of the children of Israel from off the sacrifices of their peace offerings, and have given them unto Aaron the priest and unto his sons by a statute for ever from among the children of Israel', Lev. vii. 32, 34. 'And the wave breast and heave shoulder shall ye eat in a clean place; thou, and thy sons, and thy daughters with thee: for they shall be thy due, and thy sons' due, which are given out of the sacrifices of peace offerings of the children of Israel', Lev. x. 14.

PAGE 268, l. 2. *that Comfort should be given* It was the principle of Bunyan's church to admit all without distinction who were 'visible saints' and to put no obstacles in the way of the scrupulous.

PAGE 270, ll. 35 ff. Cf. 'I am therefore for holding communion thus, because the edification of souls in the faith and holiness of the gospel, is of greater concernment than an agreement in outward things', *A Confession of My Faith*, ii. 611. 'When we attempt to force our brother beyond his light, or to break his heart with grief, to trust him beyond his faith, or to bar him from his privileges, how can we say I love. To make that the door to communion which God hath not; to make that the including, excluding charter, the bar, bounds, and rule of communion, is for want of love', *Peaceable Principles and True*, ii. 653.

PAGE 271, l. 8 marg. *Promises* Displaced in the early editions and now restored to its proper position in the text as a gloss on 'Crutches'.

l. 21. *against a Dog* Cf. p. 188, l. 25.

PAGE 272, ll. 26–27. Cf. note on p. 87, ll. 5–6.

l. 36. *arch*: notable, supereminent.

PAGE 273, l. 19. *Mr. Mnason, a Cyprusian* The name and character are borrowed from Acts xxi. 16: 'One Mnason of Cyprus, an old disciple with whom we should lodge.'

PAGE 274, l. 18. *stamped with his Foot* To summon the servants from the kitchen below.

PAGE 275, l. 8. *need of an Item*: a hint; an intimation.

ll. 11–12. *much more moderate now then formerly* i.e. since the Declaration of Indulgence of 1672 giving freedom of worship to Nonconformists.

PAGE 277, ll. 31–32. *a Monster out of the Woods* As the following description of its seven heads and ten horns shows, this is the beast of Rev. xvii. 3, representing the Church of Rome. See Bunyan's posthumous treatise *Of Antichrist and his Ruin*, especially ii. 47–50.

PAGE 278, ll. 19–20. *Attempts upon the Children* refers to proselytizing.

l. 21. *valiant Worthies*: the preachers of the 'Morning Exercises against Popery' in 1675: Baxter, Owen, Manton, and others.

PAGE 283, l. 8. *a Lesson*: the older term for a suite or sonata.

PAGE 284, l. 15. *the Wain*: 'Charles's Wain', the Great Bear.

PAGE 285, l. 21. *some new places* A further series of emblems like those in the Interpreter's House.

PAGE 286, l. 23. *washing of an Ethiopian* A common emblem theme; found in Whitney, *Choice of Emblemes*, p. 57. See Freeman, p. 216. The previous emblem of the two men Prejudice and Ill-Will on Mount Innocent fruitlessly casting dirt on the godly man is simply this emblem in reverse.

PAGE 287, l. 26. *the Glass was one of a thousand* The Bible: 'For if any be a hearer of the word, and not a doer, he is like unto a man beholding his natural face in a glass', James i. 23. Cf. *Book for Boys and Girls*, Emblem xxxix. iii. 759, and the metaphor occurs in a poem by the Baptist Abraham Cheare:

> If morn by morn you in this glass will dress you,
> I have some hopes that God will by it bless you

(in Henry Jessey, *A Looking-Glass for Children* (1673), p. 27).

PAGE 290, ll. 19–20. *hear your Horse dash* The saying is not recorded in the usual collections.

l. 28. *Sampson* Judges xv. 15.

PAGE 291, l. 20. *a man of his Hands* Proverbial: usually 'a tall man of his hands': Tilley, M163. John Ray, *A Collection of English Proverbs* (1678), p. 82.

l. 35. *a Serpent* Presumably Apollyon, though he is not slain by Christian.

PAGE 292, ll. 29–30. *whether we shall know one another* The view that one will be reunited at death with those one has known is expressed in *One Thing is Needful*, verses 69, 71. Bunyan seems to have believed in an immediate enjoyment of the beatific vision for each individual; see H. B. Workman, *Theology*, xvii (1928), 123–9.

PAGE 295, ll. 11 ff. The simple accomplishment of this, Bunyan's most famous lyric, has been much commented on; there are verbal reminiscences of Amiens' song in *As You Like It* (cf. *P.P.* ed. Edmund Venables, Oxford, 1900, p. 480).

ll. 37 f. *Bryers and Thorns* '. . . when wee are in our passage allured to turne out of the right path into the by-waies of sin and wickednesse . . . the Lord casteth into our way these Thornes and Bryars of affliction and tribulation', John Downame, *The Christian Warfare* (4th ed., 1634), p. 932.

PAGE 297, l. 24. *takes a view of his Book or Map*

> The Book of Books;
> On which who looks
> As he should do, aright, shall never need
> Wish for a better light
> To guide him in the night.

Harvey, *The Synagogue*, xiv. 2–6.

PAGE 300, l. 15. Cf. Ps. cxv. 13.

PAGE 301, l. 9. *Madam Bubble* The bubble is used throughout Quarles's *Emblemes* as an image of the world's vanity.

PAGE 302, ll. 16–17. *Feasting . . . Food* Emended from 'Cheating . . . Good' in the early editions, which makes little sense; on the evidence of the *Church Book* a handwriting confusion between 'F' and 'G' might indeed be possible in the conjectural Bunyan hand (there are examples on pp. 54, 67, and 70), less so between 'Ch' and 'F'.

PAGE 304, l. 29. *a Post come*   The summons to each pilgrim follows an impressively regular formula, so that the whole final episode has a marked rhythm, an almost musical pattern of recurrence and variation. There is the letter from the Celestial City, the emblematic token of its authenticity, the bequest of each one before crossing the river, and their last words. The use throughout of the imagery of death from Ecclesiastes xii was habitual at Puritan death-beds, as may be seen from Edward Bagshaw, *Life and Death of Mr. Bolton* (3rd ed. 1635), p. 34: 'The night before hee died, when the doores without began to be shut, and the daughters of Musicke to be brought low . . . .'

PAGE 311, l. 11. *His Name has been to me as a Civit-Box*   The more exotic language and musical rhythm again evokes the manner of Canticles, though there is no particular reminiscence.

l. 20. Eccl. xii.

ll. 35–37. This Third Part planned by Bunyan was never written, or it would have been published by Doe with the other posthumous works in the Folio of 1692. A spurious Third Part was published in 1692.

APPENDIX

THE SLEEPING PORTRAIT

THE 'sleeping portrait' with the inscription '*R. W.*' was the work of Robert White, an artist of considerable reputation in his day. He was born in London in 1645. His natural aptitude for drawing and etching was developed under the tutelage of David Loggan. 'What distinguished him', says Walpole,[1] 'was his admirable success in likenesses.' White's method was first to make pencil drawings of his 'heads' on vellum and then to use these as a basis for the engravings. The sleeping portrait first inserted in the third edition, 1679, and the later engraving in *The Holy War*, 1682, are made from such a sketch. This pencil sketch was presented in 1799 to the British Museum by its owner, the Rev. Clayton M. Cracherode, and is reproduced as the frontispiece to the present edition. Two other contemporary portraits of Bunyan are extant. The oil-painting by Thomas Sadler, a friend and pupil of Sir Peter Lely's, is in the National Portrait Gallery, Room IX, No. 1311. The inscription on the frame tells us that it was painted when Bunyan was fifty-six years of age, six years later than White's pencil drawing. The other contemporary portrait is the engraving made by John Sturt and used as a frontispiece in the Folio of Bunyan's *Works* in 1692. Charles Doe, the personal friend of Bunyan and the man chiefly responsible for this first folio edition, says of Sturt's engraving: 'His Effigies was cut in Copper from an Original paint done to the life (by his very good Friend a Limner).'[2] Who the limner was is not known. Compared with the pencil drawing of Robert White or with the oil-painting of Thomas Sadler, Sturt's engraving is, as Brown describes it, 'harsh and unpleasing'. Each of these has been used many times as a basis for later engravings.[3] In the Huntington copy of the fifth edition, 1680, and in the Lenox copy of the sixth, 1681, the sleeping portrait is replaced by a bust-portrait of Bunyan with the inscription: *I. Sturt Sc.* | *John Bunyan* | *Printed for Nath. Ponder in the Poultry* | (the last line repeated in the Huntington copy). In the sixth edition the portrait is enclosed within a plain oval border; in the Folio of 1692, within an elaborately figured oval, much larger than the former. There are slight differences in detail, but a strong resemblance in general outline.

In the British Museum copy of the seventh edition the frontispiece is not the sleeping portrait, which is inserted between the Author's Apology and the text proper, but a bust-portrait of Bunyan with the inscription: *Bunyan* | *Burnford Sc.* | *[Prin]ted for Nath. Ponder in the Poultrey*. The frontispiece of the British Museum eleventh is a sleeping portrait, but inscribed: *W. Elder Sc* | *Printed for Nat: Ponder in the Poultry*. It resembles very closely the sleeping portrait inscribed with the initials '*R. W.*'

---

[1] Horace Walpole, *Anecdotes of Painting*, with additions by the Rev. James Dallaway, 3 vols., London (1849), iii. 947–53.　　　　[2] *Works*, iii. 767.

[3] For a fairly complete account of these see Brown, pp. 385–6, and Addenda by Frank Mott Harrison, pp. 412–14.

All three of these men, Sturt, Burnford, and Elder, were contemporaries of Robert White. Sturt, in fact, was apprenticed to White at the age of seventeen. In the edition published by J. Clarke in 1728, twenty-two copper plates engraved by J. Sturt were inserted. The frontispiece to this 'Two and Twentieth edition', as it is called, is also a sleeping portrait which displays no originality but is merely a modification of the earlier conception of Robert White. O Burnford, Walpole tells us that he was 'known by a print of William Salmon, chymist, 1681', and of William Elder that he was contemporary with Robert White, that he was a Scotsman, and that his best work was a plate of Ben Jonson. (Walpole, *op. cit.*, iii. 956–7.)

INDEX TO THE TEXT

PRINTED IN GREAT BRITAIN
AT THE UNIVERSITY PRESS, OXFORD
BY VIVIAN RIDLER
PRINTER TO THE UNIVERSITY